# New Essential Mathematics
## FOR
# G C S E

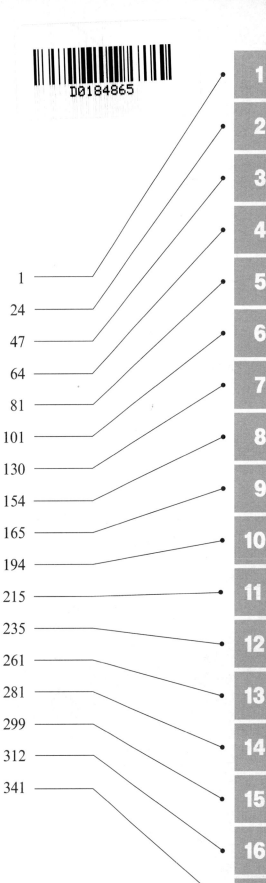

18
19
20
21
22
23
24
25
26
27
28
29

# About this book

**New Essential Mathematics for GCSE** will help you prepare to achieve your best grade in your GCSE mathematics examination.

You can use this book throughout your course, and you can also use it to help you revise before your examination.

# Thorough preparation for Intermediate tier examinations

**New Essential Mathematics for GCSE** provides complete coverage of the Intermediate tier examination topics so you can be confident you have covered everything you need to know for your examination.

Each topic is covered in a unit of work that provides:
- clear explanations of the key ideas and skills
- worked examples showing you how to answer questions
- carefully graded exercises that take you up to examination standard

# Special features are:

- **worked examination questions** with examiners' tips showing you how to gain marks
- **test yourself questions** at the end of each unit; use these to see how you are doing, and which topics you may need to review
- **revision routemaster** at the end of the book; this will help you decide whether you can tackle certain **key questions** and **topics** which are highly likely to appear in GCSE exam papers in mathematics
- **summaries of key points** at the end of each unit to help you revise

# Finding your way around

To find your way around this book use the:

**edge marks** – shown on the front pages – these help you get to the right unit quickly

**contents list** – this lists the key headings in each unit with a description of the mathematical content covered

**index** – at the end of the book

# Contents

# 7 Basic algebra

# 8 Forming equations

# 9 Straight line graphs

# 10 Manipulating algebra

# 11 Solving linear equations

# 12 Graphs of curves

# 13 Trial and improvement

# 14 Properties of shapes

# 15 Position and movement

# 16 Symmetry and angles

# 17 Transformations

# 18 Length, area and volume

# 19 Pythagoras' theorem

# 20 Trigonometry in 2-D

# 21 Using appropriate measures

# 22 Accurate drawings

# 23 Handling data

# 24 Statistical diagrams

# 25 Measures of average and spread

# 26 Cumulative frequency

# 27 Scatter diagrams

# 28 Simple probability

# 29 Combining probabilities

# SEG Modular Syllabus Matching

This spread shows you how SEG's modular syllabus is covered in this book.

# Module 2: Statistics and probability

# Module 3: Terminal module

**Authors of this book**
David Kent
Christine Medlow
Keith Pledger
Roy Woodward
with Andrew Killick

Heinemann Educational Publishers
Halley Court, Jordan Hill, Oxford OX2 8EJ
a division of Reed Educational & Professional Publishing Ltd

OXFORD FLORENCE PRAGUE MADRID
ATHENS MELBOURNE AUCKLAND
KUALA LUMPUR SINGAPORE TOKYO
IBADAN NAIROBI KAMPALA JOHANNESBURG
GABORONE PORTSMOUTH NH (USA) CHICAGO
MEXICO CITY SAO PAULO

First edition published 1996
New edition 1997

97  98  99  10  9  8  7  6  5  4  3  2  1

ISBN:  0 435 50444 4

Designed and typeset by Keyword Typesetting Services Limited, Wallington, Surrey
Printed in Great Britain by Bath Press
Cover design: Richard Knights

**Acknowledgements**
The Publishers would like to thank the following Exam Boards for permission to reproduce questions
from past examination papers. The questions are coded as follows:

[**London**] – London Examinations
[**SEG**] – Southern Examining Group
[**MEG**] – Midland Examining Group
[**WJEC**] – Welsh Joint Education Council
[**NEAB**] – Northern Examinations and Assessment Board

The authors and publishers would like to thank for permission to reproduce the following photographs:
p281 Brian Shuel/Collections and Hans Rheinhard/Bruce Coleman Ltd.; p373 Mike Hewitt/Allsport;
p424 Tony Smith/ Allsport; p426 Hulton Deutsch/Allsport; p538 Associated Sports Photography; p546
Tony Duffy/Allsport; p553 Clive Brunskill/Allsport. The Ordnance Survey maps on pages 453 and 454
are reproduced with the permission of the controller of HMSO, Crown Copyright Reserved.

# 1 Introducing number

## 1.1 Introduction

This unit revises the basic concepts of whole numbers, fractions, decimal fractions and percentages, and the relationships between them.

To help you develop your understanding of these concepts, and to practise your basic number skills, most topics use non-calculator methods.

## 1.2 Ordering numbers

This set of numbers has been written in random order.

21, 534, 19, 82, 222, 89, 115, 104, 56, 6, 1255, 34, 27

In statistics you will sometimes need to find the value of the middle number when the numbers are written in size order.

If you write the numbers in size order, with the smallest first, you have

6, 19, 21, 27, 34, 56, 82, 89, 104, 115, 222, 534, 1255

$$\downarrow$$

The middle number is 82.

### Exercise 1A

1. Write each of these sets of numbers in size order, smallest first. Write down the value of the middle number.
   (a) 3, 13, 9, 25, 16, 42, 31, 48, 24
   (b) 56, 84, 31, 29, 66, 89, 44, 12, 63
   (c) 112, 342, 245, 671, 532, 865, 339, 999, 465
   (d) 432, 76, 189, 777, 521, 98, 67, 223, 52
   (e) 221, 8, 7, 45, 1221, 67, 10, 100, 132

2. In an election the number of votes for each party is shown in the table opposite.
   (a) Rewrite the number of votes in size order, largest first.
   (b) Which party won the election?
   (c) How many votes were cast altogether?
   (d) How many more votes than New Labour did the Old Conservatives get?

(e) If the Superior Students Party had trebled their number of votes, what position would they have achieved?

| New Labour | 19 675 |
| Superior Students Party | 285 |
| Old Conservative | 23 543 |
| Social Democrats | 884 |
| Roaring Radicals | 453 |
| Anti Alien Party | 34 |
| Tired Teachers Party | 0 |
| Liberal Democrats | 12 332 |

## 1.3 Multiplying by 10 and by 100

Multiplying a number by 10 moves each digit *one* place value column to the *left*.

$$\begin{array}{ccc} H & T & U \\ & 3 & 4 \\ \times 10 & \diagup & \diagup \\ 3 & 4 & 0 \end{array} \qquad 34 \times 10 = 340$$

*Remember*: if there are no units you must write in a zero.

Multiplying a number by 100 moves the digits *two* place value columns to the *left*.

$$\begin{array}{cccc} Th & H & T & U \\ & & 3 & 4 \\ \times 100 & \diagup & \diagup \\ 3 & 4 & 0 & 0 \end{array} \qquad 34 \times 100 = 3400$$

*Remember*: if you have no units and no tens you must write in 2 zeros.

### Exercise 1B

1. How many places to the left does each digit move if you multiply by
   (a) 1000  (b) 10 000

2. Write down the answers to
   (a) $46 \times 10$  (b) $10 \times 29$  (c) $10 \times 342$
   (d) $28 \times 100$  (e) $341 \times 100$  (f) $100 \times 871$
   (g) $21 \times 1000$  (h) $1000 \times 52$  (i) $10 \times 1000$

### Example 1

A box of matches contains 47 matches.

How many matches are there in 30 boxes?

The problem can be solved using this non-calculator method:

$30 = 3 \times 10$ so multiplying by 30 is the same as multiplying by 3 and then by 10.

In 3 boxes there will be $3 \times 47$ matches:    $3 \times 47 = 141$

In 30 boxes there will be $10 \times 141$ matches:    $10 \times 141 = 1410$

30 boxes contain 1410 matches.

### Exercise 1C

1. A box of tissues contains 38 tissues. How many tissues are there in 40 boxes?

2. There are 52 playing cards in a pack. How many cards are there in:
   (a) 10 packs  (b) 30 packs  (c) 80 packs
   (d) 100 packs  (e) 200 packs  (f) 400 packs?

3. Use your answers to question **2** to find how many cards there are in:
   (a) 60 packs  (b) 130 packs  (c) 160 packs
   (d) 210 packs  (e) 240 packs  (f) 450 packs.

4. Using non-calculator methods only, show 3 different ways to find the number of playing cards in 90 packs.

5. Sanjit has 120 boxes of Christmas cards in his shop. Each box contains 25 cards. How many Christmas cards does Sanjit have altogether?

# 1.4 Dividing by 10 and by 100

Dividing a number by 10 moves each digit *one* place value column to the *right*.

$$\begin{array}{c} H\ T\ U\ .\ t \\ 3\ 4\ 0\ . \\ \div 10\ \searrow \searrow \searrow \\ 3\ 4\ .\ 0 \qquad 340 \div 10 = 34 \end{array}$$

Dividing a number by 100 moves the digits *two* place value columns to the *right*.

$$\begin{array}{c} Th\ H\ T\ U\ .\ t\ h \\ 3\ 4\ 0\ 0\ . \\ \div 100\ \searrow \searrow \searrow \searrow \\ 3\ 4\ .\ 0\ 0 \qquad 3400 \div 100 = 34 \end{array}$$

---

### Exercise 1D

1. Write down the answers to
   (a) $140 \div 10$  (b) $560 \div 10$  (c) $3280 \div 10$
   (d) $3700 \div 100$  (e) $56\,300 \div 100$  (f) $8000 \div 100$
   (g) $56\,000 \div 1000$  (h) $560 \times 10 \div 100$
   (i) $34 \div 100 \times 1000$

2. 1500 fireworks are to be packed in boxes. How many boxes will they fill if there are:
   (a) 10 fireworks in each box
   (b) 100 fireworks in each box?

---

### *Example 2*

A page of stamps contains 40 stamps. A post office has 4800 stamps. How many pages of stamps is this?

$$40 = 10 \times 4$$

So dividing by 40 is the same as dividing by 10 and then dividing by 4.

$$\begin{aligned} 4800 \div 40 &= 4800 \div 10 \div 4 \\ &= 480 \div 4 \\ &= 120 \end{aligned}$$

$$\begin{array}{r} 120 \\ 4{\overline{\smash{)}480}} \end{array}$$

There are 120 pages of stamps.

---

### Exercise 1E

1. In Nottsford College there are 3200 students. Each teaching group has 20 students. How many teaching groups are there?

2. A syndicate of 30 people wins £33 600 on the National Lottery. If the prize is shared equally, how much does each person receive?

3. A wood merchant orders 28 boxes of wood screws. Each box contains 100 screws. He opens all the boxes and re-packs the screws in packets of 40 to sell. How many packets does he have to sell?

4. Sally wants to divide £4400 by 25. Use a non-calculator method to show how she can do this:
   (a) starting by dividing by 10
   (b) starting by dividing by 100.

## Worked exam question 1

In the week before a General Election, a politician made speeches on every day of the week.

The table shows the lengths of time of the speeches.

| Monday | 40 minutes |
|---|---|
| Tuesday | 55 minutes |
| Wednesday | 28 minutes |
| Thursday | 39 minutes |
| Friday | 48 minutes |
| Saturday | 42 minutes |
| Sunday | 41 minutes |

(a) Work out the total length of time for which the politician spoke in the week. Give your answer in hours and minutes.

$$40 + 55 + 28 + 39 + 48 + 42 + 41 = 293 \ min$$

**Do:**
Show all your working

$$4 \ hours = 240 \ min$$

Remember that 1 hour = 60 minutes

$$293 - 240 = 53 \ min$$

.....4..... hours .....53..... minutes

(b) (i) Write the times in order of length of time, starting with the longest.

55    48    42    41    40    39    28

Check that you have written down all 7 numbers

..............................................................

(ii) State the middle value.

55    48    42    ④1    40    39    28

**Do:**
Cross off one number from each end of the line. Continue until there is only one left. This is the middle value

.....41..... minutes
(London)

# 1.5 Negative numbers

Numbers can be positive or negative. Zero is taken as neither positive nor negative.

A number line to show positive and negative numbers looks like this:

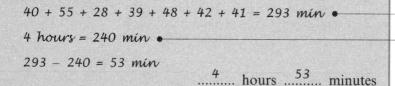

In the real world zero can be set at any point that is convenient.

The freezing point of water is taken as zero degrees (0°) in the Celsius scale.

Sea level is taken as zero for measuring the height of land. Above sea level is positive, below sea level is negative.

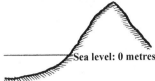

Sea level: 0 metres

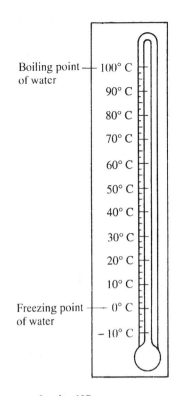

Boiling point of water — 100° C

Freezing point of water — 0° C

### Example 3

At midday on 1 January the temperatures in five cities were:

Bradford −4 °C
Glasgow −6 °C
Birmingham 0 °C
Bristol 2 °C
London 4 °C

(a) Which city was the coldest?

(b) What was the difference in temperature between Bradford and London?

First draw a temperature scale and mark on it the temperatures for the five cities.

(a) From the temperature scale you can see that Glasgow was the coldest, at −6 °C.

(b) Counting down the scale you can see that London was 8° warmer than Bradford.

London 4 °C
Bristol 2 °C
Birmingham 0 °C
Bradford −4 °C
Glasgow −6 °C

If you have money in a bank account, you have a **credit** (positive) balance.

If you are overdrawn and owe the bank money you have a **debit** (negative) balance.

In calculations you can use positive numbers to represent money you have and negative numbers to represent money you owe.

### Example 4

Shane has £10 and he owes Afsan £6. He pays Afsan the money he owes him.

How much does Shane have left?

Using a positive number for the money Shane has and a negative number for the money he owes, the calculation is

$$10 + -6 = 4$$

Shane has £4 left.

## Exercise 1F

1. Arrange these temperatures in order, coldest first.
   (a) −6 °C, 5 °C, −2 °C, 8 °C, 3 °C, −9 °C
   (b) −10 °C, −5 °C, −7 °C, −4 °C, −16 °C, 0 °C
   (c) −45 °C, 19 °C, −7 °C, 0 °C, −1 °C, 1 °C, −15 °C
   (d) −8 °C, −9 °C, −10 °C, −11 °C, −12 °C, −13 °C

2.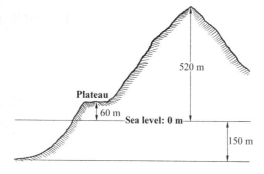

   (a) What is the difference in level between the top of the mountain and the bottom of the sea?
   (b) What would be the difference in level between the top of the mountain and the bottom of the sea if zero level was moved to the plateau?

3. A group of students get together to discuss how much money they have and how much money they owe each other.
   (a) Jagjit has £12 and owes Mark £9. Jagjit pays Mark the money he owes him.
   How much does he have left?
   (b) Julie owes Jenny £4 and also owes Karen £8.
   How much does Julie owe altogether?
   (c) Karl has £15 and owes Shirley £21. Karl gives Shirley all the money he has.
   How much does he still owe her?
   (d) John has £10 but owes Keith £14.
   What is the difference between the amount that John has and the amount he owes?
   (e) Mandeep owes Sanjay £9 and also owes Leroy £7.
   What is the difference between what he owes Sanjay and what he owes Leroy?

   (f) Carol has £7 in one pocket and £13 in another pocket.
   What is the difference between the two amounts she has in her pockets?

4. Write down each part of question **3** as a numerical sum. Use positive numbers to represent money a person has and negative numbers to represent money a person owes.

5. Write down the answer to:
   (a) $+5 + +6 =$      (b) $+5 + -3 =$
   (c) $-2 + +8 =$      (d) $-2 + -4 =$
   (e) $-3 + +6 =$      (f) $+5 + -4 + -3 =$

6. Write down the answer to:
   (a) $+5 - 6 =$      (b) $-2 - -4 =$
   (c) $+8 - +6 =$      (d) $-3 - -4 =$
   (e) $+8 - +5 =$      (f) $-4 - -3 - -2 =$

7. Lucy's bank balance is £64 debit. She needs to buy books costing a total of £120 for her college course.
   How much money does she need in total to buy her books and pay the bank what she owes?

8. Copy and complete these number patterns.
   (a) 4      7      10      13      ?      ?
   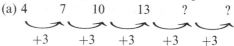
       +3     +3     +3     +3     +3

   (b) 7      5      3      1      ?      ?
       −2     −2     −2     −2     −2

   (c) 8      4      0      −4      ?      ?
       −4     −4     −4     −4     −4

   (d) −8   −6      −4      −2      ?      ?
       +2     +2     +2     +2     +2

   (e) 4      1      −3      −8      ?      ?
       −3     −4     −5     −6     −7

## Worked exam question 2

| Day | Mon | Tues | Wed | Thurs | Fri | Sat |
|---|---|---|---|---|---|---|
| Noon | −3°C | −2°C | 0°C | −3°C | 2°C | −3°C |
| Midnight | −8°C | −8°C | −6°C | −10°C | −6°C | −5°C |

The table shows the temperature at noon and at midnight in Basingstoke on six days in January.

(a) Write down the lowest temperature shown in the table.

................ −10 .... °C ●

**Do:**
Notice that the lowest temperature is the negative number with the largest numerical value

(b) (i)  On which day shown was there the biggest difference between Noon and Midnight temperatures?

............... *Friday* ●

Check each pair of numbers carefully

(ii)  How much was that difference in temperature?

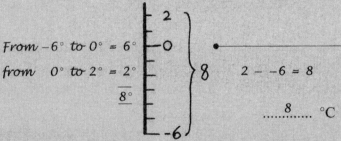

*From* −6° *to* 0° = 6°
*from*  0° *to* 2° = 2°
          $\overline{8°}$

$2 - -6 = 8$

.......... 8 ...... °C

Draw a thermometer to help you

The temperature at noon Sunday was 5°C higher than the temperature at noon Saturday.

(c) What was the temperature at noon Sunday?

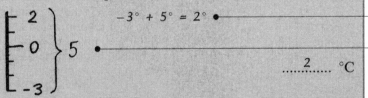

−3° + 5° = 2° ●

.......... 2 ...... °C

**Do:**
Start at −3 and add 5

Draw a thermometer to help you

The temperature at midnight Sunday was 6°C lower than the temperature at midnight Saturday.

(d) What was the temperature at midnight Sunday?

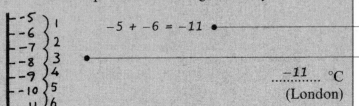

−5 + −6 = −11 ●

.......... −11 ...... °C
(London)

**Do:**
Start at −5 and add another −6

Draw a thermometer to help you

## 1.6 Fractions

A group of students was asked how they travelled to college on a Wednesday. The results were:

4 walked
15 used their own car
6 had a lift in a friend's car
2 used public transport
3 cycled

To find the fraction of the class that used a particular type of transport, you must first find the total number of students in the group. You can do this by adding together all the different responses in the survey:

$$4 + 15 + 6 + 2 + 3 = 30$$

Of the 30 students, 4 walked to college. You can say 4 out of 30 walked: $\frac{4}{30}$

Of the 30 students, 15 travelled by car. You can say 15 out of 30 went by car: $\frac{15}{30}$

---

### Exercise 1G

1. Using the results above, write down the fraction of the group that:
   (a) travelled in a friend's car
   (b) used public transport
   (c) cycled.

2. In a survey on a second group of 32 students, it was found that $\frac{4}{32}$ of the group used public transport, $\frac{19}{32}$ used their own car and the rest used other forms of transport.
   Write down:
   (a) the total number of students in this second group
   (b) the number that used public transport
   (c) the number that used other forms of transport
   (d) the fraction of the group that used other forms of transport.
   (e) Of the 19 students that used their own car, 5 drove cars that had fitted CD players. What fraction of those who travelled to college by car did not have a fitted CD player?

3. The same survey on a third group of students gave these results:
   $\frac{1}{2}$ of the group used their own car
   $\frac{1}{3}$ of the group walked to college
   The person doing the survey forgot to write down the number of students in the group. He remembered that there were more than 30 students, but less than 40.
   (a) Explain why the number of students in the group could not be 33.
   Write down:
   (b) the number of students in the group
   (c) the number of students who neither used their own car nor walked to college
   (d) the fraction that neither used their own car nor walked to college.

4. In a class of 120 students studying Mathematics, 60 completed the coursework option and 40 completed the 100% terminal examination option. The rest failed to complete the course.
   Write down:
   (a) the fraction of the class who completed the coursework option
   (b) the fraction of the class who completed the 100% terminal examination option
   (c) the fraction of the class who did not complete the course.

5. Before laying the bricks for a new house a trench has to be dug for the foundations. Tom can dig the trench in 4 hours but Claire would take 5 hours.
   (a) What fraction of the trench can each of them dig in 1 hour?
   (b) What fraction could Tom dig on his own in 3 hours?
   (c) How long would it take Claire, working on her own, to dig half the trench?

6. In a set of counters 4 are blue, 6 are green, 3 are yellow and 7 are red.
   Write down the fraction that is:
   (a) blue          (b) green          (c) red

7. Amerjit makes two spinners for an experiment. The first spinner is made from a regular hexagon and the second from an irregular hexagon.

   (a) What fraction of the regular hexagon is shaded?
   (b) Why is it difficult to state the fraction shaded on the irregular hexagon?

---

When using fractions in everyday conversation we often use them as approximate measures. For example 'half an apple' does not mean *exactly* half an apple, since apples are irregular shapes and difficult to cut in half exactly.

However, in mathematics you have to be more precise. One half $(\frac{1}{2})$ means one of two *equal* parts. The fraction $\frac{3}{8}$ means 3 parts out of 8 equal parts.

$\frac{2}{3}, \frac{4}{5}, \frac{7}{9}$ are all fractions. The top number is called the **numerator**. The bottom number is called the **denominator**.

This diagram shows two toffees and one mint.

It is **wrong** to write the fraction of toffees is $\frac{2}{3}$ without saying what the thirds represent.

It is **correct** to write '$\frac{2}{3}$ of the sweets are toffees'. The three items (toffees and mint) are described by a common term – sweets.

### Example 5

Look at the word          MATHEMATICS

Write a sentence involving fractions about:

(a) the Ts     (b) the vowels     (c) the consonants

> Vowels are:
> a, e, i, o, u

(a) $\frac{2}{11}$ of the letters are Ts.     (b) $\frac{4}{11}$ of the letters are vowels.     (c) $\frac{7}{11}$ of the letters are consonants.

---

### Exercise 1H

1. The diagram shows a collection of shapes.
   Write a sentence involving fractions about:
   (a) the square shapes
   (b) the triangular shapes
   (c) the square shapes that have holes in them.

2. This sort of information often appears on packets of soap powder and chocolate wrappers.
   (a) What is the manufacturer trying to imply?
   (b) Why could the information be misleading?

## 1.7 Calculating with fractions

In shops you sometimes see articles marked $\frac{1}{2}$ *price* or *reduced by* $\frac{1}{3}$.
The next example shows you how to find the price you pay when
the price is reduced by a fraction.

### *Example 6*

A coat costing £246 is reduced by $\frac{1}{3}$. Find the new price.

Start by finding $\frac{1}{3}$ of £246. One third is the same as dividing by 3:

$$\frac{1}{3} \text{ of £246} = \frac{£246}{3} = £82.$$

The price of the coat is reduced by £82.

The new price is the original price minus the reduction:

$$£246 - £82 = £164$$

The new price is £164.

### *Example 7*

In a sale the price of a fridge is reduced by $\frac{2}{5}$. If the original price
was £165, find

(a) the reduction in price        (b)   the sale price.

(a) Start by finding $\frac{1}{5}$ of £165.

One fifth is the same as dividing by 5:

$$\frac{1}{5} \text{ of £165} = \frac{£165}{5} = £33$$

If one fifth equals £33 then two fifths must equal $2 \times £33 = £66$.

The price reduction of the fridge is £66.

(b) The sale price is £165 − £66 = £99

---

### Exercise 1I

1. In the January Sales, Planet Superstores reduces
   the price of all its goods by $\frac{1}{3}$. Find the sale price
   of:
   (a) a television set, original price £654.
   (b) an electric toaster, original price £27.
   (c) a lawn mower, original price £309.
   (d) a computer, original price £1845.

2. A vending machine sells 2976 drinks in a week.
   Of this total,
   $\frac{1}{4}$ are coffee, $\frac{1}{8}$ are tea, $\frac{1}{3}$ are chocolate and $\frac{7}{24}$ are
   orange.
   How many drinks of each type are sold?

3. Gail, Roy, Sally and Mark set out on a 60 km
   walk. Gail completes $\frac{1}{2}$ of the walk, Roy $\frac{4}{5}$, Sally
   $\frac{5}{6}$ and Mark $\frac{7}{12}$. Find:
   (a) the distance each person walked

(b) who walked the furthest.

4. Gordon Rice builds a garage for a customer.
   The cost of building the garage is broken down
   as follows:

   The total cost of the garage is £3040. Write
   down the cost for each item on the list.

   | Digging the foundations | $\frac{3}{80}$ |
   |---|---|
   | Laying the base | $\frac{1}{5}$ |
   | Building the garage | $\frac{7}{40}$ |
   | Labour | $\frac{1}{2}$ |
   | Profit | $\frac{7}{80}$ |

5. Suzanne, Andrew and Gaynor inherit £12 000 from their aunt. Suzanne receives $\frac{1}{3}$, Andrew $\frac{1}{5}$ and Gaynor the rest. Find:
   (a) how much Suzanne receives
   (b) how much Andrew receives
   (c) how much Gaynor receives
   (d) the fraction of the inheritance that Gaynor receives.

6. Of all the letters posted last week at Boxton post office, $\frac{3}{8}$ were sent first class, with a postcode, and $\frac{3}{5}$ were sent second class, with a postcode. On all the rest the postcode had been omitted.

   If the total number of letters posted was 26 160, find:
   (a) the number of letters with a postcode
   (b) the number of letters without a postcode
   (c) the fraction of the total number of letters that were without a postcode.

7. Four friends share a sum of money. Joan receives $\frac{1}{3}$ of it, Jatinder $\frac{1}{4}$, Tristan $\frac{1}{6}$ and Ken the rest. If Joan's share is £240 find:
   (a) the total amount of money
   (b) Jatinder's share
   (c) Tristan's share
   (d) the fraction of the total amount that Ken receives.

---

## Worked exam question 3

An orange drink is made by mixing water with concentrated orange juice. $\frac{3}{4}$ of the orange drink is water.

How many litres of water will be in 12 litres of orange drink?

$\frac{1}{4}$ *of 12 = 12 ÷ 4 = 3*

............................................................................................................................

*So* $\frac{3}{4}$ *of 12 = 3 × 3 = 9*

....9.... litres

(MEG)

**Do:**
Show your working
Remember that $\frac{3}{4}$ of 12 is $\frac{3}{4} \times 12$

# 1.8 Decimals

This set of numbers has been written in random order:

1.28,  1.25,  2.54,  1.8,  2.56,  1.74,  2.38

We want to write them in size order with the smallest first.

None of these numbers has anything in the tens column or above. So the first step is to find the numbers with the lowest value in the unit column.

|  |  | U . t h |
|---|---|---|
| *Remember*: 1.28 means | 1 unit | 1 |
|  | 2 tenths | 0 . 2 |
|  | 8 hundredths | 0 . 0 8 |
|  |  | 1 . 2 8 |

In this set there are four numbers with 1 in the unit column:

①.28,       ①.25,       ①.8,       ①.74

As there are several numbers with the same value in the units column, you now look for the lowest value in the tenths column.

In this case there are two numbers with 2 in the tenths column.

　　　　1.②8,　　　1.②5

Since the number of tenths is equal, you need to check the hundredths column to see which is smaller:

　　　　1.2⑧,　　　1.2⑤

Five is less than eight so you now know that the smallest number is 1.25, and the next is 1.28.

The next lowest value will be 1.74 followed by 1.8 giving

　　　　1.25,　　　1.28,　　　1.74,　　　1.8

Using the same method with the numbers that have 2 in the units column, you can now write the numbers in size order:

1.25,　1.28,　1.74,　1.8,　2.38,　2.54,　2.56

---

### Exercise 1J

**1.** Write each of these sets of numbers in size order, lowest first:
(a) 3.4, 3.1, 2.9, 4.2, 2.15, 4.25
(b) 2.98, 2.87, 2.66, 2.99, 2.01, 2.55
(c) 4.4, 6.8, 2.0, 1.6, 6.9, 3.2, 5.1
(d) 5.81, 9.76, 4.64, 9.01, 5.79, 4.975
(e) 2.543, 9, 8.0, 5.43, 2.555, 8.01, 3.87

**2.** (a) Use a calculator to work out:
　(i) $2.4 \times 3.9$　(ii) $6.2 \times 2.1$　(iii) $4.6 \times 2.5$
　(iv) $7.3 \times 1.4$　(v) $5.2 \times 3.1$　(vi) $12.2 \times 0.8$
(b) Write your answers in size order, with the smallest first.

**3.** (a) Use a calculator to work out
　(i) $14.8 \div 9.8$　(ii) $3.6 \div 2.4$　(iii) $0.8 \div 0.6$
　(iv) $132.7 \div 86.8$　　(v) $6.2 \div 3.9$
(b) Write your answers in size order, smallest first.

---

## 1.9 Changing fractions to decimals

0.5 is the decimal equivalent of $\frac{1}{2}$.

To change a fraction into its decimal equivalent you divide the numerator by the denominator $1 \div 2 = 0.5$

---

### Exercise 1K

**1.** Change these fractions into their equivalent decimals:
(a) $\frac{3}{4}$　　(b) $\frac{2}{5}$　　(c) $\frac{9}{20}$
(d) $\frac{7}{25}$　　(e) $\frac{1}{8}$　　(f) $\frac{3}{8}$
(g) $\frac{2}{3}$　　(h) $\frac{4}{9}$　　(i) $\frac{7}{12}$

**2.** Keith's total marks for each of his subjects over a term are shown in the report opposite:
(a) Rewrite all the subject marks as decimals.
(b) Rewrite the marks in size order with the best result first.

| EASTROSE COLLEGE | |
|---|---|
| **NAME :** Keith Ledger | |
| **SUBJECT** | **MARK** |
| English | $\frac{32}{40}$ |
| French | $\frac{38}{50}$ |
| German | $\frac{21}{25}$ |
| Science | $\frac{17}{20}$ |
| Maths | $\frac{82}{100}$ |

3. Eight pieces of wood are measured, and their lengths are found to be 2 m 45 cm, 2449 mm, 248 cm, 2.34 m, 2.62 m, 241 cm, 2457 mm, 2 m 57 cm.
   Write all the lengths in size order, smallest first, using the same unit of measurement.

4. Jamie buys a packet of digestive biscuits. The packet contains 15 biscuits. For a science project Jamie has to weigh each biscuit. These are his results.

   | 21.4 g | 19.9 g | 18.8 g | 20.3 g | 20.8 g |
   | 19.8 g | 22.1 g | 21.9 g | 20.6 g | 23.1 g |
   | 18.6 g | 19.6 g | 21.4 g | 21.7 g | 20.8 g |

   (a) Write down the weight of the lightest biscuit and the heaviest biscuit.
   (b) Copy and complete this table.

   | Interval | Tally | Frequency |
   | --- | --- | --- |
   | 18.0 to 18.9 | 11 | 2 |
   | 19.0 to 19.9 | | |
   | 20.0 to 20.9 | | |
   | 21.0 to 21.9 | | |
   | 22.0 to 22.9 | | |
   | 23.0 to 23.9 | | |
   | | | Total 15 |

5. Last year eight students ran 100 m in the college sports day. Their times were:

   | Jessie | 14.35 s |
   | --- | --- |
   | Jasvinder | 14.76 s |
   | Jenny | 13.98 s |
   | Suzanne | 15.05 s |
   | Rani | 14.96 s |
   | Sally | 13.94 s |
   | Gaynor | 14.80 s |
   | Jean | 15.00 s |

   (a) Who won the race?
   (b) Who came third?
   (c) This year Sally has improved her time by 1.1 seconds. The other seven students' times are exactly the same time as last year. Write down who came first, second and third in the race last year.

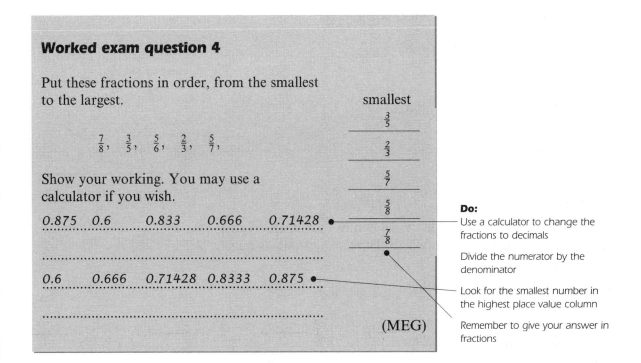

## Worked exam question 4

Put these fractions in order, from the smallest to the largest.

$$\frac{7}{8}, \quad \frac{3}{5}, \quad \frac{5}{6}, \quad \frac{2}{3}, \quad \frac{5}{7},$$

Show your working. You may use a calculator if you wish.

0.875    0.6    0.833    0.666    0.71428

0.6    0.666    0.71428    0.8333    0.875

smallest

$\frac{3}{5}$

$\frac{2}{3}$

$\frac{5}{7}$

$\frac{5}{8}$

$\frac{7}{8}$

(MEG)

**Do:**
Use a calculator to change the fractions to decimals

Divide the numerator by the denominator

Look for the smallest number in the highest place value column

Remember to give your answer in fractions

## 1.10 Percentages

Percentages are used frequently in everyday life. A **percentage** is a fraction out of 100.

For example:

- 12% means $\frac{12}{100}$
- 1% means $\frac{1}{100}$
- 49% means $\frac{49}{100}$
- 10% means $\frac{10}{100}$ which is $\frac{1}{10}$ or 0.1.

So finding 10% of an amount is the same as finding $\frac{1}{10}$ of an amount: you divide by 10 or multiply by 0.1.

### *Example 8*

Find these percentages of £240:

(a) 10%  (b) 25%  (c) $33\frac{1}{3}$%  (d) 50%  (e) 62.5%

(a) $10\% = \frac{1}{10}$

$\frac{1}{10}$ of 240 is $\frac{1}{10} \times 240 = £24$

or $\frac{1}{10} = 0.1$ so 10% of 240 is $0.1 \times 240 = £24$

(b) $25\% = \frac{25}{100} = \frac{1}{4}$

$\frac{1}{4}$ of 240 is $\frac{1}{4} \times 240 = £60$

or $\frac{1}{4} = 0.25$ so 25% of 240 is $0.25 \times 240 = £60$

(c) $33\frac{1}{3}\%$ of 240 is $\frac{33\frac{1}{3}}{100} \times 240 = £80$

or $0.333 \times 240 = £80$

> *Notice that $\frac{1}{3} = 0.333333\ldots$*
> *We shorten this to 0.333 for the calculation.*

(d) 50% of 240 is $\frac{50}{100} \times 240 = £120$

(e) 62.5% is $\frac{5}{8}$

$\frac{5}{8} \times 240 = £150$

> *Notice that $62.5\% = 0.625$*
> *and $\frac{5}{8} = 0.625$*
> *So $62.5\% = \frac{5}{8}$*

### *Example 9*

At Eastrose College, 34% of the students travel to college by car. There are 3600 students at the college. How many students travel to college by car?

You need to find 34% of 3600.

$34\% = \frac{34}{100}$

34% of 3600 is $\frac{34}{100} \times 3600 = 1224$

1224 students travel to college by car

## Exercise 1L

1. Find 10% of each amount.
   (a) £420  (b) £256  (c) £445
   (d) £14  (e) £65  (f) £92
   (g) £22.50  (h) £64.90  (i) £135.80

2. Find 25% of each amount.
   (a) £2400  (b) £3420  (c) £1380
   (d) £340  (e) £600  (f) £225
   (g) £88  (h) £45  (i) £12

3. Of all the students at Eastrose College, 26% travel to college by public transport.
   (a) How many students travel to college by public transport?
   (b) How many students do not travel by public transport?

4. At a recent Derby County football match, there were 28 000 spectators. Of these 35% were 'away' supporters.
   (a) How many 'away' supporters were there?
   (b) How many 'home' supporters were there?
   (c) What percentage of the spectators were 'home' supporters?

5. The table shows the percentage of students at Millbank College who wear glasses.

|  | Wear glasses | Do not wear glasses | Total |
|---|---|---|---|
| Male students | 8% | 34% | 42% |
| Female students | 16% | 42% | 58% |
| Total | 24% | 76% | 100% |

If 5250 students attend the college, find:
   (a) the number of males who wear glasses
   (b) the number of females who wear glasses
   (c) the number of students who wear glasses
   (d) the number of males attending the college
   (e) the number of females attending the college.

6. In a Mathematics examination there were 1600 candidates. The table below shows the percentage of candidates obtaining each grade.
   (a) How many candidates obtained a grade C?
   (b) How many candidates obtained a grade A or B?
   (c) How many candidates obtained a grade C, D or E?
   (d) How many candidates did not achieve a grade?

| Grade | Percentage |
|---|---|
| A | 13% |
| B | 15% |
| C | 24% |
| D | 19% |
| E | 10% |
| F | 8% |
| G | 6% |

---

*Example 10*

Kelly needs to work out 29% of £35

$29\% = \frac{29}{100} = 0.29$

so 29% of £35 is $0.29 \times 35 = £10.15$

*Example 11*

Joe works in a hardware shop. He has to charge Value Added Tax (VAT) on the items he sells. VAT is currently 17.5% of the price of each item.

Work out the VAT on a socket set priced at £128

$17.5\% = \frac{17.5}{100} = 0.175$

so 17.5% of 128 is $0.175 \times 128 = £22.40$

The VAT added to the price is £22.40

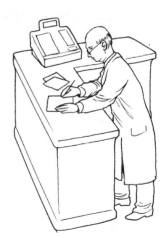

*Example 12*

A catering company gives a 15% discount for early payment.

Work out (a) the discount (b) the total price paid on a bill of £850

(a)  15% of £850 is 0.15 × 850 = £127.50

The discount is £127.50

(b)  The total price paid is £850 − £127.50 = £722.50

---

Here is a quick way of finding the discount price:

The percentage of the bill left after discount will be

$$100\% - 15\% = 85\% \quad = \quad \frac{85}{100} \quad = \quad 0.85$$

So the amount left after discount is 0.85 × £850 = £722.50

---

### Exercise 1M

1. Norman, Wesley and Shaz win a competition prize of £2488. They agree to share the prize so that Norman has 39%, Wesley has 28% and Shaz has 22%. The rest of the money they give to charity. Find:
   (a) the percentage they give to charity
   (b) the amount that each receives.

2. The current rate of VAT is 17.5% of an item's price. Find the amount of VAT to be added to these prices:
   (a) A TV set, £400 before VAT

   (b) A washing machine, £480 before VAT
   (c) A fridge, £80 before VAT
   (d) A computer, £640 before VAT
   (e) A CD player, £150 before VAT

3. A shop gives an end-of-season discount of 12.5% on a set of garden furniture. Before the discount the furniture was priced at £256. Find:
   (a) the amount by which the price is reduced
   (b) the new price of the furniture.

---

### Worked exam question 5

The basic price of a camera is £360. VAT is added at the rate of 17.5%.

Calculate the amount to be paid for the camera.

*17.5% of £360 is 0.175 × 360 = £63*

*Cost of camera = £360 + £63 = £423*

**Do:**
Add the VAT to the basic price

(MEG)

# 1.11 Fractions, decimals and percentages

Shaminder obtained these marks at half term for three of the subjects she studied.

English:      43/50
Science:      54/60
Maths:        35/40

To convert a fraction into its decimal equivalent, you divide the numerator by the denominator. So in decimal form Shaminder's results are:

English:      $43 \div 50 = 0.86$
Science:      $54 \div 60 = 0.9$
Maths:        $35 \div 40 = 0.875$

Now all the results are given as decimals you can compare them.

Shaminder obtained her highest score in Science, followed by Maths and then English.

You usually give examination results as percentages. To change a decimal into a percentage you multiply by 100.

English:      $0.86 \times 100 = 86\%$
Science:      $0.9 \times 100 = 90\%$
Maths:        $0.875 \times 100 = 87.5\%$

## Example 13

In a recent survey of reported car accidents, it was found that 3 in every 8 motorists had exceeded the speed limit.

Write this as a fraction, a decimal and a percentage.

As a fraction, 3 in every $8 = \frac{3}{8}$.

As a decimal, 3 in every $8 = 3 \div 8 = 0.375$.

As a percentage, 3 in every $8 = 0.375 \times 100 = 37.5\%$.

---

## Exercise 1N

You may use a calculator to help you with this exercise.

1. These are Matthew's results for his half term tests. Copy and complete the table.

| Subject | Mark | Decimal equivalent | Percentage |
|---------|------|-------------------|------------|
| English | 28/50 | $28 \div 50 = ?$ | $? \times 100 =$ |
| Science | 33/60 | | |
| Maths | 23/40 | | |

2. Change these fractions into percentages.
   (a) $\frac{1}{2}$        (b) $\frac{3}{5}$        (c) $\frac{11}{20}$
   (d) $\frac{28}{40}$       (e) $\frac{37}{50}$       (f) $\frac{23}{40}$
   (g) $\frac{42}{60}$       (h) $\frac{36}{90}$       (i) $\frac{21}{50}$

3. Out of a year group of 240 students, 60 turned up for football trials and 18 were chosen for the football squad.
   (a) What percentage of those at the trials were selected for the squad?
   (b) What percentage of the year group turned up for trials?
   (c) What percentage of the year group were selected for the squad?

4. During a probability experiment with a four-sided spinner, Luke obtains these results. Copy and complete his table.

| Colour | Number of times | Percentage of total number of spins |
|--------|-----------------|-------------------------------------|
| Red    | 12              |                                     |
| Yellow | 22              |                                     |
| Green  | 28              |                                     |
| Blue   | 18              |                                     |

You can use the same method for changing fractions to decimals and percentages when the numbers are not whole numbers.

*Example 14*

An article costing £12.50 is reduced by £2.40.

Find the percentage reduction.

As a fraction, £2.40 out of £12.50 $= \dfrac{2.4}{12.5} = \dfrac{24}{125}$

As a decimal, £2.40 out of £12.50 $= 2.4 \div 12.5 = 0.192$.

As a percentage, £2.40 out of £12.50 $= 0.192 \times 100 = 19.2\%$.

**Exercise 10**

1. In each part, express the first quantity as a percentage of the second.
   (a) 4.5 m, 7.2 m      (b) 3.4 g, 12.8 g
   (c) 6.6 ml, 1.2 ml    (d) 0.5 km, 1.8 km
   (e) 73.5 cm, 108 cm   (f) £2.24, 1243 p

2. Jimmy the jeweller makes an alloy by mixing 1.6 kg of silver with 8.4 kg of copper. What percentage of the alloy is
   (a) copper   (b) silver?

3. In Nottsford village a new housing estate is to be built. It is expected that the population of the village will increase by $\frac{3}{8}$.
   (a) Write this increase as a decimal and then as a percentage.
   (b) If the village population is currently 560, what will it be once the estate is established?

4. Due to rising costs, Bradbury's increase the price of one brand of chocolate bar by 7%. Write this increase as
   (a) a decimal
   (b) a fraction out of 100

5. Helen rolled a die and obtained the results below.
   (a) How many times was the die rolled?
   (b) Express each number in the right-hand column as a fraction of the total number of throws.
   (c) Express each number in the right-hand column as a percentage of the total number of throws.

| Number on dice | Number of times obtained |
|----------------|--------------------------|
| 1              | 4                        |
| 2              | 8                        |
| 3              | 6                        |
| 4              | 10                       |
| 5              | 5                        |
| 6              | 7                        |

**6.** Helen carried out a second experiment using a
five-sided spinner. Her results were:
(a) Write the results as fractions.
(b) The spinner was spun 400 times. Work out
the number of times each colour was
obtained.

| Colour | Percentage of spins |
|--------|---------------------|
| red | 13% |
| yellow | 19% |
| blue | 23% |
| green | 20% |
| white | 25% |

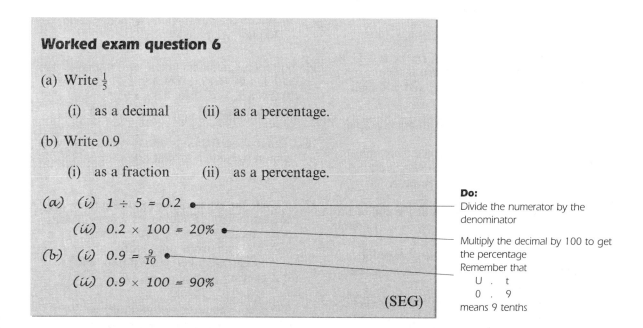

**Worked exam question 6**

(a) Write $\frac{1}{5}$

    (i)  as a decimal    (ii)  as a percentage.

(b) Write 0.9

    (i)  as a fraction    (ii)  as a percentage.

(a)  (i)  $1 \div 5 = 0.2$

    (ii)  $0.2 \times 100 = 20\%$

(b)  (i)  $0.9 = \frac{9}{10}$

    (ii)  $0.9 \times 100 = 90\%$

                        (SEG)

**Do:**
Divide the numerator by the
denominator

Multiply the decimal by 100 to get
the percentage
Remember that

    U  .  t
    0  .  9

means 9 tenths

## Exercise 1P (Mixed questions)

**1.** Arrange these numbers in size order, smallest
first. Write down the value of the middle
number.
(a) 13, 8, 34, 87, 65, 101, 4, 88, 50
(b) 123, 7, 0, 81, 432, 143, 3400, 65, 56

**2.** (a) Work out:
    (i) $23 \times 4$    (ii) $16 \times 5$    (iii) $30 \times 3$
    (iv) $25 \times 2$    (v) $71 \times 1$
(b) Write your answers in size order, smallest
first.

In questions **3** to **6**, do not use a calculator. Show
all your working.

**3.** A fishing club arranges a day's outing for its
members. The cost of the outing works out at
£57 per person.
(a) How much does it cost for 10 members to
go on the outing?

(b) The trip is such a success that a second
outing is arranged for the following week.
This time 30 people sign up to go. Find the
total cost of the second outing.
(c) The fishing club now arranges a weekend
outing, at a cost of £64 per person. What is
the total cost for 230 members?

**4.** Saroja sells fireworks in boxes of 25. She has
240 boxes. How many fireworks does she have
altogether?

**5.** Willhampton 6th Form College has 4800
students.
(a) Each registration group has 30 students.
How many teaching groups are there?

5. (b) The college has 400 car parking spaces for students. How many students could travel to college by car and park there if each car contained
   (i) the driver only
   (ii) the driver plus one passenger
   (iii) the driver plus two passengers.

6. Show how to share £3800 between 25 people so that each person receives an equal amount.

7. Arrange these numbers in size order, smallest first.
   (a) 5, −7, −5, 8, 6, −3, 2
   (b) −7, 12, −3, −2, 1, 7, −15
   (c) −8, −4, −7, −9, −14, −16, −6, −10

8. At midday the temperature in Derby is 5 °C. By midnight it falls to −8 °C. What is the difference between the midday and midnight temperatures?

9. The temperature during an Autumn morning went up from −3 °C to 6 °C.
   (a) By how many degrees did the temperature rise?
   During the afternoon the temperature fell by 8 degrees from 6 °C.
   (b) What was the temperature at the end of the afternoon?                    [London]

10. In a group of 18 people, 7 wear glasses for reading and driving and 2 others wear glasses for driving only.
    (a) What fraction of the group wears glasses?
    (b) What fraction of those who wear glasses wear them for driving only?
    (c) What fraction of the group does not wear glasses?

11. In a survey carried out on dog food, the owners had to report which dog food their pets preferred.
    $\frac{1}{2}$ said Yum biscuits
    $\frac{1}{4}$ said Chunkies
    $\frac{5}{32}$ said Rebound
    (a) What is the minimum number that could have taken part in the survey?
    (b) What percentage of owners reported that their pets preferred Chunkies?

12. The diagram shows a collection of shapes.

Write a sentence involving fractions about:
(a) the round shapes
(b) the square shapes
(c) the shaded shapes.

13. A vending machine sells 1344 drinks in one day. Of these,
    $\frac{1}{3}$ are coffee          $\frac{1}{4}$ are tea
    $\frac{1}{8}$ are orange          $\frac{7}{24}$ are hot chocolate
    How many drinks of each type are sold?

14. Flurries Discount Store sells a certain make of washing machine for £352. Planet Supplies sells the same machine for £525 but in the sale offers a discount of $\frac{1}{3}$ on this model.
    (a) What is the value of the discount offered by Planet Supplies?
    (b) Which company offers the better deal? Explain your answer.

15. Write these numbers in size order, smallest first.
    (a) 1.1, 1.01, 1.15, 1.099, 1.9, 1.2
    (b) 2.4, 8.9, 7.65, 7.56, 4.32, 8.85
    (c) 14.6, 0.01, 9.99, 7.85, 34, 12, 5.543

16. Change these fractions into decimals and write them in size order, largest first.
    $\frac{2}{3}$, $\frac{3}{4}$, $\frac{7}{9}$, $\frac{3}{5}$, $\frac{5}{8}$, $\frac{9}{16}$

17. In a sale the prices of the following items are reduced by 10%. Find the amount by which each is reduced.
    (a) A TV set: normal price £650
    (b) An electric cooker: normal price £440
    (c) A camera: normal price £125.

18. 1200 people went on a protest march.
    20% of the protestors were aged 45 or over
    30% of the protestors were aged between 25 and 45
    41% of the protestors were aged between 15 and 25
    9% of the protestors were aged 15 or under
    Find the number of protestors in each age group.

19. Write down the decimal equivalents of these fractions:
    (a) $\frac{4}{5}$    (b) $\frac{3}{4}$    (c) $\frac{5}{16}$    (d) $\frac{2}{9}$

20. Write these decimals as percentages:
    (a) 0.12    (b) 0.65    (c) 0.66    (d) 0.895

21. Write these fractions as percentages:
    (a) $\frac{2}{5}$    (b) $\frac{7}{8}$    (c) $\frac{9}{10}$    (d) $\frac{7}{9}$

22. Avtar scored 12 out of 15 in an end-of-unit test. What was her score as:
    (a) a decimal          (b) a percentage?

23. At Sound Audio all prices are reduced by $\frac{1}{4}$ in the sale. A compact disc player originally cost £356. Find
    (a) the sale price
    (b) the percentage reduction.

24. At Maestro Music, the price of a similar compact disc player is reduced from £360 to £300. Find:
    (a) the actual reduction
    (b) the reduction as a fraction of the original price
    (c) the reduction as a decimal fraction of the original price
    (d) the reduction as a percentage of the original price.

25. A new housing estate is to be built in the Shelby School catchment area. It is estimated that the number of pupils who attend the school will increase from 400 to 560. Find
    (a) the actual increase in the school population
    (b) the increase as a fraction of the original number of pupils

(c) the increase as a decimal fraction of the original number of pupils
(d) the increase as a percentage of the original number of pupils.

26. Three sisters own a machine tool company. Brenda is the eldest and owns $\frac{1}{2}$ of the shares, Carol owns $\frac{2}{5}$ and Maureen is the youngest and owns $\frac{1}{10}$ of the shares.
    (a) What fraction of the shares do Carol and Maureen own between them?
    (b) What percentage of the shares does each sister own?
    (c) If a total dividend of £2000 is paid to shareholders how much does each sister receive?

27. John works as an accountant at Eastland Bank. On 1st January he receives a 7% pay raise. What is his pay rise as:
    (a) a fraction        (b) a decimal?

28. VAT is currently 17.5%. Write this as
    (a) a decimal        (b) a fraction.

## Test yourself

| | |
|---|---|
| QUESTION | **1**. Multiply 27 by 40 |
| ANSWER | 1080       *If your answer is incorrect review page 2, Section 1.3 on multiplying by 10* |

| | |
|---|---|
| QUESTION | **2**. Divide 1800 by 40 |
| ANSWER | 45       *If your answer is incorrect review page 3, Section 1.4 on dividing by 10* |

| | |
|---|---|
| QUESTION | **3.** The midnight temperature was $-5\,°C$, the midday temperature was $8\,°C$. What is the difference between the midday temperature and the midnight temperature? |
| ANSWER | $13\,°C$       *If your answer is incorrect review page 4, Section 1.5 on negative numbers* |

| | |
|---|---|
| QUESTION | **4**. Write down the answers to<br>(a) $4 + -3$    (b) $-4 + -6$    (c) $-3 - -2$ |
| ANSWER | (a) 1   (b) $-10$   (c) $-1$       *If your answers are incorrect review page 4, Section 1.5 on negative numbers* |

**5.** In a group of 24 students 10 wear glasses.

QUESTION    Write down the fraction of the group that does **not** wear glasses.

ANSWER    $\frac{14}{24}$                *If your answer is incorrect review page 8, Section 1.6 on calculating with fractions*

---

QUESTION    **6.** Find $\frac{2}{5}$ of 35

ANSWER    14                *If your answer is incorrect review page 10, Section 1.7 on fractions*

---

QUESTION    **7.** Change these fractions to decimals: $\frac{2}{5}$   $\frac{1}{4}$   $\frac{3}{8}$.
Write your answers in size order, smallest first.

ANSWER    0.25,   0.375,   0.4                *If your answer is incorrect review page 12, Section 1.9 on decimals*

---

QUESTION    **8.** Find 32% of £84

ANSWER    £26.88                *If your answer is incorrect review page 14, Section 1.10 on percentages*

---

**9.** 24% of all students at a college study Mathematics. There are 3600 students.

QUESTION    How many students study mathematics?

ANSWER    864                *If your answer is incorrect review page 14, Section 1.10 on percentages*

---

QUESTION    **10.**   (a)   Change 0.86 to a percentage.
(b)   Change 51% to a fraction.
(c)   Change $\frac{4}{5}$ to a percentage.

ANSWER    (a)   86%   (b)   $\frac{51}{100}$                *If your answers are incorrect review page 17,*
(c)   80%                *Section 1.11 on fractions, percentages and decimals*

---

QUESTION    **11.**   Express 4.2 m as a percentage of 17.5 m.

ANSWER    24%                *If your answer is incorrect review page 17, Section 1.11 on fractions, percentages and decimals*

---

**12.** An article costing £2.40 is reduced by 80p.

QUESTION    Find the percentage reduction.

ANSWER    $33\frac{1}{3}$%                *If your answer is incorrect review page 17, Section 1.11 on fractions, percentages and decimals*

## Summary of key points to remember

1. Multiplying a number by 10 moves each digit *one* place value column to the *left*.

   H T U
     3 2
   ×10
     3 2 0

2. Multiplying a number by 100 moves each digit *two* place value columns to the *left*.

   Th H T U
       3 2
   ×100
     3 2 0 0

3. When ordering negative numbers the negative number with the largest numerical value is the smallest. For example −6 is smaller than −4.

4. The difference between two temperatures is the number of degrees between them. You can use a temperature scale to find the difference.

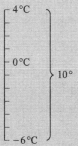

5. The fraction $\frac{4}{5}$ means 4 parts out of 5. 4 is called the **numerator** and 5 is called the **denominator**.

6. To find $\frac{3}{5}$ of an amount, find $\frac{1}{5}$ and then multiply by 3.

   To find $\frac{3}{5}$ of 20

   $\frac{1}{5}$ of 20 = 4
   $\frac{3}{5}$ of 20 = 3 × 4 = 12

7. When ordering decimals look for the number that has the lowest number in the highest place value. If there are two or more numbers with the same value look for the smallest digit in the next place value column.

8. • To find 10% of an amount divide the amount by 10.

   • To find 1% of an amount divide the amount by 100.

   • To find 12% of an amount (i) find 10% then (ii) find 1%. Add two lots of 1% to the 10% to give 12%.

9. • To change a fraction into a decimal divide the numerator by the denominator. You can use a calculator to help you.

   • To change a fraction into a percentage divide the numerator by the denominator and then multiply by 100.

   • To change a decimal to a percentage multiply the decimal by 100.

# 2 Properties of number

## 2.1 Introduction

In this unit you will learn about the properties of number that are tested in the GCSE examination. These include:

- **factor** and the **highest common factor**
- **multiple** and the **lowest common multiple**
- **prime** numbers
- **square** numbers and **square roots**
- **cube** numbers and **cube roots**
- numbers written in **standard form**

These properties of number have been a source of fascination and research for mathematicians over the centuries. They are also very useful.

For example, suppose that you wanted to lay a row of tiles across a wall.

If the width of a tile divides exactly into the width of the wall then you will be able to use a whole number of tiles. Otherwise you will need to use part of a tile.

The work on factors and multipliers is all about solving this type of problem.

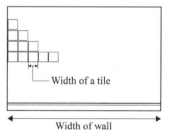

Width of a tile

Width of wall

## 2.2 Factors

Here are all the different ways of multiplying two whole numbers together to make 24.

$$1 \times 24 = 24$$
$$2 \times 12 = 24$$
$$3 \times 8 \ = 24$$
$$4 \times 6 \ = 24$$

The numbers 1, 2, 3, 4, 6, 8, 12 and 24 all divide into 24 exactly: there is no remainder. These numbers are called the factors of 24.

The **factors** of a number are all the *whole numbers* that divide into it without a remainder.

## Example 1

Write down all the factors of 50. You may use a calculator if you wish.

| | |
|---|---|
| $50 \div 1 = 50$ | so 1 and 50 are factors |
| $50 \div 2 = 25$ | so 2 and 25 are factors |
| $50 \div 3 = 16.66\ldots$ | not factors |
| $50 \div 4 = 12.5$ | not factors |
| $50 \div 5 = 10$ | so 5 and 10 are factors |
| $50 \div 6 = 8.33$ | not factors |
| $50 \div 7 = 7.14$ | not factors |
| $50 \div 8 = 6.25$ | not factors |
| $50 \div 9 = 5.55$ | not factors |
| $50 \div 10 = 5$ | so 5 and 10 are factors |

We have already found that 5 and 10 are factors, so we can stop dividing into 50.

The factors of 50 are 1, 2, 5, 10, 25 and 50.

To find the factors of a number divide it by 1, by 2, by 3 and so on. Stop when you get factors that you have already found.

## Exercise 2A

**1.** Using the method of Example 1, write down all the factors of:
(a) 10    (b) 15    (c) 21    (d) 49

**2.** Find all the factors of:
(a) 40    (b) 72    (c) 100    (d) 144

**3.** (a) Write down all the factors of
(i) 33    (ii) 67    (iii) 100    (iv) 151

(b) Which of the numbers has the most factors?
(c) Which of the numbers has the fewest factors?

**4.** Which of these numbers is 'the odd one out', and why?
11,   17,   21,   31,   43

## Example 2

Find the largest number that will divide into both 54 and 78.

Find the factors of 54:

| | |
|---|---|
| $54 \div 1 = 54$ | so 1 and 54 are factors |
| $54 \div 2 = 27$ | so 2 and 27 are factors |
| $54 \div 3 = 18$ | so 3 and 18 are factors |
| $54 \div 4 = 13.5$ | not factors |
| $54 \div 5 = 10.8$ | not factors |
| $54 \div 6 = 9$ | so 6 and 9 are factors |
| $54 \div 7 = 7.714$ | not factors |
| $54 \div 8 = 6.75$ | not factors |
| $54 \div 9 = 6$ | so 9 and 6 are factors |

Stop: because we have found these factors already.

The factors of 54 are 1, 2, 3, 6, 9, 18, 27 and 54.

Find the factors of 78:

$78 \div 1 = 78$    so 78 and 1 are factors
$78 \div 2 = 39$    so 2 and 39 are factors
$78 \div 3 = 26$    so 3 and 26 are factors
$78 \div 4 = 19.5$  not factors
$78 \div 5 = 15.6$  not factors
$78 \div 6 = 13$    so 6 and 13 are factors
$78 \div 7 = 11.14$ not factors
$78 \div 8 = 9.75$  not factors
$78 \div 9 = 8.67$  not factors
$78 \div 10 = 7.8$  not factors
$78 \div 11 = 7.09$ not factors
$78 \div 12 = 6.5$  not factors
$78 \div 13 = 6$    so 6 and 13 are factors

Stop: because we have found these factors already.

The factors of 78 are 1, 2, 3, 6, 13, 26 and 39, and the factors of 54 are 1, 2, 3, 6, 9, 18, 27 and 54.

From these lists you can see that the *largest* number that divides into both 54 and 78 is 6.

In Example 2 you saw that 1, 2, 3 and 6 are factors of both 54 and 78. You can say that 1, 2, 3 and 6 are the **common factors** of 54 and 78.

The **highest common factor** of two numbers is the largest number that is a factor of both of them. In Example 2, 6 is the highest common factor of 54 and 78.

---

## Exercise 2B

**1.** Find the highest common factor of:
   (a) 15 and 35            (b) 32 and 64
   (c) 72 and 108           (d) 125 and 150
   (e) 29 and 49            (f) 28 and 112

**2.** (a) Multiply 6 by 16       (b) Multiply 8 by 20
   (c) Find the highest common factor of your
       answers to (a) and (b).

**3.** A rectangular field measures 154 m by 144 m. The farmer who owns the field has to erect a fence all the way round it. To keep the cost down the support posts are positioned as far apart as possible.

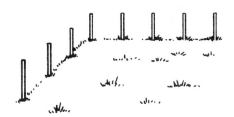

The support posts must be equally spaced and there must be a post at each corner.

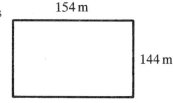

154 m

144 m

How far apart should the farmer place the posts?

**4.** The diagram shows the floor of a rectangular kitchen. The floor is to be covered by a whole number of square tiles. The tiles are all to be identical in size and as large as possible.
Find:
(a) the size of the tiles
(b) the number of tiles required.

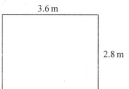

3.6 m

2.8 m

## 2.3 Simplifying fractions

Fractions can be simplified if the numerator (top) and the denominator (bottom) have a common factor.

When there is no common factor the fraction is in it's simplest form.

*Example 3*

Simplify $\dfrac{9}{12}$

9 and 12 have a common factor of 3 so we can divide the top and the bottom by 3.

$$\frac{9}{12} = \frac{9 \div 3}{12 \div 3}$$
$$= \frac{3}{4}.$$

*Example 4*

Express $\dfrac{18}{30}$ as a fraction in its simplest form.

18 and 30 have a common factor of 2

so
$$\frac{18}{30} = \frac{18 \div 2}{30 \div 2}$$
$$= \frac{9}{15}$$

9 and 15 have a common factor of 3

so
$$\frac{9}{15} = \frac{9 \div 3}{15 \div 3}$$
$$= \frac{3}{5}.$$

3 and 5 have no common factor so

$$\frac{18}{30} = \frac{3}{5} \quad \text{in its simplest form.}$$

### Exercise 2C

**1.** Express each of these fractions in its simplest form.

(a) $\frac{8}{20}$    (b) $\frac{48}{100}$    (c) $\frac{18}{24}$    (d) $\frac{40}{1000}$    (e) $\frac{12}{36}$    (f) $\frac{16}{40}$

## 2.4 Prime numbers

A number that has two and only two factors is called a prime number.

- 3 is a prime number because it has only two factors: 1 and 3
- 7 is a prime number because it has only two factors: 1 and 7

All numbers can be made by multiplying some prime numbers together.

For example, 30 can be made by multiplying together the prime numbers 2, 3 and 5:

$2 \times 3 \times 5 = 30$

*1 is not a prime number, because it only has one factor.*

## Exercise 2D

1. Which of these numbers are prime numbers?
   5,  13,  15,  21,  27,  31,  39,  41

2. Explain, with reasons, why these numbers are **not** prime numbers:
   9,  15,  25,  33,  49,  65,  100

3. Explain why:
   (a) 2 is a prime number
   (b) 1 is not a prime number
   (c) no even number, except the number 2, can be prime.

4. Write down all the prime numbers that are less than 50.

5. Make these numbers by multiplying together prime numbers. You may use the same prime number more than once.
   (a) 10     (b) 12     (c) 24     (d) 30

6. (a) Copy and complete this number pattern.
   $2 \times 3 + 1 =$
   $2 \times 3 \times 5 + 1 =$
   $2 \times 3 \times 5 \times 7 + 1 =$
   (b) Write down the next line of the number pattern. Work out the answer.
   (c) What do your four answers have in common?

7. (a) Write down all the factors of 18.
   (b) How many factors does 18 have?
   (c) Write down the factors that are prime numbers.

8. Write down all the factors of 42 that are prime numbers.

## 2.5 Prime factors

The factors of 12 are 1, 2, 3, 4, 6 and 12

The factors of 12 that are prime numbers are 2 and 3. These are called the **prime factors** of 12.

You can use tree diagrams to find the prime factors of a number. Suppose you wanted to find the prime factors of 60. You could do it like this.

Starting number:

Split into 2 numbers:

Keep splitting until all the numbers are prime:

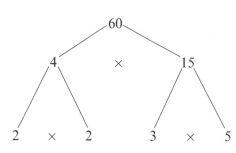

**Check**: $2 \times 2 \times 3 \times 5 = 60$.

The prime factors are 2, 3 and 5. (You only list each prime number once.)

### Exercise 2E

You will need a calculator for this exercise.

1. Copy and complete this tree diagram to confirm that the prime factors of 60 are 2, 3 and 5.

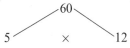

2. Copy and complete this diagram to find the prime factors of 252.

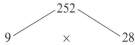

3. Given that:
   $10 \times 77 = 770$ and $11 \times 70 = 770$
   (a) Draw a tree diagram to find the prime factors of 770.
   (b) Draw a second tree diagram to check your answer.

4. By drawing tree diagrams, or by any other method, find the prime factors of these numbers.
   (a) 525     (b) 1386     (c) 2600

5. Is 1007 a prime number? Explain your answer.

## 2.6 Multiples

These numbers are taken from the 4 times table.

| 4, | 8, | 12, | 16, | 20, | 24, ... |
|---|---|---|---|---|---|
| $(1 \times 4)$ | $(2 \times 4)$ | $(3 \times 4)$ | $(4 \times 4)$ | $(5 \times 4)$ | $(6 \times 4)$ |

The numbers are called **multiples** of 4. Any whole number that can be written as 'something $\times$ 4' or '4 $\times$ something' is a multiple of 4.

The number $12 = 3 \times 4$. You can say it is the 3rd multiple of 4.

### Exercise 2F

1. Write down:
   (a) the 7th multiple of 4
   (b) the 8th multiple of 4
   (c) the 12th multiple of 4.

2. These numbers are all multiples of 6:
   6,   12,   18,   24,   30,   36,   42.
   (a) Write down the next three multiples of 6.
   (b) What is the 12th multiple of 6?

3. (a) List all the multiples of 3, up to 45.
   (b) List all the multiples of 5, up to 45.
   (c) List all the numbers up to 45 that are multiples of both 3 and 5.

4. (a) List five numbers that are multiples of both 2 and 5.
   (b) List four numbers that are multiples of both 4 and 6.
   (c) List three numbers that are multiples of both 4 and 7.
   (d) List two numbers that are multiples of both 11 and 12.

*Example 5*

Manjit and Sanjeev are bell-ringers. Manjit rings his bell every 5 seconds and Sanjeev rings his bell every 8 seconds. If Manjit and

Sanjeev start by ringing their bells together, how long will it be before they ring them together again?

Starting at time zero, Manjit will ring his bell at these times (in seconds):

0,  5,  10,  15,  25,  30,  35,  *40*,  45,  50...

Starting at time zero, Sanjeev will ring his bell at these times (in seconds):

0,  8,  16,  24,  32,  *40*,  48,  56,  64...

They will ring their bells together again 40 seconds after the start.

In Example 3 Manjit's times are multiples of 5 and Sanjeev's times are multiples of 8.

40 is a multiple of both 5 and 8 and we say that 40 is a **common multiple** of 8 and 5.

Other common multiples of 8 and 5 are 80 and 120. (You can check this.)

The **lowest common multiple** of two numbers is the smallest number that is a multiple of both of them.

In Example 6, 40 is the lowest common multiple of 8 and 5.

## Exercise 2G

1. Tom, Hilary and Greta are bell-ringers. Tom rings his bell every 3 seconds, Hilary rings her bell every 4 seconds and Greta rings her bell every 5 seconds. They all ring their bells together at time zero.
   (a) When do Tom and Hilary next ring their bells together?
   (b) When do Hilary and Greta next ring their bells together?
   (c) When do Tom and Greta next ring their bells together?
   (d) When do all three bells next ring together?

2. Belam has a set of 6 g weights, Avery has a set of 8 g weights and Flo has a set of 9 g weights. Find the smallest mass that can be weighed by all three people.

3. The Radbury Chocolate company makes Easter eggs. The eggs are sold in boxes of two different sizes. One size holds 3 Easter eggs and the other holds 7.

   (a) A customer wants 35 Easter eggs. How many boxes holding 3 eggs and how many boxes holding 7 eggs does she buy?
   (b) Show how these orders for Easter eggs can be supplied using a mixture of boxes of 3 and 7.
      (i) an order for 20 eggs
      (ii) an order for 32 eggs
      (iii) an order for 50 eggs.

4. Joan wants to buy 11 Easter eggs. What difficulties will she have if she insists on having only *full* boxes of eggs?

5. Radbury's also make and sell chocolate Christmas Santas. These Santas are packed in boxes of 5 and boxes of 8.
   (a) Show how an order for 64 Santas could be supplied.
   (b) Could Radbury's supply an order for 37 Santas using full boxes only?
   (c) Radbury's decide to have a minimum order of 28. Can you give a reason why?

# 2.7 Square numbers

Here is a number sequence.

| 1 | 4 | 9 | 16 | 25 | 36... |
|---|---|---|----|----|-------|
| $(1 \times 1)$ | $(2 \times 2)$ | $(3 \times 3)$ | $(4 \times 4)$ | $(5 \times 5)$ | $(6 \times 6)$ |

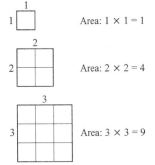

The numbers 1, 4, 9, 16, 25, 36, ... are called **square numbers**.

Square numbers are formed by multiplying a whole number by itself, as you do when you find the area of a square.

To check whether or not a number is a square number, ask yourself whether it could represent the area of a square.

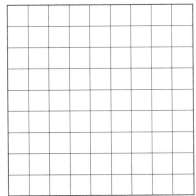

81 is a square number.

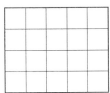

20 is *not* a square number.

16 is a square number because $4 \times 4 = 16$.

You can write $4 \times 4$ as $4^2$

So $4^2 = 16$

You read $4^2$ as '4 squared'.

You can find the square of a number using a calculator. For example, to find $12^2$:

Enter     [1] [2]

Press     [$x^2$]

The answer is   *144*

---

## Exercise 2H

**1.** The area of a square is 81 square units. What is the length of one side?

**2.** Which of these numbers are square numbers?
(a) 30  (b) 100  (c) 125  (d) 144  (e) 150

**3.** Write down the values of these square numbers.
(a) $5^2$  (b) $15^2$  (c) $25^2$  (d) $34^2$  (e) $45^2$

**4.** Write 'true' or 'false' for each of these statements.
(a) $3^2 + 4^2 = 5^2$         (b) $4^2 + 5^2 = 6^2$
(c) $4^2 + 4^2 = 8^2$         (d) $6^2 + 8^2 = 10^2$
(e) $5^2 + 12^2 = 13^2$       (f) $7^2 + 24^2 = 25^2$
(g) $8^2 + 9^2 = 17^2$        (h) $10^2 + 24^2 = 26^2$

## 2.8 Square roots

Because $225 = 15 \times 15$, 15 is called the **square root** of 225. Finding the square root is like finding the side of a square when you know its area.

Area = 1, side = 1
Square root of 1 is 1

Area = 4, side = 2
Square root of 4 is 2

Area = 9, side = 3
Square root of 9 is 3

The square root of 225 is written as $\sqrt{225}$

So we have          $15 \times 15 = 225$

    or                  $15^2 = 225$

    and                $\sqrt{225} = 15$

You can find the square root of a number using a calculator.
To find $\sqrt{169}$

    Enter     ⌂1⌂ ⌂6⌂ ⌂9⌂

    Press     ⌂√⌂

    The answer is  $13$

---

### Exercise 21

**1.** (a) A square tile has an area of $49\,\text{cm}^2$. What is the length of one side?
(b) What is the square root of 49?

**2.** (a) Another square tile has an area of $100\,\text{cm}^2$. What is the length of one side?
(b) What is the square root of 100?

**3.** Find the square root of:
(a) 16    (b) 64    (c) 121    (d) 196
(e) 441   (f) 576   (g) 1024   (h) 1849

**4.** The instructions for finding the length of the missing side of this type of triangle are:
● find the squares of both the given sides
● add the two answers together
● find the square root of this answer
Use the instructions to find the length of the missing side of these triangles.

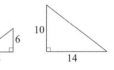

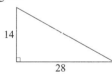

---

## 2.9 Cubes

Here is another number sequence.

    1          8          27          64          125

$(1 \times 1 \times 1)$   $(2 \times 2 \times 2)$   $(3 \times 3 \times 3)$   $(4 \times 4 \times 4)$   $(5 \times 5 \times 5)$

The numbers 1, 8, 27, 64, 125... are called **cube numbers**. Cube numbers are formed by multiplying a whole number by itself and then by itself again, as you do when you find the volume of a cube.

To check whether or not a number is a cube number, ask yourself whether it could represent the volume of a cube.

Volume: $1 \times 1 \times 1 = 1$

Volume: $2 \times 2 \times 2 = 8$

Volume: $3 \times 3 \times 3 = 9$

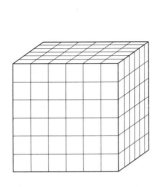 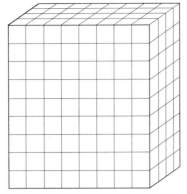

216 is a cube number.          300 is **not** a cube number.

You can see that 216 is a cube number because $6 \times 6 \times 6 = 216$.

300 is not a cube number because no whole number multiplied by itself and then by itself again gives you 300.

$$6 \times 6 \times 6 = 216$$
$$7 \times 7 \times 7 = 343$$

300 is between 216 and 343.

You can write $6 \times 6 \times 6 = 6^3$

You read $6^3$ as '6 cubed'.

You can find the cube of a number using a calculator.

To find $7^3$

Enter      $\boxed{7}$

Press      $\boxed{x^y}$ $\boxed{3}$

The answer is $\mathsf{343}$

---

### Exercise 2J

**1**. Find the cube of these numbers. Use your calculator if you need to.
   (a) 4      (b) 7     (c) 11     (d) 21

**2**. (a) What is the value of
   (i) $1^3 + 2^3$   (ii)  $1^3 + 2^3 + 3^3$
   (iii) $1^3 + 2^3 + 3^3 + 4^3$

(b) What type of numbers are all three answers?

**3**. Are either of these statements true?
   (a) $(1 + 2 + 3 + 4)^2 = 1^3 + 2^3 + 3^3 + 4^3$
   (b) $(1 + 2 + 2 + 4)^2 = 1^3 + 2^3 + 2^3 + 4^3$

---

## 2.10  Cube roots

Because $216 = 6 \times 6 \times 6$, 6 is called the **cube root** of 216.

The cube root of 216 is 6.

This is written as

$$\sqrt[3]{216} = 6$$

Calculators have different ways of finding cube roots. If you have any difficulty you should refer to your calculator manual.

Here are two ways that work on some calculators.

| Enter | Press | Press | Press | Output |
|-------|-------|-------|-------|--------|
| [2][1][6] | [INV] | [xʸ] | [3] | 6 |
| [2][1][6] | [2nd] | [ˣ√ȳ] | [3] | 6 |

You need to check the method for *your own* calculator.

*Example 6*

A cube has a volume of 21 952 cm³. Find:

(a) the length of one side

(b) the area of one face of the cube.

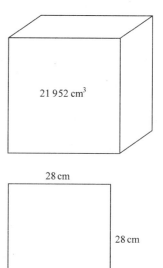

(a) The volume of the cube is 21 952 cm³ so the length of one side will be the cube root of 21 952.

The cube root of 21 952 = 28 (*check*: 28 × 28 × 28 = 21 952)

So the length of one side is 28 cm.

(b) The area of one face is $28^2$

$28^2 = 784$

The area of one face is 784 cm².

### Exercise 2K

1. What is the cube root of 32 768?

2. Find the cube root of:
   (a) 512   (b) 343   (c) 1000   (d) 1728   (e) 3375

3. A cube has a volume of 27 cm³. Find:
   (a) the length of one side
   (b) the area of one face.

4. A cube has a volume of 9261 cm³. Find:
   (a) the length of one side
   (b) the area of one face.

5. The area of one face of a cube is 361 cm². Find:
   (a) the length of one side
   (b) the volume of the cube.

6. For a charity event, some students assembled one million small plastic cubes to form a massive cube. How many small cube faces could be seen on one face of the finished massive cube?

## Worked exam question 1

Here is a sequence of numbers.

$$2, 3, 5, 8, 13, 21, 34, 55, 89, \ldots$$

(a) Work out the next number in the sequence after 89.

*2 + 3 = 5, 3 + 5 = 8, 5 + 8 = 13 etc.*

*55 + 89 = 144* •      144 •
.....................

**Do:**
Show your working

Check your answer. Use a
calculator if you wish

(b) From the sequence above,

   (i) write down a prime number,   *2 or 3 or 5 or 13 or 89*
.......................................

Give one answer

   (ii) write down a cube number,

$$8 = 2 \times 2 \times 2 \qquad \underset{\ldots\ldots\ldots}{8}$$

   (iii) write down a multiple of 17.

$$34 = 2 \times 17 \qquad \underset{\ldots\ldots\ldots}{34}$$

**Don't:**
Rush through the question

(c) From the sequence above, write down two numbers which
have a difference of 13.   *21 and 8*
*(or 34 and 21)* •

**Do:**
Give one answer

(London)

## Worked exam question 2

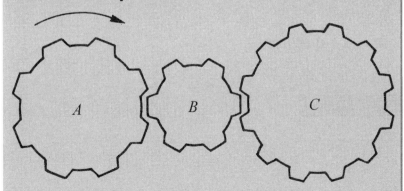

The diagram shows three interlocking cog wheels.

Wheel *A* has 8 cogs.

Wheel *B* has 6 cogs.

Wheel *C* has 12 cogs.

(a) Wheel *A* turns clockwise. In which direction does wheel *B* turn?

(a) ...*Anti-clockwise*...

(b) Wheel *A* makes 3 complete revolutions.

(i) How many complete revolutions does wheel *B* make?

*4.*            *3 × 8 = 24 = 4 × 6* ●————————

*24 is the LCM of 6 and 8*

(b)(i) ....*4*....

**Do:**
Show your working

(ii) How many complete revolutions does wheel *C* make?

*Wheel B  6 × 4 = 24*                                                                                  ●

*Wheel C  12 × 2 = 24*

(b)(ii) ....*2*....

(MEG)

## 2.11 Powers of 10

Scientists and engineers often have to work with powers of 10.

Some examples of **powers of 10** are

$10^2 = 10 \times 10 = 100$
$10^3 = 10 \times 10 \times 10 = 1000$
$10^7 = 10 \times 10 \times 10 \times 10 \times 10 \times 10 \times 10 = 10\,000\,000$

We can build a table of values:

| $10^4$ | $10^3$ | $10^2$ | $10$ |
|--------|--------|--------|------|
| 10 000 | 1000   | 100    | 10   |

     ⌣      ⌣      ⌣
× by 10   × by 10   × by 10

To go from right to left across this table we keep

● adding 1 to the power in the top row

● multiplying by ten in the bottom row.

To go from left to right in this table we need to reverse the process.

So we keep

- subtracting 1 from the power in the top row

- dividing by 10 in the bottom row.

| $10^4$ | $10^3$ | $10^2$ | $10^1$ | $10^0$ | $10^{-1}$ | $10^{-2}$ |
|---|---|---|---|---|---|---|
| 10 000 | 1000 | 100 | 10 | 1 | $\frac{1}{10}$ (or 0.1) | $\frac{1}{100}$ (or 0.01) |

$\div 10 \quad \div 10 \quad \div 10 \quad \div 10$

From the table you can see that

$$10^1 = 10$$
$$10^0 = 1$$
$$10^{-2} = \tfrac{1}{100} \text{ or } 0.01 \text{ or } \tfrac{1}{10^2}$$

and so on.

- $10^3$ is read as 'ten cubed' or 'ten to the power of 3'

- $10^{-2}$ is read as 'ten to the power of minus 2'.

### Example 7

(a) Write each of these powers of 10 in figures.

   (i)  $10^5$    (ii)  $10^6$    (iii)  $10^{-3}$

(b) Write each of these numbers as powers of 10.

   (i)  1000    (ii)  100 000 000    (iii)  1    (iv)  0.0001

(a)  (i)  $10^5 = 10 \times 10 \times 10 \times 10 \times 10 = 100\,000$

    (ii)  $10^6 = 10 \times 10 \times 10 \times 10 \times 10 \times 10 = 1\,000\,000$

    (iii)  $10^{-3} = \dfrac{1}{10^3} = \dfrac{1}{10 \times 10 \times 10} = \dfrac{1}{1000} = 0.001$

(b)  (i)  $1000 = 10 \times 10 \times 10 = 10^3$

    (ii)  $100\,000\,000 = 10 \times 10 \times 10 \times 10 \times 10 \times 10 \times 10 \times 10$
$$= 10^8$$

    (iii)  $1 = 10^0$

    (iv)  $0.0001 = \dfrac{1}{10\,000} = \dfrac{1}{10 \times 10 \times 10 \times 10} = \dfrac{1}{10^4} = 10^{-4}$

You can also do calculations with numbers multiplied by powers of ten.

*Example 8*

Work out $3000 \times 400$

$$3000 \times 400 = 3 \times 1000 \times 4 \times 100$$
$$= 3 \times 4 \times 1000 \times 100$$
$$= 3 \times 4 \times 10^3 \times 10^2$$
$$= 12 \times 10^3 \times 10^2$$
$$= 12 \times 10^5$$
$$= 1\,200\,000$$

**Exercise 2L**

1. Write each of these powers of 10 in figures.
   (a) $10^2$   (b) $10^4$   (c) $10^0$   (d) $10^{-2}$

2. Write each of these numbers as powers of 10.
   (a) $10\,000$   (b) $1\,000\,000\,000$   (c) $0.000001$

3. Work out:
   (a) $300 \times 5000$   (b) $14\,000 \div 20$
   (c) $3 \times 10^2 \times 4 \times 10\,000$   (d) $\dfrac{60\,000}{2 \times 10^3}$

4. Write these numbers as powers of 10:
   (a) one thousand   (d) one million
   (b) ten thousand   (e) one hundred thousand
   (c) ten   (f) ten $\times$ ten $\times$ ten

5. Write these as powers of 10:
   (a) $\dfrac{1}{10^4}$   (b) $\dfrac{1}{10^6}$   (c) $\dfrac{1}{10}$

6. Write these as powers of 10:
   (a) $\frac{1}{1000}$   (b) $\frac{1}{10\,000}$   (c) $\frac{1}{100\,000}$

7. Write these as decimals:
   (a) $10^{-4}$   (b) $10^{-7}$   (c) $10^{-5}$

8. Copy and complete this table:

| Power of 10 | $10^3$ | $10^2$ | $10^1$ | $10^0$ | $10^{-1}$ | $10^{-2}$ | $10^{-3}$ |
|---|---|---|---|---|---|---|---|
| Number | | | | 1 | 0.1 | | |

## 2.12 Large numbers

It is often necessary to find a short way of writing a large number, such as $5\,000\,000$ or $10\,200\,000$. A number with lots of zeros in it is difficult to read.

When large numbers are used in newspaper reports, for example, they must be easy to read and understand. In a report about a city with a population of $2\,000\,000$ this number can be written as 2 million. In the same way £$5\,200\,000$ can be written £5.2 million.

*Example 9*

Write $4\,260\,000$

(a) as a number of millions   (b) as a number $\times 10^6$

Use decimals where necessary.

(a) $4\,260\,000 = 4.26$ million   (b) $4\,260\,000 = 4.26 \times 10^6$

## Exercise 2M

**1**. Write these numbers as a number of millions. Use decimals where necessary.
(a) 6 000 000    (b) 3 400 000    (c) 7 800 000
(d) 5 500 000    (e) 2 650 000    (f) 7 642 000

**2**. Write these numbers as a number $\times 10^6$. Use decimals where necessary.
(a) 3.1 million  (b) 4.3 million  (c) 0.5 million
(d) 2 400 000    (e) 7 800 000    (f) 8 600 000
(g) 4 000 000    (h) 9 000 000    (i) 400 000

## 2.13 Standard form

In mathematics and science large numbers are often written as a number between 1 and 10 multiplied by a power of ten.

For example, 2 000 000 can be written $2 \times 10^6$
5 200 000 can be written $5.2 \times 10^6$
1 350 000 can be written $1.35 \times 10^6$

When a number is written in this way we say it is written in **standard form** or **standard index form.**

$72.4 \times 10^3$ is *not* in standard form because 72.4 is not between 1 and 10.

You can convert it to standard form like this:

$$72.4 \times 10^3 = (7.24 \times 10) \times 10^3$$
$$= 7.24 \times 10 \times 10 \times 10 \times 10$$
$$= 7.24 \times 10^4$$

You can change a large number in standard form into 'ordinary form' like this.

$$5.2 \times 10^4 = 5.2 \times 10 \times 10 \times 10 \times 10$$
$$= 52 \times 10 \times 10 \times 10$$
$$= 520 \times 10 \times 10$$
$$= 5200 \times 10$$
$$= 52 000$$

So $5.2 \times 10^4 = 52 000$

## Exercise 2N

**1**. Convert these numbers into standard form using a table like the one below. The first one has been done for you.
(a) 74 000    (b) 260    (c) 680 000
(d) 9 900 000    (e) 62    (f) 8

| $10^6$ | $10^5$ | $10^4$ | $10^3$ | $10^2$ | $10^1$ | $10^0$ | Standard form |
|---|---|---|---|---|---|---|---|
| | | 7 | 4 | 0 | 0 | 0 | $7.4 \times 10^4$ |

**2**. Write these numbers in standard form:
(a) 16    (b) 4300    (c) 650 000
(d) 87 000 000    (e) 670    (f) 865
(g) 9 870 000    (h) 98 500    (i) 805 000 000 000

**3**. Change these numbers from standard form to ordinary form.
(a) $4.2 \times 10^2$    (b) $6.7 \times 10^4$    (c) $5.5 \times 10^3$
(d) $7.5 \times 10^6$    (e) $6.2 \times 10^5$    (f) $7.3 \times 10^4$
(g) $2.4 \times 10^7$    (h) $1.1 \times 10^1$    (i) $7.25 \times 10^0$

**4**. Evaluate these expressions. Write your answers in standard form.
(a) $25 \times 26$   (b) $640 \times 15$   (c) $45 \times 900$   (d) $25^4$

## 2.14 Small numbers and standard form

In electronic circuits it is often necessary to measure very small electric currents. Sometimes currents as low as 0.000 000 000 08 amps are measured.

Just as it is convenient to write large numbers in standard form, it is also convenient to write very small numbers in standard form.

To write 0.041 in standard index form, you first write 0.041 as a fraction, where the numerator is a number between 1 and 10.

$$0.041 = \frac{4.1}{100} = 4.1 \times \frac{1}{100} = 4.1 \times \frac{1}{10^2} = 4.1 \times 10^{-2}$$

0.041 in standard form is $4.1 \times 10^{-2}$

You can change a small number in standard form into 'ordinary form' like this:

$$2.4 \times 10^{-3} = \frac{2.4}{10^3}$$
$$= \frac{2.4}{1000}$$
$$= 0.0024$$

### Exercise 20

1. Convert these numbers into standard form using a table like the one below. The first one has been done for you.
   (a) 0.0024        (b) 0.2
   (c) 0.000 06      (d) 0.15
   (e) 0.007         (f) 0.000 45
   (g) 0.034 60      (h) 0.001 25

   | $10^0$ | $10^{-1}$ | $10^{-2}$ | $10^{-3}$ | $10^{-4}$ | $10^{-5}$ | Standard form |
   |---|---|---|---|---|---|---|
   | 0 | 0 | 0 | 2 | 4 | | $2.4 \times 10^{-3}$ |

2. Write these numbers in standard form.
   (a) 0.002        (b) 0.15            (c) 0.000 4
   (d) 0.054        (e) 0.000 008       (f) 0.000 000 000 068
   (g) 0.346        (h) 0.09            (i) 0.005 6

3. Change these numbers into ordinary form.
   (a) $3.5 \times 10^{-1}$    (b) $6.0 \times 10^{-2}$   (c) $7.2 \times 10^{-4}$
   (d) $2.2 \times 10^{-3}$    (e) $1.35 \times 10^{-5}$  (f) $5.33 \times 10^{-6}$
   (g) $8.8 \times 10^{-10}$   (h) $4.4 \times 10^{-7}$   (i) $4.999 \times 10^{-1}$

### Worked exam question 3

The speed of light is approximately 300 000 000 m/s.

(a) Write 300 000 000 in standard index form.

$300\,000\,000 = 3 \times 100\,000\,000$

$= 3 \times 10^8$

**Do:**
Show your working

$3 \times 10^8$
.................

(b) Calculate the time, in seconds, light takes to travel
1 metre. Give your answer in standard index form.

$$time = \frac{distance}{speed} = \frac{1}{3 \times 10^8} = 3.33 \times 10^{-9}$$

**Do:**
Show your working

**Don't:**
Just read off your calculator display

$\underset{\cdots\cdots\cdots\cdots\cdots\cdots}{3.33 \times 10^{-9}}$ s

(London)

## Worked exam question 4

In the first 50 weeks of 1992, Barclays Bank dispensed £8.7 billion through its cash machines in 187 million transactions.

(a) Write as numbers in standard form

(i)  8.7 billion

(ii)  187 million

(i)  $\underline{8.7 \times 10^9}$

(ii)  $\underline{1.87 \times 10^8}$

[1 billion = 1 thousand million]

$8.7 \; billion = 8.7 \times 1000 \times 1\,000\,000$

$= 8.7 \times 10^9$

**Do:**
Show your working

$187 \; million = 187\,000\,000 = 1.87 \times 10^8$

(b) What was the average amount of cash dispensed at each transaction?

(b) £ $\underline{\quad 46.52 \quad}$

$$\frac{8.7 \times 10^9}{1.87 \times 10^8} = 4.652 \times 10^1$$

$$= 46.52$$

(c) Show your working for a rough estimate to (b) to check that your answer is of the right order of magnitude.

$8.7 \longrightarrow 10 \qquad 187 \longrightarrow 200$

$$\frac{10\,000\,000\,000}{200\,000\,000} = 50$$

Source of data: *The Times*, 26 December 1992

(MEG)

### Exercise 2P (Mixed questions)

1. (a) Write down the next two numbers in this sequence.
      10, 15, 20, 25, 30, 35, . . . , . . .
   (b) All the numbers are multiples of a certain number. What is that number?
   (c) Two prime numbers are factors of every number in the sequence. Write down these two prime numbers.

2. Here is a set of numbers:
   41, 45, 56, 64, 72
   Write the number which is
   (a) a square number    (c) a prime number
   (b) a multiple of 12    (d) a factor of 280.

3. Using the digits 2, 3, 4, 5 and 6 only, write down:
   (a) a prime number greater than 30
   (b) a multiple of 13
   (c) two numbers that add up to 85
   (d) a number which when subtracted from 75 gives a square number as the answer.

4. The sports club is open every night. Faz, Brian and Carol all join the club on the same Saturday for their first training session. After that Faz trains every third day, Brian every fourth day and Carol every fifth day.
   (a) After how many days will all three students train together again?
   (b) What day of the week will it be?

5. An adult flea usually covers 30 cm in one jump.

   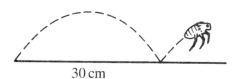

   30 cm

   (a) How many jumps will an adult flea make to cover 4.5 m? (Note: 100 cm = 1 m)
   (b) A young flea covers 25 cm in one jump.

   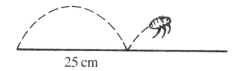

   25 cm

   A young flea and an adult flea both start off at the same time, from the same point, and jump in the same direction. How far will they go before they land at the same point again?

6. Rita plays 'Roll-a-ball' at a village fête. She has to roll six balls, all of which must 'score' (that is, enter a numbered compartment). It is possible for more than one ball to go into each compartment. When she has rolled four of them, the position is as shown on this diagram.
   (a) What is her score so far?
   (b) In order to win a prize, her total score must be a square number. Show that there are two ways that she can win a prize with the last two balls.

7. (a) Draw a tree diagram to show that
      $360 = 2^3 \times 3^2 \times 5$
   (b) Express 560 as a product of its prime factors.
   (c) Given that $360 \times 560 = 201\,600$, express $210\,600$ as a product of its prime factors.

8. (a) The diameter of the earth is approximately 12 700 km. Express this distance in standard index form.
   (b) The diameter of Mars is approximately $6.79 \times 10^3$ km. Work out the difference between the diameter of the Earth and the diameter of Mars, giving your answer in standard index form.

9. Tony read in a book that the Eiffel Tower is $2.95 \times 10^5$ mm tall.
   (a) Change $2.95 \times 10^5$ into ordinary form.
   (b) How high is the Eiffel Tower in metres? (Note: 10 mm = 1 cm and 100 cm = 1 m.)

10. It is claimed that in America there are on average 27 lightning strikes every minute.
    (a) How many lightning strikes are there, on average, in a day?
    (b) How many lightning strikes will America receive on average in a year?
    (c) Give your answer to part (b) in standard index form.

11. The National Lottery uses balls with the numbers from 1 to 49 on them.

11. (a) From the list of numbers write down
    (i) A square number
    (ii) A factor of 100, other than 1
    (iii) A multiple of 5
    (iv) A prime number.
  (b) Paul makes a set of cards with instructions
    on them. He draws two cards at a time to
    decide which lottery number to choose.
    Write down his first three numbers.

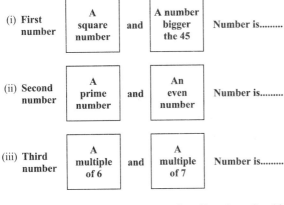

(i) **First number**  | A square number | **and** | A number bigger the 45 | **Number is.........**

(ii) **Second number** | A prime number | **and** | An even number | **Number is.........**

(iii) **Third number** | A multiple of 6 | **and** | A multiple of 7 | **Number is.........**

12. (a)
```
 1   2   3   4   5   6   7   8   9  10
11  12  13  14  15  16  17  18  19  20
21  22  23  24  25  26  27  28  29  30
31  32  33  34  35  36  37  38  39  40
```
From the numbers shown above, write down
    (i) all the multiples of 8,
    (ii) the square of 6,
    (iii) the prime factors of 70,
    (iv) the values of $3^3$, $\sqrt{25}$
  (b) Write down the next two numbers in the
    sequence
    4, 7, 10, 13, ....., ...... .                    [WJEC]

13. The number $10^{100}$ is called a googol.
    (a) Write the number 50 googols in standard
      index form.
    A nanometre is $10^{-9}$ metres.
    (b) Write 50 nanometres, in metres.
    Give your answer in standard index form.
    (c) How many nanometres are there in 10
      metres?                                      [London]

14. A number $n$, expressed in terms of its prime
    factors, is $2^6 \times 3^4 \times 11$.
    (a) Find the value of $n$.
    (b) Express $8n$ as a product of prime factors.
    (c) Find the value of $8n$, giving your answer in
      standard form.                               [SEG]

15. Centuries ago, a man promised to give his wife
    some grains of rice.
    He took a chess board
    and placed:
      one grain on the first
      square,
      two grains on the
      second square,
      four grains on the
      third square,
      eight grains on the
      fourth square,
      and so on.
    If he had completed all 64 squares on the
    chessboard he would have used approximately
    $1.845 \times 10^{19}$ grains of rice.
    One grain of rice weighs about 0.01 grams.
    Calculate an estimate of the weight of rice used.
    Give your answer in tonnes, correct to one
    significant figure.
    [1 tonne = 1000 kg.]                           [MEG]

## Test yourself

**1.** Avtar is asked to write down all the factors of 18. Here is her answer: 2, 3, 6 and 9.

QUESTION   Which two factors of 18 are missing?

ANSWER   1 and 18         *If your answer is incorrect review page 24, Section 2.2 on factors*

QUESTION   **2.**   Work out the highest common factor of 1728 and 90.

ANSWER   18              *If your answer is incorrect review page 24, Section 2.2 on factors*

| | | |
|---|---|---|
| QUESTION | **3.** Write down all the factors of <br> (a) 36 (b) 50 (c) 64 (d) 120 | |
| ANSWER | (a) 1, 2, 3, 4, 6, 9, 12, <br>       18, 36 <br> (b) 1, 2, 5, 10, 25, 50 <br> (c) 1, 2, 4, 8, 16, 32, 64 <br> (d) 1, 2, 3, 4, 5, 6, 8, 10, 12, <br>       15, 20, 24, 30, 40, 60, 120 | *If your answer is incorrect review page 24, Section 2.2 on factors* |
| QUESTION | **4.** Which of these are prime numbers? <br> 17, 27, 33, 37, 43, 49 | |
| ANSWER | 17, 37, 43 | *If your answer is incorrect review page 27 Section 2.4 on prime numbers* |
| QUESTION | **5.** Show how 90 can be made by multiplying together prime numbers. | |
| ANSWER | $2 \times 3 \times 3 \times 5 = 90$ | *If your answer is incorrect review page 28, Section 2.5 on prime factors* |
| QUESTION | **6.** Write down the first six multiples of 7. | |
| ANSWER | 7, 14, 21, 28, 35, 42 | *If your answer is incorrect review page 29, Section 2.6 on multiples* |
| QUESTION | **7.** List four numbers that are multiples of both 5 and 6. | |
| ANSWER | 30, 60, 90, 120 <br> (Other answers possible. <br> If in doubt see your teacher.) | *If your answer is incorrect review page 29, Section 2.6 on multiples* |
| QUESTION | **8.** Which of these are square numbers? <br> 4, 8, 20, 30, 36, 50, 64 | |
| ANSWER | 4, 36, 64 | *If your answer is incorrect review page 31, Section 2.7 on square numbers* |

**9.** The area of a square is $121 \, \text{cm}^2$.

| | | |
|---|---|---|
| QUESTION | (a) What is the length of one side? | |
| ANSWER | 11 cm | |
| QUESTION | (b) Write down the square root of 121. | |
| ANSWER | 11 | *If your answers are incorrect review page 32, Section 2.8 on square roots.* |
| QUESTION | **10.** Work out $\sqrt[3]{1728}$ | |
| ANSWER | 12 | *If your answer is incorrect review page 33, Section 2.10 on cube roots* |

QUESTION    **11**.  Write these numbers in standard form:
      (a)   270     (b)   8900    (c)   785 000
      (b)   0.089   (e)   0.95    (f)   0.000 037

ANSWER    (a)   $2.7 \times 10^2$          *If your answer is incorrect review page 38, Section*
        (b)   $8.9 \times 10^3$          *2.12 and page 39, Section 2.13 on standard form*
        (c)   $7.85 \times 10^5$
        (d)   $8.9 \times 10^{-2}$
        (e)   $9.5 \times 10^{-1}$
        (f)   $3.7 \times 10^{-5}$

---

QUESTION    **12**.  Write these numbers in ordinary form:
      (a)   $4.5 \times 10^1$    (b)   $6.65 \times 10^4$    (c)   $3.1 \times 10^6$
      (d)   $7.5 \times 10^{-3}$  (e)   $5.41 \times 10^{-4}$  (f)   $5.55 \times 10^{-1}$

ANSWER    (a)   45                *If your answer is incorrect review pages 38–40,*
        (b)   66 500           *Section 2.12, Section 2.13 and Section 2.14 on*
        (c)   3 100 000       *standard form*
        (d)   0.0075
        (e)   0.000 541
        (f)   0.555

---

QUESTION    **13**.  Work out $4 \times 10^8 - 4 \times 10^6$.
      Give your answer in standard form.

ANSWER    $3.96 \times 10^8$            *If your answer is incorrect review page 38, Section*
                              *2.12 and page 39, Section 2.13 on standard form*

## Summary of key points to remember

**1**. The **factors** of a number are all the whole numbers that divide into it without a remainder.

**2**. The **highest common factor** of two numbers is the largest number that is a factor of both of them.

**3**. A number that has two and only two factors is called a **prime number**. These two factors are the number itself and 1.

**4**. All numbers can be made by multiplying prime numbers together. For example, $30 = 2 \times 3 \times 5$; $12 = 2 \times 2 \times 3$

**5**. You can use tree diagrams to find the prime factors of a number.

The prime factors of 60 are 2, 3 and 5.

**6**. Any number that can be written in the form

    $n \times$ a number

is a multiple of $n$.

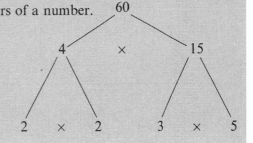

for example, $10(= 5 \times 2), 20(= 5 \times 4), 35, 45$ are multiples of 5.

$30 = 6 \times 5$, so 30 is the 6th multiple of 5.

7. The **lowest common multiple** of two numbers is the smallest number that is a multiple of both of them.

   For example, the lowest common multiple of 4 and 6 is 12.

8. Square numbers are formed by multiplying a whole number by itself, as you do when you find the area of a square.

9. The square root of whole number is the factor of a number that when multiplied by itself makes the number.

   Finding a square root is like finding the side of a square when you know its area.

   For example, $9 \times 9 = 81; \sqrt{81} = 9$

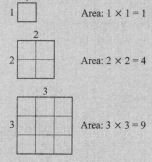

10. A cube number is formed by multiplying a whole number by itself and then by itself again, as you do when you find the volume of a cube.

    For example, $6 \times 6 \times 6 = 216$

11. Finding a cube root is like finding the side of a cube when you know its volume.

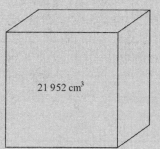

21 952 cm³

12.

| Power of 10 | $10^4$ | $10^3$ | $10^2$ | $10^1$ | $10^0$ | $10^{-1}$ | $10^{-2}$ | $10^{-3}$ | $10^{-4}$ |
|---|---|---|---|---|---|---|---|---|---|
| Number | 10 000 | 1000 | 100 | 10 | 1 | 0.1 | 0.01 | 0.001 | 0.0001 |

13. A number written as a number between 1 and 10 multiplied by a power of 10 is written in standard form.

    For example, $72000 = 7.2 \times 10^4$

14. This can appear in your GCSE formulae sheet as $a \times 10^n$ where $1 \leqslant a < 10$ and $n$ is a whole number (positive or negative).

# 3 Estimation and approximation

## 3.1 Introduction

In the real world it is often desirable to approximate numbers.

Suppose that a sports reporter is writing an article about the British Grand Prix. The car that she is writing about took a curve at 78.897 49 km per hour. It will have more impact if she writes 79 km per hour or even 80 km per hour.

If 98 675 people go to a pop concert, a newspaper will probably report this figure as 100 000. The figure has been rounded up to the nearest ten thousand.

This unit covers several different methods of giving calculated answers in a meaningful and relevant form. To do this we usually use approximations to estimate results.

---

**Exercise 3A**

1. Rewrite the following figures as if you were reporting them in a general newspaper.
   (a) The top speed of a test plane is 1547.987 km/h
   (b) The population of Athens is 3 097 000.
   (c) The highest summer temperature ever recorded in Britain was 37.777° C.
   (d) The electrical current used by a computer is 0.985 A.
   (e) 14 651 people watched Derby Rovers play Blackburn County.

---

## 3.2 Nearest appropriate values

GCSE exam questions sometimes ask you to give your answers 'to the nearest 10', or 'to the nearest whole number'.

### *Example 1*

(a) Tristan has done a calculation on his calculator. The number on the display is 5687.

   Write this number to the nearest 10.

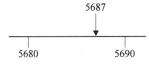

(b) Daniel has calculated two values as 26.7 and 19.1. Write these numbers to the nearest whole number.

(a) 5687 lies between 5680 and 5690

   It is nearer to 5690 than to 5680.

   So the answer is 5690 to the nearest 10.

(b) 26.7 lies between 26 and 27. It is nearer to 27. So the answer is 27 to the nearest whole number.

19.1 lies between 19 and 20. It is nearer to 19 than 20. So the answer is 19 to the nearest whole number.

### Exercise 3B

1. Write these numbers to the nearest 10.
   (a) 279      (b) 149      (c) 34
   (d) 5436     (e) 9299     (f) 3343
   (g) 8        (h) 3        (i) 9.9

2. Write these numbers to the nearest whole number.
   (a) 3.9      (b) 7.3      (c) 57.8
   (d) 0.75     (e) 0.25     (f) 80.4
   (g) 4.05     (h) 5.55     (i) 2.099

3. Rewrite these expressions, giving each number to the nearest whole number.
   (a) $3.2 \times 5.9$   (b) $3.8 \times 4.3$   (c) $7.4 \times 3.9$
   (d) $12.4 \times 2.8$   (e) $5.1 \times 4.9$   (f) $0.65 \times 5.89$

4. 37 438 people voted for the Labour party in a recent by-election.
   (a) Write this number to
      (i) the nearest 10
      (ii) the nearest 100
      (iii) the nearest 1000
      (iv) the nearest 10 000.
   (b) You have been asked to write a report on the election for the local newspaper. Which 'headline' figure will you use, and why?

## 3.3 Numbers of decimal places

Sometimes you need to work with or give results to a given number of decimal places. The number of decimal places you are asked for is the **degree of accuracy**.

*Example 2*

Rinford Listie runs 100 m in 10.56 seconds.

Calculate his average speed in metres per second (ms⁻¹).

Give your answer

(a) to the nearest whole number      (b) to one decimal place

(c) to two decimal places.

His average speed in metres per second is

$$\frac{\text{total distance}}{\text{total time}} = \frac{100}{10.56} \, \text{m s}^{-1}$$

Using a calculator:

Enter [1][0][0] [÷] [1][0][.][5][6][=]

The answer is $9.469697$

(a) $9.469\,697 \, \text{m s}^{-1}$ lies between $9 \, \text{m s}^{-1}$ and $10 \, \text{m s}^{-1}$. It is nearer to 9 than to 10.

So the speed is $9 \, \text{m s}^{-1}$ to the nearest whole number.

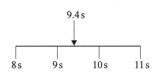

(b) $9.469\,697\,\text{m s}^{-1}$ lies between $9.4\,\text{m s}^{-1}$ and $9.5\,\text{m s}^{-1}$. It is nearer to 9.5 than 9.4.

So the speed is $9.5\,\text{m s}^{-1}$ to one decimal place.

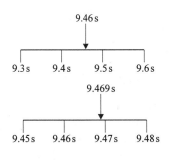

(c) $9.469\,697\,\text{m s}^{-1}$ lies between $9.46\,\text{m s}^{-1}$ and $9.47\,\text{m s}^{-1}$. It is nearer to 9.47 than 9.46.

So the speed is $9.47\,\text{m s}^{-1}$ to two decimal places.

When you are asked to give a figure to 2 decimal places your answer should have 2 digits after the decimal point.

To ensure your answer is as accurate as possible, work out the answer to 3 decimal places and then round it to 2 decimal places.

*Always work to one or more decimal places than you need*

### Example 3

(a) Write 46.382 67 correct to one decimal place.

(b) Write 46.382 67 correct to two decimal places.

(a) There must be **one** digit after the decimal point.

To make your answer as accurate as possible, consider the figure to two decimal places. Look at the interval in which 46.38 lies.

46.38 is nearer to 46.4 than it is to 46.3. Therefore, 46.382 67 correct to one decimal place is 46.4.

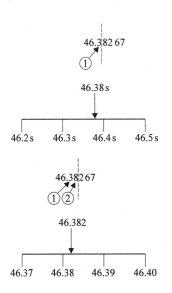

(b) There must be **two** digits after the decimal point.

To make your answer as accurate as possible, consider the figure to **three** decimal places. Look at the interval in which 46.382 lies

46.382 is nearer to 46.38 than it is to 46.39. Therefore, 46.382 67 correct to **two decimal places** is 46.38.

So, in general, if the number after the decimal place is less than 5, we round down. If the number after the decimal place is 5 or more, we round up.

### Exercise 3C

**1.** Copy this interval diagram.

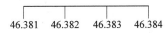

(a) Mark the position of 46.3826 on the diagram.

(b) Write 46.382 67 correct to three decimal places.

**2.** Josie runs 1500 m in 4.86 minutes.
(a) Use a calculator to find her average speed in metres per minute. Write down the number from the calculator display.
(b) Give her average speed in metres per minute correct to:
  (i) the nearest whole number
  (ii) one decimal place
  (iii) two decimal places
  (iv) three decimal places.

3. This table shows the times taken to run 400 m by the first three athletes in a race.

| Name | Time |
|------|------|
| R White | 45.4826 |
| M. Ronson | 45.4768 |
| R. King | 45.4817 |

(a) Write these times correct to two decimal places.
(b) Write down the names of the athletes in the order in which they finished the race.

4. Write these numbers to the degree of accuracy given.
   (a) 134.27 (1 d.p.)    (b) 0.67381 (4 d.p.)
   (c) 1.999 (1 d.p.)     (d) 1.999 (2 d.p.)
   (e) 17.9932 (3 d.p.)   (f) 2.00672 (4 d.p.)

5. Write the answers to the degree of accuracy stated
   (a) 24.56 × 3.87 correct to 3 d.p.
   (b) 3.764 × 2.593 correct to 3 d.p.
   (c) 2.888 × 3.777 correct to 2 d.p.
   (d) 13.799 × 12.752 correct to 1 d.p.

6. An approximate value of $\pi$ is 3.141 592 7. Write $\pi$ correct to
   (a) two decimal places
   (b) four decimal places.

# 3.4 Significant figures

Sometimes you will be asked to give a value to a number of significant figures. This is another way of giving you the degree of accuracy required.

For example, 46 192 people attended a pop concert held at Manorview Stadium. The event was reported in the Manorview Times with this headline:

The headline gave the number 46 192 correct to two significant figures.

It is essential to include enough zeros to maintain the correct place values of the two significant figures. The number is 46 000, and not 46.

When you give approximations of numbers, remember that your figures must be meaningful and useful, and approximately correct.

As another example, David obtained this reading in an experiment:

If you give this number to three decimal places, the figure is 0.006. However, if you give it to three significant figures, the figure is *not* 0.006.

When you give a decimal number to a certain number of significant figures, you count from the highest place value of a digit that is not zero. In this case the zeros indicate that there are no units, no tenths, and no hundredths. Keep these zeros to maintain the place value of the first significant figure, which is the 6, representing 6 thousandths.

So 0.006 284 7 correct to three significant figures is 0.006 28.

*Example 4*

(a) Write 10.4768 correct to three significant figures.

(b) Write 10.4768 correct to four significant figures.

(a) You must give three significant figures, starting from the highest place value:

     To give a figure that is as accurate as possible, look at the interval in which 10.47 lies. 10.47 is nearer to 10.5 than it is to 10.4. Therefore, 10.4768 correct to three significant figures is 10.5.

(b) You must give four significant figures, starting from the highest place value:

     To give a figure that is as accurate as possible, look at the interval in which 10.476 lies. 10.476 is nearer to 10.48 than it is to 10.47. Therefore, 10.4768 correct to four significant figures is 10.48.

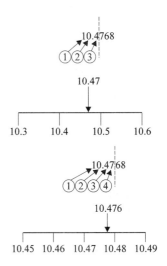

*Example 5*

Write 7886 correct to two significant figures:

The answer is 7900.

*Example 6*

Write 0.000 078 86 correct to 2 s.f.

The answer is 0.000 079.

---

### Exercise 3D

1. Write each of these numbers correct to the number of significant figures stated.
   (a) 3248   (3 s.f.)
   (b) 8419   (3 s.f.)
   (c) 1.2513 (2 s.f.)
   (d) 0.0386 (2 s.f.)
   (e) 84.341 (3 s.f.)

2. Oil costs £0.142 per litre.
   Calculate the cost of 975 litres of oil. Give your answer in pounds, correct to 2 significant figures.

3. Calculate $(3.14)^2$, giving your answer correct to 3 significant figures.

4. Find $\sqrt{21}$ correct to 2 significant figures.

5. Tom has to do the sum $3.87 + 1.16$ giving his answer correct to 2 significant figures. He writes 3.87 correct to 2 significant figures. Then he writes 1.16 correct to 2 significant figures. Then he adds together the answers to what he has done.
   Explain why this process will give him the *wrong* answer.

## 3.5 Estimating and approximating

In solving real-life problems it is often helpful to make approximations to help you establish estimated results.

For example, suppose that you need to drive from Manchester to London and back. The road atlas gives the distance between these two cities as 204 miles – so the return distance is 408 miles. Suppose also that your car does an average of 38 miles to a gallon of petrol. You can use all of this information to work out an estimate of the number of gallons of petrol you will need.

To one significant figure, 408 miles is rounded to 400 miles. Also to one significant figure, 38 miles per gallon is rounded to 40 miles per gallon. So the estimate of the number of gallons needed is $400 \div 40 = 10$ gallons.

In your GCSE examination it is always good practice to look at your final answer and ask yourself 'Does this answer seem reasonable?' In order to do this quickly you need to be able to estimate an answer of the question you have just completed.

This section shows you how to make and use estimates.

Rashpal's calculator is 'on the blink'. There is no decimal point in the calculated figures.

When Rashpal uses his calculator to calculate $2.592 \times 8.84$, the calculator displays

$$229 1328$$

Using whole numbers *below* the numbers in the expression gives $2 \times 8 = 16$. 16 is the **lower limit** of the expression.

Using whole numbers *above* the numbers in the expression gives $3 \times 9 = 27$. 27 is the **upper limit** of the expression.

The value of $2.592 \times 8.84$ must lie somewhere between these lower and upper limits. The only possible correct value for the expression is 22.913 28, since this is between 16 and 27.

$$2 \times 8 = 16 \text{ (lower limit)}$$
$$2.592 \times 8.84 = 22.913\,28$$
$$3 \times 9 = 27 \text{ (upper limit)}$$

Rashpal then tries another expression. He uses his calculator to calculate $20.4 \div 5.6$. The calculator displays the number

$$364285 7 1$$

Rashpal uses some approximations to work out the correct value for the expression.

20.4 is approximately equal to 20.

5.6 is approximately equal to 5.  $20 \div 5 = 4$.

Therefore, $20.4 \div 5.6$ must equal 3.642 857 1.

When you estimate values, use whole numbers that are convenient. In the above example, 5.6 is actually nearer to 6 than to 5. However, $20 \div 6$ is not as easy to work out as $20 \div 5$.

Note that when you are doing exam questions on this topic you *must not use a calculator* to answer any of the questions unless the question instructs you to do so.

## Exercise 3E

1. The values of the expressions below have been calculated by Rashpal's broken calculator. Work out the lower and upper limits of the values. Correct the values given below by inserting a decimal point in the correct place.
   (a) $3.4 \times 2.5 = 85$    (b) $5.6 \times 7.23 = 40488$
   (c) $2.42 \times 1.93 = 46706$
   (d) $10.63 \times 12.64 = 1343632$
   (e) $3.2 \times 5.1 \times 4.7 = 76704$
   (f) $2.9 \times 0.32 \times 8.7 = 80736$

2. Estimate the values of the expressions below, giving your answers to the nearest whole number.
   (a) $36 \div 5$      (b) $47 \div 8$      (c) $103 \div 11$
   (d) $148 \div 49$    (e) $239 \div 31$    (f) $197 \div 19$
   (g) $281 \div 41$    (h) $796 \div 98$    (i) $352 \div 58$
   (j) $\dfrac{53 \times 3}{49}$    (k) $\dfrac{38 \times 5}{19}$    (l) $\dfrac{24 \times 11}{59}$

3. Rashpal's broken calculator has been used to calculate the values of the expressions below. Correct the values by inserting a decimal point in the correct position.
   (a) $29.6 \div 9.8 = 30204082$
   (b) $43.8 \div 7.8 = 56153846$
   (c) $89.1 \div 17.2 = 51802325$
   (d) $4.45 \div 0.52 = 85576923$
   (e) $(20.3 \times 3.8) \div 9.67 = 79772492$
   (f) $(4.9 \times 5.1) \div 2.6 = 96115384$
   (g) $(16.3 \times 5.9) \div 0.251 = 38314741$

4. Find the approximate cost of:
   (a) eight books costing £1.98 each
   (b) 12 packets of sweets costing 99p each
   (c) five screwdrivers costing £3.04 each
   (d) four radios costing £39.99 each
   (e) 90 razor blades costing 51p each.

5. The area of a rectangle is $34.88 \, \text{cm}^2$. One of its sides has a length of 6.9 cm. Rashpal's broken calculator gives this number for the length of the other side:

   $$5 0 5 5 0 7 2 5$$

   (a) Give the length of the other side correct to two decimal places.
   (b) Estimate the perimeter of the rectangle.

6. Rashpal's broken calculator calculates that the length of one side of the following square is 12247449 cm.
   (a) What is the length of the side correct to four significant figures?
   (b) Use the answer to part (a) to calculate the length of one side of a square with an area of $15\,000 \, \text{cm}^2$.
   (c) What is the length of one side of a square with an area of $1500 \, \text{cm}^2$? Give your answer to 1 decimal place.

   150 cm²

## Example 7

Estimate the area of the piece of stair carpet shown below:

7.3 m

0.47m

Calculate the actual area of the carpet and compare it with your estimate.

First estimate the area of the stair carpet. 0.47 is approximately $\frac{1}{2}$, and 7.3 is approximately 7. So an estimate of the area is $\frac{1}{2}$ m × 7 m = 3.5 m².

0.47 m × 7.3 m is approximately 3.5 m².

Now calculate the actual area of the carpet.
0.47 m × 7.3 m = 3.431 m².

The estimate is 3.5 m². Difference 3.5 − 3.431 = 0.069 m².

The estimate is close to the actual area.

---

### Exercise 3F

1. Calculate approximate answers to:
   (a) 0.51 × 26.2
   (b) 0.251 × 18.4
   (c) 0.74 × 40
   (d) 0.201 × 99.9
   (e) 0.402 × 59.9
   (f) 0.52 × 0.48
   (g) 0.52 × 0.48 × 16.4
   (h) 0.74 × 20.2 × 0.51
   (i) (83 × 0.246) ÷ 5
   (j) (0.98 × 55.9) ÷ 7
   (k) 0.76 × 41.2 × 0.49
   (l) 0.76 × 41.2 ÷ 0.49

2. (a) Estimate the area of the top face of this strip of wood:

   58.9 cm
   0.59 cm

   (b) Compare your estimate with the actual area of the face.

3. (a) Show which whole numbers could be used to estimate the answers to these calculations.

   (i) $\dfrac{4.99 \times 20.2}{9.7}$

   (ii) $\dfrac{6.3 \times 198.4}{3.98}$

   (iii) $\dfrac{2.93 \times 15.4}{4.31}$

   (iv) $\dfrac{6.87 \times 33.9}{7.89}$

   (v) $\dfrac{0.48 \times 29.3}{2.6}$

   (vi) $\dfrac{0.28 \times 69.4}{8.89}$

   (vii) $\dfrac{92.7 \times 44.9}{14.6 \times 10.6}$

   (viii) $\dfrac{4.67 \times 13.5}{6.55 \times 2.33}$

   (b) Use your approximations to estimate the answers.
   (c) Use a calculator to calculate the actual answers. Give your answers to an appropriate number of significant figures.
   (d) Compare your estimates with your actual answers. Comment on the differences.

4. (a) Estimate the value of 5.5² to the nearest whole number.
   (b) Work out the exact value of 5.5².

(c) What is the difference between your estimate and the exact value?

5. (a) Estimate the values of:
   (i) 3.5²     (ii) 4.5² (iii) 6.5²     (iv) 7.5²
   (b) Work out the exact values.
   (c) Compare your estimates with your exact values.
   (d) Write down what you notice.
   (e) Write down the exact value of 10.5².

6. Jenny is using Pythagoras' theorem to find the length of side BC of this triangle.
   To do this, she uses the formula

   $$BC = \sqrt{4.7^2 + 6.4^2}$$

   Estimate BC to the nearest whole number.

   B
   4.7
   A     6.4     C

7. A bus travels 45.2 km in 2 h 30 min. (Note: 1000 m = 1 km.) Estimate its average speed in:
   (a) metres per minute
   (b) kilometres per hour.

8. Joanne uses a calculator to work out the value of 5.76 × 6.24. She writes down her answer as 359.424.
   (a) Write down a simple calculation that she can use to check her answer.
   (b) Use a calculator to calculate the correct answer. Write down all the numbers on the calculator display.
   (c) Write down the actual answer correct to:
   (i) one decimal place
   (ii) two significant figures.

**9**. Jean has to work out the value of

$$\frac{49.53}{3.1 \times 3.9}$$

(a) Show which whole numbers Jean can use as approximations to estimate the answer.

(b) Estimate the answer using these whole numbers.

(c) Use your calculator to work out the actual answer. Give your answer correct to two decimal places.

---

## Worked exam question 1

An astronaut recently spent 438 days in the Russian space station, orbiting the Earth.

Write 438 days in weeks, to the nearest week.

$438 \div 7 = 62.57142857$ ● ——————— **Do:** Show your working

$= 63 \ rounded \ up$ ● ——————— Round your answer

............63...... weeks
(MEG)

## Worked exam question 2

Use your calculator to find $\sqrt{75}$, correct to the nearest whole number.

$\sqrt{75} = 8.660254038$ ● ——————— Show your working

——————— Use your calculator correctly

............9......
(MEG)

Round to the nearest whole number

**Don't:**
Write the calculator display in the answer space

## Worked exam question 3

The size of the crowd at a football match is given as 34 700 to the nearest hundred.

(i) What was the lowest number that the crowd could be?

$34\,650$

(ii) What was the largest number that the crowd could be?

$34\,750$

(NEAB)

**Do:**
Read the question carefully

**Don't:**
Rush into it

## Worked exam question 4

Work out $\frac{3}{5}$ of 264 metres.

Give your answer in metres, correct to 3 significant figures.

$\frac{3}{5} \times 264 = 158.4$ ● ——————— **Do:** Show your working

............158...... m
(London)

Use your calculator

**Don't:**
Confuse decimal places and significant figures

## 3.6 Errors

When you use approximations and make estimates there will be some errors in your calculators.

For example, when the return distance from Manchester to London is given as 408 miles this should really be quoted as

>       408 miles, correct to the nearest mile

This actually means that the distance is between 407.5 miles and 408.5 miles, or, more strictly

>       $407.5 \leqslant \text{distance} < 408.5$

The 407.5 would be *rounded up* to 408 and the 408.5, which strictly is *not quite* 408.5, would be rounded down to 408.

So the quoted distance of 408 miles, correct to the nearest mile has an **error** of ±0.5 miles and there is an *approximation* interval of 1 mile, that is from 407.5 miles to 408.5 miles.

Suppose we now go back to the problem of driving a car from Manchester to London and back. The car does an average of 38 miles to a gallon of petrol.

We saw that we could estimate the number of gallons of petrol needed for the journey as

>       $400 \div 40 = 10$

The actual number of gallons is

>       $408 \div 38 = 10.74$  (correct to 2 d.p.)

So the *estimate* of 10 leads to an *error* of

>       $10.74 - 10 = 0.74 \, \text{gallon}$

The error is 0.74 gallons.

### *Example 8*

The number of students attending Folks College is 2800 to the nearest hundred.

Write down:

(a) the largest possible number

(b) the smallest possible number of students attending the college.

2800 is given to the nearest hundred.

(a) The largest possible number that would be rounded down to 2800 is 2849.

(b) The smallest possible number that would be rounded up to 2800 is 2750.

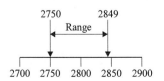

*Example 9*

A length of wood is laid on the floor.

Three students measure it.

Harry gives the length as 2 m.

Gail gives the length as 2.0 m.

Leroy gives the length as 2.00 m.

Which measurement is correct?

Harry's length of 2 m is correct to the nearest metre. So the actual length could be any value between 1.5 m and 2.5 m.

Gail's length of 2.0 m is given to the nearest tenth of a metre. The actual length could be between 1.95 m and 2.05 m.

Leroy gives the length as 2.00 m. This means that the actual measurement is anywhere between 1.995 m and 2.005 m.

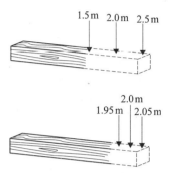

You could summarise all of this in a table.

| Least length (metres) | | Measurement | | Largest length (metres) |
|---|---|---|---|---|
| 1.5 | $\leqslant$ | Harry's | $<$ | 2.5 |
| 1.95 | $\leqslant$ | Gail's | $<$ | 2.05 |
| 1.995 | $\leqslant$ | Leroy's | $<$ | 2.005 |

The approximation interval gives the limits of accuracy of a measurement. It should be chosen to give measurements to a realistic accuracy. For example, if you measure a room to the nearest metre you can make a rough estimate for how much a new carpet for the room will cost. But these measurements will not be accurate enough when you cut the carpet to fit.

## Exercise 3G

**1**. Copy and complete the table, which shows the number of students, to the nearest hundred, at various colleges.

| College | Attendance | Smallest possible number | Largest possible number |
|---|---|---|---|
| Folks | 2800 | 2750 | 2849 |
| Westown | 2400 | | |
| Eastgrove | 800 | | |
| Northbury | 1600 | | |
| Southfold | 1000 | | |

2. (a) If the actual number of students attending the colleges in question **1** is the smallest possible number at all five colleges, what is the total student population at the five colleges?
  (b) The actual number of students at each college is given in the table.

| College | Number of students |
|---------|---------------------|
| Folks | 2740 |
| Westown | largest possible number |
| Eastgrove | smallest possible number |
| Northbury | largest possible number |
| Southfold | 999 |

Work out the total student population of the five colleges.

3. A manufacturer makes plastic strips. In the firm's catalogue, the length of a strip is given as 5 cm to the nearest centimetre. This means that the actual length of a strip can be any length between 4.5 cm and 5.5 cm.
  (a) Some of these strips are placed end to end in a row. Write down the smallest and largest possible lengths of a row of

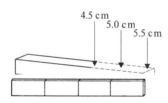

    (i) 2 strips   (ii) 5 strips   (iii) 6 strips
  (b) Two of the strips are placed side by side. Write down the smallest and largest possible differences between their lengths.

4. (a) This sign shows the distances to two towns. The distances given are to the nearest kilometre. What are the smallest and largest possible distances between the two towns?
  (b) Two walkers meet at the signpost. One sets off towards Norby, and the other to Keding. What is the smallest and largest possible differences between the distances they have to walk?

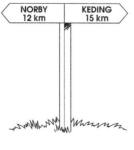

5. The population of Borrowcott is 6000 to three significant figures.
  (a) Give the smallest possible size of the population.
  (b) Give the approximation interval for the population.

6. In a report the population of Borrowcott is given as 6000 to *two* significant figures.
  (a) Give the approximation interval for the population.
  (b) Which approximation interval, question **5**(a) or **6**(a) gives the most useful information? Why?

7. The population of Leding is 356 000 to the nearest thousand. The population of Redchester is 542 000, also to the nearest thousand.
  (a) Give the approximation interval for each population.
  (b) Give the approximation interval for the total population of the two cities.
  (c) Give the largest and smallest possible differences between the populations of the two cities.

8. The information below is given in many reference books.

| Unit | Equivalent unit | |
|------|------|------|
| 1 inch | 2.54 | centimetres |
| 1 yard | 91.4 | centimetres |
| 1 litre | 1.76 | pints |
| 1 tonne | 1.016 | tonnes |
| 1 kilometre | 0.621 | mile |
| 1 mile | 1.609 | kilometres |

Copy this table. Add a third column and list the approximation intervals for each equivalent unit.

9. The sides of a rectangle are measured as 5.6 cm and 4.8 cm.
  (a) Give the approximation intervals for these two measurements.
  (b) Calculate the largest and smallest possible values for the perimeter.
  (c) Calculate the largest and smallest possible values for the area of the rectangle.

10. Darren runs 100 m. His average speed is given as $7.692\,307\,7\,\mathrm{m\,s^{-1}}$
  (a) Give a realistic approximation of this speed.
  (b) Write down the interval approximation for your answer.

11. (a) Javed measures the length of a pipe as 20 cm. What is the maximum possible length of the pipe?
    (b) Fara measures the length of the same pipe as 20.0 cm. What are the smallest and largest possible values of the length of the pipe?

12. The length of each side of a square is 2.8 cm, correct to two significant figures.
    (a) Give the largest possible length of each side.
    (b) Calculate the largest and smallest possible values for the perimeter.

---

## Worked exam question 5

1. Kathleen has to calculate the height of a tower. She knows that the answer can be found by completing this calculation

$$\frac{2.9 \times 35.6}{3.9}$$

(a) Show which whole numbers can be used to estimate the height of the tower.

   *2.9 is approximately equal to 3.*

   *35.6 is approximately equal to 36.*

   *3.9 is approximately equal to 4.*

   *The height is approximately $\frac{3 \times 36}{4}$*

**Do:**
Use simple whole numbers to make an estimate

Explain why you have used each approximation

(b) Using your approximations, calculate an estimate of the height.

   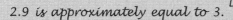

   $$\frac{3 \times \overset{9}{\cancel{36}}}{\underset{1}{\cancel{4}}} = 3 \times 9 = 27$$

**Do:**
Show all your working

(c) Using a calculator, calculate the actual height of the tower, giving your answer correct to three significant figures.

   $$\frac{2.9 \times 35.6}{3.9} = 26.471795$$

   *= 26.5 correct to three significant figures*

**Do:**
Check that you have written your answer to the correct number of significant figures, remembering to 'round up' if necessary

(d) Compare the estimated height with the actual height. Comment on the difference.

   *The estimated height is 27 m.*

   *The actual height is 26.5 m*

   *The estimated height gives a good approximation to the actual height. The error is +0.5 m.*

**Do:**
Compare your answers. If your estimate is very different from the calculated answer, check both again

State whether or not you think your estimated answer is a good one

## Worked exam question 6

The length, correct to two significant figures, of each side of a square is 4.7 cm.

(a) Give the largest possible length of each side.

*4.7 is in the interval 4.65 to 4.75*

*The largest possible length is 4.75 cm.*

(b) Calculate the smallest possible perimeter for the square.

*Smallest possible perimeter = 4 × smallest possible*
*lengthof side*

*= 4 × 4.65*

*=18.6 cm*

(c) What is the difference between the smallest possible perimeter, and the largest possible perimeter?

*smallest perimeter = 4 × 4.65 = 18.6*
*largest perimeter = 4 × 4.75 = 19.0*
*difference: 19.0 – 18.6 = 0.4cm*

The lengths of each side of this shape are given as 4.7 cm.

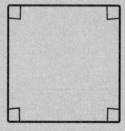

(d) Explain why the shape may not be a square.

*If the length of each side is given as 4.7 cm, the*
*actual lengths of each pair of sides can be any*
*length between 4.65 cm and 4.75 cm. This means*
*that the length of the pairs of sides may not be*
*equal. Therefore, the shape may be a rectangle and*
*not a square.*

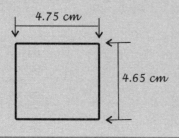

**Do:**
Check carefully which limit you are being asked to give (to two significant figures) means that the correct answer could be in the interval 4.65 to 4.75

**Do:**
Find the perimeter by multiplying the length by 4

**Don't:**
Forget to subtract the smaller perimeter from the larger one to find the difference

**Do:**
Remember that to form a square all the sides must be exactly the same length

## Exercise 3H (Mixed questions)

**1.** A formula is $v = \dfrac{14.8}{2.8 \times 5.2}$

(a) Calculate the value of $v$. Give your answer correct to 1 decimal place.

(b) Write down a simple calculation which could be used to check that your answer in part (a) is sensible.

**2.** Stephanie ran 100 metres.
The distance was correct to the nearest metre.

(a) Write down the shortest distance Stephanie could have run.

Stephanie's time for the run was 14.8 seconds. Her time was correct to the nearest tenth of a second.

(b) Write down:

(i) her shortest possible time for the run,

(ii) her longest possible time for the run. [London]

**3.** Use the formula $y = \dfrac{50 - 25}{\sqrt{(1 - 0.6^2)}}$

to calculate the value of $y$.
Give your answer correct to 1 decimal place.
Show all necessary working.

**4.** This formula is used in science: $f = \dfrac{6.7 \times 4.5}{6.7 + 4.5}$

(a) Calculate the value of $f$. Write down all the digits shown in your calculator display.

(b) (i) The distances in part (a) were measured to the nearest tenth of a centimetre. Write your answer to part (a) to an appropriate degree of accuracy.

(ii) Explain why you chose this degree of accuracy.

**5.** Roy calculated that $\dfrac{253}{36} = 14.5$

(a) Write down an approximate value for 253 and for 36.
Use them to estimate the answer to $\dfrac{253}{36}$
Do not use a calculator.

(b) What does this suggest about Roy's answer? [MEG]

**6.** (a) A parcel is weighed on digital scales which record weight correct to the nearest one pound. The scales record 12 pounds. What is the least possible weight of the parcel?

(b) (i) Convert 12.35 pounds to kilograms, taking 1 kg to be 2.2 pounds. Write down all the figures shown on your calculator display.

(ii) Write down your answer to part (b)(i) correct to the nearest kilogram. [MEG]

**7.** (a) The height of Snowdon above sea level is 3560 feet correct to the nearest whole number.
State the greatest and least possible values of this height.

(b) 1 mile = 1609 m
1 mile = 5280 feet
Use this information to express 3560 feet in metres.
[MEG]

**8.** Samina is working out the area of a rectangle. She does this calculation: $5755 \times 19 = 523\,705$.

(a) Write down a calculation that you could do as an estimate to check her answer, without using a calculator.

(b) (i) Write down your answer to your calculation in part (a).

(ii) Was Samina right? [MEG]

**9.** Press the $\pi$ button on your calculator. Write down the value of $\pi$:

(a) correct to 3 significant figures

(b) correct to 3 decimal places.

**10.** The area of a rectangle is given by the formula
Area = length × width
Calculate the area of a rectangle with
length  = 4.83 cm
width  = 2.18 cm
Give your answer correct to 3 significant figures.

**11.** (a) Work out $0.27 \times 0.35$

(b) Give your answer to part (a) correct to 2 significant figures.

**12.** 1 yard = 36 inches.
1 inch = 2.54 centimetres.
Change 1 yard to centimetres. Give your answer correct to 1 decimal place.

# Test yourself

**1.** The lowest winter temperature recorded at Easton last year was −16.816 27 °C.

QUESTION    (a)   Report the temperature in appropriate terms for a weather forecast.

ANSWER          −17 °C                        *If your answer is incorrect, review page 47, Section 3.2 on rounding.*

QUESTION    (b)   Write −16.816 27 correct to the nearest whole number, to one decimal place, and to two decimal places.

ANSWER          −17, −16.8 and             *If your answers are incorrect, review pages 48 and 49,*
                −16.82                      *Section 3.3, Examples 2 and 3 on decimal places.*

**2.** During an electronics experiment, Angela measures a voltage as 12.4837 V.

QUESTION    Give this voltage correct to three significant figures, and to two significant figures.

ANSWER          12.5 V and 12 V             *If your answers are incorrect, review page 51, Section 3.4, Examples 4, 5 and 6 on significant figures.*

**3.** 2367 students attend Gough College.

QUESTION    Give the number of students correct to three significant figures, two significant figures, and one significant figure.

ANSWER          2370, 2400 and 2000         *If your answers are incorrect, review page 51, Section 3.4, Examples 4, 5 and 6 on significant figures.*

**4.** Gary measures the difference between the lengths of two metal rods, and writes down the difference as 0.006 749 m.

QUESTION    Give 0.006 749 correct to three decimal places, and to three significant figures.

ANSWER          0.007 and 0.006 75          *If your answers are incorrect, review pages 48, Section 3.3 Examples 2 and 3, and page 51, Section 3.4, Examples 4, 5 and 6 on decimal places and significant figures.*

**5.** Kerry and Ian have to do some calculations in science. All of their numbers contain decimals.

QUESTION    Use whole number approximations to estimate the values of
            (a)   $3.89 \times 4.78$
            (b)   $39.6 \div 7.89$
            (c)   $\dfrac{5.8 \times 9.77}{6.88}$

| ANSWER | 20, 5 and 9 | *If your answers are incorrect, review pages 53 and 54, Section 3.5, Example 7 on approximating.* |

**6.** In a recent charity race, there were 1900 competitors, to the nearest 100.

| QUESTION | Write down the smallest possible and the largest possible number of competitors. |
| ANSWER | 1850 and 1949 | *If your answers are incorrect, review page 56, Section 3.6, Example 8 on errors.* |

**7.** Paul measures the length of his garden shed as 2.34 m.

| QUESTION | What is the smallest possible length of the shed? |
| ANSWER | 2.335 m | *If your answer is incorrect, review page 57, Section 3.6, Example 9 on errors.* |

## Summary of key points to remember

1. When you **approximate numbers** in the real world, your approximations must be useful and realistic.

2. When you have to give a number to $x$ **decimal places**, there should be $x$ digits after the decimal point. To ensure that your answer is accurate, work out your answer to $x + 1$ decimal places, and then give it correct to $x$ decimal places.

3. When you have to give a number to $x$ **significant figures**, write down $x$ digits from the original number, starting from the non-zero digit that has the highest place value. Look at the $(x + 1)$th digit of the original number, and round up the $x$th digit of your number if necessary. Make sure you add enough zeros to maintain the original place values of the digits.

4. You can **estimate** the value of an expression by using **whole numbers** to approximate the figures in the expression.

5. When you use or give an approximation you should always state the **degree of accuracy** it is given to: for example to three decimal places, or to two significant figures, or to the nearest hundred.

6. When a value is given to a degree of accuracy, the actual value can be anywhere in the approximation interval, which depends on the degree of accuracy.

   For example, if the number of students is 2800 to the nearest hundred, then the approximation interval is

   $2750 \leqslant$ number of students $< 2849$

# 4 Mental calculations

## 4.1 Non-calculator methods

This unit shows you non-calculator methods of long multiplication and long division, and how to use the method of 'trial and improvement' to obtain approximate answers. These methods are applied to solving problems using multiplication and division and unitary methods.

In your GCSE exam you may be given an instruction such as 'without using a calculator, work out the answer to . . .'.

When you are told to use a non-calculator method to solve a problem, you **must not use a calculator** to work out the answer.

This is just one situation where you may need to use long multiplication or division.

## 4.2 Long multiplication

### *Example 1*

Pat buys 32 packets of nails. Each packet contains 64 nails. Work out how many nails he has.

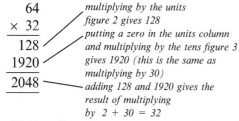

```
     64
  ×  32
    128      multiplying by the units
             figure 2 gives 128
   1920       putting a zero in the units column
             and multiplying by the tens figure 3
   2048      gives 1920 (this is the same as
             multiplying by 30)
             adding 128 and 1920 gives the
             result of multiplying
             by 2 + 30 = 32
```

Pat has 2048 nails.

### *Example 2*

Cheryl buys 32 boxes of Christmas cards to sell in her shop. Each box contains 24 cards.

How many Christmas cards does Cheryl buy?

```
     32
  ×  24
    128      multiplying by 4
    640      multiplying by 20
    768
             the result of multipling by  4 + 20 = 24
```

Cheryl buys 768 Christmas cards.

---

### Exercise 4A

Do not use a calculator for this exercise.

1. Calculate:
   (a) $17 \times 10$  (b) $10 \times 26$  (c) $141 \times 10$
   (d) $17 \times 20$  (e) $135 \times 20$  (f) $18 \times 30$
   (g) $21 \times 100$  (h) $34 \times 100$  (i) $14 \times 200$
   (j) $122 \times 200$  (k) $211 \times 300$  (l) $234 \times 400$

2. There are 64 nails in a packet.
   How many nails will there be in 24 packets?

3. Calculate:
   (a) $12 \times 41$  (b) $13 \times 35$  (c) $14 \times 82$
   (d) $15 \times 36$  (e) $16 \times 67$  (f) $15 \times 124$

4. Bertie Brayn reckons he's found an even quicker method for working out $19 \times 62$. It uses multiplying by 10 and then subtraction. Can you suggest Bertie's method?

5. There are 24 Christmas cards in a box.
   How many cards will there be in 26 boxes?

6. Calculate:
   (a) $13 \times 26$  (b) $14 \times 39$  (c) $15 \times 44$
   (d) $21 \times 64$  (e) $24 \times 18$  (f) $42 \times 53$
   (g) $36 \times 72$  (h) $59 \times 21$  (i) $98 \times 81$

## Example 3

Joan counts how many days there are until Christmas. She finds that there are 297 days.

How many hours is this?

There are 24 hours in one day. We need to calculate $297 \times 24$

```
    297
  × 24
  ─────
  1188 ──── multiplying by 4
  5940 ──── multiplying by 20
  ─────
  7128
```

There are 7128 hours until Christmas.

---

### Exercise 4B

Do not use a calculator for this exercise.
**1**. How many hours are there in 126 days?

**2**. Calculate:
   (a) $114 \times 45$   (b) $132 \times 59$   (c) $145 \times 31$   (d) $213 \times 82$   (e) $312 \times 64$
   (f) $362 \times 48$   (g) $485 \times 52$   (h) $634 \times 75$   (i) $883 \times 86$   (j) $234 \times 447$

---

## 4.3 Problems involving division

You can solve division problems without using a calculator by long division:

## Example 4

A prize of £168 was shared equally between 12 people.

Work out how much each person received.

Follow these steps:

12 divides into 16        12 divides into 48        *So 12 divides into 168*
**1** time remainder 4    **4** times exactly       *14 times*

```
      1                         14
12 )168                    12 )168
    12                         12↓
    ──                         ──
     4                         48
                               48
                               ──
                                0
```

*So 12 divides into 168 14 times*

**Each person receives £14**

## Example 5

Mrs Hammond teaches a class of 29 infants. She has 667 red counters to be used for a number investigation. She wants each child to have an equal share of the counters.

How many counters should she give each child?

29 divides into 66      29 divides into 87      *So 29 divides into 667*
**2 times remainder 8**    **3 times exactly**      *23 times*

$$\begin{array}{r} 2 \\ 29 \overline{)667} \\ 58 \\ \hline 8 \end{array}$$
    
$$\begin{array}{r} 23 \\ 29 \overline{)667} \\ 58\downarrow \\ \hline 87 \\ 87 \\ \hline 0 \end{array}$$

**She should give 23 counters to each child.**

---

### Exercise 4C

Do not use a calculator for this exercise.

**1.** Mrs Hammond has 754 blue counters to share equally among the 29 children. How many counters does each child receive?

**2.** Calculate:
(a) $224 \div 16$     (b) $306 \div 18$     (c) $408 \div 17$     (d) $364 \div 28$     (e) $372 \div 31$     (f) $551 \div 29$

---

*Example 6*

Find the remainder when 373 is divided by 24.

24 divides into 37      24 divides into 133      *So 24 divides into 373*
**1 time remainder 13**    **5 times remainder 13**      *15 times remainder 13*

$$\begin{array}{r} 1 \\ 24 \overline{)373} \\ 24 \\ \hline 13 \end{array}$$
    
$$\begin{array}{r} 15 \\ 24 \overline{)373} \\ 24\downarrow \\ \hline 133 \\ 120 \\ \hline 13 \end{array}$$

**The remainder is 13.**

---

### Exercise 4D

**1.** Find the remainder when 427 is divided by 24.

**2.** Find the remainder in these calculations.
(a) $145 \div 12$    (b) $243 \div 21$    (c) $243 \div 31$

(d) $315 \div 25$    (e) $562 \div 32$    (f) $535 \div 27$
(g) $642 \div 19$    (h) $723 \div 43$    (i) $799 \div 53$
(j) $856 \div 44$    (k) $943 \div 64$    (l) $999 \div 99$

---

## 4.4 Solving problems mentally

Craig has been asked to work out $80 \times 0.2$ in his head.

He rearranges the problem to make it easier.

$$80 \times 0.2$$
$$8 \times 10 \times 0.2$$
$$8 \times 2 = 16$$

So $80 \times 0.2$ gives the same answer as $8 \times 2 = 16$

*Example 7*

Work out $60 \div 0.2$ mentally.

First rearrange the problem to make it easier:

$$60 \div 0.2$$

$$(600 \div 10) \div 0.2$$

$$600 \div (10 \times 0.2)$$

$$600 \div 2 = 300$$

So $60 \div 0.2$ gives the same answer as $600 \div 2 = 300$

## Exercise 4E

Do not use a calculator for this exercise.

1. Work out mentally:
   (a) $25 \times 0.2$    (b) $34 \times 0.1$    (c) $50 \times 0.4$
   (d) $22 \times 0.3$    (e) $35 \times 0.5$    (f) $224 \times 0.2$
   (g) $800 \times 0.3$    (h) $450 \times 0.4$    (i) $600 \times 0.12$
   (j) $400 \times 0.11$    (k) $300 \times 0.02$    (l) $800 \times 0.04$

2. Work out mentally:
   (a) $40 \div 0.2$    (b) $600 \div 0.4$    (c) $200 \div 0.5$
   (d) $300 \div 0.1$    (e) $120 \div 0.3$    (f) $150 \div 0.5$
   (g) $26 \div 0.13$    (h) $480 \div 0.12$    (i) $6.0 \div 0.15$
   (j) $2.4 \div 0.2$    (k) $8.8 \div 0.22$    (l) $36 \div 0.09$
   (m) $0.56 \div 0.007$    (n) $0.64 \div 0.16$

3. Work out mentally:
   (a) $(30 \times 0.8) \div 2$      (b) $(40 \times 0.5) \div 4$
   (c) $(80 \times 0.2) \div 10$      (d) $(50 \times 0.4) \div 0.2$
   (e) $60 \times 0.6 \div 0.3$      (f) $400 \times 0.6 \div 0.8$
   (g) $200 \times 0.01 \div 0.5$      (h) $600 \times 0.5 \div 2.5$
   (i) $(50 \times 0.4) \div 0.2$      (j) $50 \times (0.4 \div 0.2)$
   (k) $(400 \times 0.6) \div 0.8$      (l) $400 \times (0.6 \div 0.8)$
   (m) $24 \times 0.8 \div 0.4$      (n) $24 \div 0.8 \times 0.4$

4. Eight different rectangles each have area $24\,\text{cm}^2$. The table gives the length or the width of each one.
   Copy and complete the table.

| Area (cm²) | Length (cm) | Width (cm) |
|---|---|---|
| 24 | 12 | |
| 24 | | 3 |
| 24 | | 4 |
| 24 | 1.0 | |
| 24 | 0.5 | |
| 24 | | 60 |
| 24 | 0.2 | |
| 24 | 0.02 | |

5. Six different rectangles each have perimeter 24 cm. The table gives the lengths of each rectangle.
   Copy and complete the table.

| Perimeter | Length | Width | Area |
|---|---|---|---|
| 24 | 8 | | |
| 24 | 6 | | |
| 24 | 2 | | |
| 24 | 1 | | |
| 24 | 0.2 | | |
| 24 | 0.1 | | |

6. Copy and complete these number patterns:
   (a) $40 \times 80 = 3200$      (b) $40 \div 80 = 0.5$
      $40 \times 8 = 320$             $40 \div 8 =$
      $40 \times 0.8 =$              $40 \div 0.8 =$
      $40 \times 0.08 =$            $40 \div 0.08 =$
      $40 \times 0.008 =$          $40 \div 0.008 =$

7. John and Jamie are having an argument. John says that if you multiply two numbers together you always get an answer bigger than both numbers. Jamie disagrees.
   Who do you agree with and why?

8. Is this statement always true?
   'If you divide one number by another the answer is always smaller than the bigger of the two numbers.'
   If you disagree, give an example to show why.

## Worked exam question 1

Do not use a calculator to answer this question. Show all your working clearly.

There are 13 forms in year 7. Each form has 28 pupils

How many pupils are there in year 7?

$$10 \times 28 = 280$$

$$1 \times 28 = 28$$

$$1 \times 28 = 28$$

$$1 \times 28 = 28$$

$$\overline{13 \times 28 = 364}$$

(NEAB)

**Do:**
Read the question carefully
13 forms of 28 pupils means
$13 \times 28$ pupils in year 7

Find 10 lots of 28 and then a further 3 lots

## Worked exam question 2

29 students plan an activities holiday. The cost of the holiday works out to £128 per person.

(Do not use a calculator for any part of this question. You must show all your workings and clearly identify each answer.)

(a) Work out the total cost of the holiday.

$$10 \times 128 = 1280$$
$$10 \times 128 = 1280$$
$$5 \times 128 = 640$$
$$2 \times 128 = 256$$
$$2 \times 128 = 256$$
$$\overline{29 \times 128 = 3712}$$

*The total cost of the holiday is £3712*

Note that the cost for one student is £128, so the total cost will be £128 × 29

Use a non-calculator method and show each stage of your working clearly.

(b) Work out whether your answer to part (a) is reasonable.

*29 is approximately 30.*

*128 is approximately 130.*

*30 × 130 = 3 × 1300 = 3900*

*3900 is close to 3712, and so the answer to part (a) is reasonable.*

**Do:**
Show which approximations you are going to use, and why you are going to use them

(c) A deposit of 15% must be paid on each booking. Find
15% of £128.

$$10\% \text{ of } £128 = £12.80$$
$$\underline{5\% \text{ of } £128 = \phantom{0}6.40}$$
$$15\% \text{ of } £128 = £19.20$$

*A deposit of £19.20 is required for each booking.*

Find 10% of £128 by dividing 128
by 10
5% is half of 10%

Remember to add the two
percentages together

## 4.5 Trial and improvement

When a joiner makes a new door he usually makes it too big. He
tries the door in the frame, then planes some wood off the side and
tries it in the frame again. If it is still too big he planes off some
more wood and tries it in the frame again. He continues this
process until the door fits the frame.

In mathematics you can use a similar process to find an answer to
a problem. You first make a guess of the answer. Then try your
guess in the problem to see if it 'fits'. If your guess is not correct,
improve it and try again. You need to continue this process until
you have a satisfactory solution to the problem. This method of
solving problems is called **trial and improvement**.

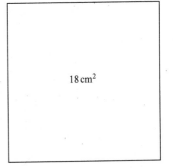

*Example 8*

Calculate the length of the side of this square. The area of the
square is $18 \text{ cm}^2$.

Your value for the side should give a value for the area that is
correct to three decimal places.

First measure the length of the side on the diagram. This gives a
value of 4.2 cm.

Area of square = length × length

Try $\quad 4.2 \times 4.2 = 17.64$ (this is not big enough)
so try $\quad 4.3 \times 4.3 = 18.49$ (this is too big)

So the answer lies between 4.2 and 4.3

Now try $\quad 4.24 \times 4.24 = 17.978$ to 3 d.p. (not big enough)
so try $\qquad 4.25 \times 4.25 = 18.062$ to 3 d.p. (too big)

So the answer lies between 4.24 and 4.25

Now try $\quad 4.243 \times 4.243 = 18.003$ to 3 d.p. (too big)
so try $\qquad 4.242 \times 4.242 = 17.995$ to 3 d.p. (not big enough)

So the answer lies between 4.242 and 4.243

18 cm²

Now try   $4.2425 \times 4.2425 = 17.999$ to 3 d.p. (not big enough)
so try      $4.2426 \times 4.2426 = 18.000$ to 3 d.p. (correct)

So a length of 4.2426 cm gives a square area of 18 cm$^2$ correct to 3 decimal places.

---

### Exercise 4F

1. (a) Measure the length of one side of this square as accurately as you can.

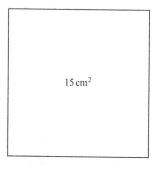

15 cm$^2$

   (b) Multiply your measurement by itself and see how close you are to the correct area.
   (c) Use the trial and improvement method to find the length of one side correct to 3 decimal places.

2. For her maths homework Pat has to find the angle at the centre of a circle when it is divided into 7 equal sectors. She knows the answer can be found by dividing 360° by 7, but the 'division' button on her calculator is broken. Pat finds the angle correct to 4 significant figures using only the multiplication button and the trial and improvement method.
   Solve Pat's problem showing all your working.

3. Use the trial and improvement method to find the length of this rectangle.

8.2 cm$^2$        1.4 cm

   Your value for the length should give a value for the area that is correct to 4 decimal places. Show all your working.

4. Use a trial and improvement method to find the cube root of 10 correct to 3 decimal places. Show all your working.

---

### Worked exam question 3

Roberta is trying to work out the square root of 31. The square root key on her calculator is not working and so she decides to use a trial and improvement method to find the answer.

(a) Complete the following equations:

   $5.5^2 =$   *30.25*

   $5.6^2 =$   *31.36*

   $5.55^2 =$   *30.8025*

**Do:**

Use your calculator to find $5.5^2$ by using the  $x^2$  key or by calculating $5.5 \times 5.5$

Write down all the figures on your calculator display

(b) Continue this trial and improvement method to find the square root of 31, where 31 is correct to three decimal places.

   $5.55^2 = 30.8025$ *(not enough)*

   $5.56^2 = 30.9136$ *(not enough)*

Write down the full calculator display for each stage

$5.57^2 = 31.0249$ *(too much)*

$5.565^2 = 30.969225$ *(not enough)*

$5.568^2 = 31.002624$ *(just too much)*

$5.5678^2 = 31.000397 = 31.000$ *correct to three decimal places*

$\sqrt{31} = 5.568$ *correct to three decimal places*

Find your answer correct to 4 d.p. and then round it down to 3 d.p.

## 4.6 Unitary methods

If you are told that a gardener can plant out 960 seedlings in 3 hours, you can work out how many she plants out in 1 hour.

You can then use this information to calculate how many seedlings she could plant out in 4 hours, 5 hours, or any other length of time.

When you work out

- how many seedlings a gardener plants in *one* hour

- how far a car travels in one hour

- how much petrol you can buy for £1

you are using a **unitary method**.

'Unitary' means one unit; for example

- seedlings in one hour

- kilometres in one hour

- litres for £1

### Example 9

A car travels 120 km in 3 hours at a constant speed.

How far does it travel in 2.5 hours at the same speed?

In    3 hours it travels    120 km

In    1 hour it travels    $120 \div 3 = 40$ km

So in  2.5 hours it travels $2.5 \times 40 = 100$ km

### Example 10

A bottle of white correction fluid contains 24 m*l* of fluid and costs 72 p.

Find:

(a) the cost of 1 m*l*

(b) how much fluid you get for 1 p

(c) the cost of 100 ml (assuming the cost per millimetre that you found in (a)).


(a) The cost of 1 ml is the cost of 24 ml, divided by 24. The cost for 24 ml is 72 p, so

$$\text{cost of } 1 \text{ ml} = 72 \div 24 = 3 \text{ p}$$

(b) The amount of fluid you get for 1p is the amount, 24 ml, divided by the cost, 72 p:

$$\text{amount for } 1 \text{ p is } 24 \div 72 = 0.33\ldots \text{ ml}$$

(c) The cost of a 100 ml bottle is 100 times the cost for 1 ml of fluid:

$$\text{cost} = 100 \times 3 = 300\text{p}$$
$$= \text{£3.00}$$


## Exercise 4G

1. A car travelled 135 km in 5 hours at constant speed. Calculate:
   (a) how far it travelled in 1 hour
   (b) how far it travelled in 4 hours
   (c) how far it travelled in 2 hours 30 minutes.

2. A packet of digestive biscuits contains 16 biscuits and weighs 288 grams. Find:
   (a) the weight of one biscuit
   (b) the weight of 10 biscuits
   (c) the weight of 25 biscuits.

3. Find the cost, to the the nearest penny, of:

   18 tiles: £7.20

   (a) one tile
   (b) 15 tiles

4. Jackie earns £360 for a 40-hour week. Find:
   (a) her hourly rate
   (b) the amount she earns if she works exactly 24 hours, and is only paid for the hours she works.

5. On one day the exchange rate between the American dollar and the UK pound sterling is $1 = £0.5

   (a) At this exchange rate, how many dollars would you get for
      (i) £1    (ii) £8    (iii) £16?
   (b) How many pounds would you get for $12.5?

6. In Example 11 the cost of a 100 ml bottle of correction fluid was calculated as £3. Give a reason why this is unlikely to be the actual price of a 100 ml bottle.

7. A large bottle of orange squash contains 3 litres of squash and costs £1.44. The standard bottle contains 1 litre and costs 92p. (Note: 1000 ml = 1l.) Calculate:
   (a) the cost per ml of the squash in the large bottle
   (b) the amount per penny of squash in the standard bottle
   (c) which bottle is the 'best buy', and why.

8. Tony's maths notes contain 480 pages. The set of notes is 3 cm thick. Given that 10 mm = 1 cm. Find:
   (a) (i) the thickness of one page in millimetres
       (ii) the thickness of the first 50 pages.
   (b) His science notes, on the same paper, are 2.1 cm thick. How many pages do they contain?
   (c) A set of English notes, on the same paper, contains 256 pages. The notes are photocopied 4 times (on the same paper) to make 5 sets. How tall is the stack of 5 sets?

*Example 11*

Mr Pearce is building a new bungalow. He has to dig a trench by the side of the house for drains. The trench is 30 m long. He can only dig 3 m of trench per day.

(a) How long would it take him to dig the whole trench on his own?

(b) How long would it take Mr Pearce and his daughter Mabel working together to dig the trench? (Mabel digs at the same rate as Mr Pearce.)

(a) As Mr Pearce can dig 3 m of trench in one day, it would take him $30 \div 3 = 10$ days to dig the whole trench.

(b) Mr Pearce and Mabel can together dig 6 m of trench per day. Therefore, it would take them $30 \div 6 = 5$ days to dig the whole of the trench.

*Example 12*

Six window cleaners start cleaning all the windows in a tower block on Monday morning. It takes them three days to clean all the windows.

How long would it take two window cleaners working at the same speed to clean all the windows in the same tower block?

To solve this type of problem, you need to work out how long it would take for **one** cleaner to clean **all** the windows working at the same speed.

It would take one cleaner $6 \times 3 = 18$ days to clean the windows.

Therefore, two cleaners would take $18 \div 2 = 9$ days to clean the windows.

**Exercise 4H**

1. Mr Pearce decides that even working with his daughter Mabel, it would still take too long to dig the trench. He asks three more relatives to help. How long will it take Mr Pearce, his daughter Mabel and the three other relatives to dig the trench? (Assume they all dig at the same rate)

2. A second smaller trench is needed for the drains. This trench is 24 metres long and can be dug by one person at a rate of 4 metres per day. Find how long it would take to dig it if:
   (a) Mr Pearce works alone

(b) Mr Pearce and his daughter work together
(c) Mr Pearce, his daughter and his wife Sheila all work together
(d) a gang of 15 students are employed to dig the trench.

3. Mr Pearce employs 3 electricians. Working together these electricians can wire up his new bungalow in 2 days.
   (a) How long should it take one electrician working on his own to wire the bungalow?
   (b) How long should it take 2 electricians to wire up the new bungalow?

4. Caron has to complete her maths coursework. She works out that if she spends 2 hours a day it will take her 6 days to complete it. Unfortunately the deadline for handing in the coursework is only 5 days away.
   (a) How long would it take her if she spent 3 hours a day on it?
   (b) Would Caron have her coursework completed on time?

5. A group of 30 students go on a field trip. On the trip they have to perform various different tasks. Their tutor works out that it should take 1.5 hours for the 30 students to complete all the tasks. Unfortunately 12 of the students catch 'flu' and do not go on the trip.
   (a) How long would it take one student working on her own to complete all the tasks?
   (b) How long did it take the students who did go on the trip to complete all the tasks?

---

## Worked exam question 4

Molly solders components on to a circuit board for a car radio manufacturer. She is paid 24 p for each of the first 250 components that she solders.

(a) How much does she earn for soldering the first 250 components of the week?

$250 \times 0.24 = £60$ *for 250 components*

**Do:**
Note that she earns 24 p for each component. So she earns $250 \times 0.24$ for 250 components

Molly is paid 18p for each component that she solders in a week after the first 250.

(b) In her shift on the first day of the week, Molly solders 386 components. How much does she earn on that day?

*Pay: 24p each for the first 250 components*

**Do:**
Find her earnings for 250 components at 24p and $386 - 250 = 136$ components at 18p

*18p each for $386 - 250 = 136$ components.*

Use your answer to (a) in your calculation

$136 \times 0.18 = £24.48$

*Total earnings for the day are $£60 + £24.48 = £88.48$.*

In one week, Molly earns £346.20.

(c) How many components has she soldered?

*For soldering the first 250 components, Molly earns £60. For the rest, she earns 18p per component.*

Use your answer from (a) – she is paid £60 for 250 components. So she is paid $£346.20 - £60 = £286.20$ for the rest of the components

$£346.20 - £60 = £286.20$

$\dfrac{286.20}{0.18} = 1590$

*Molly soldered $250 + 1590 = 1840$ components.*

**Worked exam question 5**

It takes 100 g of flour to make 15 shortbread biscuits.
Calculate the weight of flour needed to make 24 shortbread
biscuits.

$$\frac{100}{15} = 6.666\ldots$$

$$6.666\ldots \times 24 = 160g$$ (MEG)

Work out how much flour is
needed to make one biscuit

**Don't:**
Re-set your calculator or round
this figure

**Do:**
Multiply by 24 to find the amount
of flour needed for 24 biscuits

## 4.7 Multiplication and division

You often need to solve mathematical problems in the real world,
as well as in exams. If the information is given in words, your first
question might be 'What do I do with this information?' It often
helps you decide whether to use multiplication or division in a
problem if you look at the problem first using whole numbers.

Lucy lives in Derby and her friend Charlie lives 16 miles away in
Nottingham. Lucy wants to know how far it is between the two
cities in kilometres. She looks through her maths textbook and
finds:

$$1 \text{ mile} = 1.609 \text{ km}$$

Lucy is not sure if she should multiply or divide to work out the
answer.

She uses approximations to make the problem more simple.
1 mile is approximately 2 km.

Then 16 miles is approximately 32 km.

To find this you multiply $16 \times 2$

So to solve the original problem multiply 16 by 1.609

$16 \times 1.609 = 25.74$ km to 4 significant figures.

*Example 13*

A car petrol tank holds 38.5 litres of petrol.

What is this capacity in gallons?
(1 gallon is approximately 4.55 litres.)

$$1 \text{ gallon} = 4.55 \text{ litres}$$

$$\frac{1}{4.55} \text{ gallons} = 1 \text{ litre}$$

The capacity is $38.5 \times \dfrac{1}{4.55} = 8.46$ gallons.

## Exercise 4I

1. A marathon is run over a distance of approximately 26 miles. Calculate this distance in kilometres correct to two significant figures (1 mile = 1.609 km).

2. A ream of paper contains 500 sheets of paper. Each sheet of the paper is 0.124 mm thick. What is the total thickness of
   (a) one ream of the paper?
   (b) six reams of the paper?

3. Copy the map below. Label it with the distances between the towns in miles. (1 km is approximately 0.621 miles.) Give your answers to 2 significant figures.

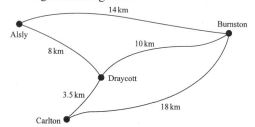

4. A petrol can holds 6.5 litres of petrol. How many gallons does it hold? (1 litre is approximately $\frac{1}{5}$ of a gallon.)

5. A ball is dropped from the top of a tower 20 m high. When the ball bounces, it rises to $\frac{5}{8}$ of the height from which it was dropped, or $\frac{5}{8}$ of the height of its last bounce.
   (a) Find the height that the ball reaches on the first bounce.
   (b) How high does the ball rise on the fourth bounce?
   (c) How many times will the ball bounce before it rises to a height of less than 1 m?

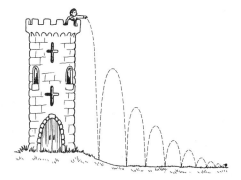

6. A pile of photocopying paper consists of 750 sheets and measures 930 mm in height: Find the following:
   (a) the thickness of one sheet of the paper
   (b) the height of a pile of 3400 sheets of the paper
   (c) the number of sheets of the paper in a pile 744 mm high.

7. A pub sells an average of 524 pints of beer a day. Find:
   (a) the number of pints of beer the pub sells in a week
   (b) the number of pints it sells in a year
   (c) the amount in litres of beer that it sells in a year (1 litre is approximately 1.76 pints).

8. A new bypass road is being built around Draycott. The first section of the bypass will be 14.5 km long. It takes 32 tonnes of tar to surface 1 km of the road. Calculate:
   (a) the number of tonnes of tar that will be needed to surface the first section of the new road
   (b) the number of tonnes of tar that will be needed to surface the second section of the bypass, which is 21.25 km long, and the same width as the first section
   (c) the mass in kilograms of tar that will be needed to surface the third section of the bypass, which is 126 m long, and the same width as the first section.
   (Note: 1000 kg = 1 tonne.)

9. A boat in a yacht race reaches a maximum speed of 25 knots. 1 knot is approximately 1.143 miles per hour, and 1 km is approximately 0.621 miles. Calculate:
   (a) the maximum speed of the boat in miles per hour
   (b) the maximum speed of the boat in kilometres per hour.

10. A gunner in a tank fires a test shell at a target 5.452 km away. However, the shell only travels 3.488 km before it hits the ground. The gunner tilts the gun up by 1°, and fires another test shell. This shell travels 0.109 km further than the first shell. By how many degrees does the gunner have to tilt the gun from its original position before a shell hits the target?

11. A new model of car called the Korolla is launched by the car manufacturer Daywoo. In its advertising, Daywoo claims that the average petrol consumption of the Korolla at a steady speed of 56 miles per hour is 50 miles per gallon. What is the petrol consumption at 56 miles per hour of the Korolla in kilometres per litre? (1 mile is 1.609 km, and 1 litre is 0.22 gallons.)

**12**. In a 12 km charity walk, Jay walks at an average rate of 64 paces per minute. The length of one of his paces is $\frac{7}{8}$ m. Work out:
(a) how many paces he takes over the whole walk
(b) how long it takes him to complete the walk.

**13**. It costs a cement company £72.56 to produce 1 tonne of ready mixed concrete. It sells concrete to the building trade at a price of £90.60 per tonne.
(a) A builder needs 24.5 tonnes of concrete. How much will he have to pay for it?
(b) A man carrying out DIY work needs $\frac{3}{4}$ tonne of concrete. How much will it cost him?
(c) A large building company is building a housing estate. It receives a bill for concrete for £10 872. How many tonnes of concrete did it order?
(d) How much profit did the cement company make from an order for cement from a builder whose bill was £1812?

**14**. Matthew Engineering Group pays its employees a mileage allowance when they use their own cars on company business. The rate is 30 p for the first 100 miles of a journey, and 18 p for any additional miles.
The distance between Derby and Cambridge is 115 miles.
(a) How much can an employee claim for a trip from Derby to Cambridge and back?
(b) Another company pays its employees a mileage allowance of 25 p per mile. How much should an employee of this company claim for a trip from Derby to Cambridge and back?

(c) Calculate the amount that an employee can claim under each system for a journey of 180 miles.
(d) For a certain distance, an employee could claim the same amount of money under both systems. Use a trial and improvement method to find this distance.

**15**. To build an alarm system, the following parts are needed:

| | |
|---|---|
| metal case | £12.50 |
| L.E.D.s | £5.65 |
| switches | £8.49 |
| resistors | £4.52 |
| microchips | £16.85 |
| wiring | £7.42 |
| alarm bells | £4.30 |

(a) What is the total cost of the parts in one alarm system?
(b) What is the cost of the parts in 25 alarm systems?
(c) How many alarm systems can be made for £1000?

**16**. Mr Kent went on holiday to Germany. He changed £2000 into deutschmarks (DM) at a rate of 2.25 DM to the pound. His hotel and other expenses were 225 DM per day for eight days. On returning home, he changed his remaining deutschmarks back into pounds. Calculate:
(a) the number of deutschmarks that he received for his £2000
(b) the total of his hotel and other expenses per day in pounds
(c) the amount of money in pounds that he returned home with.

---

## Worked exam question 6

Colin buys 28.4 litres of petrol at 52.5p a litre. The price at another garage is 46.2 p a litre. How much more petrol can Colin buy for the same money if he uses this garage?

*First garage* 28.4 × 52.5p = 1491p = £14.91

*Second garage* $\frac{1491}{46.2}$ = 32.2727

= 32.3 *litres to the nearest 0.1 of a litre*

*The difference is* 32.3 − 28.4 = 3.9 *litres*          (MEG)

**Do:**
Work out how much Colin spends on petrol at the first garage

Divide the amount of money by the cost of petrol

Give your answer to a realistic level of accuracy

### Exercise 4J (Mixed questions)

1. **Do not use a calculator when answering this question.**
   **All working must be shown.**
   Sian and David are on holiday in Spain.
   (a) They buy drinks costing 275 pesetas and 340 pesetas.
       (i) Find the total cost of their drinks.
       (ii) They pay for the drinks using a 1000 peseta note. How much change should they be given?
   (b) They stay at an hotel which has a small boat for hire. The boat can hold a maximum of 6 people.
       (i) The boat was hired 16 times in a day, and was fully loaded on each occasion. Find the total number of people who rode in the boat during that day.
       (ii) On a different day, the total number of people who rode in the boat was 132. The boat was fully loaded each time. Find how many times the boat was hired that day. [WJEC]

2. (a) The diagram shows a mineral water bottle.
       Copy the diagram and draw the approximate water level on the bottle, if it is three-quarters full.
   (b) Bottles of mineral water cost 39 p each.
       Estimate the cost of 142 bottles.
       Show how you obtained your estimate.
   (c) Without using a calculator, work out the exact cost of 142 bottles of mineral water at 39 p each.
   (You must write down enough working to show that you did not use a calculator). [MEG]

3. **Do not use a calculator in this question. Show all your working clearly**.
   Floppy discs cost 35 p each.
   You have £5 to spend on floppy disks.
   (a) How many floppy disks do you buy?
   (b) How much change do you get?

4. The area of a square is 63 cm$^2$.
   (a) Write down the length of one side to the nearest whole number.
   (b) Use a trial and improvement method to calculate the length of one side correct to 3 decimal places.

5. The length of a rectangle is 2 cm more than its width.
   (a) Calculate the area of the rectangle
       (i) when the width is 4 cm
       (ii) when the width is 5 cm.
   (b) Using a trial and improvement method, find the width of the rectangle given that its area is 32 cm$^2$.
       Give your answer in centimetres correct to one decimal place. (You must show all your trials). [MEG]

6. A cassette tape is played at $1\frac{7}{8}$ inches per second.
   (a) Calculate the length of tape played in 8 seconds.
   (b) Calculate the length of tape played in $2\frac{1}{2}$ seconds.
   (c) Calculate how long it takes for $9\frac{3}{8}$ inches of tape to be played.
   (d) Calculate the length of tape played in half an hour. Give your answer in feet and inches. (Note: 12 inches = 1 foot)  [London]

7. A group of 29 teenagers is planning an activities holiday. The holiday will cost £118 per person.
   (a) **Do not use a calculator**.
       Work out the total cost of the holiday for the group. Show all the stages in your working clearly. Write down the answer.
   You could estimate whether your answer to (a) is reasonable.
   (b) Write down a calculation you could use.
       Include the final answer to this calculation.
   A deposit of $12\frac{1}{2}$% must be paid on each holiday.
   (c) Use your calculator to find $12\frac{1}{2}$% of £118. [London]

8. A personal stereo was priced at £48. In a sale it was reduced to £42.
   (a) By what fraction was the original price reduced?
   (b) Write your fraction as a percentage. [London]

9. This recipe will make 3 glasses of Raspberry Milk Shake.
   150 ml raspberry juice
   300 ml water
   150 ml evaporated milk
     15 g sugar
   Juice of $\frac{1}{2}$ lemon
   How much raspberry juice is needed for 5 glasses?

**10**. Leroy changes £475.60 into Guilders for a
holiday in Holland.
The exchange rate is £1 = 2.68 Guilders.
There is a £5 charge for changing the money.
How many Guilders should he receive?    [SEG]

**11**. A book has 200 pages and is 2.76 cm thick.
(a) Find the thickness, in cm, of one page.

(b) Calculate the thickness of 340 pages of the
same book.

**12**. A piece of string is 406 centimetres in length. It
is to be cut up into pieces which are each 17 cm
long. Calculate:
(a) the number of 17 cm long pieces that can be
obtained
(b) the length of the small piece of string that is
left over.    [NEAB]

---

## Test yourself

**1.** An office manager orders 116 packets of 24 felt pens.

QUESTION    Work out $24 \times 116$. Do not use a calculator.

ANSWER    2784    *If your answer is incorrect, review page 64, Section 4.2, on long multiplication.*

**2.** 243 is divided by 17.

QUESTION    Find the remainder. Do not use a calculator.

ANSWER    5.    *If your answer is incorrect, review page 65, Section 4.3 on problems involving division*

**3.** Joe is laying a garden path. He is using a single line of paving slabs that are 0.2 m long. He has 600 slabs.

QUESTION    Calculate $600 \times 0.2$. Do not use a calculator.

ANSWER    120    *If your answer is incorrect, review page 66, Section 4.4 on solving problems mentally*

**4.** You want to find the square root of 44. The square root key on your calculator is not working.

QUESTION    (a)    Calculate the values of $6.6^2$, $6.7^2$, and $6.65^2$.

ANSWER    $6.6^2 = 43.56$    *If your answer is incorrect, review page 69, Section 4.5 on trial and improvement.*
$6.7^2 = 44.89$
$6.65^2 = 44.2225$

QUESTION    (b)    Between which two of the limits in part (a) does the square root of 44 lie?

ANSWER    6.6 and 6.65    *If your answer is incorrect, review page 69, Section 4.5 on trial and improvement.*

**5.** The price of twelve bars of chocolate is £3.36.

QUESTION    What is the cost of (i) one bar (ii) five bars (iii) 17 bars?

ANSWER    (i)    £0.28    (or 28 p)    *If your answer is incorrect, review page 71, Section 4.6 on unitary methods.*
(ii)    £1.40
(iii)    £4.76

6. It takes four furniture makers six days to make a sofa.

| | | |
|---|---|---|
| QUESTION | (a) | How long would it take one person to make that sofa? |
| ANSWER | | 24 days |

*If your answer is incorrect, review page 71, Section 4.6 on unitary methods.*

| | | |
|---|---|---|
| QUESTION | (b) | How long would it take three people to make that sofa? |
| ANSWER | | 8 days |

*If your answer is incorrect, review page 71, Section 4.6 on unitary methods.*

7. The 40 km walk is an Olympic Games event. 1 km = 0.621 miles.

QUESTION    What is the length of the walk in miles?

ANSWER    24.84 miles

*If your answer is incorrect, review page 75, Section 4.7 on multiplication and division.*

8. The value at one point of £1 sterling in US dollars was approximately $2.25.

QUESTION    What was the value of US$1 in pounds sterling?

ANSWER    £0.44

*If your answer is incorrect, review page 75, Section 4.7 on multiplication and division.*

## Summary of key points to remember

1. When you solve a problem using a **non-calculator method**, break the problem down into simple components. Then total the components to find the solution to the main problem. Show all your workings, and clearly identify your answer.

2. When you have to solve a **long-division problem** using a non-calculator method, you can often convert it into a multiplication problem to make it easier to solve.

3. When you have to solve a problem in your head, you can often **rearrange the numbers** to make it easier to work out.

4. When you solve a problem using a **trial and improvement method**, estimate the required value. Check how close your estimate is to the correct solution. Then change your estimate by a small amount and check again, until you have the correct answer.

5. When you solve a problem using a **unitary method**, find the appropriate value for one unit first. Then use this unit value to find the solution to the problem.

6. When you have to solve a problem and you are not sure whether you should be using multiplication or division, use approximate values to create an easier version of the problem. Solving your easier version should help you decide whether to use multiplication or division.

# 5 Ratio and percentage

This unit covers finding ratios and calculations involving sharing amounts in a given ratio. You will be shown how to calculate percentages using a calculator. Percentage calculations include fractional and percentage increase and decrease such as when prices rise or fall by a given percentage. You will also learn how to calculate the percentage profit and loss when goods are bought and sold.

## 5.1 Ratio 1

Suppose that £12 is to be shared between two people. If it is shared equally they will each receive £6.

The £12 could also be shared so that one person receives twice as much as the other. Then one would receive £8 and the other £4. We say that the £12 is shared in the **ratio** two to one, which we write 2 : 1.

### Example 1

Tony and Gaynor buy a packet of 15 pens. They share them out between them. They put all the pens in one pile:

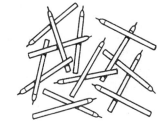

Tony takes two pens: ⊂════▷ ⊂═══▷

Then Gaynor takes three pens: ⊲═══▷ ⊲═══▷ ⊲═══▷

They carry on taking turns, with Tony taking two pens and Gaynor taking three pens, until all the pens have gone. What ratio do Tony and Gaynor share their pens out in?

Tony and Gaynor share their pens out in the ratio 2 : 3.

---

### Exercise 5A

1. (a) In Example 1, when all the pens are shared out, how many will Tony have? How many will Gaynor have?
   (b) Write down the fraction of the 15 pens that they each have. Write the fractions in their lowest terms.

   (c) Can you see a connection between the fractions and the ratio 2 : 3?

2. The packet of 15 pens cost £3.
   (a) What fraction of the £3 should Tony pay?
   (b) How much should Tony pay?
   (c) How much should Gaynor pay?

## 5.2 Sharing in ratios

Suppose that a stick of rock is to be divided into two lengths in the ratio $a : b$. The easiest way to do this is to think of the stick of rock as having length $(a + b)$. Then one share will be $\dfrac{a}{a+b}$ of the length and the other share will be $\dfrac{b}{a+b}$ of the length.

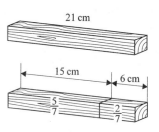

### Example 2

A length of wood 21 cm long is to be divided into two parts in the ratio 2 : 5. How long will each length be?

The ratio required is 2 : 5.

The smaller length will be 2 parts out of 7 or $\frac{2}{7}$ of 21 = 6 cm.

The larger length will be 5 parts out of 7 or $\frac{5}{7}$ of 21 = 15 cm.

A simple check is to add the two lengths to see if they come to 21 cm.

$$6 \, \text{cm} + 15 \, \text{cm} = 21 \, \text{cm}$$

### Exercise 5B

1. Errol, Paljit and Karl share a packet of 24 sweets in the ratio 1 : 2 : 3.
   (a) What fraction of the sweets does each have?
   (b) How many sweets does each have?

2. Sally, Brian and Mark share £45 in the ratio 4 : 5 : 6.
   (a) What fraction of the £45 does each person receive?
   (b) How much does each person receive?

3. Jean and Derek inherit £4000 in their Aunt Hilda's will. The will instructs that the money is to be shared in the ratio 3 : 2 in favour of Jean.
   (a) What fraction of the £4000 does each receive?
   (b) How much does each receive?
   (c) Show a simple method to check your answers.

4. Demi and Sharon share £320 in the ratio 3 : 5.
   (a) To work out how much each receives, how many parts should the £320 be divided into?
   (b) What fraction of the £320 does Demi receive?
   (c) How much does Demi receive?
   (d) What fraction does Sharon receive?
   (e) How much does Sharon receive?

5. Danny and Melissa serve food in a cafe. Danny works seven days a week but Melissa only works on Friday, Saturday and Sunday. They share their tips in the ratio of the number of days they work.
   (a) Write down the ratio in which they share their tips.
   (b) What fraction of the tips should Danny receive?
   (c) The tips in one week came to £90. How much did Melissa receive?
   (d) The following week the tips came to £72. How much did Danny receive?

6. In a GCSE mathematics examination course 80 of the final marks are for the written examination papers and the other 20 are from coursework assignments.
   (a) Write the ratio of exam marks to coursework marks.
   (b) Daly obtains a final mark of 66. The ratio of his exam marks to coursework marks was 8 : 3.
   How many coursework marks did he gain?

7. Suzanne runs a local shop. She sells three types of soap powder: New Brave, New Aireal and New Pursal. In one week she sells 864 boxes of these powders in the ratio of 1 : 2 : 3.
   (a) What fraction of the total sales are for New Pursal?

7. (b) How many of boxes of New Brave does she sell?
   (c) She makes 8 p profit on each box sold. How much profit does she make from the two best-selling lines altogether?

8. Four darts players each threw 3 rounds of 3 darts each to raise money for charity. The charity received one pound for each point scored. Between them the 4 darts players scored 1728 in the ratio 3 : 4 : 4 : 5.
   (a) What score did the best player obtain?
   (b) What was her average score each round in order to achieve this total score?
   (c) What was the lowest total score?
   (d) What was the difference in score between the highest scorer and the lowest?

## 5.3 Ratio 2

Suppose an unknown amount is shared in the ratio 2 : 3. We know that the fractional amounts will be $\frac{2}{5}$ and $\frac{3}{5}$ respectively. If we are then given the actual value of one of the shares we can calculate the value of the other share and the value of the original amount.

*Example 3*

In one season Adam and Paul scored goals in the ratio 4 : 5. Adam scored 24 goals.

(a) How many goals did Paul score?

(b) What was the total number of goals scored between them?

(a) The goals were scored in the ratio 4 : 5. So Adam scored $\frac{4}{9}$ of the total number and Paul scored $\frac{5}{9}$.

$\frac{4}{9}$ of the total is 24 (the number Adam scored)

so $\frac{1}{9}$ of the total is $24 \div 4 = 6$

and $\frac{5}{9}$ of the total is $6 \times 5 = 30$

Paul scored 30 goals.

(b) Adam scored 24 goals and Paul scored 30. So they scored a total of $30 + 24 = 54$ goals between them.

### Exercise 5C

1. Cars use more fuel in cold weather. A petrol company carried out a fuel consumption test on a certain car. They found that the winter-to-summer fuel consumption ratio over a test track was 3.5 : 4. The winter fuel consumption was 8.2 km per litre. Find the summer consumption.

2. The speed limit in French towns is 60 kilometres per hour. 5 miles is approximately equal to 8 km.
   (a) Mr Been drives through a French town at 35 miles per hour. Is he breaking their speed limit?
   (b) The maximum speed allowed on British roads is 70 miles per hour. What is this speed in kilometres per hour?

3. The average marks of three teaching groups at Midgrove college were in the ratio 4 : 5 : 7. The average mark of the middle group was 62.5. Find:
   (a) the lowest mark
   (b) the difference between the highest and lowest mark.

4. A bag contains red, blue and green counters in the ratio 5 : 7 : 11. There are 275 red counters in the bag. What is the total number of counters in the bag?

## Worked exam question 1

Anne is 12 years old and her brother Bobby is 8 years old. •———

They have £2 pocket money altogether.

The money is shared in the ratio of their ages.

(a) Calculate the amount each receives.

$$Ann \ gets \ \frac{12}{20} \times £2 = £1.20 \ •$$

$$Bobby \ gets \ \frac{8}{20} \times £2 = £0.80$$

$$= \underline{£2.00} \ •$$

Anne $\underline{£1.20}$ Bobby $\underline{80p}$

Two years ago Bobby received 30p pocket money.

Their pocket money was in the same ratio 12 : 8.

(b) Calculate how much Anne received then.

$$\frac{8}{20} \ of \ total = 30p$$

$$so \ \frac{1}{20} \ of \ total \ \frac{30}{8}p = 3.75p \ •$$

$$Anne's \ share \ is \ \frac{12}{20} \ of \ total = 3.75 \times 12 = 45p \ •$$

$\underline{45}$ p

(London)

**Do:**
Note that the ratio of their ages is 12 : 8

Note that the shares are $\frac{12}{20}$ and $\frac{8}{20}$

Check your answer is correct by adding

**Do:**
Note that the ratio is still 12 : 8

Note that Bobby received $\frac{8}{20}$ of the total

Find $\frac{1}{20}$ of the total

Multiply by 12 to find $\frac{12}{20}$ of the total

# 5.4 Percentages

In Unit 1 Number you learnt how to calculate percentages. Here we will develop a quicker method, using a calculator.

Duljit wants to find 21% of £26.

He knows he can work it out by finding

$$10\% \ of \ £26 = £2.60$$
$$10\% \ of \ £26 = £2.60$$
$$\underline{1\% \ of \ £26 = £0.26}$$

and adding to get 21% of £26 = £5.46

There is another method of finding percentages.

As a decimal fraction $10\% = \frac{10}{100} = 0.1$

As a decimal fraction $1\% = \frac{1}{100} = 0.01$

Duljit found 21% by finding

$$10\% + 10\% + 1\% = 21\%$$

which is the same as

$$0.1 + 0.1 + 0.01 = 0.21$$

So 21% of £26.50 = 0.21 × £26 = £5.46

You can use a calculator to do the multiplication.

---

**Exercise 5D**

1. Duljit wants to find 34% of £6.36. Write down the multiplication sum he should do on his calculator.

2. Hazel wants to find 58% of 11.5 kg.
   (a) What should she multiply the 11.5 kg by?
   (b) Find 58% of 11.5 kg.

3. Find 32% of £64:
   (a) by finding 10% and multiplying by 3, finding 1% and multiplying by 2 and adding the two answers together.
   (b) by multiplying £64 by 0.32.

4. Write these percentages as decimal fractions:
   (a) 25%  (b) 56%  (c) 62%  (d) 11%

   (e) 70%  (f) 7%  (g) 12.5%  (h) 67.5%
   (i) 110%  (j) 150%  (k) 243%  (l) 450%

5. Find:
   (a) 42% of 6400 g          (b) 56% of 2 m
   (c) 75% of 240 ml          (d) 5% of £2.46
   (e) 16% of 1200 cm         (f) 8% of 10 min
   (g) 120% of 800 kg         (h) 17.5% of 8 m
   (i) 117.5% of 8 m

6. In a 240 g packet of biscuits 4.7% is protein, 67.1% is carbohydrates and 8.2% is fat
   Find:
   (a) the amount of fat in grams
   (b) the amount of carbohydrates in grams.

---

# 5.5 Calculating percentages using decimals

Last year reported crime went up by 24%.

This diagram represents the percentage of crimes at the beginning of the year.

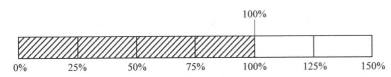

This diagram represents the percentage at the end of the year.

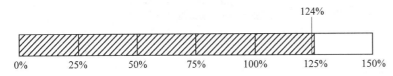

As a percentage, the number of crimes at the end of the year is:

$$100\% + 24\% = 124\% \quad \text{of the number of crimes at the beginning of the year}$$

*Example 4*

Jenny earns £28 500 a year. She gets a 15% increase.

Calculate her new salary.

After a 15% increase Jenny's salary will be $100\% + 15\% = 115\%$ of her old salary.

115% as a decimal $= \frac{115}{100} = 1.15$

So her new salary is $1.15 \times £28\,500 = £32\,775$

During 1993 house prices fell by an average of 15%.

This diagram represents the price of a house at the beginning of the year.

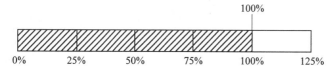

This diagram represents the price at the end of the year.

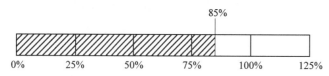

As a percentage the new value is:

$$100\% - 15\% = 85\% \text{ of the old value}$$

### Exercise 5E

1. These statements describe increases over one year. Write the end-of-year value as a percentage of the beginning-of-year value.
   (a) The number of reported crimes went up by 15%.
   (b) The student population went up 12.5%.
   (c) The rate of inflation went up by 2.5%.
   (d) The price of a car increased by 9%.
   (e) The price of a washing machine went up by 17.5%.

2. Write the new value as a percentage of the old value for these statements.
   (a) A house decreases in value by 12%.
   (b) A bank balance decreases by 11%.
   (c) Reported violent crime goes down by 5%.
   (d) The cost of a holiday goes down by 22%.

3. (a) The value of an item decreased by 34%. Write down a multiplication sum to find the new value.

   (b) The value of MJ shares falls by 34%. Before the fall the shares cost £5.25 each. What is the new price?

4. Alan weighs 82 kg before he starts a diet. He sets himself a target of losing 5% of his original weight. What is his target weight?

5. (a) Decrease £120 by 20%.
   (b) Decrease 56 kg by 25%.
   (c) Decrease 2.4 m by 16%.
   (d) Decrease £1240 by 10.5%.
   (e) Decrease 126 cm by 2%.

6. Susie invested £100 into a savings account on 1 January 1994. The interest paid was 6.5% per annum.
   (a) Write down a multiplication sum to find the amount she will have at the end of the first year.

**6**. (b) How much money did she have in her account at the end of the first year?

(c) Assuming the interest rate remains the same, copy and complete this table. Give the 'amounts' to the nearest £.

| Date | Amount |
|------|--------|
| 1 January '94 | £100 |
| 1 January '95 | |
| 1 January '96 | |
| 1 January '97 | |
| 1 January '98 | |

**7**. A lorry costing £24 000 depreciates (its value goes *down*) by 20% in its first year, 15% in its second year and 10% each year thereafter.
(a) Find the value of the lorry after 1 year.
(b) Copy and complete the table opposite. Give the value to the nearest £ each time.

| New value | £24 000 |
|-----------|---------|
| Value after 1 year | |
| Value after 2 years | |
| Value after 3 years | |
| Value after 4 years | |
| Value after 5 years | |

**8**. Molly invests her savings in an investment trust. Her savings increase by 12% in the first year and a further 8% in the second. They fall by 9.6% in the third year.
(a) Write down a multiplication sum to find the value of her savings after the first year.
(b) What should you multiply by to find the value after two years? (Be careful, it is not 2.0.)
(c) By what percentage has Molly's investment changed over the three years?

**9**. The value of an item increases by 10% in one year but falls by 10% the following year. Write the value at the end of the second year as a percentage of the original value.

## 5.6 Percentage increase and percentage decrease

Over a period of time the price of an item often changes (usually increases). In order to compare the change in price of different items it is useful to calculate the actual increase (or decrease) as a percentage of the original price. We call this the percentage increse (or percentage decrease). You can apply the same technique to other values that can change, such as lengths, weights and times.

In 1994 a cinema ticket cost £2.50.

In 1996 a ticket at the same cinema cost £4.00.

You can find the increase in the price as a percentage of the original price.

$$\text{Actual increase} = £4.00 - £2.50 = £1.50$$

Now look at the actual increase as a fraction of the original price:

$$\text{Fraction increase} = \frac{\text{actual increase}}{\text{original price}} = \frac{150}{400}$$

As a decimal fraction:

$$\frac{150}{400} = 0.375$$

And as a percentage:

$$0.375 \times 100 = 37.5\%$$

The percentage increase is 37.5% of the original price.

### Example 5

In 1994 the cost of an annual season ticket for the rail journey from Derby to London was £2568. In 1995 this was increased to £2860.

(a)  (i)    By how much was the cost increased?

    (ii)   Calculate the percentage increase, giving your answer to the nearest 0.1%.

The cost of the annual season ticket from Nottington to London was increased by 12%.

(b) Find the new cost of a season ticket if the cost before the increase was £2420.

(a)  (i)    Actual increase = £2860 − £2568 = £292

    (ii)   percentage increase $\quad = \dfrac{\text{actual increase}}{\text{original cost}} \times 100\%$

$$= \dfrac{292 \times 100}{2568}\% = 11.370\,72\%$$

    percentage increase $\quad = 11.4\%$ to nearest 0.1%

(b) Percentage increase is 12%

Increased cost as a percentage of the old cost is
$(100 + 12)\% = 112\%$ or 1.12

New price $= 1.12 \times 2420 = £2710.40$

The new season ticket costs £2710.40

### Example 6

In a sale the price of a TV set was reduced from £840 to £650.

Calculate the percentage decrease.

Actual decrease = £840 − £650 = £190

Percentage decrease $= \dfrac{\text{actual decrease}}{\text{original price}} \times 100 \ = \dfrac{190}{840} \times 100$

$$= 22.62\%$$

to the nearest 0.01%.

**Exercise 5F**

1. In 1991 an Easter egg cost £2.40.
   In 1993 a similar Easter egg cost £3.00.
   In 1996 a similar Easter egg cost £3.90.
   Find:
   (a) the fractional increase from 1991 to 1993
   (b) the fractional increase from 1991 to 1996
   (c) the percentage increase from 1991 to 1993
   (d) the percentage increase from 1993 to 1996.

2. Calculate the percentage change (to 1 decimal place) from
   (a) £36 to £48        (b) 12.5 kg to 20 kg
   (c) 2.45 m to 2.86 m   (d) 50 minutes to 1 hour

3. Before he fitted a 'fuel-saver' Jamie's car travelled 36 km on 4.5 litres of petrol. After he had fitted the fuel-saver it travelled 58.3 km on 5.5 litres.

   Find:
   (a) the fuel consumption (in km per litre) before the fuel-saver was fitted.
   (b) the fuel consumption (in km per litre) after the fuel-saver was fitted.
   (c) the percentage change in fuel consumption.

4. Calculate the percentage change (to 1 decimal place) from
   (a) £60 to £48        (b) 18 kg to 13.5 kg
   (c) 3.75 m to 2.5 m   (d) 1 minute to 45 seconds

5. As she drove up a hill Selina noticed that the speed of her car had decreased from 68 km per hour to 62.5 km per hour.
   Find:
   (a) the actual decrease in the speed of her car
   (b) the percentage decrease correct to 1 decimal place.

## 5.7 Percentage profit and percentage loss

When items are bought and re-sold, there is usually a profit or a loss. So that profits (or losses) on several items can be compared it is useful to express the profit (or loss) as a percentage of the original buying price. This is the **percentage profit** or **percentage loss**.

Wayne sells boxes of chocolates in his shop. He buys the chocolates from the wholesaler for £2.40 a box. He sells them for £3.00 a box.

You can calculate his percentage profit like this:

Actual increase = £3.00 − £2.40 = £0.60

Now look at the 60 p as a fraction of the original price.

$$\text{Fraction increase} = \frac{\text{actual increase}}{\text{original price}} = \frac{60}{240}$$

As a decimal fraction.

$$\frac{60}{240} = 0.25$$

And as a percentage.

$$\frac{60}{240} = 0.25 = 25\%$$

The percentage profit is 25%.

*Example 7*

Colin invests £1600 in a company called 'Take it and Run' Ltd.
One year later he finds his investment is only worth £1360.

Find:

(a)  his actual loss

(b)  his percentage loss.

(a)  His actual loss $= £1600 - £1360 = £240$

(b)  Fractional loss $= \frac{240}{1600}$

As a decimal fraction $\frac{240}{1600} = 0.15$

Percentage loss $= 0.15 \times 100 = 15\%$

---

**Exercise 5G**

1. Arthur Weekly buys an old car for £840. He
   spends £400 doing the car up. He then sells it
   for £1699. Calculate:
   (a) his actual profit
   (b) his percentage profit to the nearest 1%.

2. A 24-litre oil drum was exactly $\frac{1}{4}$ full. A
   mechanic took 1.5 litres from the drum. Find:
   (a) the amount of oil left in the drum.
   (b) the percentage of the original 24 litres left in
       the drum.

3. In Example 7, Colin invested £1600 with 'Take
   it and Run' Ltd. After the first year his
   investment was only worth £1360. One year later
   Colin's investment had fallen to £1080. Find:
   (a) his actual loss over the two years
   (b) his percentage loss over the two years
   (c) his percentage loss between the first and
       second year.

4. Find these percentage decreases to the nearest
   1%.
   (a) A decrease from £48 to £32.
   (b) A decrease from 5.2 kg to 3.8 kg.
   (c) A decrease from 45 cm to 39.5 cm.
   (d) A decrease from 2 min to 110 s.
   (e) A decrease from 1 metre to 45 cm.

5. This table shows the value of the Feesta car
   after a number of years from new.

| New price | £12 500 |
|---|---|
| After 1 year | £10 000 |
| After 2 years | £8600 |
| After 3 years | £7500 |
| After 4 years | £6600 |

   (a) Calculate the percentage loss in the first year
       as a percentage of the original price.
   (b) Calculate the percentage loss between the
       second and third years.

6. Sanjeev bought a house in 1984 for £64 000. In
   1989 he sold it to Danny for £85 000. In 1994
   Danny had to sell the house for £60 000.
   Calculate:
   (a) Sanjeev's percentage profit
   (b) Danny's percentage loss
   (c) the percentage change in the value of the
       house between 1984 and 1994.

---

## 5.8 More percentage calculations

The price of a carpet is reduced by 20% in the sales. It now costs
£60.

What was the price before the sale?

The sale price is $100\% - 20\% = 80\%$ of the original price
$$= 0.8 \text{ in decimal form}$$

You can represent the information in the question in a flow diagram:

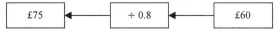

| Pre-sale price | → | × 0.8 | → | £60 |

Then draw a second flow diagram reversing the instructions:

| £75 | ← | ÷ 0.8 | ← | £60 |

The price of the carpet before the sale was £75.

*Check*: 20% of £75 = £15
$$£75 - £15 = £60 = \text{the sale price}$$

Value Added Tax, or VAT, has to be paid on most goods and services. VAT is currently 17.5%

Most retailers give prices inclusive of VAT. When they complete their accounts they have to show the price and the VAT separately.

## Example 8

A three-piece suite is sold for £1875 including VAT at 17.5%.

How much is the cost less VAT?

The total percentage cost $= 100\% + 17.5\% = 117.5\%$
$$= 1.175 \text{ as a decimal fraction}$$

| Price | → | × 1.175 | → | £1875 selling price |

Reversing the flow diagram:

| £1595.74 | ← | ÷ 1.175 | ← | £1875 |

The cost of the three-piece suite less VAT is £1595.74 to the nearest penny.

---

## Exercise 5H

1. The price of a television set has been reduced by 10% and is now £540.00.
   (a) What percentage of the pre-sale price is the sale price?
   (b) Draw a flow diagram to show this information.
   (c) Find the pre-sale price.

2. Due to increased raw material costs, a manufacturer increases the cost of the bikes that she makes by 12%. The new price is £280.
   (a) What percentage of the old price is the new price?
   (b) What was the cost of a bike before the 12% increase?

2. (c) Show a method for checking your answer to part (b).

3. The total price of a holiday is the cost of the holiday plus 17.5% VAT. In the holiday brochure the total price is quoted as £320 per person.
   (a) What percentage is the price before VAT of the total price? Give your answer to 1 decimal place.
   (b) Draw a flow diagram to show this information.
   (c) Find the price before VAT is added.

4. Due to falling orders, Johnson's Cars decreases its sales force by 8% to 161 employees. Find:
   (a) the number of employees before the decrease
   (b) the actual decrease in number.

5. After two years the value of a new moulding machine has fallen to £15 000. The depreciation is estimated at 15% per year. Find to the nearest penny:
   (a) the value of the moulding machine after the first year
   (b) the original price
   (c) the percentage decrease over the two years.

---

## Worked exam question 2

(a) The usual price of a television set is £298 plus VAT at $17\frac{1}{2}\%$.

   (i) Work out the exact value of $17\frac{1}{2}\%$ of £298.

   $$\frac{17.5}{100} = 0.175$$

   **Do:** Remember that $17.5\% = \frac{17.5}{100} = 0.175$

   $$0.175 \times 298 = 52.15$$

   **Do:** Multiply the original cost by 0.175

   (a)(i) £ 52.15

   (ii) What is the usual price of this television set?

   $$298 + 52.15 = 350.15$$

   **Do:** Add VAT to original cost

   (a)(ii) £ 350.15

(b)

GANNET STORE BARGAIN OFFER! You pay no VAT!

BERRIES STORE SALE! $\frac{1}{6}$ OFF USUAL PRICES

Gannet Store and Berries Store are selling larger television sets at reduced prices. The usual price of these sets in both stores is £423 (£360 plus £63 VAT).

   (i) Calculate the difference between the reduced prices in the two stores. Show your working clearly.

   Gannet store reduction £63

   **Do:** Notice that Gannet Store's reduction is the VAT

   Berries store $\frac{1}{6} \times 423 = £70.5$ reduction

   **Do:** Find $\frac{1}{6}$ of the usual price for the Berries Store reduction

   Difference = £70.5 − £63 = £7.50

   **Do:** Subtract to find the difference

   (b)(i) £ £7.50

(ii)   Which of the stores gives the bigger reduction?

(b)(ii) .....*Berries* •

(MEG)

**Do:**
Compare the two reductions

## 5.9 Fractional changes

Shops often reduce the prices of goods they sell by a percentage, such as '10% off'. Sometimes the reductions are given as fractions such as '$\frac{1}{3}$ off', or 'half price'. This section shows you how to calculate increases and decreases given in fractions.

In a sale at Bartons Stores there is $\frac{1}{3}$ off all marked prices.

Grant buys a coat in the sale.

This diagram represents the normal cost of the coat.

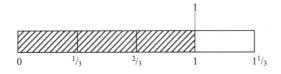

This diagram represents the sale price.

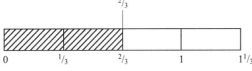

As a fraction the sale price is

$$1 - \tfrac{1}{3} = \tfrac{2}{3} \text{ of the original price.}$$

### Example 9

Jean sees a new dress in Emeld's Stores. The cost of the dress is £231. For one day only the cost is reduced by $\frac{1}{4}$.

How much does the dress cost to buy?

$\frac{1}{4}$ off means that the 'one day only' price will be $1 - \tfrac{1}{4} = \tfrac{3}{4}$ of the original price

$$\tfrac{3}{4} \times 231 = \text{£}173.25$$

The dress costs £173.25 in the sale.

The cost of goods can increase as well as decrease.

After a poor harvest the price of coffee increases by $\frac{1}{4}$.

This diagram represents the original price.

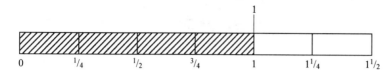

This diagram represents the new price.

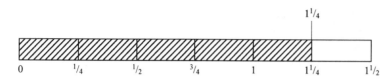

As a fraction the new price is

$$1 + \tfrac{1}{4} = 1\tfrac{1}{4} \text{ of the old price}$$

## Example 10

Ajay notices that the price of petrol has increased by $\tfrac{1}{5}$ over a period of two years. Two years ago petrol cost 48p per litre.

How much does it cost now?

An increase of $\tfrac{1}{5}$ means the new price is $1 + \tfrac{1}{5} = 1\tfrac{1}{5} = \tfrac{6}{5}$ the price two years ago.

$$\tfrac{6}{5} \times 48 = 57.6 \text{ p}$$

Now petrol costs 57.6 p per litre.

---

## Exercise 5I

1. Write the new price as a fraction of the original price:
   (a) after a $\tfrac{1}{4}$ discount
   (b) after a $\tfrac{1}{5}$ reduction
   (c) when the price is reduced by $\tfrac{3}{8}$
   (d) when the price is reduced by $\tfrac{1}{2}$
   (e) when there is $\tfrac{3}{10}$ off all goods.

2. To help build trade during the recession, Leon decided to reduce the cost of everything he sold by $\tfrac{1}{5}$.
   (a) What fraction of the original cost does he now charge?
   (b) How much does he now charge for:
      (i) a washing machine originally costing £504

(ii) a computer originally costing £1248
(iii) a compact disc player originally costing £356?

3. What fraction would you multiply by to find the new price of an item after
   (a) the price is increased by $\tfrac{1}{3}$
   (b) the price is increased by $\tfrac{3}{5}$
   (c) the price is reduced by $\tfrac{5}{8}$?

4. In Barleyton there are two electrical shops. They both sell Sunny video cameras for £780. On 1 January Nixons increases the price by $\tfrac{1}{8}$ and Curies increases the price by 10%
   (a) Write down the multiplication sum to find Nixons new price.
   (b) Write down the multiplication sum to find Curies' new price.

**5**. Which of these represents the best buy?

**6**. Eastgrove College has a new wing built on to its main building. As a result the college can increase its number of students by $\frac{3}{8}$.

   (a) By what number must you multiply to find the new total number of students?
   (b) What is the decimal equivalent of this number?
   (c) What is the percentage equivalent?
   (d) The number of students before the increase was 1648. What is the new student population?

**7**. Four students were given these puzzles to solve.
Paul:                    Gwen:

Toby:                    Paljit:

They worked out the answers.
(a) Who had the largest amount?
(b) Who had the smallest amount?

**8**. To combat rising costs, Browntrees had to make a decision. They could either increase the cost of a chocolate bar by $\frac{1}{5}$ or decrease the weight by $\frac{1}{5}$.
If you were the manufacturer what would be your decision and why?

**9**. During one year an investment increases by 10%. The next year the value decreases by $\frac{1}{4}$.
   (a) What is the percentage change over the two years?
   (b) What is the fractional change?

**10**. Floyd and Jackie are having an argument. Jackie has won £1000 on the National Lottery. Floyd says that if she spends 25% of it in the first year and then 25% of its remaining value each year it will only last 4 years. Jackie says Floyd is wrong and that it will last much longer than that.
Who do you agree with and why?

---

## Worked exam question 3

(a) Ahmed has a Renault 3 car.

He is given a reduction of 45% of his car insurance because he has not had a car accident.

| KENT CAR INSURANCE | |
| --- | --- |
| RENAULT 3 | £570 per year |
| FORD FOXY | £360 per year |

This is called a 'No Claims' reduction.

Calculate the price Ahmed has to pay to insure his car.

$0.55 \times 570 = £313.50$

Ahmed pays £313.50

(b) Barbara has a Ford Foxy car.

After taking her 'No Claims' reduction off she has to pay £234 to insure her car.

**Do:**
Notice that 45% reduction means that Ahmed pays
100% − 45% = 55% and
55% = 0.55

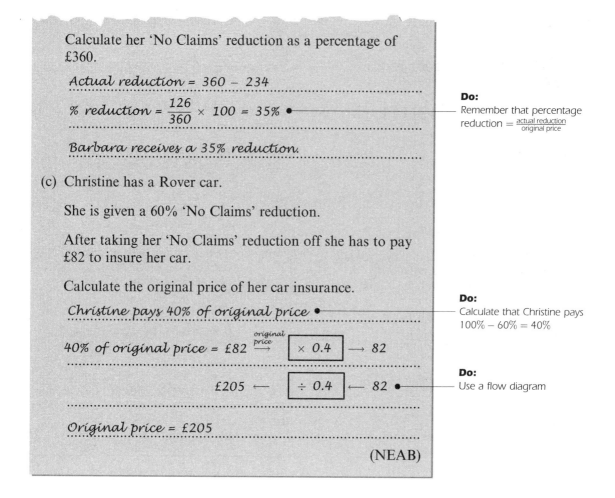

Calculate her 'No Claims' reduction as a percentage of £360.

*Actual reduction = 360 – 234*

*% reduction = $\frac{126}{360} \times 100 = 35\%$* •

*Barbara receives a 35% reduction.*

**Do:**
Remember that percentage reduction = $\frac{\text{actual reduction}}{\text{original price}}$

(c)  Christine has a Rover car.

She is given a 60% 'No Claims' reduction.

After taking her 'No Claims' reduction off she has to pay £82 to insure her car.

Calculate the original price of her car insurance.

*Christine pays 40% of original price* •

**Do:**
Calculate that Christine pays 100% – 60% = 40%

*40% of original price = £82* $\xrightarrow{\text{original price}}$ $\boxed{\times\ 0.4}$ $\longrightarrow$ *82*

*£205* $\longleftarrow$ $\boxed{\div\ 0.4}$ $\longleftarrow$ *82* •

**Do:**
Use a flow diagram

*Original price = £205*

(NEAB)

---

### Exercise 5J (Mixed questions)

1. Three football players score 18, 15 and 12 goals respectively. Their club pays out £6000 in bonus money to these players. They share the bonus in the same ratio as the goals they score.
Calculate the share of the bonus for each player.                                    [WJEC]

2. Tony bought a second-hand car for £7500. It decreased in value each year by 8% of its value at the beginning of that year. Calculate the value of the car 2 years after he bought it.      [WJEC]

3. In 1992 Nadir's total fuel bill was £480. In 1993 it was £552.
What is the percentage increase in Nadir's fuel bill from 1992 to 1993?                  [WJEC]

4.
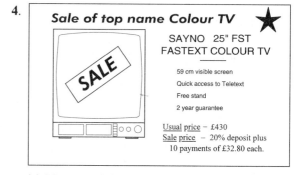

**Sale of top name Colour TV** ★

SAYNO  25" FST
FASTEXT COLOUR TV
___
59 cm visible screen
Quick access to Teletext
Free stand
2 year guarantee
___
Usual price – £430
Sale price – 20% deposit plus
10 payments of £32.80 each.

(a) How much is the deposit?
(b) How much is the total of the monthly payments?
(c) Work out the total amount you pay for the TV set at the Sale Price.
(d) How much do you save by paying the Sale Price instead of the Usual Price?      [London]

5. Three friends Helen, Sara and Mark agree to share the total money received for any job in the ratio 5:4:6.
   (a) The total money received for a job was £12. Calculate Sara's share.
   (b) Mark's share for another job was £6.24. Calculate the total money received for this job                [WJEC]

6. (a) Work out 5% of £180
   (b) The price of a portable electronic typewriter in 1988 was £180. The price in 1989 was 5% more than the 1988 price. What was the price in 1989?                [London]

7. Kurt's father has decided to buy him a drum kit. The recommended price is £1000 (plus VAT at 15%). By paying cash Kurt's father gets a discount of 10%.
   (a) Work out the discount on the £1000 recommended price.
   (b) What is the cash price?
   VAT at 15% is added.
   (c) What is the VAT on the cash price?
   (d) What price does Kurt's father actually pay for the drum kit?                [London]

8.

A motorist needs to buy a tyre, size 155 SR-13.
(a) How much does he pay for the tyre, including VAT?
When a new tyre is fitted to a car, there are two additional charges:
£1 plus 15% VAT for a valve,
£1.60 plus 15% VAT for wheel balancing.
(b) Work out the total additional charge for a new tyre.
(c) Work out the total cost of tyres and additional charges to a motorist who has her car fitted with four new 175/70 SR-13 tyres.                [London]

9. Anne sends a box of computer discs to Herr Brunn in Germany. The packet weighs 180 g.
   Postage for packet to Germany

| Not over | £ | p |
| --- | --- | --- |
| 20 g | | 23 |
| 60 g | | 39 |
| 100 g | | 55 |
| 150 g | | 74 |
| 200 g | | 92 |
| 250 g | 1 | 10 |
| 300 g | 1 | 30 |

(a) Find the cost of the postage to Germany.
Herr Brunn pays for the discs by sending a cheque for 400 marks. The exchange rate is 3.17 marks for the £.
(b) Convert 400 marks to £.
The discs, the postage and the packing cost Anne £75 in total.
(c) Calculate the profit that Anne made by selling the discs to Herr Brunn.
(c) Hence, express this profit as a percentage of Anne's total costs of £75.                [London]

# Test yourself

**1.** £5000 is shared out in the ratio 3 : 2.

QUESTION    (a)    What fraction of the £5000 is the smaller share?

ANSWER    $\frac{2}{5}$    *If your answer is incorrect, review page 82, Section 5.2 on sharing in ratios.*

QUESTION    (b)    How much is the larger share?

ANSWER    £3000    *If your answer is incorrect, review page 82, Section 5.2 on sharing in ratios.*

**2.** Tom and Brenda agree to share a sum of money in the ratio 4 : 7. Tom's share is £220.

QUESTION    (a)    What fraction of the money does Brenda receive?

ANSWER    $\frac{7}{11}$    *If your answer is incorrect, review page 82, Section 5.2 on sharing in ratios.*

QUESTION    (b)    How much money is shared out?

ANSWER    £605    *If your answer is incorrect, review page 82, Section 5.2, Example 2 and page 83, Section 5.3, Example 3.*

QUESTION    **3.** Find 12.5% of 45 kg.

ANSWER    5.625 kg    *If your answer is incorrect, review page 84, Section 5.4 on percentages.*

**4.** A sales manager receives a 15% increase in salary.

QUESTION    (a)    What percentage of the old salary will the manager's new salary be?

ANSWER    115%    *If your answer is incorrect, review page 85, Section 5.5, Example 5.*

QUESTION    (b)    The manager's old salary is £18 500. Calculate the manager's new salary.

ANSWER    £21 275    *If your answer is incorrect, review page 85, Section 5.5, Example 4.*

**5.** Delroy is very ill. While he is ill, his body weight drops by 30%.

QUESTION    (a)    What is Delroy's new weight, expressed as a percentage of his old weight?

ANSWER    70%    *If your answer is incorrect, review page 85, Section 5.5 on calculating percentages.*

QUESTION    (b)    Before he was ill, Delroy weighed 84 kg. What is his new weight?

ANSWER    58.8 kg    *If your answer is incorrect, review page 85, Section 5.5 on calculating percentages.*

**6**. Anne buys a new car for £12 500. Two years later, she sells it for £8500.

| | |
|---|---|
| QUESTION | What is the actual loss and the percentage loss? |
| ANSWER | £4000, 32%    *If your answer is incorrect, review page 89, Section 5.7 on percentage loss.* |

**7**. The price of a season ticket to watch the local football team is increased from £200 to £230.

| | |
|---|---|
| QUESTION | What is the percentage increase? |
| ANSWER | 15%    *If your answer is incorrect, review page 87, Section 5.6 on percentage increase.* |

**8**. Over one year the value of David's car falls from £8400 to £5600.

| | |
|---|---|
| QUESTION | Find the percentage decrease in the value of the car. |
| ANSWER | $33\frac{1}{3}\%$    *If your answer is incorrect, review page 87, Section 5.6 on percentage decrease.* |

**9**. The price of a coat is reduced by 10% in a sale. It is sold in the sale for £72.

| | |
|---|---|
| QUESTION | (a) What is the sale price of the coat, expressed as a percentage of the pre-sale price. |
| ANSWER | 90%    *If your answer is incorrect, review page 90, Section 5.8 on percentage calculations.* |

| | |
|---|---|
| QUESTION | (b) What is the pre-sale price of the coat? |
| ANSWER | £80    *If your answer is incorrect, review page 90, Section 5.8 on percentage calculations.* |

**10**. The price of a holiday is £325 including VAT. The current rate of VAT is 17.5%.

| | |
|---|---|
| QUESTION | What is the price of the holiday before VAT has been added? |
| ANSWER | £276.60 (to the nearest penny)    *If your answer is incorrect, review page 91, Section 5.8, Example 8.* |

**11**. Helen notices that her weight has increased by $\frac{1}{5}$ over the past two years.

| | |
|---|---|
| QUESTION | (a) What is Helen's new weight as a fraction of her weight two years ago? |
| ANSWER | $\frac{6}{5}$ or $1\frac{1}{5}$    *If your answer is incorrect, review page 93, Section 5.9 on fractional changes.* |

| | |
|---|---|
| QUESTION | (b) Helen weighed 55 kg two years ago. How much does she weigh now? |
| ANSWER | 66 kg    *If your answer is incorrect, review page 93, Section 5.9 on fractional changes.* |

## Summary of key points to remember

1.  If an amount is divided in the ratio of 4 : 7 then one person receives $\frac{4}{11}$ of the amount and the other receives $\frac{7}{11}$.

2.  If an amount is divided in the ratio $a : b$ then one person receives $\frac{a}{a+b}$ of the amount and the other receives $\frac{b}{a+b}$.

3.  To find 17% of an amount multiply the amount by $\frac{17}{100} = 0.17$

4.  To find a percentage of an amount, multiply the amount by the percentage in decimal form.

5.  If an amount is decreased by 12% then the new amount as a percentage of the original amount is $100 - 12 = 88\%$.

6.  If an amount is increased by 25% then the new amount as a percentage of the original amount is $100 + 25 = 125\%$

7.  If you are given a price after a percentage change and asked to find the original price use flow diagrams to help you.

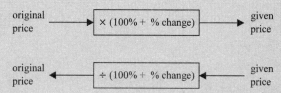

8.  If a known amount is increased or decreased by a fraction, to calculate the new amount work out what fraction of the original amount the new amount represents. Then multiply the original amount by this fraction.

    For example, if an amount is increased by $\frac{1}{5}$ then the new amount is $1 + \frac{1}{5} = \frac{6}{5}$ of the original amount.

# 6 Money and measures

## 6.1 Introduction

This unit brings together many of the ideas introduced in the earlier units, to tackle problems involving direct proportion, compound measures and compound interest. It also shows you how to do calculations with numbers written in standard form.

## 6.2 Direct proportion

There are many examples in the real world where one variable is affected by another variable. For example, the faster you drive your car, the greater your fuel consumption; the harder you exercise, the faster your heart beats.

Jack and Jill take part in a sponsored run. They each receive £1 per kilometre they run. If they run 0 km then they receive no money (£0). If Jack runs 5 km he receives £5. If Jill runs *double* his distance (10 km) she receives *double* the money that Jack receives (£10).

This is an example of **direct proportion**.

Two variables are directly proportional if *both* these statements are true:

- When one variable is zero, the other variable is zero.

- When one variable changes the other variable changes in the *same ratio*.

We can write

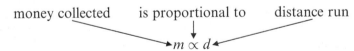

money collected     is proportional to     distance run

$$m \propto d$$

The symbol $\propto$ means 'is proportional to'.

### Example 1

In a science experiment Arif filled a cylinder with a steady flow of water. He recorded the height of the water in the cylinder at different times.

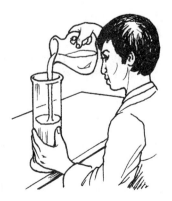

| Height of water (cm) | 6 | 10 | 15 | 18 | 24 | 30 |
|---|---|---|---|---|---|---|
| Time taken (s) | 7.5 | 8 | 12 | 14.4 | 19.2 | 24 |

Plot a graph of the height of the water (vertical axis) against time (horizontal axis).

What conclusions can you draw from the graph?

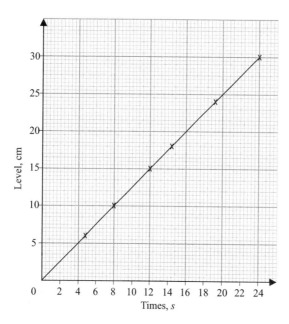

When the time is zero, the height of water is zero.

From the graph,  at time 8 s the height is 10 cm
at time 16 s the height is 20 cm

As one variable (time) doubles, so does the other variable (height), so the height of the water and the time are in direct proportion.

In general, if the graph of one variable plotted against another is a straight line which passes through (0, 0), then the two variables are in direct proportion.

A straight line graph through the origin has an equation of the form $y = mx$, where $m$ is the gradient. So if two variables are in direct proportion they are connected by a rule $y = mx$, and you can find the value of $m$ from the graph.

### Example 2

The height of a tree is directly proportional to the shadow it casts. At 3 pm a tree 8 m tall casts a shadow 10 m long.

(a) Find a rule connecting the height of a tree and the length of its shadow at 3 pm.

(b) At 3 pm the shadow of another tree is 8 m long. How tall is the tree?

(c) At 3 pm, how long is the shadow of a tree 10 m tall?

(a) Since the relationship is directly proportional you can represent the information on a graph.

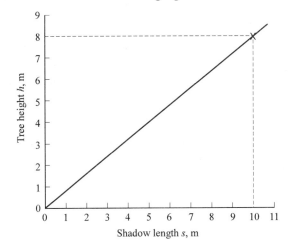

The rule is of the form $y = mx$, where $m$ is the gradient.

$$\text{Gradient} = \frac{\text{vertical distance}}{\text{horizontal distance}} = \frac{8}{10} = 0.8$$

So the rule is $h = 0.8\,s$

(b) Shadow of length 8 m: $s = 8$

The height of the tree is $\quad h = 0.8 \times 8$
$$h = 6.4\,\text{m}$$

(c) Tree 10 m tall: $h = 10$
$$h = 0.8\,s$$

So:

$$s = \frac{h}{0.8}$$

The length of the shadow is $\dfrac{10}{0.8} = 12.5\,\text{m}$

## Exercise 6A

1. Given that $w \propto t$ and $w = 6$ when $t = 4$ find:
   (a) $t$ when $w$ doubles in values
   (b) $w$ when $t$ halves in value.

2. Given that $a \propto b$ and $a = 12$ when $b = 8$, find:
   (a) $b$ when $a$ increases to 36
   (b) $a$ when $b$ decreases to 2

3. Given that $d \propto s$ and $d = 18$ when $s = 15$, find:
   (a) $s$ if $d$ decreases by 6
   (b) $d$ if $s$ increases to 25

4. In which of the graphs opposite is $r$ directly proportional to $s$?

(a)
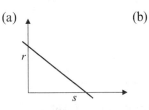

(b)
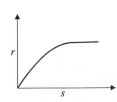

(c)
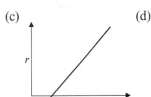

(d)
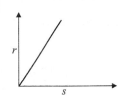

5. Which of the following are examples of direct proportionality? Explain your answers.
(a) Profit made by selling goods.
(b) Final examination results and effort put into work.
(c) Area of a square and the length of one side.
(d) The area of a rectangle with one side of constant length and the length of the other side variable.
(e) Time and distance travelled at a constant speed.
(f) The height ($h$) of a student and the amount they weigh.

6. The length of the shadow of a tree ($s$) is directly proportional to the height of the tree ($h$).

At 5 pm a tree 18 m tall casts a shadow 12 m long.
(a) Sketch a graph to show this information.
(b) Find a rule connecting $h$ and $s$.
(c) Find $h$ when $s = 14.5$
(d) Find $s$ when $h = 16$, giving your answer correct to 2 decimal places.

7. The area of a shape is directly proportional to its length. A length ($l$) of 14 cm gives an area ($a$) of 42 cm$^2$
(a) Sketch a graph of this information.
(b) Work out a rule connecting $a$ and $l$.
(c) What is the area of a shape with length 24.4 cm?
(d) Find $l$ when $a = 14.6$ cm$^2$ giving your answer to 2 decimal places.

## 6.3 Using ratio to find the rule

If two variables are in direct proportion then when one variable changes the other variable changes in the same ratio.

For example,

- if one variable doubles then the other variable doubles.

- if one variable decreases by 10% then the other variable decreases by 10%.

We can use the constant ratio to find the rule connecting two variables that are in direct proportion.

### Example 3

The mass of a gold statue is directly proportional to its height. A statue measuring 8.2 cm has a mass of 1.148 kg.

Find the mass of a similar statue with a height of 15.5 cm.

Instead of drawing a graph you can put this information into a table:

| Mass ($m$) | 1.148 | ? |
|---|---|---|
| Height ($h$) | 8.2 | 15.5 |

The mass to height ratio $m{:}h$ is 1.148 : 8.2

To find the rule first divide the ratio

$$\frac{1.148}{8.2} = 0.14 \quad \text{or} \quad \frac{\text{mass}}{\text{height}} = 0.14$$

So the rule connecting mass and height is $m = 0.14h$

When $h = 15.5$

$$m = 0.14 \times 15.5 = 2.17$$

The mass of the second statue is $2.17\,\text{kg}$.

## Exercise 6B

1. These tables show two variables in direct proportion to each other. Calculate the missing values correct to 1 decimal place.

(a)
| w | 8.4 | ? |
|---|---|---|
| h | 8 | 14 |

(b)
| h | 12.0 | 16.8 |
|---|---|---|
| s | 10.5 | ? |

(c)
| p | 7.8 | ? |
|---|---|---|
| l | 6.8 | 37.6 |

(d)
| a | 10.4 | 20.8 |
|---|---|---|
| p | ? | 23.9 |

2. For each table in **question 1**, write a rule connecting the two variables, correct to 1 decimal place.

3. A table lamp casts a shadow of a vase on to a wall $1.4\,\text{m}$ away from it. The height of the shadow of the vase is $11.2\,\text{cm}$. The table lamp is moved away from the wall and the shadow starts to 'grow'.
   (a) Find a rule connecting the distance from the wall $d$ and $h$ the height of the shadow.
   (b) How far is the lamp away from the wall when the height of the shadow is $25.6\,\text{cm}$?

4. The voltage ($V$) across a resistor is directly proportional to the current (in amps) ($I$) flowing through it.
   (a) Write down the readings from the two meters in the diagram.
   (b) Write down a rule connecting the voltage ($V$) and the current ($I$).
   (c) Calculate the current when the voltage increases to $11.52$ volts.
   (d) Calculate the voltage when the current is $2.46$ amps.

5. Given that $r \propto t$ and $r = 2.4$ when $t = 12.8$, find correct to 2 decimal places:
   (a) $r$ when $t = 8.9$    (b) $t$ when $r = 3.1$

---

## Worked exam question 1

The cost of white correction fluid is directly proportional to the amount of fluid in the bottle.

Floyd buys a $20\,\text{m}l$ bottle for £1.18.

(a) Find a rule connecting the cost and the amount of fluid.

(b) Find the cost of a bottle containing $70\,\text{m}l$ of fluid.

(c) How much fluid, to the nearest $\text{m}l$, is there in a bottle that costs 76p?

(a) $\dfrac{118}{20} = 5.9$ •————————————————

The rule is

$C = 5.9a$  Where $C$ = the cost in pence
$\qquad\qquad a$ = the amount of fluid

**Do:**
Use ratio to find the rule connecting one variable with the other

(b) $C = 5.9a$ •————————————————
$C = 5.9 \times 70$
$C = 413$

The cost is 413p or £4.13.

Use the rule you found in (a) to find the cost

(c)    $C = 5.9a$   or   $a = \dfrac{C}{5.9}$ •————————————————

$\qquad\qquad a = \dfrac{76}{5.9} = 12.88$

$\qquad\qquad\quad = 13\ ml$ to the nearest $ml$

Divide each side by 5.9 to rearrange the formula

## Worked exam question 2

Two female weight lifters wish to find who is the stronger.

They decide to measure 'strength' by dividing their 'lifts' by their 'body weights'.

This table shows their lifts and their body weights.

| Name | Lift | Body weight |
|---|---|---|
| Lorraine Costanzo | 237.5 kg | 90 kg |
| Ruthi Shafir | 213 kg | 67.5 kg |

(a) Work out the measure of strength for Lorraine

$237.5 \div 90 = 2.6388$ •————————————————
$\qquad\qquad = 2.64$ to 2 d.p.

**Do:**
Divide the strength by the lift

(b) If Ruthi had the same strength as Lorraine, what would her lift be?

$L = 2.64 \, B$ •————————————————————

$= 2.64 \times 67.5$ •————————————————————

$= 178.125$

(MEG)

**Do:**
Find the rule connecting the strength and the lift

Calculate Lorraine's lift using the rule

## 6.4 Compound measures

Information is often given in terms of two measurements.

For example,

- the speed of a car in kilometres per hour.
- the fuel consumption of a bus in kilometres per litre.
- the density of a metal in grams per cubic centimetre.

These combinations of two measurements are called **compound measures**.

## 6.5 Average speed

The average speed of a vehicle is defined as

$$\frac{\text{total distance travelled by the vehicle}}{\text{total time for the journey}}$$

The average speed is usually calculated in kilometres per hour, which we write as $\text{km h}^{-1}$

*Example 4*

Derby is 205 km from London.

A train travelled from Derby to London in 2.75 hours.

Find its average speed for the journey.

$$
\begin{aligned}
\text{Average speed} &= \frac{\text{total distance}}{\text{time taken}} \\
&= \frac{205}{2.75} \\
&= 74.5 \text{ km per hour (to 1 d.p.)}
\end{aligned}
$$

In a travel problem you may be given times in hours and minutes. The calculations will be easier if you change the minutes into a decimal fraction of an hour.

There are 60 minutes in 1 hour.

So  24 minutes $= \frac{24}{60} = 0.4$ hour

   30 minutes $= \frac{30}{60} = 0.5$ hour

---

### Exercise 6C

1. The Flying Scotsman took 7.15 hours to travel from Edinburgh to London, a distance of 632 km. Calculate the average speed of the train in km per hour correct to 1 decimal place.

2. Keith travelled 56 miles from Nottingham to Stoke by bus. The journey took 1.65 hours. Calculate the average speed of the bus in miles per hour correct to 1 decimal place.

3. Change these minutes into decimal fractions of hours. Give your answer correct to 2 decimal places where appropriate.
   (a) 15 minutes   (b) 36 minutes   (c) 48 minutes
   (d) 20 minutes   (e) 45 minutes   (f) 4 minutes

4. Mandy drove for 1 hour 12 minutes. How long was her journey in
   (a) minutes       (b) hours?

---

*Example 5*

Joe walks to college each morning. He leaves his flat at 8 am and arrives at the college at 8.24 am. The distance between Joe's flat and the college is 1.2 km.

Find his average walking speed in:

(a) metres per minute       (b)  km per hour       (c)  miles per hour (1 km = 0.62 miles)

(a) Distance travelled is 1.2 km $= 1.2 \times 1000 = 1200$ m

   Time taken $= 24$ minutes

   Average speed $= \frac{1200}{24} = 50$ metres per minute

(b) Distance travelled is 1.2 km

   Time taken $= \frac{24}{60} = 0.4$ hour

   Average speed $= \frac{1.2}{0.4} = 3$ km per hour

(c) Distance travelled is $1.2 \times 0.62 = 0.744$ miles

   Time taken $= \frac{24}{60} = 0.4$ hour

   Average speed $= \frac{0.744}{0.4} = 1.86$ miles per hour

Sometimes you are asked for an answer in hours and minutes. You have to convert times such as 2.6 hours into hours and minutes.

1 hour $= 60$ minutes

0.6 hour $= 0.6 \times 60 = 36$ minutes

So 2.6 hours $= 2$ hours 36 minutes

## Exercise 6D

1. Change these times in hours into hours and minutes giving your answer to the nearest minute.
   (a) 0.3 hour   (b) 5.4 hours  (c) 3.75 hours
   (d) 6.28 hours (e) 3.96 hours (f) 9.48 hours

2. It took Shane 2 hours 24 minutes to complete the maths examination paper. It took Jack 2.25 hours to complete the same paper.
   (a) Who took the longest time and by how much to complete the examination paper?

3. Roy and Gail set out at 10 am for a 25 km walk. They walk for 2 hours 12 mins and then rest for 45 minutes before completing their walk in a further 2.15 hours. Calculate:
   (a) The total time it took to complete the 25 km walk.
   (b) Their average speed for the journey to 1 significant figure.

4. A train travels at 60 km per hour for 2.5 hours and then 50 km per hour for a further 3 hours 18 minutes. Calculate:
   (a) How far the train travels altogether.
   (b) How long the total journey takes.
   (c) The average speed for the journey.

## 6.6 Density

The density of a substance is its mass per unit volume. To calculate density divide the mass by the volume

$$\text{density} = \frac{\text{mass}}{\text{volume}}$$

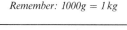

Remember: 1000g = 1 kg

Density is usually measured in grams per cubic centimetre.

A block of gold has a volume of 540 cm³ and a mass of 6.156 kg.

The density of the block is

$$\text{density} = \frac{\text{mass}}{\text{volume}} = \frac{6156\,\text{g}}{540\,\text{cm}^3} = 11.4\,\text{grams per cm}^3$$

*Example 6*

A cast iron pipe is 2 metres long with a cross-sectional area of 14 cm². The mass of the pipe is 210 kg. Calculate:

(a) The volume of metal in the pipe.

(b) The density of cast iron in grams per cm³

(a) Volume = cross-sectional area × length
    = 14 × 200
    = 2800 cm³

(b) Density = $\dfrac{\text{mass}}{\text{volume}} = \dfrac{210\,000}{2800} = 75$ grams per cm³

## Exercise 6E

1. A cast iron pipe has a mass of 360 kg and a density of 7.5 grams per cm³. Its cross-sectional area is 15 cm². Calculate:
   (a) The volume of metal in the pipe.
   (b) The length of the pipe in metres.

2. The density of aluminium is 2590 kilograms per m³. Find:
   (a) The mass of a piece of aluminium which has a volume of 3.5 m³
   (b) The volume of a piece of aluminium whose mass is 1200 kg.

3. This diagram shows the cross section of a prism. The prism has a volume of 850 cm³ and a mass of 8.5 kg. Calculate the density of the material of which it is made in grams per cm³.

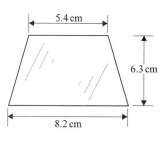

# 6.7 Other compound measure calculations

*Example 7*

The average fuel consumption of a car is measured in kilometres per litre.

A car uses 16 litres of petrol in travelling 200 km.

Find its average fuel consumption.

Average fuel consumption $= \frac{200}{16} = 12.5$ km per litre

## Exercise 6F

1. Calculate the average fuel consumption of a car that travels 406 km on 28 litres of petrol.

2. Greg sets off with a full tank of petrol on a journey of 450 km. When he arrives, his petrol gauge indicates $\frac{1}{4}$ full. A full tank of petrol holds 48 litres.
   (a) Calculate the average fuel consumption for his journey.
   (b) If the average fuel consumption remains the same, how much further can he travel before he runs out of petrol?

3. At a steady speed of 56 km per hour, the fuel consumption of Jaswinder's car is 42 km per litre of petrol.
   (a) How far will her car travel on 30 litres of petrol at 56 km per hour?
   (b) How much petrol will her car use on a journey of 150 km, where the average speed is 56 km per hour? Give your answer to the nearest litre

   (c) How far does the car travel on 1 litre of petrol at a steady speed of 56 km per hour?

4. Charlie fits a 'standard' 4.5 V battery into his personal stereo. The battery costs £2.40 and lasts for 280 hours. He replaces the 'standard' battery with a 'super platinum' battery which costs £4.68 but lasts for 600 hours.
   (a) Find the cost in pence per hour for each battery. Give your answers to 2 decimal places.
   (b) Find the time per £ for each battery to the nearest hour.
   (c) Which type of battery is the best buy? Explain your answer.

5. A bus travelling at 60 km per hour uses petrol at an average consumption of 7.5 km per litre.
   (a) Find the consumption in litres per km to 2 decimal places.
   (b) (i) How far will the car travel in 20 minutes?
   (ii) How much petrol will it use?

## Worked exam question 3

A bus has a petrol tank in the shape of a cylinder. The cylinder is 156 cm long and has a diameter of 42 cm.

(a) Calculate the volume of the cylinder

(i) in cm$^3$ correct to 4 significant figures

$$Volume = \pi r^2 h$$
$$= 3.142 \times 21 \times 21 \times 156$$
$$= 216\ 157\ cm^3$$
$$= 216\ 200\ cm^3\ to\ 4\ s.f.$$

**Do:**
Use the formula for volume of a cylinder

Use a calculator to find the answer

(ii) in litres, correct to the nearest whole number

$$= \frac{216\ 157}{1000} = 216.157$$
$$= 216\ litres\ to\ the\ nearest\ whole\ number$$

The bus uses petrol at a rate of 12.5 litres for every 100 km travelled.

(b) (i) What is the fuel consumption in km per litre?

$$Fuel\ consumption = \frac{100}{12.5} = 8\ km\ per\ litre$$

**Do:**
Divide the distance travelled by the amount of petrol used, to find the consumption in km per litre

(ii) How far can the bus travel on a full tank of petrol?

$$8 \times 216 = 1728\ km$$

Multiply the consumption by the amount of petrol the tank can hold

## 6.8 Compound interest

When you invest money in a bank or building society your money earns interest. The amount of interest is usually quoted as a percentage paid annually. If the interest is paid directly to you each year and you don't add it to your account, it is called **simple interest**.

If the interest is added to your account, then the next year you are paid interest on your savings and interest on your interest from the previous year. This is called **compound interest**.

### Example 8

Karen invests £500 in a building society account. The account pays interest at an annual rate of 8% per annum. Karen will be paid the interest directly each year.

How much interest will she receive over the next 6 years?

This problem is about simple interest.

8% interest on £500 for 1 year = £40

8% interest on £500 for 6 years = £40 × 6
$$= £240$$

She will receive £240 interest over the next 6 years.

### Example 9

Liam invests £500 in an account that pays 8% per annum. At the end of each year interest of 8% of the balance of the account is paid into the account.

So at the end of the first year

$$8\% \times £500 = £40$$

in interest is paid into his account. The new balance will be £540.

At the end of the second year Liam's balance will be £500 + £40 = £540.

So at the end of the second year

$$8\% \times £540 = £43.20$$

in interest is paid into his account. The new balance will be £583.20.

To find compound interest, you can simplify the calculation as follows.

The percentage value of an account at the beginning of the year is 100%. The percentage value of the same account at the end of the year will be:

$$100\% + \text{percentage interest}$$

For Liam's account in the example above, the percentage value at the end of the year is

$$100\% + 8\% = 108\% \text{ or } 1.08 \text{ as a decimal}$$

The value of Liam's account can be calculated directly by multiplying its beginning of year value by 1.08.

$$500 \times 1.08 = £540$$

The balances over the next 6 years are shown in the table:

| End of the | Value at beginning of year | Calculation | Value at end of year |
|---|---|---|---|
| 1st year | £500 | 500 × 1.08 | £540 |
| 2nd year | £540 | 540 × 1.08 | £583.20 |
| 3rd year | £583.20 | 583.20 × 1.08 | £629.86 |
| 4th year | £629.86 | 629.86 × 1.08 | £680.24 |
| 5th year | £680.24 | 680.24 × 1.08 | £734.66 |
| 6th year | £734.66 | 734.66 × 1.08 | £793.44 |

After 6 years the value of the investment will be £793.44.

### Exercise 6G

1. Copy Liam's compound interest table. Using the memory facilities on your calculator, extend the table to find how much the original investment would have grown to after 10 years.

2. How does £500 invested at 8% compound interest for 10 years compare with £500 invested at 6% simple interest for 10 years?

3. How many years will it take the £500 to treble in value when invested:
   (a) at 8% compound interest
   (b) at 8% simple interest?

4. On 1 January Surjit invested £1000 in an investment account that pays compound interest

at 10.2%. Calculate the balance in his account:
(a) at the end of the 1st year
(b) at the end of the 4th year
(c) at the end of the 8th year.

5. Sean rents a house at a monthly rent of £320. In the rent agreement it states that the rent will be increased each year by the annual inflation rate. Assuming an annual inflation rate of 3.5%, find:
(a) the amount of rent paid in the first year
(b) the monthly rent increase imposed at the end of the first year
(c) the monthly rent paid during the second year
(d) the monthly rent to be paid after the sixth year.

---

### Worked exam question 4

The National Currency Bank offered the following.

> INVEST WITH US FOR FIVE YEARS AND WE WILL ADD 7% TO THE VALUE OF YOUR INVESTMENT EACH YEAR.

Alan invested £2000 with them.

(a) How much was his investment worth after one year?

**Do:** Find the percentage value after one year = 100% + 7% = 107%

$2000 \times 1.07 = £2140$

Multiply the investment by 1.07 to find the value after one year

(b) How much was his investment worth after five years?

After 1 year    2140

2 years $1.07 \times 2140 = 2289.80$

**Do:** Multiply the value at the end of each year by 1.07

3 years $1.07 \times 2289.80 = 2450.08$

4 years $1.07 \times 2450.08 = 2621.59$

5 years $1.07 \times 2621.59 = 2805.10$

after 5 years the investment is worth £2805.10

(MEG)

## 6.9 Standard form

Writing numbers in standard form is covered in Unit 2 Properties of number. In this section you will learn how to carry out calculations where the numbers are written in standard form. These techniques are useful for calculations with very large numbers, such as $3.0 \times 10^8$, and very small numbers such as $1.6 \times 10^{-7}$.

### Example 10

Calculate $(2.4 \times 10^2) \times (1.2 \times 10^3)$

When multiplying numbers in standard form it is best to group the numbers together and group the powers of 10 together.

$$(2.4 \times 10^2) \times (1.2 \times 10^3)$$
$$= 2.4 \times 1.2 \times 10^2 \times 10^3$$
$$= 2.88 \times 10^2 \times 10^3$$
$$= 2.88 \times 10^5$$

*Note*: when you multiply powers of 10 you *add* the powers.

### Example 11

Calculate $(2.4 \times 10^5) \div (1.2 \times 10^2)$

$$= (2.4 \div 1.2) \times (10^5 \div 10^2)$$
$$= 2.0 \times 10^3$$

*Note*: when you divide powers of 10 you *subtract* the powers.

### Example 12

The mean distance from the Sun to the Earth is $1.5 \times 10^8$ km. The speed of light is 300 000 km per second.

(a) Write the speed of light in standard form.

(b) Calculate how long it takes for light from the Sun to reach the Earth.

(a) Speed of light $= 300\,000 = 3.0 \times 10^5$ km per second

(b) Time $= \dfrac{\text{distance from Sun}}{\text{speed of light}}$

$$= \dfrac{1.5 \times 10^8}{3 \times 10^5}$$
$$= 5 \times 10^2$$
$$= 500 \text{ seconds}$$

## Exercise 6H

For this exercise use the speed of light = $3.0 \times 10^8$ metres per second.

1. The mean distance from the Sun to Saturn is $1.43 \times 10^9$ km. Calculate, in hours and minutes, how long it takes the light from the Sun to reach Saturn.

2. The distance light travels in a year is called a 'light year'.
   (a) Calculate the distance light travels in a 'light year'. Give your answer in standard form.
   (b) The furthest known object from the Earth is $1.5 \times 10^{10}$ light years away.
   How far is this in kilometres? Give your answer in standard form correct to three significant figures.

3. A human heart beats, on average, 72 beats per minute.
   (a) How many times does the heart beat in a year?
   (b) Alice died on her 92nd birthday. Calculate the approximate number of times her heart beat during her life time.
   Give your answer correct to 3 significant figures in standard form.

4. Given the 'ideal' conditions of food, moisture and warmth some food bacteria can divide into 2 every 20 minutes. This is called binary fission.
   (a) A ham sandwich is left on a plate in the 'ideal' bacteria breeding conditions for 4 hours. Use the formula
   $$n = 2^{t/20} \quad \text{where } n = \text{the number of bacteria}$$
   $$t = \text{the time in minutes}$$
   to calculate the number of bacteria after 4 hours. Give your answer in standard form.
   (b) A second sandwich contains $2.1 \times 10^6$ bacteria. Using a trial and improvement method, calculate the approximate time the

sandwich had been in the 'ideal' breeding conditions.

5. A 'dot' on a piece of paper has a circumference of 0.18 cm.
   Calculate the radius of the dot, giving your answer in standard form correct to 2 significant figures.

6. When a nuclear reactor starts up electric currents as low as 0.000 000 000 007 amps have to be measured.
   (a) Write down 0.000 000 000 007 amps in standard form.
   (b) The voltage across a resistor is calculated using the formula
   $$V = IR \quad \text{where } I = \text{the electric current in amps}$$
   $$R = \text{the resistance in ohms}$$
   What is the voltage across a $5.2 \times 10^5$ ohm resistor when the current from part (a) passes through it?

7. Einstein's formula for the energy, $E$ joules of a body of mass $m$ kilograms is
   $$E = mc^2 \quad \text{where } c = \text{the speed of light } (3.0 \times 10^8 \text{ metres per second})$$
   (a) Calculate the energy of a body with a mass of 500 kg.
   (b) The energy of a body is $2.5 \times 10^7$ joules. Calculate the mass of the body, giving your answer in standard form.

8. Work out the answer to
   $$\frac{(2.3 \times 10^7) \times (3.6 \times 10^{-2})}{8.75 \times 10^{-5}}$$
   Give your answer in standard form correct to 2 significant figures.

---

### Worked exam question 5

During 1987/8 there were 23 million telephone directories printed.

(a) Write this number in standard form.

$2.3 \times 10^7$

**Do:**
Remember that a number in standard form only has one digit in front of the decimal point

One tonne is equal to $10^3$ kg. The directories used 27 350 tonnes of paper.

(b) Write this in kilograms in standard form.

$27350 \times 10^3 = 27350000$ •—————————— Multiply the tonnes by $10^3$

$= 2.735 \times 10^7$ *kg*

(c) What was the average mass of paper in one directory?

Divide the total mass by the number of directories

$(2.735 \times 10^7) \div (2.3 \times 10)^7$ •

$\approx 1.189$ *kg*

(MEG)

---

## Exercise 6I (Mixed questions)

1. There are approximately 150 thousand ants in a tropical ant colony.
   (a) Write 150 thousand in standard form.
   (b) Each ant eats an average $2.4 \times 10^{-3}$ kilograms of food per day. Calculate the total average amount of food eaten by 150 thousand ants in one day. Give your answer in kilograms.    [NEAB]

2. Work out the value of
   $$(4.6 \times 10^{-2}) \times (8.3 \times 10^4)$$
   giving your answer in standard index form.    [London]

3. Sally takes out a six-year policy with an insurance company. This policy costs her £100 each year, starting at the beginning of year one. The company pays a compound interest rate of 8%.
   (a) Copy and complete this table.

| End of year | Value plus annual payment | Interest earned | Current total |
|---|---|---|---|
| 1st | 100 | $100 \times 0.08$ | £108 |
| 2nd | $108 + 100$ | $208 \times 0.08$ | £224.64 |
| 3rd | $224.64 + 100$ | | |
| 4th | | | |
| 5th | | | |
| 6th | | | |

(b) How much is Sally's policy worth after the end of the 10th year?

4. (a) Light takes about 12 minutes and 40 seconds to reach the planet Mars from the Sun. Light travels at approximately 299 800 kilometres per second. Calculate the approximate distance of the Sun from Mars. Give your answer in standard form correct to 2 significant figures.
   (b) The distance from the Earth to the Moon is approximately 384 400 km. The distance from the Earth to the Sun is approximately $1.496 \times 10^8$ km.
   Use these approximations to express the ratio
   distance of         .   distance of
   Earth to Moon   :   Earth to Sun
   in the form $1 : n$ where $n$ is a whole number.
   (c) Light travels at the rate of approximately 186 000 miles per second. Light takes 12 years to reach Earth from a particular star. Find the approximate distance of this star from the Earth. Give your answer in standard form correct to 3 significant figures.    [NEAB]

5. Chantelle went on a business strip to the United States and returned to Britain via Germany. Before starting out she checked two exchange rates and found that
   £1 was equivalent to 1.56 US dollars
   £1 was equivalent to 2.45 German marks
   Calculate the exchange rate between the US and Germany in:
   (a) marks per dollar    (b) dollars per mark.

# 6.10 Earning money

People doing different jobs earn money, or are paid money in different ways.

**Hourly rate**

Joe works for an electrical components company. He is paid £5.24 per hour – that is his **hourly rate**.

Joe works a 40 hour week so his total pay for a week is

$$5.24 \times 40 - £209.60$$

**Overtime**

Some weeks Joe has to work over his allocated 40 hours. When he does this he is paid at an **overtime** rate. The overtime rate is $1\frac{1}{2}$ times his hourly rate.

So when Joe works overtime, he is paid

$$5.24 \times 1\frac{1}{2} = £7.86 \text{ per hour}$$

*Example 13*

Cathy works as cleaner at the Sports Centre. She is paid £3.60 per hour.

She works a 35 hour week.

When she works overtime, Cathy is paid an overtime rate of $1\frac{1}{2}$ times her hourly rate.

One week, Cathy worked for 50 hours.

Calculate her total pay for that week.

Cathy worked for 35 hours at £3.60 per hour

She did $50 - 35 = 15$ hours overtime

Her overtime rate was $1\frac{1}{2} \times £3.60 = £5.40$

So she worked for 15 hours at £5.40 per hour

Her total pay was $(3.60 \times 35) + (5.40 \times 15) = £126 + £81 = £207$

**Salary**

Some people are paid an annual **salary**, rather than an hourly rate.

Look at this advertisement for a job as a clinical psychologist.

It means that the person who gets this job will be paid £17,161 irrespective of how many hours she or he works.

*Note*: £17 161 per annum (per year) is equivalent to

$$17\,161 \div 52 = £330.02 \text{ per week.}$$

XYZ Health Authority

New Town Hospital

Appointment of_____

**CLINICAL PSYCHOLOGIST**
(Salary: £17,161 per annum)

Apply with C.V.  to Hospital Administrator
New Town hospital, Newtown,
Any street, Any where

**Tel. 1234 567 8910**

If we assumed that the clinical psychologist worked for 40 hours a week then £330.02 per week is equivalent to

$$330.02 \div 40 = £8.2505 \text{ or } £8.25 \text{ per hour.}$$

### Example 14

Alex takes a job in a bank.

She is paid a salary of £12 064 per annum.

(a) Calculate her equivalent weekly wage. Alex works for 37.5 hours per week.

(b) Calculate her equivalent hourly rate.

(a) Her equivalent weekly wage is $12\,064 \div 52 = £232$

(b) Her equivalent hourly rate is $232 \div 37.5 = £6.18666$ or £6.19 correct to the nearest penny.

---

### Exercise 6J

1. Barbara works as a children's nurse. Her salary is £18 490 per annum.
   (a) Calculate her equivalent weekly wage.
   (b) She works for 36 hours per week. Calculate her equivalent hourly rate.

2. Matthew has a choice of two jobs. The first job pays a rate of £5.42 per hour. The second job pays a salary of £11 500 per annum. Matthew will have to work for 40 hours per week in either job. Which of the two jobs will pay Matthew the most? Explain your answer.

3. Asif normally works for 37 hours per week. His hourly rate is £4.80.
   When he works overtime his overtime rate is $1\frac{1}{2}$ times his hourly rate.
   Last week Asif worked for 55 hours.
   Calculate his total pay for last week.

4. Shoona works in a book shop. She is paid £4 per hour. She normally works for 35 hours per week. When she works overtime, she is paid an overtime rate of $1\frac{1}{4}$ times her hourly rate. One week, just before Christmas, Shoona works for 52 hours. Calculate her total pay for that week.

---

### Piecework

Some people are paid neither a salary nor an hourly rate. They are paid on a **piecework** basis. They are paid for each piece of work they do.

For instance, during the Autumn, Maureen works picking apples. She is paid £2.50 per basket of apples she picks.

### Example 15

Maureen picks apples. She is paid on a piecework basis of £2.50 per basket of apples picked.

One week she picks 120 baskets of apples.

(a) Calculate her total pay for the week.

(b) During that week, Maureen worked for 50 hours. Calculate her equivalent hourly rate of pay.

(a) Her total pay was $2.50 \times 120 = £300$

(b) Her equivalent hourly rate was $300 \div 50 = £6$ per hour

---

### Exercise 6K

1. Alice has her own business cleaning cars.
   She charges £2.25 per car.
   In a typical week Alice will clean 102 cars and this takes her 45 hours.
   (a) Calculate Alice's pay for a typical week.
   (b) Calculate Alice's typical equivalent hourly rate.

2. Neil picks strawberries during the summer holiday.
   He is paid £1.20 per box of strawberries he picks.
   The table opposite shows the number of boxes he picks one week. He does not work on Sunday.

(a) Calculate Neil's total pay for that week.
(b) During that week, Neil worked for 52 hours. Calculate his equivalent hourly rate.

| Day | Boxes |
|-----|-------|
| Mon | 23 |
| Tues | 31 |
| Wed | 37 |
| Thurs | 28 |
| Fri | 34 |
| Sat | 26 |

---

### Commission

There are people, such as sales representatives, who receive pay on a **commission** basis. Usually they are paid a percentage of the value of the sales they make.

### *Example 16*

Juliet sells cosmetics.

Her company pays her £20 per day.

They also pays her a commission of 10% on all the sales she makes.

Yesterday, Juliet sold £327 worth of cosmetics.

Calculate her total pay for the day.

Juliet's pay was £20 + 10% of £327

$$= 20 + 32.70$$
$$= £52.70$$

## Exercise 6L

1. This table refers to the same Juliet as in Example 17. It shows her sales during one week.
   (a) Calculate her total pay for the week.
   (b) Juliet had to work for 52 hours that week. Calculate her equivalent hourly rate.

   | Day | Sales |
   |-----|-------|
   | Mon | 327 |
   | Tues | 418 |
   | Wed | 207 |
   | Thurs | 196 |
   | Fri | 485 |

2. After leaving college, Gary took a job selling cars.
   He is paid a salary of £5 400 per annum and commission of 10% of the profit he makes on deals.
   In his first year of work he made profits of £92 600.
   (a) Calculate Gary's total pay for his first year of work.
   (b) Calculate Gary's equivalent weekly wage.
   (c) During the year Gary worked for a total of 1620 hours.
   Calculate his equivalent hourly rate of pay.

## 6.11 Deductions from your earnings

However you earn your money, there are two major deductions from your earnings.

These are:

- **National Insurance** – this pays for the National Health Service, pensions, etc.

- **Income tax** – this pays for a wide range of public services such as the police, road, defence, etc.

### National Insurance

The table below shows the National Insurance rates set in 1992.

| Weekly wage (£) | National Insurance Rate |
|-----------------|-------------------------|
| 0 – 51. 99 | 0% |
| 52 – 390 | 2% on first £52 per week plus 9% on the remainder |
| 390 + | 2% on first £52 per week plus 9% on £338 |

*Example 17*

David earns £138 per week.

Calculate his weekly National Insurance contribution.

David pays 2% of £52 then 9% on the difference between his total wage and £52. The difference in David's case is $138 - 52 = £86$

So his National Insurance contribution is 2% of 52 + 9% of 86

$$= 1.04 + 7.74$$
$$= £8.78 \text{ per week}$$

## *Example 18*

Melanie earns £12 per hour as an editor.

She works for 44 hours per week.

(a) Calculate her weekly earnings.

(b) Calculate her National Insurance contribution per week.

(a) Her weekly earnings are $12 \times 44 = £528$

(b) She pays 2% National Insurance on £52 then 9% on £338. So her National Insurance contribution is 2% of 52 + 9% of 338

$$= 1.04 + 30.42$$
$$= £31.46 \text{ per week.}$$

---

### Exercise 6M

**1**. Jim works as a computer sales person. He is paid £150 per week plus a commission of 5% of all the sales he makes. Last week Jim made £4600 worth of sales.
(a) Calculate Jim's earnings for last week.
(b) Calculate Jim's National Insurance contribution for last week.

**2**. Alison earns £21 840 per year.
(a) Calculate her equivalent weekly wage.
(b) Calculate her weekly National Insurance contribution.

**3**. Calculate the **maximum** weekly National Insurance contribution any person can make.

---

### Income Tax

The vast majority of people have income tax deducted from their pay before they receive that pay. The pay is deducted by the employer who then pays the tax to the Government. This system of payment is called Pay As You Earn, or P.A.Y.E. for short.

To work out an income tax contribution is quite complicated.

Firstly, we work out a person's **taxable** income. This is done by the formula

taxable income = total income − allowances

The total income is the amount they earn in a given period (usually a week, month or year).

For a single person the current allowance is £3445. A married couple will get this allowance plus another £1720, making £5165. There are other allowances which can be claimed by some people, but we will keep Example **19** and Exercise **6N** simple by just using the single person's allowance.

Then the taxable income is multiplied by a rate of taxation. These rates change nearly every April; in April 1996 the new rates were:

20% on the first £3900 of taxable income
24% on the remainder up to £25 500 taxable income
40% on everything above £25 500

This gives the amount of tax which has to be deducted by the employer.

### Example 19

Kay works as a director of a large company. Her annual salary is £60 000.

She is not married.

Calculate her annual and monthly income tax contribution.

Kay's taxable income is $60\,000 - 3445 = £56\,555$

She pays income tax on

> 20% of £3900
>
> 24% of (£25 500 − 3900)
>
> 40% of (£56 555 − 25 500)

So she pays

> 20% of 3900 + 24% of 21 600 + 40% of 31 055
>
> $= 780 + 5184 + 12\,422$
>
> $= £18\,386$

Her monthly income tax contribution is $18\,386 \div 12 = £1532.17$ correct to the nearest penny.

---

### Exercise 6N

1. Mandy earns £16 200 per year as a community nurse. She is not married.
   Calculate her monthly income tax contribution.

2. Colin works as a fitter. He is not married. He is paid £6.02 per hour and works a 37 hour week. He works for 46 weeks each year. Last year he also worked a total of 100 hours overtime. His overtime rate is $1\frac{1}{2}$ times his hourly rate.
   Calculate:
   (a) Colin's earnings last year.
   (b) Colin's income tax contribution for last year.

---

## 6.12 Borrowing money

It is a common practice these days for people to borrow money to pay for something, such as a house, car, holiday, furniture, etc. We usually borrow the money from a bank, building society or Hire Purchase company.

The way the system works is simple. You borrow the money from the bank (say), the bank charges interest which they add on to the amount you borrow. Then you pay the money back, amount borrowed plus interest, over a number of weeks, months or years.

## Mortgage

For most people, the largest amount of money they borrow is likely to be for the purchase of a house. This is usually done through what is called a **mortgage**. In many cases the mortgage is paid off over a 25-year period.

How much you can borrow will depend on your income. Most banks and building societies use one of these formulae to calculate the maximum mortgage they will give you.

For a single borrower:

Formula 1:        Up to 3 times the borrowers annual income

For joint borrowers:

Formula 2:        Up to 2 times the larger annual income plus the smaller annual income.

Formula 3:        Up to $2\frac{1}{2}$ times the joint annual income of the borrowers.

But these formulae vary from one bank or building society to another and over time.

The bank or building society will also only lend you a percentage (usually a maximum of 90% or 95%) of their valuation of the house you are going to buy. You have to pay the remainder, usually as a deposit before the day you actually become the owner of the house.

### Example 20

Alan and Jenny want to buy a flat which is valued at £52 000.

The building society agrees with this valuation but will lend Alan and Jenny only 90% of the valuation. The seller has asked for a 10% deposit.

(a) Calculate the deposit Alan and Jenny must pay.

The building society says that they will lend Alan and Jenny $2\frac{1}{2}$ times their joint income.

(b) Calculate the joint income Alan and Jenny require in order to obtain the mortgage they need.

(a) The deposit they require is 10% of 52 000 = £5200

(b) The amount they need to borrow is 52 000 − 5200 = £46 800

So        2.5 × joint income    = 46 800
          joint income         = 46 800 ÷ 2.5
          joint income         = £18 720

Alan and Jenny were successful in getting the mortgage they required. For the next 25 years they will be paying a mortgage of £372.50 per month.

This means that over the 25 years they will pay a total of $372.50 \times 12 = £4470$ per year or $4470 \times 25 = £111\,750$ plus their £5200 deposit.

So they will actually pay £116 950 for their house.

To borrow £46 800 and pay back £111 750 seems as if Alan and Jenny will be paying back a lot of money, relative to the amount they borrow. But we need to remember that over the years inflation changes monetary values and house prices usually rise in line with inflation.

If we had 5% inflation over 25 years then it would be like a compound interest rate of 5%, and $(1.05)^{25} = 3.386$.

So £46 800 today will be $46\,800 \times 3.386 = £158\,404.80$

in 25 years time – if we have 5% inflation. But rates of interest and inflation can vary greatly over a period of time.

---

### Exercise 60

1. Mary earns £11 200 per year. For a mortgage she can borrow up to 3 times her annual salary. She wishes to buy a flat which her building society values at £35 000. They will give her a mortgage of 95% of their valuation of the flat. The remainder must be paid by Mary as a deposit.
   (a) Calculate the deposit Mary must find.
   (b) Will Mary will be able to get the mortgage she requires? Give your reasons.

2. Warim and Sarah have saved £7000 towards buying a house.
   Warim's salary is £12 000 per year. Sarah's salary is £15 400 per year.
   The building society agrees to give them a mortgage worked out as (2 × Sarah's salary) + Warim's salary
   (a) Calculate the maximum mortgage the building society will give to Warim and Sarah.
   (b) Calculate the maximum price they can pay for a house.

---

### Bank Loans

Depending on your status, whether you have a regular job etc., banks will usually lend you money to buy a car, holiday or something else. This is usually called a **bank loan**.

### *Example 21*

Maxine has saved £1000 towards buying a car. The car costs £6000. Maxine's bank agrees to loan her the extra money over a 5-year period.

The bank adds an interest charge of £2860.

Calculate the amount Maxine will have to pay back to the bank each month.

Maxine borrows 6000 − 1000 = £5000

The interest is £2860 so she has to pay back to the bank
5000 + 2860 = £7860 over 5 years.

5 years is 5 × 12 = 60 months.

So she pays back 7860 ÷ 60 = £131 per month.

---

## Exercise 6P

1. Sandra and Jim are given a bank loan of £3000 to buy some new furniture. The loan is over a 3-year period. They have to pay the bank £115 per month.
   (a) Calculate the total Sandra and Jim will pay to the bank.
   (b) Calculate the interest being charged by the bank.

2. Keith and Mary decide to buy a caravan. The caravan costs £9500. Keith and Mary have saved £1500 but they need to raise the rest of the money through a bank loan. The bank agrees to let them have the necessary loan, over a 5-year period. The bank charges £2941 interest.
   (a) Calculate the total amount Keith and Mary will have to pay to the bank.
   (b) Calculate the amount they will pay to the bank each month.

---

### Overdrafts

Another way of borrowing money is to agree an **overdraft facility** with your bank.

This means that you can actually have a *negative* amount in your bank account. The bank then charges interest on this negative amount. Sometimes the interest figure seems to be very low, but banks charge it on a monthly or three-monthly basis rather than an annual basis.

### *Example 22*

John agrees a £2000 overdraft facility with his bank. The interest is charged at 1.95% per month.

John's account is overdrawn by £2000 one month. Calculate the interest he will be charged.

The interest charge is
$$1.95\% \text{ of } 2000$$
$$= \frac{1.95}{100} \times 2000$$
$$= £39$$

---

## Exercise 6Q

1. Kim has an overdraft facility of £3000 with her bank. The bank charges interest at 2.05% per month. Calculate the amount of interest Kim will pay one month if her overdraft is
   (a) £1200    (b) £3000

2. Joseph has an overdraft facility of £2500 with his bank. He uses all of this facility one month. He finds that the bank charge interest of £50 for that month. Calculate the bank's monthly interest rate.

---

## Credit Cards

One of the most popular ways of borrowing money is through the use of **credit cards** such as Access, Mastercard, Visa, etc.

The credit card company, will give you a *limit* on your credit card facility. This is the maximum amount you can borrow. You will be charged interest on any amount which you have not paid back within a specified period.

At the end of each month the credit card company will send you a statement. The statement tells you how much you owe and the minimum repayment you must make for that month. The minimum amount is usually 5% of what you owe – 5% of your balance. If you pay back less than the full amount, you will be charged interest on the balance once the period specified by the credit card company (usually two or three weeks from the date of the statement) is over.

*Example 23*

Fiona opens her credit card account by using it to pay for a holiday costing £500.

The credit card company charge her interest at 2% per month on the balance of her account. The credit card company also asks for a minimum payment of 5% of the balance at the end of the month.

For the end of the first month, calculate:

(a) the balance of Fiona's account

(b) the minimum payment Fiona will be asked to pay.

At the end of the first month, Fiona pays the credit card company £100. She does not use the card again. For the end of the second month, calculate:

(c) the balance of Fiona's account

(d) the minimum payment Fiona will be asked to pay.

(a) The interest on £500 is 2% of 500 = £10

So her balance is £500 + £10 = £510

(b) The minimum payment will be 5% of 510

$$= 0.05 \times 510$$
$$= £25.50$$

Fiona pays £100, so she starts the second month with a balance of 510 − 100 = £410

(c) The interest on her new balance will be 2% of 410 = £8.20

So at the end of the second month her new balance will be
410 + 8.20 = £418.20

(d) Her minimum payment at the end of the second month will be
5% of 418.20

$$= 0.05 \times 418.20$$
$$= £20.91$$

---

### Exercise 6R

1. The balance on George's credit card account at the start of April is £1200. Interest is charged at a rate of 1.95% per month. The minimum monthly payment is 5% of the balance. Calculate:
   (a) the balance of George's account at the end of April
   (b) the minimum payment George should make at the end of April.

2. On the 1st January, Jenny used her new credit card to pay for a computer. The computer cost £750. The credit card company charge interest at 1.95% per month. They also ask for a minimum payment of 5% of the balance at the end of each month. Calculate:
   (a) the balance of Jenny's account at the end of January
   (b) the minimum payment Jenny will be asked to make at the end of January.
   At the end of January, Jenny makes a payment of £100 to the credit card company. On 1st February she uses the card again to buy a new coat costing £95. Calculate:
   (c) the balance of her account at the end of February
   (d) the minimum payment she will be asked to make at the end of February.

---

## Test yourself

**1.** $x$ is directly proportional to $y$.

| QUESTION | The value of $x$ is doubled. What is the new value of $y$? |
| --- | --- |
| ANSWER | The value of $y$ is doubled | *If your answer is incorrect, review page 101, Section 6.2 on direct proportion* |

**2.** $p$ is directly proportional to $r$. When $r = 40$, $p = 24$.

| QUESTION | (a) Give a rule that connects $p$ and $r$ |
| --- | --- |
| ANSWER | $p = 0.6r$ | *If your answer is incorrect, review page 101, Section 6.2 on direct proportion.* |

| QUESTION | (b) When $r = 16$, what is the value of $p$? |
| --- | --- |
| ANSWER | $p = 9.6$ | *If your answer is incorrect, review page 101, Section 6.2 on direct proportion* |

| QUESTION | (c) When $p = 20$, what is the value of $r$, to two decimal places? |
| --- | --- |
| ANSWER | $r = 33.33$ | *If your answer is incorrect, review page 101, Section 6.2 on direct proportion* |

**3.** $u$ is directly proportional to $v$.

QUESTION  Copy and complete the following table:

| $u$ | 34.50 | 16.80 |
|---|---|---|
| $v$ | 8.90 | ? |

ANSWER

| $u$ | 34.50 | 16.80 |
|---|---|---|
| $v$ | 8.90 | 4.33 |

*If your answer is incorrect, review page 104, Section 6.3, Example 3 on using ratio to find the rule.*

**4.** A car completes a journey of 49.6 km in 1.24 hours.

QUESTION  Calculate the average speed of the car.

ANSWER  40 km per hour

*If your answer is incorrect, review page 107, Section 6.5 on average speed.*

**5.** The mass of a metal bar is 4.8 kg. The volume of the bar is 420 cm$^3$.

QUESTION  Find the density of the bar in grams per cubic centimetre. Give your answer correct to two decimal places.

ANSWER  11.43 grams per cm$^3$

*If your answer is incorrect, review page 109, Section 6.6 on density.*

**6.** A motorcycle travels 270 km on 12 litres of petrol.

QUESTION  What is the average fuel consumption of the motorcycle in kilometres per litre?

ANSWER  22.5 kilometres per litre

*If your answer is incorrect, review page 110, Section 6.7, Example 7 on compound measures.*

**7.** Water is discharged from a pipe at a rate of 5 cm per second. The cross-sectional area of the pipe is 2.4 cm$^2$.

QUESTION  How much water is discharged from the pipe in 8 minutes?

ANSWER  5760 cm$^3$ = 5.76 litres

*If your answer is incorrect, review page 110, Section 6.7, Example 7 on compound measures.*

**8.** Sara invests £200 in a building society for two years. The building society pays annual compound interest at a rate of 6%.

QUESTION  What is the value of Sara's investment at the end of the two years?

ANSWER  £224.72

*If your answer is incorrect, review page 111, Section 6.8 on compound interest.*

QUESTION    **9.** Multiply $2.4 \times 10^2$ by $6.8 \times 10^3$. Give your answer in standard form.

ANSWER    $1.632 \times 10^6$    *If your answer is incorrect, review page 114, Section 6.9, Example 11 on standard form.*

QUESTION    **10.** Calculate:

$$\frac{(3.2 \times 10^{-5}) \times (4.6 \times 10^3)}{5.1 \times 10^{-7}}$$

Give your answer in standard form, to three decimal places.

ANSWER    $2.886 \times 10^5$    *If your answer is incorrect, review page 114, Section 6.9, Example 11 on standard form.*

## Summary of key points to remember

**1.** Two variables are directly proportional if *both* these statements are true:

- When one variable is zero, the other variable is zero.

- When one variable changes, the other variable changes in the same ratio.

**2.** To change a number of **minutes** into a decimal number of **hours**, divide the number of minutes by 60. To change a decimal number of hours into hours and minutes, multiply the decimal fraction part of the decimal number of hours by 60.

**3.** The average speed of a vehicle is

$$\frac{\text{total distance travelled}}{\text{total time for the journey}}$$

**4.** The average **fuel consumption** of an engine is usually measured in kilometres per litre.

**5.** The **volume of liquid** flowing from a pipe per second is equal to the cross-sectional area of the pipe multiplied by the number of centimetres of water per second flowing from the pipe.

**6.** The **density** of a substance equals its mass divided by its volume.

**7.** When **compound interest** is calculated, the interest is payable on the current balance. This balance includes any interest earned to date on the original amount of money.

**8.** To multiply two numbers in standard form:

- multiply the two numbers

- add the powers of 10.

**9.** To divide two numbers in standard form:

- divide the two numbers

- subtract the powers of 10.

# 7 Basic algebra

## 7.1 Introduction

This unit develops the branch of mathematics called 'algebra'. Algebra is a method of calculating and investigating relationships between quantities, by using letters to represent numbers. This unit starts with the substitution of numbers into expressions written in algebra. It then goes on to investigating sequences and functions using algebra.

## 7.2 The language of algebra

The language of algebra is an 'agreed' shorthand. You already know and use algebra in mathematics. For example,

'is equal to' is represented by the symbol $=$

and 'add '$a$' to '$b$' is represented by $a + b$

Like any language you need to learn its rules:

- $5a$ means $5 \times a$       *Note*: we do not include the $\times$ sign

- $abc$ means $a \times b \times c$

- $\dfrac{a}{b}$ means $a \div b$

- $a^2$ means $a \times a$       *Note*: it does **not** mean $2 \times a$

- $a^4$ means $a \times a \times a \times a$

- $\dfrac{2ab}{cd}$ means $2 \times a \times b$ divided by $c \times d$

*Example 1*

If $a = 4$, $b = 6$, $c = 2$ and $d = 5$ calculate the value of $\dfrac{ab}{cd}$

$$\frac{ab}{cd} = \frac{4 \times 6}{2 \times 5} = \frac{24}{10} = 2.4$$

Take care when using a calculator. $ab$ is divided by $(c \times d)$.

## Exercise 7A

If $a = 5$, $b = 4$ and $c = 2$, calculate the value of:

**1.** $ab$   **2.** $abc$   **3.** $ac + b$   **4.** $\dfrac{ab}{c}$   **5.** $\dfrac{ac}{b}$   **6.** $\dfrac{a + c}{b}$

**7.** $b^2$   **8.** $b^3$   **9.** $b^2 - bc$   **10.** $a^c$   **11.** $c^b$   **12.** $a^c - c^b$

# 7.3 Using brackets

You might think that it is possible to interpret an expression such as

$$3 + 4 \times 2 - 5$$

in different ways.

Most modern calculators will work this out as:

> Start with 3, then add the product $4 \times 2$,
> then take away 5.

So the result is $3 + 8 - 5 = 6$

Some calculators (and people) might interpret this expression as:

> Start with 3, then add 4, multiply by 2
> and take away 5.

This gives the result:

$$3 + 4 = 7, \text{ then } 7 \times 2 = 14, \text{ then } 14 - 5 = 9$$

Some other calculators (and people) might interpret the expression as:

> add 3 and 4, then multiply by $2 - 5$

This gives the result:

$$3 + 4 = 7, \quad 7 \times -3 = -21$$

To be absolutely clear how we wish the expression to be interpreted we can use brackets.

- $3 + (4 \times 2) - 5$         gives the result 7
- $(3 + 4) \times 2 - 5$         gives the result 9
- $(3 + 4) \times (2 - 5)$       gives the result $-21$

The **rule** for using brackets is:

> Always work out the parts in brackets first.
> Then do the rest of the calculation.

It is important that you get used to working with brackets in algebra. In algebra we only use brackets when they are absolutely necessary.

For example:

- $ab + c$ means $(a \times b) + c$   brackets not necessary
- $a(b + c)$ means $a \times (b + c)$   brackets necessary

When you substitute numbers for letters in a calculation you should *always* use brackets to make your meaning clear.

### Example 2

If $w = 12$, $x = 6$, $y = 3$ and $z = 8$ calculate the value of

(a) $wx - yz$   (b) $w(x - yz)$   (c) $\dfrac{w + x}{xy}$

(a) $wx - yz = (12 \times 6) - (3 \times 8)$
$$= 72 - 24$$
$$= 48$$

(b) $w(x - yz) = 12 \times [6 - (3 \times 8)]$
$$= 12 \times (6 - 24)$$
$$= 12 \times -18$$
$$= -216$$

(c) $\dfrac{w + x}{xy} = \dfrac{12 + 6}{(6 \times 3)}$
$$= \dfrac{18}{18}$$
$$= 1$$

### Example 3

Evaluate $\dfrac{a^2 - bc}{ac}$ where $a = 6.4$, $b = 5.3$ and $c = 2.7$

Give your answer correct to 2 decimal places (2 d.p.).

$$\frac{a^2 - bc}{ac} = \frac{(6.4)^2 - (5.3 \times 2.7)}{(6.4 \times 2.7)}$$
$$= \frac{40.96 - 14.31}{17.28}$$
$$= \frac{26.65}{17.28}$$
$$= 1.54 \text{ to 2 d.p.}$$

### Exercise 7B

1. (a) Use your calculator to work out
      $3 + 4 \times 2 - 5$. Do not press the '$=$' key until
      the end of the calculation.
   (b) Which of the two calculations does your
      calculator work out?

2. For these expressions, find the answer without
   using a calculator. Then check your answers
   using a calculator. If the two answers are
   different, try to find out why.
   If $p = 6$, $q = 4$, $r = 3$ and $s = 2$, calculate the
   value of:

   (a) $p + \dfrac{r}{s}$    (b) $\dfrac{pq}{rs}$    (c) $\dfrac{s(p+q)}{r+s}$

   (d) $p + \dfrac{qr}{s}$    (e) $\dfrac{p+qr}{s}$    (f) $\dfrac{p}{s} + qr$

   (g) $\dfrac{p}{q} + \dfrac{r}{s}$    (h) $\dfrac{p+r}{q+s}$    (i) $\dfrac{qr}{ps}$

3. Evaluate correct to 2 decimal places:

   (a) $\dfrac{ac + b^2}{abc}$    (b) $\dfrac{a^2 + bc}{c^2 - d}$

   where $a = 2.5$, $b = 6.1$, $c = 4.8$ and $d = 1.75$.

## 7.4 Using formulae

You will often need to find a quantity using a formula that has
been given to you on a formula sheet, or in an exam question.
Formulae are used in many aspects of mathematics, for example
for finding areas, speeds or temperatures.

*Example 4*

The diagram shows the end wall of a carport.

Let $b$ represent the length of the base.
Let $h$ represent the height to the top of the roof.
Let $s$ represent the height to the bottom of the roof.

Find the area of the end wall using the formula

$$\text{Area} = \frac{b(s+h)}{2}$$

when $b = 4\,\text{m}$, $s = 5\,\text{m}$ and $h = 7\,\text{m}$

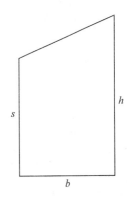

$$\begin{aligned}
\text{Area} &= \frac{b(s+h)}{2} \\
&= \frac{4(5+7)}{2} = \frac{4 \times 12}{2} \\
&= \frac{48}{2} \\
&= 24
\end{aligned}$$

The area is $24\,\text{m}^2$.

## Exercise 7C

1. Use the formula $A = \dfrac{b(s+h)}{2}$ to find the areas

   of the end walls of the carports with these
   measurements:
   (a) $b = 3\,\text{m}$, $s = 3\,\text{m}$ and $h = 4\,\text{m}$
   (b) $b = 3.5\,\text{m}$, $s = 3\,\text{m}$ and $h = 3.6\,\text{m}$
   (c) $b = 2.4\,\text{m}$, $s = 3.2\,\text{m}$ and $h = 3.5\,\text{m}$
   (d) $b = 3.2\,\text{m}$, $s = 2.75\,\text{m}$ and $h = 3.25\,\text{m}$

2. The approximate area of an
   equilateral triangle is given
   by the formula:

   $$\text{Area} = \dfrac{0.86s^2}{2}$$

   where $s$ is the length of one
   side.
   Find the area of these
   equilateral triangles giving your answer to
   1 decimal place:
   (a) $s = 2.4$  (b) $s = 6.25$  (c) $s = 18.75$

3. The total surface
   area of a cuboid is
   found by using the
   formula:

   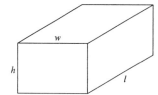

   Area $= 2(lw + lh + hw)$ where $l$ is the length, $w$
   is the width and $h$ is the height
   Find the total surface area of these cuboids:
   (a) $l = 12\,\text{cm}$, $w = 8\,\text{cm}$ and $h = 2.5\,\text{cm}$
   (b) $l = 8.5\,\text{cm}$, $w = 6.25\,\text{cm}$ and $h = 2.5\,\text{cm}$
   (c) $l = 10.4\,\text{cm}$, $w = 6.8\,\text{cm}$ and $h = 8.4\,\text{cm}$

4. The approximate volume of a cone is given by
   the formula: Volume $= 0.78d^2h$ where $d$ is the
   base diameter and $h$ is the
   vertical height
   Find the volume of these cones
   giving your answer correct to
   1 decimal place:
   (a) $d = 3.2\,\text{cm}$ and $h = 6.4\,\text{cm}$
   (b) $d = 8.5\,\text{cm}$ and $h = 12\,\text{cm}$
   (c) $d = 8.2\,\text{cm}$ and $h = 12.2\,\text{cm}$

5. The height of the back of a pick-up truck above
   ground level depends upon the weight of the
   load.

   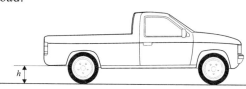

   The height is given by the formula:

   $$h = 1200 - \dfrac{w^2}{160}$$

   where $w$ is the weight in kilograms and $h$ is the
   height in millimetres.
   Find the height of the back above ground level
   when:
   (a) $w = 150\,\text{kg}$  (b) $w = 225\,\text{kg}$
   (c) $w = 320\,\text{kg}$  (d) $w = 400\,\text{kg}$

6. Find the maximum weight that can be put into
   the back of the pick-up truck in question **5**
   before it touches the ground.

   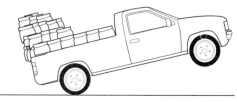

7. Joe's cottage has oak ceiling beams. He wants to
   know the maximum safe weight that one of the
   beams can support.
   Joe consults a structural engineer who gives him
   the formula:

   $$w = \dfrac{59.9td^2}{l}$$

   where $w$ is the maximum safe weight in kg, $d$ is
   the depth of the beam in cm, $t$ is the thickness of
   the beam in cm and $l$ is the length of the beam
   in cm
   Calculate the maximum safe weight for a beam
   30 cm deep, 36 cm thick and 3.6 m long.

8. The cross-sectional area of the disc below is
   given by the formula:

   $$A = 3.14(R^2 - r^2)$$

   (a) Calculate the cross-sectional area, correct to
   2 d.p. for a disc with $R = 4.2\,\text{cm}$ and
   $r = 2.8\,\text{cm}$.
   (b) Show that this alternative formula gives the
   same area:

   $$A = 3.14(R + r)(R - r)$$

   (c) Calculate the cross-
   sectional area of a
   disc with
   $R = 7.14\,\text{cm}$ and
   $r = 2.86\,\text{cm}$.

   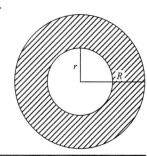

## Worked exam question 1

This formula is used in science: $f = \dfrac{uv}{u+v}$

Calculate $f$ when $u = 6.7\,\text{cm}$ and $v = 4.5\,\text{cm}$. Write down all the digits shown in your calculator answer.

$$f = \frac{6.7 \times 4.5}{6.7 + 4.5} = \frac{30.15}{11.2} = 2.691964286$$

**Do:**
Remember that uv = u + v so
uv = 6.7 × 4.5

Remember that $\dfrac{uv}{u+v}$
means (u × v) ÷ (u + v)

............................................................................

2.691964286 cm   (SEG)

Write down all your working

Write down all the digits from your calculator display

## Worked exam question 2

A formula is $v = \dfrac{a}{ut}$

(a) Calculate the value of $v$ correct to 3 decimal places when $a = 15.1$, $u = 2.9$ and $t = 5.1$

$$v = \frac{15.1}{2.9 \times 5.1} = \frac{15.1}{14.79} = 1.020\,960\,1$$

$$= 1.021 \text{ to 3 decimal places}$$

**Do:**
Remember that ut means u × t

Round the answer to 3 decimal places. Count 3 places after the decimal point. If the 4th figure is 5 or more, round up the 3rd figure

(b) Write down a simple calculation which could be used to check your answer to part (a).

15.1 *is approximately* equal to 15
2.9 *is approximately equal to* 3
5.1 *is approximately equal to* 5

Show the approximations that you are using

A *simple calculation is*   $\dfrac{15}{3 \times 5} = \dfrac{15}{15} = 1$   (London)

## Worked exam question 3

Use the formula: $A = \frac{1}{4}c\sqrt{4a^2 - c^2}$

to calculate the value of $A$ given that $c = 7.23$ and $a = 8.76$

Give your answer correct to 1 decimal place.

$A = \frac{1}{4} \times 7.23 \times \sqrt{4 \times 8.76^2 - 7.23^2}$

$A = 1.8075 \times \sqrt{254.6775}$

$A = 1.8075 \times 15.95861836$

$A = 28.84520269$   $A = 28.8$

**Don't:**
Rush through the question

**Do:**
Show all your working
Remember that
$\frac{1}{4}c\sqrt{4a^2 - c^2}$ means
$\frac{1}{4} \times c \times \sqrt{4a^2 - c^2}$

$A = 28.8$

Give your answer correct to 1 d.p.

(London)

## 7.5 Sequences

Carrying out mathematical investigations often involves working out and collecting a set of numbers. Sometimes you need to be able to predict the next numbers in the sequence.

Here is a sequence of numbers:

$$4, 7, 10, 13, 16, 19, \ldots$$

A typical exam question is:

(a) Write down the next two numbers in the sequence.

(b) Write down an expression for the $n$th term.

To answer this type of question it often helps to put the information into a table of results.

| Term | 1 | 2 | 3 | 4 | 5 | 6 |
|------|---|---|----|----|----|----|
| Value | 4 | 7 | 10 | 13 | 16 | 19 |

Look for the difference between successive terms.

| Term | 1 | 2 | 3 | 4 | 5 | 6 |
|------|---|---|---|---|---|---|
| Value difference | 4   +3 | 7   +3 | 10   +3 | 13   +3 | 16   +3 | 19 |

Here the difference is the same each time. We call it a **constant difference**. To obtain the next two numbers in the sequence you just continue the pattern.

| Term | ... | 5 | 6 | 7 | 8 |
|------|-----|---|---|---|---|
| Value difference | | 16   +3 | 19   +3 | 22   +3 | 25 |

So the next two terms of this sequence are 22 and 25.

Once you recognise how the sequence 'grows' you can continue the pattern to find the value of any term you wish to know. However, if you needed to know the value of the 1000th term continuing the pattern would be very time-consuming and very boring. This is where an expression for the $n$th term is useful.

To find an expression for the $n$th term we have to find a relationship linking the term number and its value. For example in our sequence the 5th term ($n = 5$) has **value** 16.

Look again at the table of results.

| Term | 1 | 2 | 3 | 4 | 5 | 6 | 7 | ... |
|------|---|---|---|---|---|---|---|-----|
| Value difference | 4   +3 | 7   +3 | 10   +3 | 13   +3 | 16   +3 | 19   +3 | 22 | ... ... |

The difference $(+3)$ means that each value is increasing by 3.

So the difference between the first term and any other term must be 3 time something.

For example, the difference between the

> 1st term and the 2nd term is $3 \times 1$
> 1st term and the 3rd term is $3 \times 2$
> 1st term and the 4th term is $3 \times 3$
> 1st term and the 8th term is $3 \times 7$

and so on. This means that each term is of the form $3n + c$ where $n$ is the term and $c$ is a number to be found.

Here the 1st term is 4. So using $3n + c$ with $n = 1$ gives:

$$4 = 3 \times 1 + c$$
$$c = 1$$

So an expression for the $n$th term is $3n + 1$

Once you have found an expression it is important to check that it works for another term that you were given in the question.

Using the expression $3n + 1$ for the 5th term gives $(3 \times 5) + 1 = 16$

The expression is correct.

You can use the expression for the $n$th term to find the value of any term.

For example the 1000th term $= (3 \times 1000) + 1 = 3001$

### Example 5

A sequence of numbers is given as: $3, 8, 13, 18, 23, 28, \ldots$

Find:

(a) the next two terms

(b) an expression for the $n$th term

(c) the value of the 21st term.

Put the information into a table of results and look for the difference between successive terms.

| Term | 1 | 2 | 3 | 4 | 5 | 6 |
|------|---|---|---|---|---|---|
| Value<br>difference | 3   +5 | 8   +5 | 13   +5 | 18   +5 | 23   +5 | 28 |

The constant difference is 5.

(a) the next two terms are $(28 + 5) = 33$
    and $\quad\quad\quad\quad\quad\quad (33 + 5) = 38$

(b) Each term is of the form $5n + c$

The 1st term is 3

so   $3 = (5 \times 1) + c$
$c = -2$

An expression for the $n$th term is $5n - 2$

Check against another known value:

$$4\text{th term} = (5 \times 4) - 2$$
$$= 18$$

The expression is correct.

(c) The 21st term is:

$$(5 \times 21) - 2 = 103$$

---

### Exercise 7D

1. The expression for the $n$th term of a sequence of numbers is $8n + c$. Find:
   (a) the constant difference between successive terms
   (b) the value of $c$ if the first term is 7.

2. Find the next two terms, an expression for the $n$th term and the value of the 26th term for these sequences.
   (a) $1, 6, 11, 16, 21, \ldots$   (b) $8, 12, 16, 20, 24, \ldots$
   (c) $3, 7, 11, 15, 19, \ldots$   (d) $7, 13, 19, 25, 31, \ldots$
   (e) $6, 13, 20, 27, 34, \ldots$

---

### *Example 6*

A sequence of numbers is given as: $11, 9, 7, 5, 3, \ldots$

Find:

(a) the next two terms in the sequence

(b) an expression for the $n$th term

(c) the value of the 12th term.

Putting the information into a table:

| Term | 1 | 2 | 3 | 4 | 5 |
|------|---|---|---|---|---|
| Value difference | 11  $-2$  9  $-2$  7  $-2$  5  $-2$  3 | | | | |

The constant difference is $-2$.

(a) The next two terms are   $3 - 2 = 1$
    and                      $1 - 2 = -1$

(b) Each term is of the form $-2n + c$. The 1st term is 11.

So   $(-2 \times 1) + c = 11$
$c - 2 = 11$
$c = 13$

An expression for the $n$th term is $-2n + 13$ or $13 - 2n$

Checking against the 5th term:

$$13 - (2 \times 5) = 3$$

The expression is correct.

(c) The 12th term is:

$$13 - (2 \times 12) = 13 - 24$$
$$= -11$$

---

### Exercise 7E

1. An expression for the $n$th term of a sequence is $4 - 3n$. Write down:
   (a) the constant difference between successive terms
   (b) the value of the first term.

2. An expression for the $n$th term of a sequence is $-8n + c$. Write down:
   (a) the constant difference between successive terms
   (b) the value of $c$ if the 1st term is 1.

3. Find the next two terms, an expression for the $n$th term and the value of the 21st term for these sequences.
   (a) $18, 14, 10, 6, 2, \ldots$
   (b) $13, 9, 5, 1, \ldots$
   (c) $21, 15, 9, 3, -3, \ldots$
   (d) $-4, -6, -8, -10$
   (e) $4.5, 2.0, -0.5, -3.0, \ldots$

---

## 7.6 Sequences from patterns

Number sequences often come from patterns. For example, the number of matchsticks in these patterns form a sequence. GCSE exam questions about sequences sometimes start with a pattern.

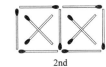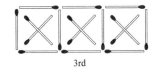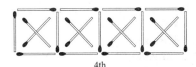

1st          2nd              3rd                    4th

---

### Exercise 7F

1. (a) Draw the next matchstick pattern in the sequence above.
   (b) Copy this table of results. Use the diagrams to complete it.

| Pattern | 1st | 2nd | 3rd | 4th | 5th |
|---|---|---|---|---|---|
| Number of matchsticks | 6 | | | | |

   (c) Find an expression for the number of matchsticks in the $n$th pattern.
   (d) How many matchsticks will there be in the 21st pattern?

2. Here is another sequence of patterns made from matchsticks.

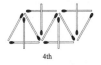

1st        2nd          3rd          4th

**2.** (a) Draw the next pattern in the sequence.
   (b) Copy and complete this table of results.

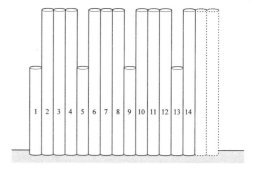

| Pattern | 1st | 2nd | 3rd | 4th | 5th | 6th |
|---|---|---|---|---|---|---|
| Number of matchsticks | 4 | 7 | | | | |

  (c) Find an expression for the number of matchsticks in the $n$th pattern.
  (d) How many matchsticks would you need to make the 55th pattern?

**3.** A fence of long and short poles in this arrangement surrounds a large field.

The 1st short pole is number 1. The 2nd short pole is number 5 and so on. Find an expression for the number of the $n$th short pole.

---

## 7.7 More sequences

Here is a sequence of numbers: $3, 7, 13, 21, 31, \ldots$

Putting the numbers in a table of results and calculating the differences we get:

| Term | 1st | 2nd | 3rd | 4th | 5th |
|---|---|---|---|---|---|
| Value<br>difference | 3    7    13    21    31<br>    +4    +6    +8    +10 | | | | |

This time the difference is *not* a constant number. When this happens the best approach is to look at the second difference, that is the difference of the differences.

| Term | 1st | 2nd | 3rd | 4th | 5th |
|---|---|---|---|---|---|
| Value<br>1st difference<br>2nd difference | 3    7    13    21    31<br>   +4    +6    +8    +10<br>     +2    +2    +2 | | | | |

The second difference gives a constant value $(+2)$.

**If the first difference is a constant** then the expression for the $n$th term is of the form $an + c$ i.e. a **linear expression.**

An expression is linear if the variable is raised to the power $1(n^1)$. The graph of a linear expression is a straight line.

**If the second difference is a constant** then the expression for the $n$th term is of the form $an^2 + bn + c$ i.e. a quadratic expression.
An expression is quadratic if the highest power of the variable is $2(n^2)$.

The value of *a is always half the second difference.*

In this case $a = 1$ (half of 2).

Now rewrite the table of results, putting each value in terms of $n^2$.

| Term | 1st | 2nd | 3rd | 4th | 5th |
|------|-----|-----|-----|-----|-----|
| Value | $3 = 1^2 + 2$ | $7 = 2 + 3$ | $13 = 3^2 + 4$ | $21 = 4^2 + 5$ | $31 = 5^2 + 6$ |

Putting the non-squared numbers in a second table:

| Term | 1st | 2nd | 3rd | 4th | 5th |
|------|-----|-----|-----|-----|-----|
| Number difference | 2   +1 | 3   +1 | 4   +1 | 5   +1 | 6 |

The non-squared numbers form a sequence with a constant difference of 1. The expression for the $n$th term of the sequence of non-squared numbers is $n + 1$.

Now putting these two results together the expression for the $n$th term of the sequence 3, 7, 13, 21, 31, . . . is $n^2 + n + 1$.

Checking for $n = 1$: $1^2 + 1 + 1 = 3$ correct

$\qquad\qquad n = 5$: $5^2 + 5 + 1 = 31$ also correct

The expression for the $n$th term is $n^2 + n + 1$.

### *Example 7*

A sequence of numbers is given as: $4, 7, 12, 19, 28, \ldots$

Find:

(a) an expression for the $n$th term

(b) the value of the 35th term.

(a) Putting the numbers in a table of results:

| Term | 1st | 2nd | 3rd | 4th | 5th |
|------|-----|-----|-----|-----|-----|
| Value difference | 4   +3 | 7   +5 | 12   +7 | 19   +9 | 28 |

The first difference is not a constant, so we find the second difference.

| Term | 1st | 2nd | 3rd | 4th | 5th |
|------|-----|-----|-----|-----|-----|
| Value 1st difference 2nd difference | 4   +3 | 7   +5   +2 | 12   +7   +2 | 19   +9   +2 | 28 |

The second difference is a constant (2). This tells us that the expression for the $n$th term is a quadratic of the form $an^2 + bn + c$, where $a$ is half of the 2nd difference constant number. So $a = 1$.

Now re-write the table of results, putting each value in term of $n^2$.

| Term | 1st | 2nd | 3rd | 4th | 5th |
|---|---|---|---|---|---|
| Value | $4 = 1^2 + 3$ | $7 = 2^2 + 3$ | $12 = 3^2 + 3$ | $19 = 4^2 + 3$ | $28 = 5^2 + 3$ |
| difference | 0 | 0 | 0 | 0 | |

The sequence 3, 3, 3, 3, . . . has $n$th term $0n + 3 = 3$

So an expression for the $n$th term of the sequence
4, 7, 11, 12, 19, 28, . . . is $n^2 + 3$

(b) The value of the 35th term is $(35)^2 + 3 = 1225 + 3$
$$= 1228$$

---

### Exercise 7G

**1.** (a) Copy and complete this table of results.

| Term | 1st | 2nd | 3rd | 4th | 5th | 6th |
|---|---|---|---|---|---|---|
| Value | 6 | 11 | 18 | 27 | | |
| 1st difference | | 5 | 7 | 9 | | |
| 2nd difference | | | 2 | | | |
| Squared pattern | $1^2 + 5$ | $2^2 + 7$ | $3^2 + 9$ | | | |

  (b) Write down an expression for the $n$th term
      of the sequence 5, 7, 9, . . .
  (c) Write down an expression for the $n$th term of
      the sequence 6, 11, 18, 27, . . .
  (d) Calculate the value of the 24th term of the
      sequence in (c).

**2.** For part of their coursework students at High
    Green College had to investigate the number of
    matchsticks needed to make a set of patterns.
    One student obtained these results:

| Pattern | 1st | 2nd | 3rd | 4th | 5th | 6th |
|---|---|---|---|---|---|---|
| Number of matchsticks | 5 | 8 | 13 | 20 | | |
| 1st difference | | | | | | |
| 2nd difference | | | | | | |
| Squared pattern | | | | | | |

  (a) Copy and complete the table.
  (b) Write down an expression for the $n$th term
      of the sequence.
  (c) Write down the value of the 25th term of the
      sequence.

**3.** For each of these number sequences write down:
    (i) the next two terms
    (ii) an expression for the $n$th term
    (iii) the value of the 25th term.
    (a) $0, 2, 6, 12, \ldots$     (b) $3, 8, 15, 24, \ldots$
    (c) $0, 1, 4, 9, \ldots$     (d) $0, 5, 12, 21, \ldots$
    (e) $8, 14, 22, 32, \ldots$     (f) $1.5, 5, 10.5, 18, \ldots$

**4.** (a) Write down the first 6 terms of the sequence
      you obtained in question **3**.
  (b) Use this sequence to help you find an
      expression for the $n$th triangle number.

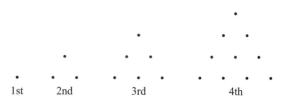

| 1st | 2nd | 3rd | 4th |

  (c) What is the 100th triangle number?

**5.** Christine studied a set of patterns. She obtained
    this table of results.

| Term | 1st | 2nd | 3rd | 4th | 5th |
|---|---|---|---|---|---|
| Value | 1 | 3 | 6 | 11 | 18 |

  Her teacher said that one of the values was
  probably wrong.
  (a) Which value do you think is wrong? Give a
      reason for your answer.
  (b) Re-write the table with the correct value.
  (c) Add 'difference' rows to your table.
  (d) Find an expression for the $n$th term of the
      corrected sequence.

**6**. Two sequences are given as: 3, 8, 15, 24, 35, . . .
and 8, 15, 24, 35, 48, . . .
(a) Write down the next three terms of both
sequences.
(b) Find an expression for the $n$th term for both
sequences.

(c) Use your results to (a) and (b) to write down
an expression for the $n$th term of the
sequence
15, 24, 35, 48, . . .
(d) Check your expression using a given value.

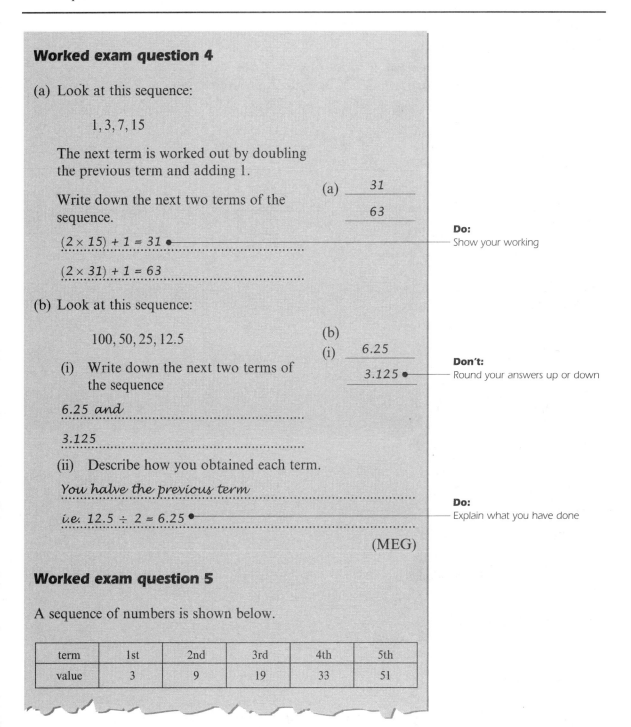

**Worked exam question 4**

(a) Look at this sequence:

    1, 3, 7, 15

The next term is worked out by doubling
the previous term and adding 1.

Write down the next two terms of the
sequence.

(a)    *31*
       *63*

*(2 × 15) + 1 = 31* —————————————————————

**Do:**
Show your working

*(2 × 31) + 1 = 63*

(b) Look at this sequence:

    100, 50, 25, 12.5

(i)  Write down the next two terms of
     the sequence

(b)
(i)    *6.25*
       *3.125*

**Don't:**
Round your answers up or down

*6.25 and* ......................................................

*3.125* ......................................................

(ii)  Describe how you obtained each term.

*You halve the previous term* .................................................

**Do:**
Explain what you have done

*i.e. 12.5 ÷ 2 = 6.25* —————————————————————

(MEG)

**Worked exam question 5**

A sequence of numbers is shown below.

| term  | 1st | 2nd | 3rd | 4th | 5th |
|-------|-----|-----|-----|-----|-----|
| value | 3   | 9   | 19  | 33  | 51  |

(a) Write down an expression for the $n$th term in this sequence.

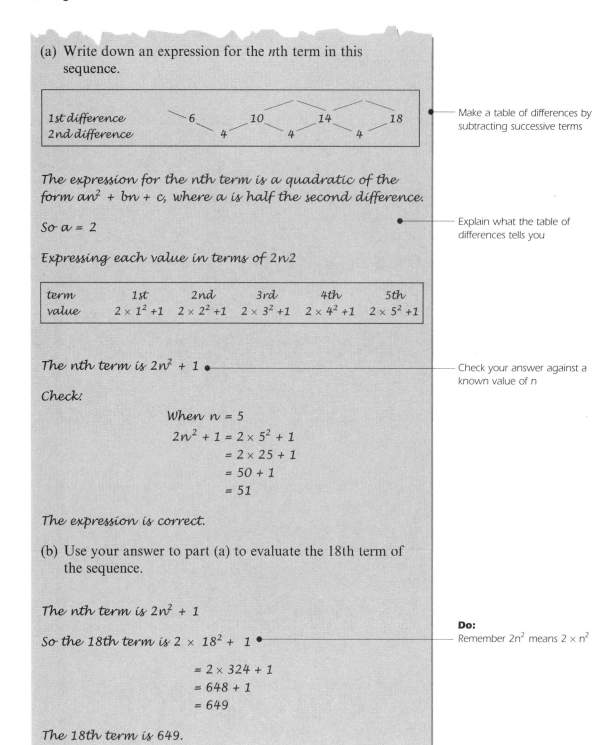

1st difference       6     10     14     18

2nd difference      4      4      4

*Make a table of differences by subtracting successive terms*

The expression for the nth term is a quadratic of the form $an^2 + bn + c$, where $a$ is half the second difference.

So $a = 2$

*Explain what the table of differences tells you*

Expressing each value in terms of $2n2$

| term | 1st | 2nd | 3rd | 4th | 5th |
|------|-----|-----|-----|-----|-----|
| value | $2 \times 1^2 + 1$ | $2 \times 2^2 + 1$ | $2 \times 3^2 + 1$ | $2 \times 4^2 + 1$ | $2 \times 5^2 + 1$ |

The nth term is $2n^2 + 1$

*Check your answer against a known value of n*

Check:

$$\text{When } n = 5$$
$$2n^2 + 1 = 2 \times 5^2 + 1$$
$$= 2 \times 25 + 1$$
$$= 50 + 1$$
$$= 51$$

The expression is correct.

(b) Use your answer to part (a) to evaluate the 18th term of the sequence.

The nth term is $2n^2 + 1$

So the 18th term is $2 \times 18^2 + 1$

**Do:**
*Remember $2n^2$ means $2 \times n^2$*

$$= 2 \times 324 + 1$$
$$= 648 + 1$$
$$= 649$$

The 18th term is 649.

## 7.8 Flow diagrams

You can use a flow diagram to break down a set of instructions into simple steps. The instruction can be given in an English sentence, or as a mathematical expression.

*Example 8*

An instruction is given as: 'think of a number, multiply it by 3 and then add 4'. What would be the answer if the number you first thought of was 5?

The instruction 'multiply by 3 and add 4' can be represented by a flow diagram:

For the number 5:

If the number you first thought of was 5 the answer would be 19.

---

### Exercise 7H

1.

    Using the flow diagram, what answer do you get if the number you first think of is:
    (a) 3          (b) 7          (c) 10?

2. Draw flow diagrams to represent the following instructions.

    Think of a number, then:
    (a) multiply by 6 and add 3
    (b) multiply by 3 and take away 7
    (c) add 4, then multiply by 5
    (d) divide by 2 and then add 8

3. Use 8 as your first number in all your flow diagrams from question **2**. Write down your answers.

---

## 7.9 Input/output diagrams

The number you put into the flow diagram is called the **input**.

The number that comes out is the **output**.

This flow diagram represents the instructions 'multiply by 2 and add 1'.

If the input is 1

the output is 3.

Try inputs 2, 3 and 4. You can show the results in an input/output diagram.

| Input | Output |
|:-----:|:------:|
| 1 | 3 |
| 2 | 5 |
| 3 | 7 |
| 4 | 9 |

## *Example 9*

Draw an input/output diagram for an input of $-2, -1, 0, 1$ in the flow diagram.

The input/output diagram is:

| Input | Output |
|:-----:|:------:|
| $-2$ | $-7$ |
| $-1$ | $-5$ |
| $0$ | $-3$ |
| $1$ | $-1$ |

## Exercise 71

1. (a) Work out the output from this flow diagram:

   (b) Copy this input/output diagram.
   Use the flow diagram to complete it.

| Input | Output |
|:-----:|:------:|
| 1 | |
| 2 | |
| 3 | |
| 4 | |
| 5 | |

2. Copy this input/output diagram.
   Use the flow diagram to complete it.

| Input | Output |
|:-----:|:------:|
| 1 | |
| 5 | |
| 6 | |
| | 15 |
| | 30 |

3. Draw input/output diagrams for:
   (a) an input of 2, 3, 4, 5, 6 in the flow diagram

   (b) an input of 3, 4, 5, 6 in the flow diagram

   → +2 → × 4 →

   (c) an input of 2, 4, 6, 8 in the flow diagram

   → −2 → −1 →

   (d) an input of 0, 2, 4, 6 in the flow diagram

   → +4 → −2 →

4. Draw an input/output diagram for:
   (a) input $-2, -1, 0, 1, 2$ in the flow diagram:

   → × 2 → +3 →

   (b) input $-3, -2, -1, 0, 1$ in the flow diagram

   → +4 → × 3 →

   (c) input $-4, -3, -2, -1, 0$ in the flow diagram:

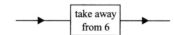

## 7.10 Functions

The instructions that tell you what to do to each number are often
written using algebra.

The instruction        $n \rightarrow 3n + 5$        is shorthand for:

'Multiply the input number by 3, then add 5'

or        $\rightarrow \boxed{\times 3} \rightarrow \boxed{+5} \rightarrow$

When instructions are written this way they are called **functions**.

### *Example 10*

The function $n \rightarrow 3n - 2$ for the set of numbers {2,3,4,5} means
'multiply the input number by 3, then subtract 2, or

$\rightarrow \boxed{\times 3} \rightarrow \boxed{-2} \rightarrow$

for input numbers 2, 3, 4, 5.

The input/output diagram is

| Input | Output |
|-------|--------|
| 2 | 4 |
| 3 | 7 |
| 4 | 10 |
| 5 | 13 |

### *Example 11*

Draw an input/output diagram for: $n \rightarrow n^2$

for the set of numbers $\{-2, -1, 0, 1, 2\}$

| Input | Output |
|-------|--------|
| −2 | 4 |
| −1 | 1 |
| 0 | 0 |
| 1 | 1 |
| 2 | 4 |

### Exercise 7J

**1.** Draw input/output diagrams for:
  (a) $n \rightarrow n - 2$      {3,4,5,6,7}
  (b) $n \rightarrow 5 - n$      {2,3,4,5,6}
  (c) $n \rightarrow 4n + 6$      {−1,0,1,2,3}
  (d) $n \rightarrow n^2$      {1,2,3,4}
  (e) $n \rightarrow n^2 + 2$      {0,2,4,6}

**2.** Draw input/output diagrams for:
  (a) $n \rightarrow n^2$      {−3,−2,−1,0,1}
  (b) $n \rightarrow n^2 - 3$      {−2,−1,0,1,2}
  (c) $n \rightarrow n^2 + n$      {−2,−1,0,1,2}
  (d) $n \rightarrow n^2 - 3n$      {−4,−3,−2,−1,0}

### *Example 12*

This is the input/output diagram for a set of instructions.

| Input | Output |
|:-----:|:------:|
| 1 | 1 |
| 2 | 3 |
| 3 | 5 |
| 4 | 7 |
| $n$ | ? |

Find the function that gives this input/output diagram.

The function is a rule that changes all the input numbers to their output numbers.

In other words we need to find an expression for the $n$th term.

From the input/output diagram we see that the constant difference is 2. So the expression must be of the form $2n + c$.

An input of 1 gives an output of 1.

so:
$$(2 \times 1) + c = 1$$
$$2 + c = 1$$
$$c = -1$$

The expression for the $n$th term is $2n - 1$. Written as a function $n \to 2n - 1$.

Checking $n \to 2n - 1$:

the rule works for all the input numbers:

$$1 \to (2 \times 1) - 1 = 1$$
$$2 \to (2 \times 2) - 1 = 3$$
$$3 \to (2 \times 3) - 1 = 5$$
$$4 \to (2 \times 4) - 1 = 7$$

The function is $n \to 2n - 1$

---

## Exercise 7K

**1.** Find the function for each of these input/output diagrams.

(a)

| Input | Output |
|:-----:|:------:|
| 1 | 3 |
| 2 | 4 |
| 3 | 5 |
| 4 | 6 |

(b)

| Input | Output |
|:-----:|:------:|
| 2 | 4 |
| 1 | 2 |
| 0 | 0 |
| −1 | −2 |
| −2 | −4 |

**1.** (c)

| Input | Output |
|-------|--------|
| 3 | 10 |
| 2 | 7 |
| 1 | 4 |
| 0 | 1 |

(d)

| Input | Output |
|-------|--------|
| 3 | 1 |
| 2 | 0 |
| 1 | −1 |
| 0 | −2 |

## Worked exam question 6

During a number investigation Terry has to double a number and then add 12 to the result.

(a) Draw a flow diagram to show this information.

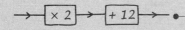

**Do:**
Remember doubling a number is the same as multiplying by 2

(b) (i)  What number does Terry get if the input number is 9?

$9 \longrightarrow \boxed{\times 2} \longrightarrow \boxed{+12} \longrightarrow 30$

Follow the flow diagram instructions in the direction of the arrows

*The output number is 30.*

(ii)  What is the input number if the output number is 44?

$? \longrightarrow \boxed{\times 2} \longrightarrow \boxed{+12} \longrightarrow 44$

*44 − 12 = 32*

**Do:**
Work backwards through the flow diagram

*32 ÷ 2 = 16*

*The input is 16.*

*Check (16 × 2) + 12 = 44*

Check your answer is sensible

(c) If the input number is $n$ use symbols to represent the instructions.

$n \longrightarrow \boxed{\times 2}$    *gives 2n*

$\boxed{+12}$    *gives 2n + 12*

Remember n × 2 is usually written as 2n. An answer of the form (n × 2) + 12 will usually score full marks

*The instructions are n $\longrightarrow$ 2n + 12*

## Worked exam question 7

The cost, in pounds, of a holiday in London may be calculated using the flow diagram.

number of nights → [ Multiply by 37 ] → [ Add 21 ] → cost
in a hotel                                              in
                                                        pounds

(a) Calculate the cost of a holiday with 3 nights in a hotel.

$(3 \times 37) + 21 = 111 + 21 = 132$ ●

£ ...132...

**Do:**
Use brackets to make your meaning clear

(b) Mr Manuel has £235. Calculate the greatest number of nights he could stay in a hotel.

[ × by 37 ] → [ + 21 ] → 235 ●

(5.78) ← [ ÷37 ] ← [ - 21 ] ← 235 ●
         214

...5...

Show your working

Work backwards through the flow diagram

(c) Write down a formula for the cost $C$, in pounds, of a holiday with $n$ nights in a hotel.

$n$ → [ ×37 ] → [ + 21 ] → $37n + 21$ ●

$37 \times n$
$37n$        $37n + 21$

$C = \dfrac{37n + 21}{}$

(London)

**Do:**
Put n into the flow diagram

---

## Exercise 7L (Mixed questions)

1. The volume, $V$ cm$^3$, of a 3-D shape is given by $V = \pi r^2 h + \frac{2}{3}\pi r^3$.
   Calculate the value of $V$ to 2 decimal places when $r = 5$ cm, $h = 7.2$ cm and $\pi = 3.14$.

2. A formula used in science is $S = ut + \frac{1}{2}at^2$
   Calculate the value of $S$
   (a) when $u = 30$, $t = 4$ and $a = 10$
   (b) when $u = -42$, $t = 5.3$ and $a = -1$

3. The first 5 terms in a sequence of numbers are:
   $3, 8, 15, 24, 35$
   (a) Work out the next two terms in this sequence.

   (b) Work out the 10th term in this sequence.
   (c) Find an expression for the $n$th term in this sequence.

4. Sarah makes a pattern using dots. The first 3 patterns are shown below.

1st          2nd              3rd

4. (a) Draw the 4th pattern.
   (b) Work out the number of dots in the 8th pattern.
   (c) Write down an expression for the number of dots in
      (i) the $n$th pattern
      (ii) the $(n+1)$th pattern.
   (d) Find, in its most simplified form, an expression for the difference between the number of dots in the $(n+1)$th pattern and the number of dots in the $n$th pattern.

5. A formula used in science is $\dfrac{1}{f} = \dfrac{1}{v} + \dfrac{1}{u}$

   Calculate the value of $f$ when $v = 5$ and $u = -2.4$ giving your answer to 3 decimal places.

6. A formula used in banking is $P = A(1 + r)^n$
   Calculate the value of $P$ when
   $A = 500$,    $r = 0.05$   and   $n = 4$

7. Here is a diagram of a simple function machine.

input → $\times\ 3$ → $-2$ → output

   Calculate the output when the input is
   (a) 5        (b) $-5$        (c) 0
   (d) $-1$     (e) $\frac{1}{2}$        (f)  $-\frac{1}{3}$

8. Here is a simple function machine.

input → $+2$ → $\times\ 5$ → output

   Calculate the *input* when the output is
   (a) 30     (b) $-5$     (c) $37\frac{1}{2}$     (d) $-18$

## Test yourself

**1.** If $a = 3$, $b = 4$ and $c = 12$ calculate the value of:

**QUESTION**    (i)   $a + b$    (ii)  $8a - 2c$    (iii)  $4a + 3b$    (iv)  $a^2 + b^2$    (v)  $a^2 + 2b - c$

**ANSWER**    (i) 7   (ii) 0   (iii) 24        *If your answer is incorrect review page 130, Section*
(iv) 25   (v) 5        *7.2 on the language of algebra*

**2.** The approximate surface area of a cylinder is given by the formula
   $A = 6.3(r^2 + hr)$

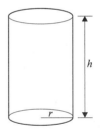

**QUESTION**    Calculate $A$ when  (a)  $r = 4$ and $h = 12$
                              (b)  $r = 2.4$ and $h = 2.4$

**ANSWER**    (a) 403.2   (b) 72.576        *If your answer is incorrect review page 133, Section 7.4 on using formulae*

**3.** Here is a sequence of numbers: 2, 9, 16, 23, 30, . . .

**QUESTION**    (a)   Write down the next two numbers in the sequence

**ANSWER**    37, 44

**QUESTION**    (b)   What is the constant difference between successive terms?

**ANSWER**    7

**QUESTION**    (c)   Write down an expression for the $n$th term.

**ANSWER**    $7n - 5$        *If your answers are incorrect review page 136, Section 7.5 on sequences*

**4.** These results come from a number pattern investigation:

| Pattern | 1st | 2nd | 3rd | 4th | 5th | 6th |
|---|---|---|---|---|---|---|
| Number of matchsticks | 4 | 10 | 16 | | | |

**QUESTION**  Copy and complete the table.

**ANSWER**

| 4th | 5th | 6th |
|---|---|---|
| 22 | 28 | 34 |

**QUESTION**  How many matchsticks would you need for the *n*th pattern?

**ANSWER**  $6n - 2$           *If your answers are incorrect review page 139, Section 7.6 on sequences from patterns*

**QUESTION**  **5.** Find an expression for the *n*th term of this sequence:
                1, 5, 11, 19, 29, . . .

**ANSWER**  $n^2 + n - 1$           *If your answer is incorrect review page 140, Section 7.7 on more sequences*

**QUESTION**  **6.** Draw an input/ouput diagram for an input of 1, 3, 5, 7, 9 in the flow diagram.

**ANSWER**

| Input | Output |
|---|---|
| 1 | 8 |
| 3 | 12 |
| 5 | 16 |
| 7 | 20 |
| 9 | 24 |

*If your answer is incorrect review page 144, Section 7.8 on flow diagrams and page 145, Section 7.9 on input/output diagrams*

**QUESTION**  **7.** Copy this input/output diagram. Use the flow diagram to complete it.

| Input | Output |
|---|---|
| 0 | |
| 2 | |
| 5 | |
| | 16 |
| | 24 |

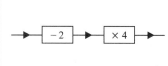

**ANSWER**

| Input | Output |
|---|---|
| 0 | −8 |
| 2 | 0 |
| 5 | 12 |
| 6 | 16 |
| 8 | 24 |

*If your answer is incorrect review page 145, Section 7.9 on input/output diagrams*

# Summary of key points

1. $ab$ means $a \times b$ $\qquad$ $\dfrac{a}{b}$ means $a \div b$

   $a^2$ means $a \times a$ $\qquad$ $\dfrac{2ab}{cd}$ means $2 \times a \times b$ divided by $c \times d$

2. When you substitute numbers for letters in a calculation, remember to use brackets to make your meaning clear.

   For example,  $ab + c$ means $(a \times b) + c$
   $\qquad\qquad\quad$ $a(b + c)$ means $a \times (b + c)$

3. When you work out a numerical expression, always work out the expression in the brackets first. For example,

   $3 + (4 \times 2) - 5 = 3 + 8 - 5$

4. To find an expression for the $n$th term of a sequence of numbers start by looking at the differences between successive terms.

   If the 1st difference is a constant the $n$th term is of the form $an + b$.

   If the 2nd difference is a constant the $n$th term is of the form $an^2 + bn + c$.

5. The number you put into the flow diagram is called the **input**.

   The number that comes out is the **output**.

   You can show the results in an input/ouput diagram.

   | Input | Output |
   |-------|--------|
   |       |        |
   |       |        |

6. When the instructions for a flow diagram are written in algebra they are called **functions**.

   $n \to 2n + 5$ is a function.

# 8 Forming equations

## 8.1 Introduction

As you saw in Unit 7 Basic algebra, Mathematicians often use letters to represent unknown numbers. Algebra is an agreed shorthand language for doing this. A letter that represents a number is called a **variable**.

This unit shows you how to write information in algebra. It also explores the differences between expressions, formulae and equations.

## 8.2 Algebraic expressions

Tom is $x$ years old and Tina is $y$ years old. An expression for the sum of their ages is $(x + y)$ years.

$x + y$ is called an **algebraic expression**.

The sum of two numbers $x$ and $y$ means $x + y$. The difference of two numbers $x$ and $y$ means $x - y$ or $y - x$.

### Example 1

$a$, $b$ and $c$ represent three numbers. Write down an expression for:

(a) the sum of the three numbers

(b) $a$ added to $b$ and then divided by $c$

(c) the average of the three numbers

(d) twice $a$ minus three times $b$.

(a) The sum means the total when all three numbers are added together. The expression is $a + b + c$

(b) $a$ added to $b$ is $a + b$. Divided by $c$ is $\dfrac{a + b}{c}$

(c) The average is the sum divided by the number of numbers

$$\frac{a + b + c}{3}$$

(d) Twice $a$ means $\quad\quad 2 \times a$ or $2a$
Three times $b$ means $\quad 3 \times b$ or $3b$
The expression is $\quad\quad 2a - 3b$

**Exercise 8A**

1. Dean is $r$ years old and Kelly is $s$ years old. Write down an expression for:
   (a) the difference in their ages
   (b) their ages multiplied together
   (c) twice Dean's age.

2. Katy is $m$ years old and Martin is $(m + 3)$ years old. Write down an expression for the sum of their ages.

3. Baljit is $x$ years old and Delroy is 5 years younger. Write an expression for:
   (a) Delroy's age
   (b) the sum of their ages
   (c) the difference of their ages
   (d) their ages multiplied together

4. (a) £420 is shared equally between 10 people. How much does each person receive?
   (b) Write an expression for the amount each person receives if £$A$ pounds is shared equally between 10 people.
   (c) Write an expression for the amount each person receives if £$A$ pounds is shared equally between $n$ people.

5. Janette buys 6 pens for £1.20. Find:
   (a) the cost of one pen
   (b) the cost of $n$ pens.
   Chris buys pens for $p$ pence each.
   (c) Write an expression for the cost of $m$ pens.

6. (a) Write down letters to represent four unknown numbers. Write down an expression for the sum of these four numbers.
   (b) Two of the numbers are equal. Write down a new expression for the sum of the four numbers.
   (c) All four numbers are equal. Write down a new expression for the sum of the four numbers.

7. The difference between two numbers is 4. Write down:
   (a) two possible expressions for the sum of the two numbers
   (b) two possible expressions for the two numbers multiplied together.

8. A cafe serves $c$ cups of coffee and $t$ cups of tea each day for $d$ days.
   Write down the meaning of these expressions in words.
   (a) $(c + t)$        (b) $(c - t)$
   (c) $(t - c)$        (d) $dc$
   (e) $d(c + t)$

9. $n$ metals bars are placed in a row of total length $t$ cm and total weight $w$ kg.
   Write down the meaning of the expressions:
   (a) $\dfrac{t}{n}$     (b) $\dfrac{w}{n}$
   (c) Explain why the expression $(t + w)$ has no meaning.

# 8.3 Constructing formulae

$n - x$ is an example of an **algebraic expression**. $a + b$, $3x - 2y$, $5z$ are all expressions.

$n = x + y$ is an example of a **formula**.

$y = mx + c$, $A = 3b$, $I = PRT$ are all formulae. A formula describes the relationship between two or more variables.

### *Example 2*

In a class of $n$ students, $x$ students are girls.

(a) Write an expression for the number of boys in the class in terms of $n$ and $x$.

(b) There are $y$ boys in the class. Write a formula connecting $n$, $x$ and $y$.

(a) There are $n$ students in total. $x$ of them are girls.
So there must be $n - x$ boys.

(b) There are $n$ students in total. $x$ are girls and $y$ are boys.
So $y = n - x$.

You can find the perimeter of a rectangle by adding the length and width together and multiplying the result by 2.

This statement can be written as a general formula using letters to represent the lengths involved. Use the letters $P$, $l$ and $w$ where

$P$ = the length perimeter
$l$ = the length
$w$ = the width

You can choose any letters to represent the lengths. You must explain what each letter represents.

To find the perimeter add the length and width together $= (l + w)$ and then multiply the result by 2 to give $2(l + w)$

The perimeter $P = 2(l + w)$

Now you have obtained this formula you can use it to find the perimeter of any rectangle.

### Example 3

(a) Find the perimeter of a rectangle with length 8 cm and width 5 cm.

(b) Find the perimeter of a rectangle with length 12.4 cm and width 3.8 cm.

(a) $P = 2(l + w) = 2(8 + 5)$
$\qquad\qquad = 2 \times 13$
$\qquad\qquad = 26$ cm

(b) $P = 2(l + w) = 2(12.4 + 3.8)$
$\qquad\qquad = 2 \times 16.2$
$\qquad\qquad = 32.4$ cm

---

### Exercise 8B

**1.** Find the perimeter of this rectangle.

10.4 cm

2.85 cm

Use the formula $P = 2(l + w)$ where $P$ is perimeter, $l$ is length and $w$ is width.

**2.** Write down a formula for the area of a rectangle. Use $A$ to represent area, $l$ to represent length and $w$ to represent width.

**3.** (a) Six identical bars of steel each weigh 52 kg. What is the total weight of the 6 bars?
(b) Write an expression for the total weight of $n$ bars of steel each weighing 52 kg.

**3.** (c) Write an expression for the total weight of $n$ bars of steel each weighing $p$ kg.
   (d) The total weight of $n$ bars of steel is $x$ kg. Each bar weighs the same.
    Write an expression for the weight of 3 of the bars in terms of $x$ and $n$.

**4.** To find the mean of 5 numbers you add the 5 numbers together and divide the result by 5.
   (a) The mean of 5 numbers $r, s, t, u, v$ is $m$. Write down a formula for $m$ in terms of $r, s, t, u, v$.
   (b) Calculate $m$ when $r = 15$, $s = 7$, $t = 8$, $u = 12$ and $v = 6$.

**5.** The area of a trapezium is found by calculating the mean of the two parallel sides and multiplying this result by the height ($h$).
   (a) Let $a$ and $b$ represent the lengths of the two parallel sides. Write down an expression for the mean of $a$ and $b$.
   (b) Write down a formula for the area of a trapezium in terms of $a$, $b$ and $h$.
   (c) Use your formula to calculate the areas of these trapeziums:

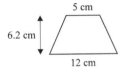 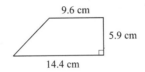

**6.** Jane earns £$n$ per hour.
   (a) Write down an expression for the amount that Jane earns in 3 hours.
    Jane works $h$ hours each week.
   (b) Write a formula for the amount £$m$ that Jane earns in a week.
   (c) Calculate the value of $m$ when $n = £6.20$ and $h = 38$.
   (d) One week Jane earned £150. Write down an expression in $h$ and $n$ for that week's earnings.

**7.** Robinsons make two charges for repairing a washing machine. The first charge is a fixed charge called the 'call-out' charge. The second charge is an hourly rate for the time it takes for the repair.
   (a) Let $P$ = the total charge in pounds
         $c$ = the call-out charge in pounds
         $r$ = the hourly rate in pounds
         $t$ = the time taken for the repair in hours.

Write down a formula for the total charge for a call-out and repair.
   (b) The call-out charge is £35 and the hourly rate is £12.50. It takes the engineer 4 hours to repair Mrs Brown's washing machine. Calculate the total charge for this repair.

**8.** Sally has 4 wall units to put along one wall in her kitchen. She wants the spaces at each end of the wall to be equal.
   (a) Write down a formula for the space, $g$, in terms of the length of the wall, $l$ and the width of a unit, $u$.
   (b) The kitchen wall is 3.6 metres long. The width of one wall unit is 600 mm. Find the length of the gap.

**9.** A widow with $s$ sons and $d$ daughters dies and leaves all her money, £$M$ to her children. The money is shared equally between the children.
   (a) Write down an expression for the amount each child receives.
   (b) Write down a formula for the amount £$A$ each child receives.
   (c) Calculate the value of $M$ when $A = 2500$, $s = 2$ and $d = 5$.

**10.** When a ball is dropped from a tower the distance $d$ metres it has fallen in $t$ seconds can be calculated from the formula $d = 5t^2$.
   (a) How far will the ball have fallen in
     (i) 2 seconds
     (ii) 5 seconds
     (iii) 7.5 seconds
   (b) How far does the ball fall between the 3rd second and the 4th second?
   (c) If the tower is 500 metres high, how long is it before the ball hits the ground?

**11.** From the top of a cliff the distance to the seaward horizon can be calculated as follows: 'Multiply the height of the cliff by 12.5, then take the square root of the answer'
   (a) Using appropriate letters, fully defined, write down a formula for finding the distance to the horizon.
   (b) Use your formula to find the distance to the horizon from the top of a cliff that is 20 m high. Give your answer correct to 1 decimal place.

## Worked exam question 1

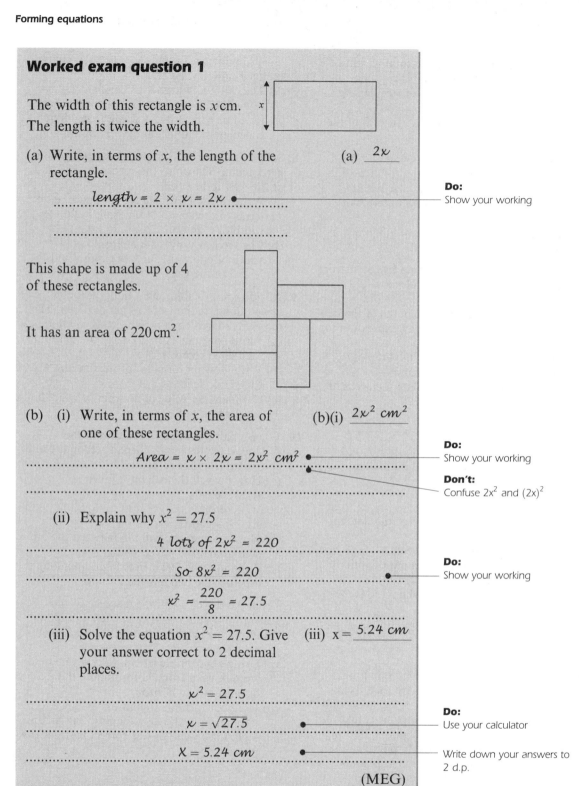

The width of this rectangle is $x$ cm.
The length is twice the width.

(a) Write, in terms of $x$, the length of the
rectangle.

(a) $\underline{2x}$

**Do:**
Show your working

$$length = 2 \times x = 2x \bullet$$

This shape is made up of 4
of these rectangles.

It has an area of 220 cm².

(b)  (i)  Write, in terms of $x$, the area of
one of these rectangles.

(b)(i) $\underline{2x^2 \ cm^2}$

$$Area = x \times 2x = 2x^2 \ cm^2 \bullet$$

**Do:**
Show your working

**Don't:**
Confuse $2x^2$ and $(2x)^2$

(ii)  Explain why $x^2 = 27.5$

$$4 \ lots \ of \ 2x^2 = 220$$

$$So \ 8x^2 = 220$$

**Do:**
Show your working

$$x^2 = \frac{220}{8} = 27.5$$

(iii)  Solve the equation $x^2 = 27.5$. Give
your answer correct to 2 decimal
places.

(iii) $x = \underline{5.24 \ cm}$

$$x^2 = 27.5$$

$$x = \sqrt{27.5} \bullet$$

**Do:**
Use your calculator

$$X = 5.24 \ cm \bullet$$

Write down your answers to
2 d.p.

(MEG)

## Worked exam question 2

When the 8.05 train to London left Derby there were $x$
passengers on board. The train stopped at Leicester, Kettering
and Luton.

(a) At Leicester 45 passengers got off and 12 new passengers got on.

Write down an expression for the number of passengers on the train when it left Leicester.

*When the train arrived at Leicester there were x passengers on board.*

*45 got off so there were (x − 45) passengers left.* •————

*12 new passengers on the train when it left Leicester.*

*(x − 45 + 12) = (x − 33)*

*There were (x − 33) passengers on the train when it left Leicester.*

**Do:**
Remember to subtract the number of passengers who got off the train and add the number who got on the train

(b) When the train left Kettering there were half as many passengers on board as when it had arrived.

Write down an expression for the number of passengers on the train when it left Kettering.

*When the train arrived in Kettering there were (x − 33) passengers.*

*When it left there were half as many,* $\dfrac{(x - 33)}{2}$ •————

**Do:**
Remember to find 'half as many' you divide by 2

(c) (i) If this pattern is repeated every day, write down a formula for the number of passengers $P$ who are on board when the train arrives at Luton.

*When the train arrived at Luton there were* •———— *(x − 33)/2 passengers on board. So the formula is:*

$$P = \frac{(x - 33)}{2}$$

**Do:**
Notice that you have two expressions for the number of passengers. These must equal each other

(ii) Use your formula to find the number of passengers who arrived at Luton when $x = 257$.

$$P = \frac{(x - 33)}{2} = \frac{(257 - 33)}{2} = \frac{(224)}{2} = 112$$

## 8.4 Constructing equations

A formula is a statement that describes the relationship between two or more variables. For example, $y = mx + c$ is a formula.

If you are given the values $y = 12$, $m = 3$ and $c = 5$ you can substitute these into the formula to give $12 = 3x + 5$, which is an **equation**. You can solve the equation to find the value of $x$.

$x^2 + 6x + 8 = 0$ is another example of an equation.

## Example 4

Sherene wants to translate this statement into an algebraic equation.

'A number is multiplied by 8, then 7 is subtracted from the answer. The result is 19.'

Sherene starts by saying:

| | |
|---|---|
| Let $n$ be the number | $n$ |
| Multiply it by 8 | $8n$ |
| then subtract by 7 | $8n - 7$ |
| The result is 19: | $8n - 7 = 19$ |

> *Note*: you can use any letter

## Exercise 8C

1. Translate these statements into equations. You do not need to solve the equations.
   (a) A number is multiplied by 5, then 3 is added. The result is 18.
   (b) If you multiply a number by 5 and then subtract 3 you are left with 42.
   (c) Four times a certain number add 15 equals 47.
   (d) Multiply a number by 7 and add 5 to get 50.
   (e) Take 4 away from a number. You are left with 12.
   (f) Take a number away from 4. The result is 12.

2. A rectangle has an area of $A$ cm$^2$. The length of the rectangle is $x$ cm. The width of the rectangle is $y$ cm.
   (a) Write down a formula connecting $A$, $x$ and $y$.
   (b) When $A = 24$, write down an equation in $x$ and $y$.
   (c) Explain why there are many solutions in $x$ and $y$ to your equation.

3. The area of a square is $A$ cm$^2$. The length of a side of the square is $x$ cm.
   (a) Write down a formula connecting $A$ and $x$.
   (b) For $A = 25$, write down an equation in $x$.
   (c) Find the value of $x$ when $A = 25$.

## Example 5

Andrew wants to translate this problem into an algebraic equation:

'Three times a number then add 5 is the same as twice the number take away 1.'

Andrew starts by saying:

| | |
|---|---|
| Let $x$ be the number | $x$ |
| Three times a number then add 5 | $3x + 5$ |
| 'is the same as' means 'equals' | $3x + 5 =$ |
| Twice the number take away 1 | $3x + 5 = 2x - 1$ |

## Exercise 8D

1. Translate these statements into equations. You do not need to solve the equations.
   (a) Three times a number then add 2 is the same as the number plus 3.
   (b) Multiplying a number by 4 and then taking away 5 gives the same result as multiplying the number by 7 and then adding 3.
   (c) Two times a number then add 1 equals the number take away 4.
   (d) Taking a number away from 10 gives the same result as multiplying the number by itself and adding 6.
   (e) A number added to 4 is then multiplied by 3. This gives the same answer as multiplying the number by 3 and subtracting 2.

2. Translate these equations into words.
   (a) $4n + 5 = 3n - 2$    (b) $2x - 3 = 4x - 5$
   (c) $6y + 2 = 3y - 12$

3. The perimeter, $P$ cm, of a square is found by multiplying the length of one of its sides by 4.
   (a) Write down a formula for the area of a square.
   (b) Write down a formula for the perimeter of a square.
   (c) Write down an equation for the length of one side of a square whose perimeter has the same numerical value as its area.
   (d) What is the length of one side of a square whose perimeter and area have the same numerical value?

---

## Worked exam question 3

Rashpal is $\frac{1}{4}$ of her mother's age. Rashpal is $x$ years old.

(a) Write an expression in terms of $x$ for:

   (i) her mother's age

   *Rashpal is $\frac{1}{4}$ of her mother's age. This means that her mother must be 4 times older than Rashpal.*

   *If Rashpal is $x$ years old her mother is $4x$ years old.*

   (ii) Rashpal's age in 5 years' time

   *Rashpal is $x$ years old now.*

   *In 5 years' time she will be $(x + 5)$ years old.* ●——— **Do:**
   Remember to use a + sign when adding two quantities

   (iii) her mother's age in 5 years time.

   *her mother is $4x$ years old now.*

   *In 5 years' time she will be $(4x + 5)$ years old.*

(b) In 5 years' time Rashpal will be $\frac{1}{3}$ of her mother's age.

   Write an equation in $x$ to represent this statement.

   *In 5 years' time Rashpal's mother will be $(4x + 5)$ years old.*

   *This is 3 times Rashpal's age in 5 years' time. Rashpal's age in 5 years' time will be $(x + 5)$.*

   *3 times $(x + 5)$ is $3(x + 5)$*
   *So          $3(x + 5)$ is the same as $4x + 5$*
   *           $3(x + 5) = 4x + 5$* ●——— **Do:**
   Remember that an equation needs two parts that are equal to each other

### Exercise 8E (Mixed questions)

1. Alison is given £20 for her birthday. She uses the £20 to start saving for her holiday. Then each week she adds £4 to her savings. She does not spend any of her savings. After $n$ weeks, Alison will have saved £$S$. Write down a formula connecting $S$ and $n$.

2. A bus has a top deck and a lower deck. There are $x$ seats on the lower deck. There are 3 less seats on the top deck than on the lower deck.
   (a) Write down an expression for the number of seats on the bus.
   There are 41 seats on the bus.
   (b) Write down an equation in $x$.
   (c) Find the value of $x$.

3. A car-hire company charges customers £40 per day and 25 pence for each mile driven.
   A customer hires a car for a day and drives $x$ miles. The customer is charged £$C$.
   Write down a formula for $C$ in terms of $x$.

4. For the triangle ABC shown here, the length of BC is half the length of AB (all lengths are in centimetres).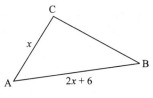
   (a) Write down an expression for the length of BC.
   The perimeter of the triangle ABC is $P$ cm.
   (b) Write down a formula for $P$ in terms of $x$.
   (c) Given that $P = 20$ cm, write down an equation for $x$.

5. The formula for the area, $A$, of a circle of radius $r$ is $A = \pi r^2$.
   A sheet of metal is in the shape of a rectangle with a semi-circular end-piece. Write down an expression for the area of this sheet of metal in terms of $x$ and $\pi$.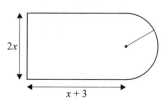

## Test yourself

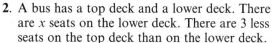

QUESTION **1.** If Charlotte is $y$ years old now, how old was she (a) 5 years ago (b) $x$ years ago?

ANSWER (a) $(y - 5)$ years old   *If your answer is incorrect review page 154,*
(b) $(y - x)$ years old   *Section 8.2 on algebraic expressions*

---

**2.** Tony sells $n$ hot dogs and $m$ hamburgers every day for $d$ days.

QUESTION Write an expression for:
(a) the total number of hot dogs and hamburgers he sells in one day
(b) the total number of hot dogs he sells in one week
(c) the total number of hot dogs and hamburgers he sells in $d$ days

ANSWER (a) $n + m$   (b) $7n$   *If your answer is incorrect review page 154,*
(c) $d(n + m)$   *Section 8.2 on algebraic expressions*

---

**3.** In a box of $S$ sweets 12 are mints and the rest, $t$, are toffees.

QUESTION (a) Write a formula for the total number of sweets in the box.

ANSWER (a) $S = 12 + t$

---

QUESTION (b) Use your formula to find the number of toffees if there are 30 sweets in the box.

ANSWER (b) 18 toffees   *If your answer is incorrect review page 155, Section 8.3 on constructing formulae*

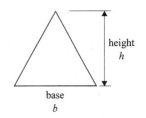

**4.** The area of a triangle is found by multiplying the length of the base $b$ by the height $h$ and dividing by 2.

---

QUESTION    (a)   Write a formula to find the area $A$ of a triangle.

ANSWER    (a)    $A = \dfrac{bh}{2}$

---

QUESTION    (b)   Find the area of a triangle with base 12.4 cm and height 8.2 cm.

ANSWER    (b)    $A = 50.84\,\text{cm}^2$

---

QUESTION    (c)   The area of a triangle is 24 cm².
Write an equation to represent this information.

ANSWER    (c)    $24 = \dfrac{bh}{2}$        *If your answer is incorrect review page 155,*
*Section 8.3 on constructing formulae and page 159,*
*Section 8.4 on constructing equations*

---

**5.** I think of a number, multiply it by 3 and then add 4. The result is 19.

---

QUESTION    (a)   Translate this statement into an algebraic equation.

ANSWER    (a)    $3n + 4 = 19$        *If your answer is incorrect review page 159,*
*Section 8.4 on constructing equations*

---

QUESTION    (b)   Solve the equation

ANSWER    (b)    $n = 5$        *If your answer is incorrect review page 159, Section*
*8.4 on constructing equations*

---

**6.** Jackie is $x$ years old. She is 3 times older than her sister Sarah.

---

QUESTION    Write down in terms of $x$:
(a)   Sarah's age now
(b)   Sarah's age in 6 years' time
(c)   Jackie's age in 6 years' time.

ANSWER    (a)  $\dfrac{x}{3}$  (b) $\dfrac{x}{3} + 6$  (c) $x + 6$   *If your answers are incorrect review page 159,*
*Section 8.4 on constructing equations*

---

In 6 year's time the sum of Jackie's and Sarah's ages will be 36.

---

QUESTION    (d)   Write down an equation to represent this information.

ANSWER    (d)    $(x + 6) + \left(\dfrac{x}{3} + 6\right) = 36$   *If your answers are incorrect review page 159,*
*Section 8.4 on constructing equations*

## Summary of key points to remember

1. The **sum** of two numbers $x$ and $y$ means $x + y$. The difference of two numbers $x$ and $y$ means $x - y$ or $y - x$.

2. $4n + 3$ is an example of an **algebraic expression**.

3. $P = 4n + 3$ is an example of an **algebraic formula**. It describes the relationship between two variables.

4. $8 = 4n + 3$ is a example of an **algebraic equation**. You can solve it to find the value of $n$.

# 9 Straight line graphs

## 9.1 Introduction

When you are dealing with physical quantities, such as length, time, or temperature, you sometimes need to find a relationship between them. For example, you may want to find the relationship between the distance a car has travelled and the time it has been travelling.

Drawing a graph creates a visual picture of the relationship between two quantities. The graph can help you to understand this relationship.

This gives you two ways of finding a relationship between two quantities:

1  Using the input/output values of a function.

2  Using the graph techniques developed in this unit.

## 9.2 Graphing functions

In Unit 7 you drew input/output diagrams for functions. This is the part of the input/output diagram of $x \rightarrow 2x - 1$.

| Input | Output |
|:-----:|:------:|
| 0 | −1 |
| 1 | 1 |
| 2 | 3 |
| 3 | 5 |
| 4 | 7 |

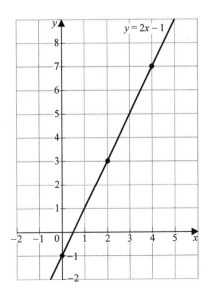

You can write the inputs and outputs together as a pair of coordinates:

$$(0, -1), (1, 1), (2, 3), (3, 5) \text{ and } (4, 7)$$

You can then plot these points on a coordinate diagram and join them to give a graph of $x \rightarrow 2x - 1$. The formula for the graph of $x \rightarrow 2x - 1$ is $y = 2x - 1$. The 'name' of the graph is $y = 2x - 1$.

## Exercise 9A

**1.** Here are input/output diagrams for two functions:

| Input | Output |
|-------|--------|
| 3 | 11 |
| 2 | 8 |
| 1 | 5 |
| 0 | 2 |
| −1 | −1 |

| Input | Output |
|-------|--------|
| 4 | 2 |
| 2 | 4 |
| 0 | 6 |
| −2 | 8 |
| −4 | 10 |

(a) Write the inputs and outputs of each diagram as pairs of coordinates.

(b) Find the rule for each function and express it in the form $x \rightarrow ?$

(c) Plot the points for each function on a coordinate diagram. Join them with a straight line.

(d) Write the 'name' of each graph in the form $y = ?$

(e) What is the connection between your answers to (b) and (d)?

**2.** For each of the following functions (i) draw an input/output diagram. (ii) write down the pairs of coordinates. (iii) plot the points on a coordinate diagram. (iv) draw and label the graph.

|  |  | inputs |
|--|--|--------|
| (a) | $x \rightarrow 3x - 2$ | $\{-1, 0, 1, 2, 3\}$ |
| (b) | $x \rightarrow x + 2$ | $\{-2, -1, 0, 1, 2, 3\}$ |
| (c) | $x \rightarrow 3 + 2x$ | $\{-1, 0, 1, 2, 3, 4\}$ |
| (d) | $x \rightarrow 6 - x$ | $\{-3, -2, -1, 0, 1, 2\}$ |
| (e) | $x \rightarrow -2x - 3$ | $\{-2, -1, 0, 1, 2, 3\}$ |

**3.** This is a graph of a function.

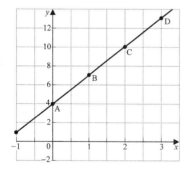

(a) Write down the coordinates of points A, B, C and D.

(b) Draw an input/output diagram for these coordinates.

(c) Use the input/output diagram to work out a formula in the form $y = ax + c$.

**4.** (a) From each of these graphs choose at least four points and write down their coordinates.

(i)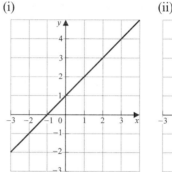

(ii)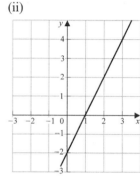

(b) Draw an input/output diagram for these coordinates.

(c) Find the rule for each function. Write it in the form $x \rightarrow ?$

(d) Write the name of the graphs in the form $y = ?$

**5.** Find the rules for the functions shown in these graphs. Write them in the form $x \rightarrow ?$
Write the names of the graphs in the form $y = ?$

(a)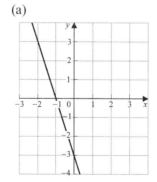

(b)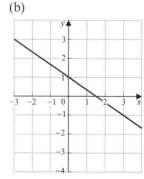

# 9.3 Gradient of a straight line graph

This is a graph of
$y = x$.

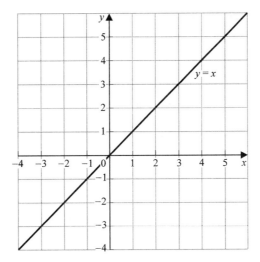

If we rotate the line
anticlockwise the line
gets steeper.

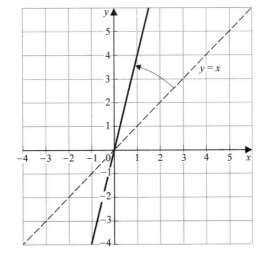

If we rotate the line
clockwise the line
gets less steep.

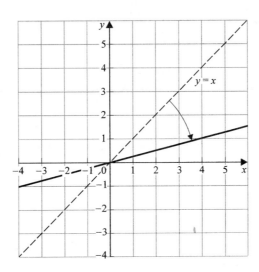

The measure of steepness of a graph is called its **gradient**. In the formula of a line of the form $y = mx$, $m$ is the gradient.

The line $y = x$ ($y = 1x$) has gradient 1.

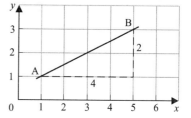

### Example 1

To find the gradient of this line:

(i) work out the vertical distance from A to B.

(ii) work out the horizontal distance from A to B.

(iii) divide: $\dfrac{\text{vertical distance from A to B}}{\text{horizontal distance from A to B}}$

The gradient of this line $m = \frac{2}{4} = \frac{1}{2}$

The gradient of this line, $\frac{1}{2}$, is less steep than the gradient of the line $y = x$.

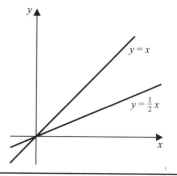

### Exercise 9B

1. (i) For each line: write down the gradient.
   (ii) State whether it is steeper or less steep than the line $y = x$.
   (a) $y = 4x$       (b) $y = 1.5x$
   (c) $y = \frac{1}{2}x$       (d) $y = 0.6x$
   (e) $y = \frac{4}{3}x$       (f) $y = \frac{3}{4}x$

2. Work out the gradients of these lines.

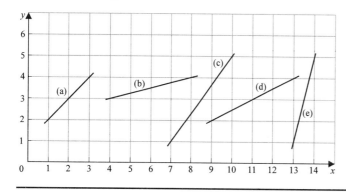

3. (a) Write down the coordinates of points A and B.
   (b) Work out the gradient of the line AB.

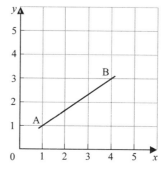

### Example 2

Find the gradient of the straight line joining the points $(3, 3)$ and $(5, 12)$.

Sketch the information given.

Work out:

(i) the vertical distance between the two points. This is the difference between the $y$ coordinates.

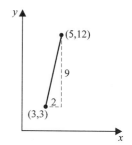

(ii) the horizontal distance between the two points. This is the difference between the $x$ coordinates.

The gradient $m = \dfrac{\text{difference in } y \text{ coordinates}}{\text{difference in } x \text{ coordinates}}$

$\qquad = \dfrac{12 - 3}{5 - 3} = \dfrac{9}{2} = 4.5$

---

### Exercise 9C

1. Find the gradient of the straight line joining the points A and B.

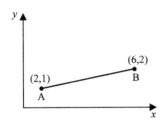

2. Sketch the pairs of coordinate points. Find the gradient of the straight line joining them.
   (a) $(0, 0)$ and $(7, 3)$     (b) $(0, 0)$ and $(6, 3)$
   (c) $(2, 2)$ and $(6, 4)$     (d) $(1, 2)$ and $(7, 10)$
   (e) $(-1, 1)$ and $(9, 5)$    (f) $(5, 4)$ and $(9, 16)$

3. The line $y = x$ is rotated clockwise until it lies along the $x$-axis.
   (a) What is the gradient of the new line?
   (b) What is the equation of the new line?

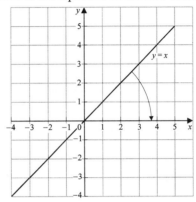

---

## 9.4 Positive and negative gradients

*Example 3*

Find the gradients of these two lines:

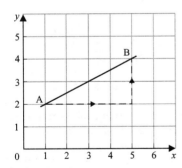

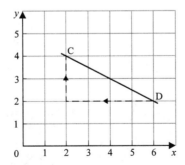

Vertical distance from A to B = 2

Horizontal distance from A to B = 4 in the positive direction →

Gradient $= \frac{2}{4} = \frac{1}{2}$

Vertical distance from C to D = 2

Horizontal distance from C to D = 4 in the negative direction ←

Gradient $= \frac{2}{-4} = -\frac{1}{2}$

Both lines have the same steepness but the gradients are not the same. One gradient is positive and the other is negative.

Graphs that run this way are positive.

Graphs that run this way are negative.

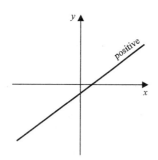

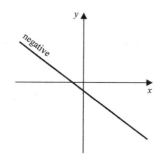

*Example 4*

Find the gradient of the line passing through the points $(2, 6)$ and $(6, 4)$.

First sketch the information.

Use the sketch to help find the gradient.

Vertical distance $\qquad 6 - 4 = 2$

Horizontal distance $\qquad 2 - 6 = -4$

Gradient $= \frac{-4}{2} = -2$

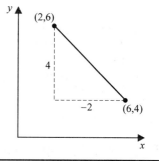

### Exercise 9D

1. Work out the gradients of these lines.

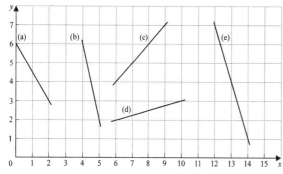

(b) What is the gradient of the line passing through points A and C?

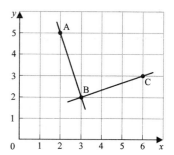

2. Sketch the pairs of coordinate points. Find the gradient of the straight line joining them.
   (a) $(0, 4)$ and $(4, 2)$    (b) $(1, 7)$ and $(3, 1)$
   (c) $(5, 2)$ and $(7, 7)$    (d) $(-4, 7)$ and $(-7, 4)$
   (e) $(-1, 0)$ and $(6, -1)$    (f) $(1, 2)$ and $(4, 4)$
   (g) $(-1, -3)$ and $(2, 4)$    (h) $(4, 2)$ and $(-3, -4)$
   (i) $(-2, 5)$ and $(2, -1)$    (j) $(5, 10)$ and $(-5, 2)$

3. (a) Find the gradients of the lines AB and BC.

4. Martin works out the gradient of several lines. He puts his findings in a table of results.

| Line | (a) | (b) | (c) | (d) | (e) | (f) | (g) | (h) |
|---|---|---|---|---|---|---|---|---|
| Gradient | $-3$ | $\frac{-5}{2}$ | $\frac{1}{3}$ | $0.5$ | $\frac{3}{6}$ | $\frac{-2}{5}$ | $\frac{-5}{-2}$ | $0.4$ |

(a) How many of the lines have negative gradients?
(b) How many lines have a gradient less than 1?
(c) Which lines are parallel to each other?
(d) Work out which pairs of lines are at right angles to each other?

## 9.5 Straight line graphs not through the origin

Here is a graph of $y = x$

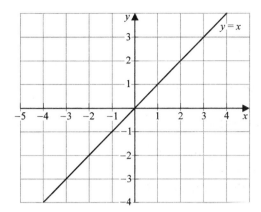

The line can be translated up:

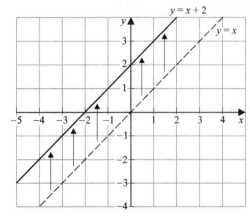

The line $y = x$ has moved up 2. This is $+2$.

The **equation** of the line is now $y = x + \underline{2}$.

The line crosses the $y$-axis at $y = +2$.

$+2$ is the $y$-intercept.

The line can be translated down:

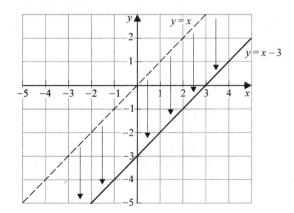

The line $y = x$ has moved down 3. This is $-3$.

The **equation** of the line is now $y = x - \underline{3}$.

The line crosses the $y$-axis at $y = -3$.

$-3$ is the $y$-intercept.

*Remember*: translating a graph upwards moves it in a positive direction ↑
translating a graph downwards moves it in a negative direction ↓

The formula of a straight line is the relationship between the $x$-coordinate and the $y$-coordinate. All straight lines have a formula of the form $y = mx + c$ where $m$ is the gradient and $c$ is the $y$-intercept.

*Note*: Sometimes the word 'equation' is used instead of 'formula' when talking about straight line graphs, as in the following example.

### Example 5

A straight line has the equation $y = 3x + 2$. Write down the gradient and the $y$-intercept.

$y = mx + c$
$y = 3x + 2$
The gradient $= 3$, the $y$-intercept $= 2$.

---

### Exercise 9E

1. The equation of the line AB is $y = 2x$
   (a) The line AB is translated up 2 to give line CD. Write down the equation of the line CD.
   (b) The line AB is translated down 3 to give line EF. Write down the equation of the line EF.

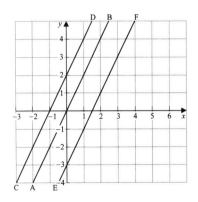

2. Write down:
   (a) the gradient of line (i)
   (b) the equation of line (i)
   (c) the equation of line (ii)

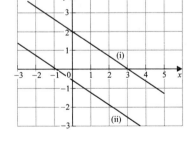

3. Copy the diagram on the right.
   (a) On your diagram draw the line $y = \frac{1}{2}x$
   (b) Use this line to draw the line $y = \frac{1}{2}x - 3$

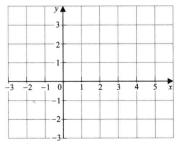

4. Write down the gradient and the $y$-intercept of these lines. Do not draw the lines.
   (a) $y = 5x + 6$   (b) $y = -5x - 4$
   (c) $y = \frac{3}{4}x - \frac{1}{2}$   (d) $y = 0.6x + 1.8$

5. Sketch the line $y = 5x + 12$. Then sketch the line $y = 5x + 15$ on the same axes.
   The line $y = 5x + 15$ is reflected in the line $y = 5x + 12$ to give a new line.
   Write down the equation of the new line.

6. Write down the equations of these lines.

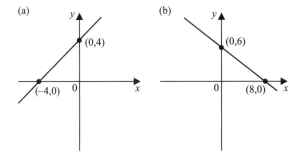

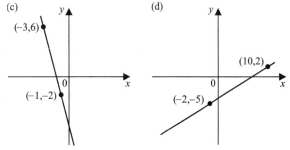

## 9.6 Drawing straight line graphs

All straight line graphs have a formula of the form $y = mx + c$, where $m$ is the gradient and $c$ is the amount of translation from $(0, 0)$.

$c$ is called the $y$-intercept and is the value of $y$ where the line crosses the $y$-axis.

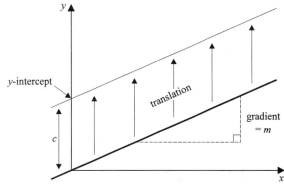

### Exercise 9F

1. (a) Copy and complete this table:

| $x$ | 1 | 2 | 3 | 4 | 5 | 6 |
|---|---|---|---|---|---|---|
| $y$ | 0 | 2 | 4 | 6 | | |

   (b) Plot the points on graph paper. Join them with a straight line.
   (c) By using your graph or otherwise, write down the value of the gradient and the $y$-intercept of the line.
   (d) Write down the equation of the line.

2. (a) Copy and complete this table:

| $x$ | $-2$ | $-1$ | 0 | 1 | 2 | 3 | 4 |
|---|---|---|---|---|---|---|---|
| $y$ | 2 | 0 | $-2$ | $-4$ | | | |

   (b) Plot each point on graph paper. Join them with a straight line.
   (c) Write down the equation of the line.

3. In a 'think of a number' game the instructions are 'think of a number, multiply by 3 and then add 4'.
   (a) Draw a table of the answers you get when the starting number is 3, 5 and 8.
   (b) Plot the points from your table on graph paper. Join them with a straight line.
   (c) Find the equation of the line.
   (d) Use your graph to find the starting number when the answer is 14.

## 9.7 Using graphs to solve problems

*Example 6*

Peter wins £30 in a 'spot the ball' competition. He decides to save the money towards a holiday. Each week after his win he saves a further £8.

(a) Draw a table to show the amount Peter has saved during the first 7 weeks.

(b) Write down a formula for working out Peter's savings, $S$, after $n$ weeks.

(c) Explain, with reasons, what a graph of the savings formula would look like.

(d) Sketch the graph of the formula.

(a)

| Week | 0 | 1 | 2 | 3 | 4 | 5 | 6 | 7 |
|------|---|---|---|---|---|---|---|---|
| Amount saved | 30 | 38 | 46 | 54 | 62 | 70 | 78 | 86 |

(b) The constant difference between his weekly savings is £8. This tells us two things:

 (i)   the relationship is linear

 (ii)   it is of the form $S = 8n + c$

Looking at the 1st week with savings of £38

$$38 = (8 \times 1) + c$$

So $c = 30$ and the formula is $S = 8n + 30$

(c) The formula    $S = 8n + 30$

is of the form   $y = mx + c$

The graph must be a straight line. The gradient is 8 and the $y$-intercept is 30.

(d)

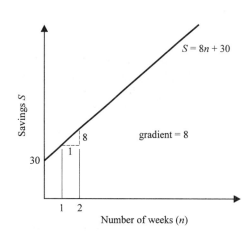

## Worked exam question 1

June is getting married. She wants to hire a hall for her wedding reception. She obtains two quotations giving the charges.

(a) The local church hall charges £30 plus £10 per guest.

    (i) Complete the table for the charges made by the church hall.

| Number of guests | 10 | 30 | 50 | 70 | 90 |
|---|---|---|---|---|---|
| Charge (£) | 130 | 330 | 530 | 730 | 930 |

    (ii) On the grid opposite plot the points and draw a graph to show the charges mades.

(b) (i) The local hotel has a function room. Their charges are calculated from the formula:

$$C = \frac{5N}{2} + 500$$

    where $C$ is the charge and $N$ is the number of guests. Complete this table for the charges made by the hotel.

| Number of guests | 0 | 20 | 40 | 80 |
|---|---|---|---|---|
| Charge (£) | 500 | 550 | 600 | 700 |

    (ii) On the grid opposite plot the points to show the charges made by the hotel.

(c) What do the two graphs tell you about the charges made?

*The graphs cross between 62 and 63 guests. Where the graphs cross is where the charges for the church hall and the hotel are the same. For up to 62 guests the hire of the church hall is cheaper. For 63 guests and over the hire of the hotel is cheaper*

---

**Do:**
Calculate the charges according to the rule: multiply the number of guests by 10 and add on 30

Show your working

$(50 \times 10) + 30 = 530$
$(70 \times 10) + 30 = 730$
$(90 \times 10) + 30 = 930$

**Do:**
Calculate the charges according to the formula: multiply the number of guests by 5, divide by 2 and add on 500

Show your working

$\dfrac{5 \times 20}{2} + 500 = 550$
$\dfrac{5 \times 40}{2} + 500 = 600$
$\dfrac{5 \times 80}{2} + 500 = 700$

**Do:**
Say where the graphs cross and what it means that the graphs cross

Explain when the church hall is cheaper and when the hotel is cheaper

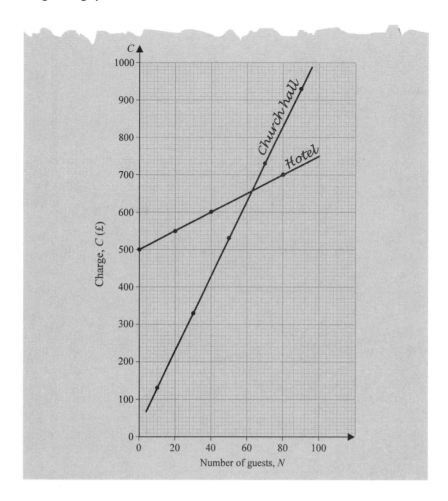

### Exercise 9G

1. The instructions for finding the total cooking time for a turkey are: 'Cook for 45 minutes per kilogram and add 20 minutes'
   (a) Copy and complete this table:

   | Weight (kg) | 1 | 2 | 3 | 4 | 5 | 6 |
   |---|---|---|---|---|---|---|
   | Cooking time (min) | 65 | 110 | | | | |

   (b) Find a formula for working out the total cooking time of a turkey weighing $n$ kilograms.
   (c) Explain how your formula is related to the straight line formula $y = mx + c$. Sketch the graph of your formula.

2. When a ball is dropped from the top of a tower it always bounces back to a quarter of the height of the tower.

   (a) Copy and complete this table:

   | Height of tower $h$ (metres) | 0 | 4 | 8 | 12 | 16 | 20 | 24 |
   |---|---|---|---|---|---|---|---|
   | Height ball bounced $b$ (metres) | 0 | 1 | 2 | | | | |

   (b) On squared paper draw a graph of height $h$ against bounce $b$.
   (c) Write down a formula connecting $h$ and $b$.
   (d) Use your graph to find $b$ when $h = 15$.
   (e) Use your graph to find $h$ when $b = 2.4$.

3. Abdul orders 24 boxes of chocolates to sell over Christmas.
   He finds that he sells 4 boxes of chocolates a day. He does not order any more boxes.

3. (a) Copy and complete this table:

| Number of days ($d$) | 0 | 1 | 2 | | | | |
|---|---|---|---|---|---|---|---|
| Number of boxes left ($n$) | 24 | 20 | | 12 | 8 | | 0 |

(b) Find a formula connecting the number of boxes of chocolates and the number of days.
(c) Sketch a graph of your formula.
(d) Explain how your formula relates to the general formula of a straight line $y = mx + c$.

4. The speedometer on Selina's car developed a fault. She took it to the garage to be checked. The mechanic took the car for a test drive and found these results

| Speedo meter reading, $S$ (mph) | 10 | 20 | 25 | 45 | 60 |
|---|---|---|---|---|---|
| True reading, $T$ (mph) | 12 | 20 | 23 | 42 | 56 |

(a) Draw axes with $S$ horizontal from 0 to 80 and $T$ vertical also from 0 to 80.
(b) Plot the points and draw a straight line through as many points as you can.
(c) Find the equation of the line.
(d) When Selina's speedometer indicates 30 mph what is her true speed?
(e) The legal maximum speed in the UK is 70 mph. What is the reading on the speedometer when the true speed is 70 mph?

5. Peter decides to go on a diet in order to lose weight. However his bathroom scales are not very accurate and so he takes them to his local hardware shop to be tested.
The shop finds these results:

| Indicated weight (kg) | 5 | 15 | 30 | 45 | 55 |
|---|---|---|---|---|---|
| True weight (kg) | 3 | 15 | 32 | 49 | 63 |

(a) Plot these values on graph paper.
(b) Find the equation of the best line you can draw to fit this data.
(c) Peter's true weight is 75 kg. He loses 10 kg. How much weight do his scales indicate that he has lost?

6. Toby has a remote-controlled model car. He carried out an experiment to see how far it could travel in a certain amount of time.
These were his results:

| Time taken $T$ (seconds) | 2 | 3 | 4 | 5 | 6 |
|---|---|---|---|---|---|
| Distance $D$ (metres) | 28 | 40 | 52 | 64 | 76 |

Toby wanted to find a relationship between the distance travelled and the time taken.
(a) On graph paper draw these axes and draw a graph of $D$ against $T$.
(b) Find a relationship between $T$ and $D$ in the form $T = aD + c$ giving the values of $a$ and $c$.

# 9.8 Drawing graphs of ax + by = c

We have looked at lines whose equations are written in the form $y = mx + c$. This is called 'gradient–intercept form'. $m$ is the gradient and $c$ is the amount of translation from $(0,0)$, or where the line cuts the $y$-axis.

Sometimes the formula of a line is not given in the form $y = mx + c$.

*Example 7*

Draw a graph of the equation $3x + 2y = 6$

We could rearrange the equation in the form $y = mx + c$ but this is not necessary.

To draw the line, first find where it crosses both axes.

Where the line crosses the $y$-axis $x = 0$, so
$$(3 \times 0) + 2y = 6$$
$$y = 3$$

The line crosses the $y$-axis at the point $(0, 3)$.

Where the line cuts the $x$-axis $y = 0$, so
$$3x + (2 \times 0) = 6$$
$$3x = 6$$
$$x = 2$$

which gives the point $(2, 0)$.

The two points $(0, 3)$ and $(2, 0)$ are on the line $3x + 2y = 6$.

We can plot them and join them with a straight line.

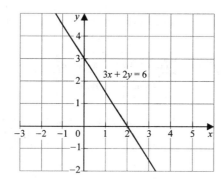

### Exercise 9H

1. Use the method of Example 7 to draw graphs of these equations.
   (a) $3x + 4y = 12$    (b) $2x + 6y = 12$
   (c) $5x + 2y = 10$    (d) $3x - 2y = 6$
   (e) $4y - 2x = 8$    (f) $3x + 5y = 15$
   (g) $3x + 4y = -12$    (h) $4x - 2y = -10$
   (i) $2x + 2y = 7$

2. (a) Draw these two lines on the same set of axes.
      (i) $x + y = 3$  (ii) $2x - y = -6$
   (b) Write down the coordinates of the point where the two lines intersect.

## 9.9 Finding points on the line ax + by = c

Substituting $x = 0$ and $y = 0$ into an equation sometimes gives values that are difficult to plot accurately on graph paper.

*Example 8*

$$\text{Draw the line } 2x + 3y = 8$$
$$\text{When } x = 0 \quad 3y = 8$$
$$y = 2.3333\ldots$$

which is not easy to plot accurately.

It is better to try another value of $x$.

When $x = 1$

$$2 + 3y = 8$$
$$3y = 6$$
$$y = 2$$

which gives the point $(1, 2)$

when $y = 0$     $2x = 8$
$$x = 4$$

which gives the point $(4, 0)$

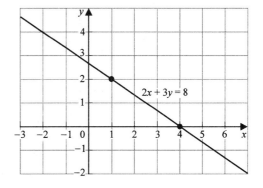

The two points $(1, 2)$ and $(4, 0)$ are on the
line $2x + 3y = 8$.

We plot them and join them with a straight line.

---

**Exercise 9I**

1. Draw the graphs of these equations.
   - (a) $3x + y = 2$      use $x = 0$ and $y = -1$
   - (b) $3x + 2y = 7$      use $x = 1$ and $y = -1$
   - (c) $5x - 4y = 1$      use $x = 5$ and $y = 1$
   - (d) $4x - 3y = 11$      use $x = 2$ and $y = 3$
   - (e) $2x + 5y = 12$      use $x = 1$ and $y = 0$

2. Draw the graphs of these equations. Choose
   your own values of $x$ and $y$.
   - (a) $4x - 3y = 1$      (b) $2x + 3y = 19$
   - (c) $2x - 5y = 8$      (d) $3x + 4y = 0$
   - (e) $2x + 3y = 2.5$      (f) $6x + 3y = 51$

---

# 9.10 Simultaneous equations

A pair of equations that can both be satisfied by one value of $x$
and one value of $y$ are called **simultaneous equations**.

For example:

$$x + y = 3$$
$$2x - y = -6$$

are both satisfied by the values $x = -1$ and $y = 4$.

In an exam you may be asked to solve simultaneous equations by
a graphical method. To do this you need to draw the graphs of the
equations on a coordinate diagram and find the cordinates of the
point where they cross.

### Example 9

Solve these simultaneous equations by a graphical
method

$$x + y = 3$$
$$2x - y = -6$$

Draw a graph of $x + y = 3$

When $x = 0$, $y = 3$, which gives the point $(0, 3)$

When $y = 0$, $x = 3$, which gives the point $(3, 0)$

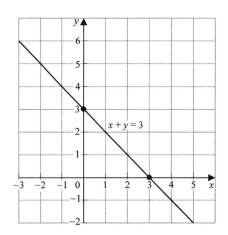

Draw a graph of $2x - y = -6$ on the same axes.

When $x = 0$, $y = 6$, which gives the point $(0, 6)$

When $y = 0$, $2x = -6x = -3$

which gives the point $(-3, 0)$

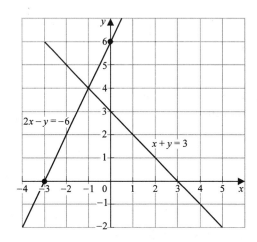

From the graph we see that the two lines cross at the point $(-1, 4)$.
The values $x = -1$ and $y = 4$ must satisfy both the equations.
Check that these values satisfy both the equations:

$$-1 + 4 = 3 \quad \text{correct}$$
$$-2 - 4 = -6 \quad \text{correct}$$

So $x = -1$ and $y = 4$ are correct solutions of the simultaneous equations

$$x + y = 3$$
$$2x - y = -6$$

### Exercise 9J

1. (a) Plot the two equations $x - y = 1$ and
   $x + 2y = 7$ on a set of axes.
   (b) Use your graph to show that the solution to
   the simultaneous equations
   $$x - y = 1$$
   $$x + 2y = 7$$
   is $x = 3$ and $y = 2$

2. Solve these pairs of simultaneous equations by a
   graphical method.
   (a) $x + 3y = 0$              (b) $x - 2y = 1$
       $x - 3y = 6$                  $2x + y = 2$
   (c) $x - y = 0$               (d) $4x - 2y = 7$
       $3x - y = -2$                $x + 3y = 7$

   (e) $4x + 3y = 9$            (f) $5x + 3y = 1$
       $2x + 5y = 15$              $2x + 3y = -5$
   (g) $2x + 3y = 29$          (h) $2x - 5y = 8$
       $3x + 2y = 16$              $3x - 7y = 11$

3. (a) Try to solve the simultaneous equations
   $x + y = 4$ and $3x + 3y = 18$ by a graphical
   method.
   (b) Comment on what you notice.

4. (a) Try to solve the simultaneous equations
   $2x + 3y = 12$ and $8x + 12y = 48$ by a
   graphical method.
   (b) Comment on what you notice.

## 9.11 Inconsistent equations

When two lines are parallel to each other their equations are called
**inconsistent** and they have no solutions.

The equations in Exercise **9J** question **3** are inconsistent. The first
equation is $x + y = 4$. The second is $3x + 3y = 18$. Dividing
$3x + 3y = 18$ by 3 it becomes $x + y = 6$.

But $x + y$ cannot equal 4 and 6 at the same time. The two lines are
parallel.

When the two equations give the same line they are said to have
infinitely many solutions. Every point on the line fits both
equations. For example, in Exercise 9J question 4 the two
equations give the same line and so have infinitely many solutions.

### Exercise 9K

Study these pairs of simultaneous equations. Try to decide which have (a) one solution, (b) no
solution (c) infinitely many solutions.

1. $3x + 2y = 18$    2. $3x + 5y = 12$    3. $3x + 4y = 24$    4. $4x - 5y = 9$
     $9x + 6y = 54$     $12x + 20y = 48$      $x + 2y = 18$     $-8x + 10y = -18$

### Worked exam question 2

The cost of a journey with Sylvester Taxis is £0.80 a mile.

(a) Work out the cost of using Sylvester Taxis for journeys of 10, 30 and 50 miles.

(a) miles  cost

**Do:**
Show your working

$10 \times 80 = 800p = £8$

$30 \times 80 = 2400p = £24$

$50 \times 80 = 4000p = £40$

10  £ __8__

30  £ __24__

50  £ __40__

(b) Plot this information on the grid opposite and join the points with a straight line.

The cost of a journey with Ekebusi Motors is worked out by the formula

$$\text{Cost in £} = \frac{D}{2} + 12$$

where $D$ is the distance in miles.

(c) Work out the cost of using Ekebusi Motors for journeys of 10, 30 and 50 miles.

(c) miles  cost

**Do:**
Substitute the values for D into the formula

$Cost = \frac{10}{2} + 12 = £17$

$Cost = \frac{30}{2} + 12 = £27$

$Cost = \frac{50}{2} + 12 = £37$

10  £ __17__

30  £ __27__

50  £ __37__

(d) Plot this information on the same grid and join the points with a straight line.

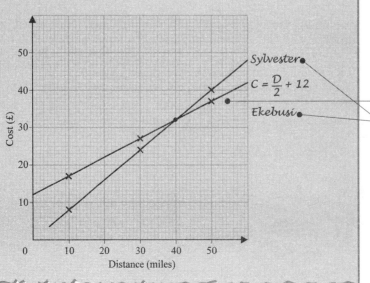

**Do:**
Mark the points with crosses

Label your lines

(e)  Use your graph to find the distance for which the costs are the same.

(e) __40__ miles

**Do:**
Mark where the lines cross on the graph

*lines meet when distance = 40 miles*

..................................................................................................................

..................................................................................................................

(MEG)

## Worked exam question 3

Solve the simultaneous equations

$$7x + 2y = 14$$
$$5x + 4y = 20$$

*7x + 2y =14*

*When x = 0   2y = 14*
                *y = 7*     *which gives the point (0, 7)*

*When y = 0   7x = 14*
                *x = 2*     *which gives the point (2, 0)*

**Do:**
Find two points on each line

Make x = 0 and solve for y

Make y = 0 and solve for x

*5x + 4y = 20*

*When x = 0   4y = 20*
                *y = 5*     *which gives the point (0, 5)*

*When y = 0   5x = 20*
                *x = 4*     *which gives the point (4, 0)*

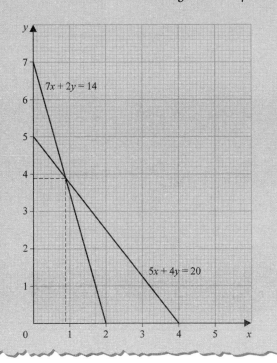

*The lines intersect at the point x = 0.9, y = 3.9*
*Check*

$$7x + 2y = (7 \times 0.9) + (2 + 3.9)$$
$$= 14.1$$

*The solutions are correct to 1 decimal place.*

**Do:**
Check your answer by substituting back in one of the equations

## Worked exam question 4

Fifty-one students went to a pop concert.

Let $x$ represent the number of men.

Let $y$ represent the number of women.

The number of women is related to the number of men by the two equations

$$x + y = 51$$
$$y = 2x + 3$$

The line $x + y = 51$ has been drawn.

(a) Draw the line $y = 2x + 3$.

*When x = 0, y = 3*
*When x = 10, y = 20 + 3*
*= 23*

**Do:**
Find 2 points on the line

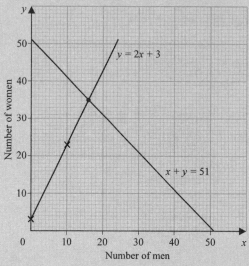

**Do:**
Show your working

Plot your points on the graph and join them with a straight line

**Do:**
Mark on the graph where the two lines cross

Explain where you found the answer on the graph

(b) Use the graph to write down the number of men and women who went to the pop concert.

*lines cross when men = 16 women = 35*

..........16.......... men

..........35.......... women

(SEG)

# 9.12 Conversion graphs

A conversion graph is a straight line graph which is used to convert from one measurement to another measurement.

Some common examples of conversion graphs are for changing a temperature measured in °C to °F, changing miles to kilometres or changing from one currency to another.

### Example 10

5 miles is approximately the same distance as 8 kilometres.

Draw the graph for converting kilometres to miles.

Use the graph to convert

(a) 14 kilometres to miles

(b) 14 miles to kilometres.

5 miles = 8 kilometres and 0 miles = 0 kilometres, so join the two points to make a straight line.

It is a good idea to extend this line so that you can use it to convert higher values.

(a) Draw a line across from 14 kilometres until it reaches the line, then draw down to find that 14 kilometres is approximately 8.8 miles.

(b) Draw a line up from 14 miles until it reaches the line, then draw across to find that 14 miles is approximately 22.4 kilometres.

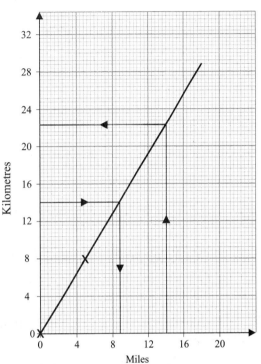

---

### Exercise 9L

1 This graph can be used to convert between degrees Celsius (°C) and degrees Fahrenheit (°F).

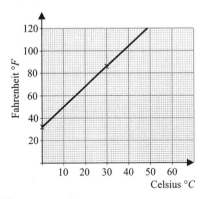

Convert
(a) 0°C to °F
(b) 45°C to °F
(c) 100°F to °C.

2 This graph can be used to convert between gallons and litres.

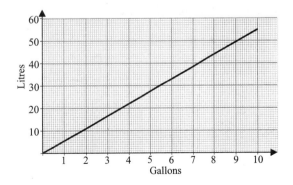

Use the graph to convert
(a) 6 gallons to litres
(b) 44 litres to gallons
(c) 55 litres to gallons.

## 9.13 Distance - time graphs

Distance - time graphs are used to show information about journeys. The horizontal axis is used for time and the vertical axis is used for distance.

### *Example 11*

Kaylesh travels by car from her home in London to Nottingham and back. She leaves homes at 7 am and travels 90 miles in 2 hours when she stops to have a cup of coffee for 30 minutes. She then drives a further 50 miles and arrives in Nottingham at 10.30 am.
She leaves Nottingham at 2 pm and drives straight back, arriving home at 4.30 pm.

(a) Draw a distance - time graph to illustrate her journey.

(b) Calculate her average speed for each section of her journey.

(a) The total distance from London to Nottingham is 140 miles so the vertical axis goes up to 140.

The horizontal axis starts at 7 am and ends at 4.30 pm.

For the first section, she starts at 7 am, 0 miles away and finishes at 9 am, 90 miles away.

For the second section, she stays at 90 miles away for 30 minutes until 9.30 am.

For the third section, she finishes 140 miles away at 10.30 am.

For the fourth section, she stays 140 miles away until 2 pm.

For the last section, she travels the 140 miles back home, arriving at 4.30 pm.

So the graph looks like this:

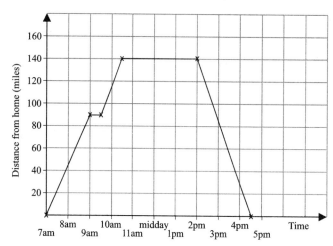

(b) average speed $= \dfrac{\text{distance travelled}}{\text{time taken}}$

First section:  average speed $= \dfrac{90 \text{ miles}}{2 \text{ hours}}$

$= 45$ m.p.h.

Second section: no speed as she has stopped.

Third section:  average speed $= \dfrac{50 \text{ miles}}{1 \text{ hour}}$

$= 50$ m.p.h.

Fourth section: no speed as she has stopped.

Fifth section:  average speed $= \dfrac{140 \text{ miles}}{2\frac{1}{2} \text{ hours}}$

$= 56$ m.p.h.

---

## Exercise 9M

1. Alison leaves her home at 9 am. She runs 1500 metres in 6 minutes then she stops for 14 minutes. She runs the 1500 metres back home which takes her 10 minutes.
   Draw a distance-time graph for Alison's run.

2. Mary walks from her home to the shops and back. Her journey is represented by this distance-time graph

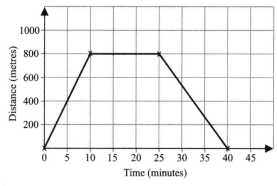

(a) How far is it to the shop?
(b) How long was Mary in the shop?
(c) Calculate Mary's average speed in metres per hour, on her journey from the shop back to her home.
Mary left home at 11.50 am.
(d) What time did Mary get back home from the shop?

3. The railway journey from Sudbury to Marks Tey is 15 miles each way. A train leaves Sudbury at 06.30 and travels at a constant speed to Marks Tey. It arrives at Marks Tey at 06.50 and waits there for 15 minutes before returning to Sudbury at the same speed as the outward journey.
   (a) At what time will the train arrive back at Sudbury?
   (b) Draw the distance-time graph for the trains journey from Sudbury to Marks Tey and back.

4. This distance-time graph represents Ravi's journey from his home to school and back.

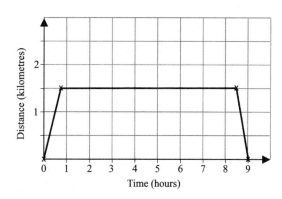

Describe fully what the three sections OA, AB and BC, of the graph represent.

### Exercise 9N (Mixed questions)

1. A ball is dropped from a height of $h$ metres. It bounces back to a height of $b$ metres.
   The ball bounces back to $\frac{2}{5}$ of the height from which it is dropped.
   (a) Write down a formula connecting $b$ and $h$.
   (b) For values of $h$ from 0 to 20 m plot the graph of $b$ against $h$.

2. Draw these graphs. Find the gradient and the $y$-intercept for each one.
   (a) $y = 3x + 1$       (b) $y = 2x - 5$
   (c) $y = -x + 3$       (d) $y - x = 1$
   (e) $y = -2x + 1$      (f) $y = 3 - x$
   (g) $y + 3x = 2$       (h) $2y - 5x = 6$
   (i) $3y + 2x = 5$      (j) $2x - 6y = 8$

3. (a) For values of $x$ from $-5$ to 5, draw the graphs of
   $$y = -x + 3$$
   $$2y - 3x = 2$$
   (b) Use your graphs to solve the simultaneous equations:

$$y = -x + 3$$
$$2y - 3x = 2$$

4. By drawing suitable graphs, solve the simultaneous equations:
   $$2y + x = 3$$
   $$y - 3x = 5$$

5. A company pays its travelling sales people by one of two schemes of payment.
   Under **scheme A** the company pays a sales person:
   'A fixed payment of £30 per day plus 50p for every mile travelled'.
   Under **scheme B** the company pays a sales person:
   'A fixed payment of £12 per day plus 70p for every mile travelled'.
   By drawing suitable graphs, or otherwise, work out the distance a sales person has to travel in one day for the company to pay out the same amount under each scheme.

---

## Test yourself

**1.** The function $x \rightarrow 4x - 2$ has input $\{0, 2, 4, 6, 8\}$

QUESTION   (a)   Draw an input/output diagram.

ANSWER

| Input | Output |
|-------|--------|
| 0 | −2 |
| 2 | 6 |
| 4 | 14 |
| 6 | 22 |
| 8 | 30 |

*If your answer is incorrect review page 165, Section 9.2 on graphing functions*

---

QUESTION   (b)   Write down the inputs and outputs as pairs of coordinates.

ANSWER   $(0, -2)(2, 6)(4, 14)(6, 22)$
$(8, 30)$

*If your answer is incorrect review page 165, Section 9.2 on graphing functions*

**QUESTION**    (c)    Plot the points on a coordinate diagram. Join them with a straight line.

**ANSWER**

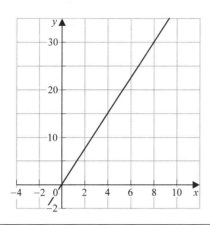

*If your answer is incorrect review page 165, Section 9.2 on graphing functions*

---

**2.**

**QUESTION**    Work out the gradients of these two lines.

(a)

(b)

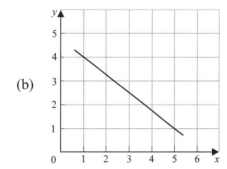

**ANSWER**    (a) $\frac{2}{6} = \frac{1}{3}$    (b) $\frac{-3}{-4} = -\frac{3}{4}$    *If your answer is incorrect review page 169, Section 9.4 Example 3 on positive and negative gradients*

---

**3.**    The equation of line AB is $y = 2x - 4$

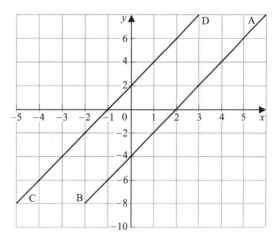

**QUESTION**   Write down the equation of the line CD.

**ANSWER**   $y = 2x + 2$    *If your answer is incorrect review page 171, Section 9.5 on graphs not through the origin*

---

**4.**

**QUESTION**   Work out the equations of these lines.

**ANSWER**

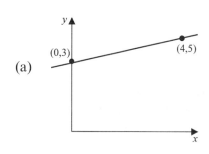

(a)

(b)

**ANSWER**   (a)   $y = \frac{1}{2}x + 3$    *If your answer is incorrect review page 173,*
(b)   $y = -2x + 6$    *Section 9.6 on drawing straight line graphs*

---

**5.**

**QUESTION**   Write down two pairs of coordinates that you could use to plot a graph of the equation $3x + 5y = 15$

**ANSWER**   $(0, 3)(5, 0)$    *There are other possible answers. See your teacher.*

---

**6.**   The graph of $y = 2x + 3$ is drawn on the axes below.

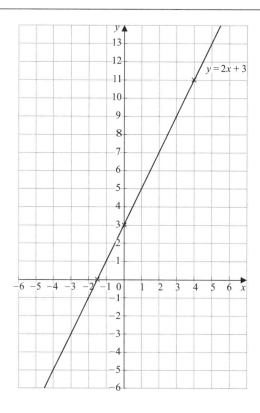

**QUESTION**    (a)    Copy the axes. On the same axes plot the graph of $3x - y = 1$

**ANSWER**

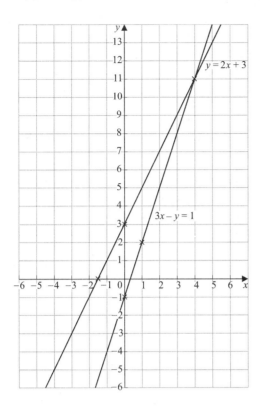

*If your answer is incorrect review page 177, Section 9.8 on drawing graphs of $ax + by = c$*

---

**QUESTION**    (b)    Use your graphs to solve the simultaneous equations

$$y = 2x + 3$$
$$3x - y = 1$$

**ANSWER**    $x = 4$, $y = 11$

*If your answer is incorrect review page 179, Section 9.10 on simultaneous equations*

---

7.    Jenny owns a small motorbike. One day she leaves home at 12:00 noon. She rides to a café, has a meal at the café and then rides back home. This graph represents Jenny's journey.

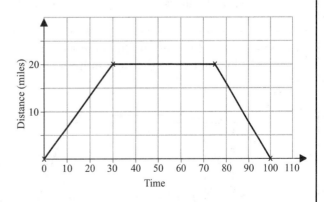

| | |
|---|---|
| **QUESTION** | (a)   How far is it from Jenny's home to the café? |
| **ANSWER** | 20 miles                    *If your answer is incorrect review page 186, Section 9.13 on Distance - time graphs* |

| | |
|---|---|
| **QUESTION** | (b)   Work out Jenny's average speed on the journey from her home to the café. |
| **ANSWER** | 40 m.p.h.                    *If your answer is incorrect review page 186, Section 9.13 on Distance - time graphs* |

| | |
|---|---|
| **QUESTION** | (c)   How much time did Jenny spend at the café? |
| **ANSWER** | 45 minutes                    *If your answer is incorrect review page 186, Section 9.13 on Distance - time graphs* |

| | |
|---|---|
| **QUESTION** | (d)   At what time did Jenny arrive back home? |
| **ANSWER** | 13:40 (or 1:40 pm)                    *If your answer is incorrect review page 186, Section 9.13 on Distance - time graphs* |

**QUESTION**   This graph can be used to convert between miles and kilometres.

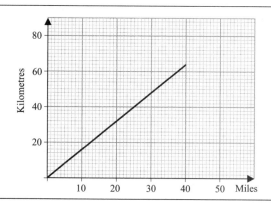

| | |
|---|---|
| **QUESTION** | (e)   Use the graph to convert:<br>      (i)    30 miles to kilometres<br>      (ii)   60 kilometres to miles |
| **ANSWER** | (i) 48 km                    *If your answer is incorrect review page 185, section*<br>(ii) 37.5 miles               *9.12 on conversion graphs* |

| | |
|---|---|
| **QUESTION** | (f)   Re-draw the travel graph at the start of question 7, showing the distance in kilometres to the time in hours |
| **ANSWER** | 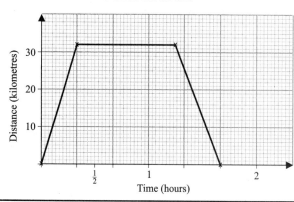          *If your answer is incorrect review page 186, Section 9.13 on Distance - time graphs* |

# Summary of key points to remember

1. The measure of steepness of a graph is called its **gradient**.

2. To find the gradient of a line divide the vertical distance between two points by the horizontal distance between the same two points.

   For the line AB

   $$\text{gradient} = \frac{\text{vertical distance from A to B}}{\text{horizontal distance from A to B}}$$

   $$= \frac{2}{4} = \frac{1}{2}$$

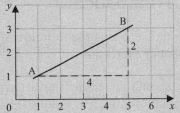

3. The amount of vertical translation of a line from the point $(0,0)$ is called the $y$-intercept.

   The $y$-intercept is the value of $y$ where the line crosses the $y$-axis.

4. All straight line graphs have a formula of the form $y = mx + c$ where $m$ is the gradient and $c$ is the $y$-intercept.

5. To plot a graph of a straight line given in the form

   $$ax + by = c$$

   first make $x = 0$ and solve for $y$

   then make $y = 0$ and solve for $x$.

   If this gives values that are difficult to plot, try other values of $x$.

6. To find the solution of two simultaneous equations by a graphical method, draw the graphs of the two equations on the same set of axes. The solution is the value of $x$ and $y$ where the two lines cross.

7. Two simultaneous equations whose graphs are parallel lines have no solution. The equations are called **inconsistent**.

8. Two simultaneous equations whose graphs are the same line have infinitely many solutions.

# 10 Manipulating algebra

## 10.1 Introduction

This unit explains the techniques of manipulating **algebraic** (or **symbolic**) **expressions**.

You should remember that letters, such as $x$ or $b$, can be used to represent numbers or quantities, and that:

- $2x$ means 2 multiplied by $x$

- $3b$ means 3 multiplied by $b$

- $x^2$ means $x \times x$
  $x^2$ is read '$x$ squared'

- $y^3$ means $y \times y \times y$
  $y^3$ is read '$y$ cubed'

- $7r^2$ means $7 \times r \times r$ which is the same as $r \times r \times 7$.

The terms $2x$, $3b$, $x^2$, $y^3$ and $7r^2$ are algebraic expressions. Note that $x$ can mean $1x$, which equals $1 \times x$. It can also just mean $x$.

$2t$ is an **expression**. $y = 2t$ is a **formula**, and $2t = 6$ is an **equation**.

In this unit you will learn how to collect together the terms in algebraic expressions. You will also learn the role that brackets play in algebra, what the term 'factorising' means, what a 'quadratic expression' is, and how to rearrange formulae.

This branch of algebra is extremely important, especially you need to know the techniques covered in this unit to achieve the higher grades at GCSE.

## 10.2 Collecting like terms

If you have a long algebraic expression it may be sensible to shorten or **simplify** it.

It can sometimes help to think of the expression in terms of a physical image. For example, suppose that $3b$ means 3 black discs (●●●), and $2w$ means 2 white discs (○○).

Then, if you are asked to simplify the expression

$$3b \quad + \quad 2w + \quad 4b \quad + w$$
$$(\bullet\bullet\bullet + \circ\circ + \bullet\bullet\bullet\bullet + \circ)$$

'simplify' can be taken to mean 'put all the black discs together and all the white discs together', and so

$$3b + 2w + 4b + w = \quad 7b \quad + \quad 3w$$
$$(\bullet\bullet\bullet\bullet\bullet\bullet\bullet + \circ\circ\circ)$$

### Example 1

Simplify these expressions:

(a) $2x + 4y + 4x + 3y$  (b) $5a + 3b + 4a - b - 2a$

(a) $2x + 4y + 4x + 3y$

Putting all the $x$ terms and the $y$ terms together gives

$$2x + 4x + 4y + 3y$$

which gives

$$6x + 7y$$

(b) $5a + 3b + 4a - b - 2a$

Putting all the $a$ terms and all the $b$ terms together gives

$$5a + 4a - 2a + 3b - b$$

which is

$$7a + 2b$$

Doing these problems using mental pictures such as black and white discs can help with initial understanding. Another way of tackling them is to use cards with the terms of the expressions written on them.

For example, you can work out the problems in Example 1 using cards:

Write each term with its plus or minus sign, on a separate card:

$$2x + 4y + 4x + 3y$$

| $2x$ | $+4y$ | $+4x$ | $+3y$ |
|------|-------|-------|-------|

Then re-arrange the cards so that all the $x$ terms are together and all the $y$ terms are together.

| $2x$ | $+4x$ | $+4y$ | $+3y$ |
|------|-------|-------|-------|

So the expression is equal to $6x + 7y$

The cards for the second problem are:

| $5a$ | $+3b$ | $+4a$ | $-b$ | $-2a$ |

which are re-arranged into the following order:

| $5a$ | $+4a$ | $-2a$ | $+3b$ | $-b$ |

You can then see that the expression is equal to $7a + 2b$.

When you use cards, you must remember to write on each card the plus or minus **sign** that belongs to the term. (Sometimes, the term at the beginning of an expression does not have a sign in front of it. This means that it is positive.)

*Example 2*

Simplify the expression

$$3s + 4t - 5s + 6t - s - 3t$$

Write the terms on cards as follows:

| $3s$ | $+4t$ | $-5s$ | $+6t$ | $-s$ | $-3t$ |

Now re-arrange the cards so that all the $s$ terms are together and all the $t$ terms are together:

| $3s$ | $-5s$ | $-s$ | $+4t$ | $+6t$ | $-3t$ |

You can then see that the expression equals $-3s + 7t$, or $7t - 3s$. (The second expression could be written $+7t - 3s$, but we can drop the positive sign in front of the $7t$, because it is the first term in the expression.)

---

### Exercise 10A

**1.** Simplify these expressions.
   (a) $5x - 3y + 2x - 3y + y - 4x$
   (b) $4a + 2b - 3b - a + 2a - b$
   (c) $s - t + 3s - 5t + 4s - t$
   (d) $3x - 2y + z - x - y + 2z$
   (e) $4x - 3y + 2z - 5x - 2y + z$
   (f) $r + r - 3s - 2r + r - s$
   (g) $x + y - z + x - y - z$
   (h) $2p - 4q - r + 2r - 3q - p$
   (i) $4x - 3y - 2x + 5y - z + 2z$

---

## 10.3 Multiplying out expressions

In Section 10.2 you used black and white discs to visualise an expression in physical terms. Using this idea again, suppose that

$3b$ means ●●● (three black discs)

$2w$ means ○○ (two white discs)

Then $3b + 2w$ means ●●● + ○○

We now double this set of discs:

(●●● + ○○) + (●●● + ○○)

This is twice $3b + 2w$.

Twice $(3b + 2w)$ is written $2(3b + 2w)$, and so

$2(3b + 2w)$ means (●●● + ○○) + (●●● + ○○)

Putting all the black discs together and all the white discs together gives (●●●●●●) + (○○○○) or $6b + 4w$.

The two sets of discs

(●●●○○) with (●●●○○) and (●●●●●●○○○○)

are just two different ways of arranging the same collection of discs. Therefore, because they are both the same collection, we can say that

$$2(3b + 2w) = 6b + 4w$$

We can confirm this by multiplication, as follows:

$$2(3b + 2w) = (2 \times 3b) + (2 \times 2w) = 6b + 4w$$

The process of going from $2(3b + 2w)$ to $6b + 4w$ is called **multiplying out**.

The reverse process, of going from $6b + 4w$ to $2(3b + 2w)$, is called **factorising**.

*Example 3*

Multiply out the expression $4(3b + 2w)$.

$$4 \times (3b + 2w) = (4 \times 3b) + (4 \times 2w)$$
$$= 12b + 8w$$

So $4(3b + 2w) = 12b + 8w$

If it helps, you can think of the expression as being four times (●●● + ○○).

In **all** of the problems in this section so far, the expressions have all had plus signs.

The next example shows you how to multiply out an expression containing a minus sign.

### Example 4

Multiply out the expression $2(5x - 3y)$

$$2 \times (5x - 3y) = 2 \times 5x - 2 \times 3y$$
$$= 10x - 6y$$

So $2(5x - 3y) = 10x - 6y$

Some expressions have a letter, rather than a number, outside the brackets.

### Example 5

Multiply out $p(3p - 2)$

$$p \times (3p - 2) = p \times 3p - p \times 2$$
$$= 3p^2 - 2p$$

So $p(3p - 2) = 3p^2 - 2p$

*Remember*: $p \times 3p$ is equal to $p \times 3 \times p$, which is the same as $3 \times p \times p$ and is written as $3p^2$. $p \times 2$ is the same as $2 \times p$, which is written as $2p$.

---

**Exercise 10B**

1. Multiply out these expressions.
   (a) $3(x + 2y)$      (b) $2(p + 3q)$
   (c) $5(3a + 2b)$      (d) $7(2r + 3s)$
   (e) $2(2b + 3w + 4r)$      (f) $3(p + 2q + s)$
   (g) $2(3a + 2b + 5c)$      (h) $3(4x + 3y)$
   (i) $4(3x + 5y)$      (j) $2(5x + y)$
   (k) $2(5a + 2b)$      (l) $2(x + 3y + z)$
   (m) $3(2u + 5v + w)$      (n) $5(3x + y + 4z)$
   (o) $3(w + 2x + 3y + 5z)$

2. Multiply out these expressions.
   (a) $2(4x - 3y)$      (b) $3(x - 2y)$
   (c) $5(x - 3y)$      (d) $4(2x - y)$
   (e) $6(2x - 4y)$      (f) $3(5a - 2b)$
   (g) $7(a - 2b)$      (h) $2(5r - 2s)$
   (i) $2(x - y)$      (j) $3(x - y)$

   (k) $3(r - 2)$      (l) $5(x - 3)$
   (m) $2(5 - x)$      (n) $2(x + 3y - z)$
   (o) $4(3x - y + z - 2w)$      (p) $5(x - 2y - 3z - 5)$

3. Multiply out these expressions. *Remember* that $x \times y$ is written as $xy$.
   (a) $x(x - 3y)$      (b) $x(2x + 4)$
   (c) $x(3x - 4)$      (d) $x(x - 3y)$
   (e) $x(2x + 3y)$      (f) $x(5x - 2y)$
   (g) $a(2a - b)$      (h) $p(4p + 3)$
   (i) $c(c - 3)$      (j) $a^2(a + b)$
   (k) $a^2(3 - a)$      (l) $x(x + 2y)$
   (m) $x(x - 1)$      (n) $p(p - 2)$
   (o) $t(3t - 5)$      (p) $2t(3t + 5)$
   (q) $\pi(r^2 - r)$      (r) $r(3 + \pi r)$
   (s) $x(x + 1)$      (t) $y(y^2 - x + 1)$

---

## 10.4 Multiplying out expressions and collecting like terms

In this section you will learn how to multiply out expressions and put all the 'like terms' together. This then creates one **simplified expression**.

- $3x$ and $2x$ are 'like terms'
  so $3x + 2x$ is equal to $5x$

- $4x^2$ and $3x^2$ are 'like terms'
  so $4x^2 - 3x^2$ is equal to $1x^2$ or $x^2$

- $2x^2$ and $3x$ are '*not* like terms'
  so $2x^2 + 3x$ cannot be simplified to give one simple expression.

### Example 6

Multiply out and simplify the expression

$$3(2x + y) + 5(3x + 2y)$$

Multiply out each set of brackets first.

$$3(2x + y) + 5(3x + 2y) = (6x + 3y) + (15x + 10y)$$
$$= 6x + 3y + 15x + 10y$$

Collecting the $x$ terms and $y$ terms together gives

$$6x + 15x + 3y + 10y = 21x + 13y$$

You need to be very careful when you multiply out and simplify expressions that include brackets and a mixture of plus and minus signs.

### Example 7

Multiply out and simplify

$$3(x + 2y) - 2(x - 3y)$$
$$3(x + 2y) - 2(x - 3y) = 3 \times x + 3 \times 2y - (2 \times x - 2 \times 3y)$$
$$= 3x + 6y - (2x - 6y)$$
$$= 3x + 6y - 2x + 6y$$
$$= 3x - 2x + 6y + 6y$$
$$= x + 12y$$

So $3(x + 2y) - 2(x - 3y) = x + 12y$

### Example 8

Multiply out and simplify

$$3(x - 5) - 2(4 - 3x)$$
$$3(x - 5) - 2(4 - 3x) = (3 \times x - 3 \times 5)$$
$$- (2 \times 4 - 2 \times 3x)$$
$$= (3x - 15) - (8 - 6x)$$
$$= 3x - 15 - 8 + 6x$$
$$= 3x + 6x - 15 - 8$$
$$= 9x - 23$$

So $3(x - 5) - 2(4 - 3x) = 9x - 23$

*Example 9*

Multiply out and simplify

$$x(3x - 2) - x(5 - x)$$

$$\overgroup{x(3x} - 2) - \overgroup{x(5} - x) = (x \times 3x - x \times 2)$$
$$- (x \times 5 - x \times x)$$
$$= 3x^2 - 2x - (5x - x^2)$$
$$= 3x^2 - 2x - 5x - (-x^2)$$
$$= 3x^2 - 2x - 5x + x^2$$
$$= 3x^2 + x^2 - 2x - 5x$$
$$= 4x^2 - 7x$$

So $x(3x - 2) - x(5 - x) = 4x^2 - 7x$

---

### Exercise 10C

1. Multiply out and simplify:
   (a) $2(3x + y) + 2(x + y)$    (b) $4(x + 3y) + 2(x + y)$    (c) $2(x + y) + 3(x + y)$
   (d) $5(x + y) + 3(x - y)$    (e) $7(x - y) + 5(x + 3y)$    (f) $4(x + 7) + 3(x + 2)$
   (g) $4(a + 2b) + 3(a - b)$    (h) $6(a + 2b) + 4(a - 3b)$    (i) $7(x + 3y) + 2(x - y)$
   (j) $3(x - y) + 2(x + y)$    (k) $4(p + 2q) + (p - q)$    (l) $5(x - 1) + 3(x - 2)$
   (m) $6(x - 3) + 2(x - 5)$    (n) $7(a - b) + 3(a + b)$    (o) $4(a + 2b) + 3(b - 2a)$
   (p) $2(x - 3y) + 3(y - 2x)$    (q) $3(y - 2x) + 2(3x + y)$    (r) $3(r - s) + 3(s - r)$

2. Multiply out and simplify:
   (a) $2(x + y) - 2(2x - y)$    (b) $3(2x - y) - 2(x - 3y)$    (c) $4(a - 2b) - 2(a + b)$
   (d) $3(r + s) - 3(r - s)$    (e) $5(p + 2q) - 5(p - q)$    (f) $5(p + 2q) - 5(p - 2q)$
   (g) $2(x + 3y) - 3(x - 2y)$    (h) $4(2x - 3y) + 3(2x + 4y)$    (i) $2(2s - t) - 4(s - t)$
   (j) $5(s + t) - 5(s - t)$    (k) $3(2a + b) - 2(a - 3b)$    (l) $2(x - y) - 5(2x - y)$
   (m) $2(3a - 2b) - 5(a - b)$    (n) $5(s - 2t) - 2(4s - t)$    (o) $4(x - 2y) - 2(3x - y)$
   (p) $7(s - 3t) + 3(s + 7t)$    (q) $2(3x - y) - 3(x - y)$    (r) $5(2x - 3y) - 2(4x - 3y)$

3. Multiply out and simplify:
   (a) $x(4x + 3) - x(2 - x)$    (b) $x(3x - 1) - x(x - 2)$    (c) $y(4y - 3) + y(y - 4)$
   (d) $x(x - y) + y(x + y)$    (e) $r(2r - s) - s(r - 2s)$    (f) $2x(3x + 1) - x(3 - x)$
   (g) $p^2(p - 1) - p(2 - p^2)$    (h) $x^2(2x - 1) - x(3 - 2x^2)$    (i) $x(1 - y) + y(x - 1)$
   (j) $x(x - 1) - 2(1 - x^2)$    (k) $p(2p + q) - q(p - q)$    (l) $p(3 - p) - p(p - 1)$
   (m) $3t(1 - t) - 4(2 - t^2)$    (n) $x^2(1 - x) - x(2 - x^2)$    (o) $y(2x + y) - x(2y - x)$

---

## 10.5 Factorising expressions

You saw in Section 10.3 that $2(3b + 2w) = 6b + 4w$ and that this multiplying out can be reversed, so that $6b + 4w = 2(3b + 2w)$

This reversed process is called **factorising**.

Note that, as $3(a + 2b) = 3a + 6b$

$3a + 6b$ can be factorised as $3(1a + 2b)$ or $3(a + 2b)$.

Also, $4(1 + 5u) = 4 + 20u$

So $4 + 20u$ can be factorised as $4(1 + 5u)$.

### *Example 10*

Factorise $6x + 2y$

You need to understand that $6x = 2 \times 3x$ and $2y = 2 \times y$

So $6x + 2y = (2 \times 3x + 2 \times y)$

Now look for what the two terms $2 \times 3x$ and $2 \times y$ have in **common**. Their common factor is 2.

Take the common factor out of the brackets like this:

$$(2 \times 3x + 2 \times y) = 2 \times (3x + y)$$

So $6x + 2y = 2(3x + y)$

### *Example 11*

Factorise completely $12x + 30y$

You can write $12x + 30y = 2(6x + 15y)$, but this has not factorised the expression completely. You need to break down the 12 and the 30 into prime factors:

$$12x + 30y = (2 \times 2 \times 3 \times x + 2 \times 3 \times 5 \times y)$$

Now you find all the factors that are common to both of the terms. In this case, the common factors are 2 and 3. Take these factors out of the bracket:

$$\begin{aligned} 12x + 30y &= (2 \times 2 \times 3 \times x + 2 \times 3 \times 5 \times y) \\ &= 2 \times 3 \times (2 \times x + 5 \times y) \\ &= 6(2x + 5y) \end{aligned}$$

### *Example 12*

Factorise completely $6x^2y + 15xy^2$

You need to break down this expression into factors.

$$6x^2y + 15xy^2 = (2 \times 3 \times x \times x \times y + 3 \times 5 \times x \times y \times y)$$

Then look at the two terms to find all the factors that they have in common. Their common factors are 3, $x$ and $y$. Take these factors out of the bracket:

$$\begin{aligned} 6x^2y + 15xy^2 &= 3 \times x \times y \times (2 \times x + 5 \times y) \\ &= 3xy(2x + 5y) \end{aligned}$$

## Exercise 10D

1. Factorise these expressions.
   (a) $3x + 6y$
   (b) $2x + 4y$
   (c) $2b + 8w$
   (d) $3x - 6$
   (e) $2x - 4$
   (f) $5x - 5$
   (g) $10 - 5a$
   (h) $3x + 15$
   (i) $5x - 30y$
   (j) $14 - 7x$

2. Factorise completely:
   (a) $6x + 15$
   (b) $9x + 12y$
   (c) $30a - 12b$
   (d) $8a - 16b$
   (e) $12x - 42y$
   (f) $15 - 9x$
   (g) $16t + 40s$
   (h) $30y + 18x$
   (i) $9x - 24y$
   (j) $36x + 24y$

3. Factorise completely:
   (a) $12a^2b + 15ab^2$
   (b) $6x^2y - 15xy^2$
   (c) $6p^3q^2 + 15p^2q^3$
   (d) $p^2q - q^3p$
   (e) $3ab - 6a^2$
   (f) $a^2 + ab$
   (g) $2x^2y + 6xy^2$
   (h) $4\pi r^2 - \pi r$
   (i) $3xy^3 - 9x^3y$
   (j) $4x^2y + 6xy^2$

---

### Worked exam question 1

Factorise completely $12p^2q - 15pq^2$.

$12p^2 q - 15 p q^2$

$= 2 \times 2 \times 3 \times p \times p \times q - 3 \times 5 \times p \times q \times q$ ●

$= 3pq \, (4p - 5q)$ ●

$3pq \, (4p - 5q)$

(London)

**Do:**
Write each term as a product of its factors

Put all the common factors outside the brackets

---

## 10.6 Quadratic expressions

A **quadratic expression** is an expression such as

$$2x^2 - 3x + 5$$

A quadratic expression has

  an $x^2$ term      ($2x^2$ in the above)
  an $x$ term       ($-3x$ in the above)
  a constant term   ($+5$ in the above).

All quadratic expressions can be written in the form

$$ax^2 + bx + c$$

where $a, b$ and $c$ are numbers.

A quadratic expression can also be written in terms of a letter other than $x$.

For example,

$$3t^2 + 5t - 1$$

is a quadratic expression in $t$.

This section explains how to multiply two expressions such as $(2x + 3)$ and $(3x - 1)$, together.

Think about the expression

$$(x + 3)(x + 5)$$

$(x + 3)(x + 5)$ means $(x + 3) \times (x + 5)$

Start by imagining a rectangle with sides of length $x + 3$ and $x + 5$. The area of this rectangle is $(x + 3)(x + 5)$.

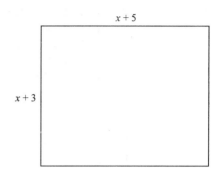

This rectangle can be partitioned like this:

From the diagram you can see that the area of the whole rectangle is

$$x^2 + 5x + 3x + 15 = x^2 + 8x + 15$$

You now have two expressions for the area of the same rectangle

$$\text{Area} = (x + 3)(x + 5)$$

and $\text{Area} = x^2 + 8x + 15$

and so you can see that

$$(x + 3)(x + 5) = x^2 + 8x + 15$$

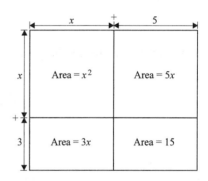

The two brackets multiplied together give a quadratic expression. This method is used again in Unit 13 for quadratic equations.

Now look at a harder problem:

$$(x + 4)(2x + 3)$$

Imagine a rectangle with sides of $x + 4$ and $2x + 3$.

The area of this rectangle is $(x + 4)(2x + 3)$.

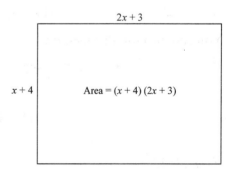

Then partition the rectangle like this:

From the diagram the area of the rectangle is given by

$$2x^2 + 3x + 8x + 12 = 2x^2 + 11x + 12$$

So $(x + 4)(2x + 3) = 2x^2 + 11x + 12$

You can use cards to help you understand the process of multiplying out. Write each term of the expression on a card, with its sign, as you did in Section **10.2**.

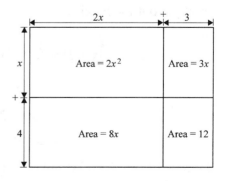

For the expression $(x + 4)(2x + 3)$ the cards are

$$\left(\boxed{x} \quad \boxed{+4}\right)\left(\boxed{2x} \quad \boxed{+3}\right)$$

Then carry out four multiplications:

$$\boxed{x} \times \boxed{2x} = 2x^2$$

$$\boxed{x} \times \boxed{+3} = 3x$$

$$\boxed{+4} \times \boxed{2x} = 8x$$

$$\boxed{+4} \times \boxed{+3} = 12$$

So $(x + 4)(2x + 3) = 2x^2 + 3x + 8x + 12$
$$= 2x^2 + 11x + 12$$

You can also think of the process as follows.

$$(x + 4)(2x + 3)$$

This gives $2x^2 + 3x + 8x + 12$

So $(x + 4)(2x + 3) = 2x^2 + 11x + 12$

You can also use this method:

$$(x + 4)(2x + 3) = x(2x + 3) + 4(2x + 3)$$
$$= 2x^2 + 3x + 8x + 12$$
$$= 2x^2 + 11x + 12$$

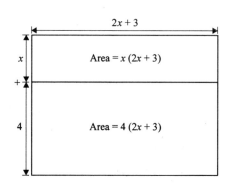

### Example 13

Expand and simplify $(x + 3)(3x + 2)$

The word 'expand' is sometimes used in exam questions. It means 'multiply out the brackets'.

$$(x + 3)(3x + 2) = (x \times 3x) + (x \times 2) + (3 \times 3x)$$
$$+ (3 \times 2)$$
$$= 3x^2 + 2x + 9x + 6$$
$$= 3x^2 + 11x + 6$$

So $(x + 3)(3x + 2) = 3x^2 + 11x + 6$

*Example 14*

Multiply and simplify $(2x + 3)(4x - 5)$

You can think of the process as

$(\boxed{2x}\boxed{+3})(\boxed{4x}\boxed{-5})$ *or* $2x(4x - 5) + 3(4x - 5)$

The first method gives

$$(2x \times 4x) + (2x \times (-5)) + ((+3) \times 4x) + ((+3) \times (-5))$$
$$= 8x^2 - 10x + 12x - 15$$
$$= 8x^2 + 2x - 15$$

So $(2x + 3)(4x - 5) = 8x^2 + 2x - 15$

You can check that the second method gives the same answer.

*Example 15*

Multiply out $(2x + 3)^2$.

You need to understand that $(2x + 3)^2$ means $(2x + 3)(2x + 3)$.

$$(2x + 3)^2 = (2x + 3)(2x + 3)$$

$$or\ [2x(2x + 3) + 3(2x + 3)]$$
$$= (2x \times 2x) + (2x \times 3) + (3x \times 2x) + (3 \times 3)$$
$$= 4x^2 + 6x + 6x + 9$$
$$= 4x^2 + 12x + 9$$

You can check that the second method gives the same answer.

---

### Exercise 10E

1. Expand and simplify:
   (a) $(x + 2)(x + 5)$
   (b) $(x + 3)(x + 7)$
   (c) $(y - 3)(y - 5)$
   (d) $(p - 2)(p - 7)$
   (e) $(x + 1)(x - 6)$
   (f) $(x - 2)(x + 5)$
   (g) $(2a + 1)(a + 3)$
   (h) $(3x + 1)(x + 5)$
   (i) $(2y + 7)(y + 1)$
   (j) $(4t + 1)(2t + 3)$
   (k) $(x + 1)(x - 1)$
   (l) $(x - 7)(x + 4)$
   (m) $(3y - 2)(y - 3)$
   (n) $(4x - 1)(x - 3)$
   (o) $(2x - 3)(x + 5)$
   (p) $(3p - 2)(p + 4)$
   (q) $(2s + 5)(s - 3)$
   (r) $(5y - 3)(2y + 1)$
   (s) $(4t - 3)(2t + 7)$
   (t) $(3x + 2)(x - 5)$

2. Multiply out:
   (a) $(3x + 2)^2$
   (b) $(2x + 5)^2$
   (c) $(2x - 3)^2$
   (d) $(5y - 2)^2$
   (e) $(4p - 3)^2$
   (f) $(2t - 1)^2$
   (g) $(3x + 1)^2$
   (h) $(4x - 1)^2$
   (i) $(5t + 3)^2$
   (j) $(6x - 5)^2$

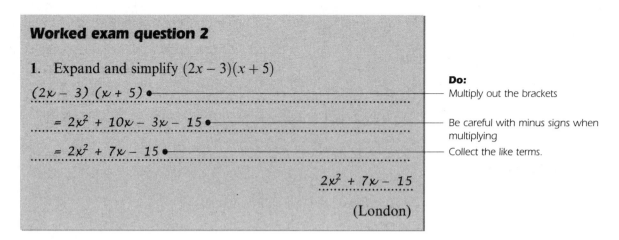

**Worked exam question 2**

**1.** Expand and simplify $(2x - 3)(x + 5)$

$(2x - 3)(x + 5)$ •————— **Do:** Multiply out the brackets

$= 2x^2 + 10x - 3x - 15$ •————— Be careful with minus signs when multiplying

$= 2x^2 + 7x - 15$ •————— Collect the like terms.

$2x^2 + 7x - 15$

(London)

## 10.7 Indices

You should remember from number work that:

$$2^3 \text{ means } 2 \times 2 \times 2$$

$2^3$ this number is called the **index** (or **power**)

The plural of index is **indices**.

$2^3$ is usually read as: 'two cubed'
or 'two to the 3'

$2^3$ can also be read as: 'two to the power of 3'
or 'two to the index 3'.

- $2^3 \times 2^4 = (2 \times 2 \times 2) \times (2 \times 2 \times 2 \times 2)$
$$= 2^7$$
$$2^3 \times 2^4 = 2^{3+4}$$

- $2^7 \div 2^4 = \dfrac{\cancel{2} \times \cancel{2} \times \cancel{2} \times \cancel{2} \times 2 \times 2 \times 2}{\cancel{2} \times \cancel{2} \times \cancel{2} \times \cancel{2}}$
$$= 2 \times 2 \times 2 = 2^3$$
$$2^7 \div 2^4 = 2^{7-4}$$

- $(2^3)^2 = 2^3 \times 2^3$
$$= (2 \times 2 \times 2) \times (2 \times 2 \times 2)$$
$$= 2^6$$
$$(2^3)^2 = 2^{3 \times 2}$$

The general rules for indices are

$$a^n \times a^m = a^{n+m}$$
$$a^n \div a^m = a^{n-m}$$
$$(a^n)^m = a^{n \times m}$$

*Remember:* $a^1 = a$, $a^0 = 1$

*Example 16*

Simplify (a) $3x^3 \times 2x^4$   (b) $8p^3 \div 2p$   (c) $(2t^2)^3$

(a) $3x^3 \times 2x^4 = 3 \times 2 \times x^3 \times x^4$

$\qquad = 6 \times x^3 \times x^4$

$\qquad = 6 \times x^{3+4}$

$\qquad = 6 \times x^7$

$\qquad = 6x^7$

(b) $8p^3 \div 2p = \dfrac{8p^3}{2p} = \dfrac{4p^3}{p}$

$\qquad = 4p^3 \div p = 4p^{3-1}$

$\qquad = 4p^2$

(c) $(2t^2)^3 = 2t^2 \times 2t^2 \times 2t^2$

$\qquad = 2 \times 2 \times 2 \times t^2 \times t^2 \times t^2$

$\qquad = 8 \times t^6$

$\qquad = 8t^6$

or $(2t^2)^3 = 2^3 \times (t^2)^3$

$\qquad = 8t^{2\times3}$

$\qquad = 8t^6$

---

**Exercise 10F**

Simplify these expressions.

(a) $3t^2 \times 4t$      (b) $5p^3 \times 3p^2$      (c) $12x^3 \div 4x$      (d) $16x^2 \div 8x$

(e) $(2t^3)^2$      (f) $(3x^2)^3$      (g) $8x \div 4x^3$      (h) $(2x)^3 \times (3x^2)^4$

(i) $(x^3y)^2$      (j) $(5xy^2)^3$      (k) $10y^2 \times 5y^3$      (l) $4r^2 \times 8r$

(m) $(2x)^4 \div 4x^2$      (n) $(5x^3)^2 \div 25x$      (o) $x^{-3} \times x^5$      (p) $(x^{-3})^{-2}$

(q) $(x^{-1})^{-3}$      (r) $(4x)^2 \times 3x^2$      (s) $t^3 \div t^{-2}$      (t) $(8x)^2 \div x^{-3}$

---

# 10.8 Rearranging formulae

Instructions for cooking a turkey:

> 'Allow 45 minutes per kilogram and then add on an extra 30 minutes'.

Thus the time $t$ taken to cook a turkey using these instructions is given by

$$t = 45w + 30$$

where $w$ is the weight in kilograms of the turkey, and $t$ is the time in minutes.

You can use this formula to calculate the cooking time for any weight of turkey.

Suppose that we want to know the maximum weight of turkey that can be cooked in a given time. To do this you need to rearrange the formula $t = 45w + 30$ so that it is in the form $w = \ldots$ . You can do this using a loop diagram.

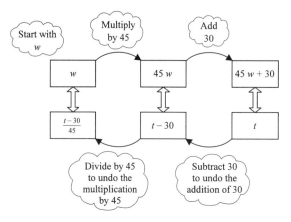

This gives the formula

$$w = \frac{t - 30}{45}$$

where $w$ is the maximum weight that can be cooked in a given time $t$.

You can solve the same problem in a different way.

Start with the formula

$$t = 45w + 30$$

Then subtract 30 from both sides of the formula:

$$t - 30 = 45w + 30 - 30 = 45w$$

So $t - 30 = 45w$

Now divide both sides of the formula by 45:

$$\frac{t - 30}{45} = \frac{45w}{45} = w$$

So $w = \dfrac{t - 30}{45}$

You may want to look at this section again after you have read Unit 11.

By rearranging the formula $t = 45w + 30$ so that

$$w = \frac{t - 30}{45}$$

you have made $w$ the **subject** of the formula.

## Example 17

Make $x$ the subject of the formula

$$y = 7 + 3x$$

Subtract 7 from both sides of the formula:

$$y - 7 = 7 + 3x - 7$$
$$y - 7 = 7 - 7 + 3x$$
$$y - 7 = 3x$$

Now divide both sides of the formula by 3:

$$\frac{y - 7}{3} = \frac{3x}{3}$$

So $x = \dfrac{y - 7}{3}$

## Example 18

Make $t$ the subject of the formula

$$m = 5 - 3t$$

Subtract 5 from both sides of the formula:

$$m - 5 = 5 - 3t - 5$$
$$m - 5 = -3t$$

Divide both sides of the formula by $-3$:

$$\frac{m - 5}{-3} = \frac{-3t}{-3}$$
$$= t$$

So $t = \dfrac{m - 5}{-3}$

Note that this can be written as

$$t = \frac{5 - m}{3}$$

## Example 19

Make $x$ the subject of the formula

$$y = mx^2 + k$$

Subtract $k$ from both sides of the formula:

$$y - k = mx^2 + k - k$$
$$y - k = mx^2$$

Divide both sides of the formula by $m$:

$$\frac{y - k}{m} = \frac{mx^2}{m}$$

$m$ can be cancelled out for the right-hand term:

$$\frac{y - k}{m} = x^2$$

So $x^2 = \dfrac{y - k}{m}$

Now take the square root of both sides

$$\sqrt{x^2} = x = \sqrt{\frac{y - k}{m}}$$

---

### Exercise 10G

Make $x$ the subject of these formulae.

(a) $y = 3x + 2$     (b) $y = 5x - 3$     (c) $y = ax + b$     (d) $y = k - 3x$
(e) $y = a\sqrt{x} + b$     (f) $y = t - kx$     (g) $y = 3x^2 + 1$     (h) $y = 4 - 3x^2$
(i) $y = m\sqrt{x} - c$     (j) $y = 2(k - a\sqrt{x})$     (k) $y = 3(7 - kx^2)$     (l) $y = a(mx - b)$

---

### Worked exam question 3

The cost, $C$ pence, of printing $n$ party invitations is given by

$$C = 120 + 40n$$

Find a formula for $n$ in terms of $C$.

$C - 120 = + 40n - 120$        **Do:** Subtract 120 from each side

$C - 120 = 40n$        Divide both sides by 40

$\dfrac{C - 120}{40} = \dfrac{40n}{40}$

$n = \dfrac{C - 120}{40}$

**Don't:** Forget that a formula states that something equals something else — remember to include '$n =$' in your answer

(London)

## Exercise 10H (Mixed questions)

1. Factorise completely:
   (a) $3x + 9$
   (b) $5 - 10x$
   (c) $8t + 12$
   (d) $5x + 15y$
   (e) $x^2 - 6x$
   (f) $x^2y + xy^2$
   (g) $2p^2q^2 - 4pq$
   (h) $a^3b - 2ab^2$
   (i) $4s^2t + 6st^2$
   (j) $\pi r^2h + 2\pi r^3$

2. Expand and simplify:
   (a) $(x + 4)(x + 7)$
   (b) $(y + 3)(y + 2)$
   (c) $(x + 5)^2$
   (d) $(2x + 1)(x + 3)$
   (e) $(3x - 2)(x - 1)$
   (f) $(4y - 3)(y + 1)$
   (g) $(x - 3)(x + 3)$
   (h) $(2t - 1)(2t + 1)$
   (i) $(3s + 2)(s - 3)$
   (j) $(2x - 5)(x + 3)$

3. Simplify:
   (a) $a^3 \times a^2$
   (b) $2b^2 \times 3b^5$
   (c) $10b^2 \div b$
   (d) $15a^7 \div 5a^2$
   (e) $\dfrac{a^2b}{a}$
   (f) $\dfrac{a^3b^2}{ab}$
   (g) $\dfrac{4x}{2x^3}$
   (h) $\dfrac{p^3q^3}{pq}$
   (i) $\dfrac{16t^7}{4t^6}$
   (j) $\dfrac{72x^5y^2}{30x^2y^3}$

4. Re-arrange these formulae to make the letter in brackets the subject.
   (a) $y = 3x - 5$ $\quad(x)$
   (b) $y = mx + c$ $\quad(x)$
   (c) $y = a - bx$ $\quad(x)$
   (d) $y = ax^2 - b$ $\quad(x)$
   (e) $s = ut + vt$ $\quad(t)$
   (f) $V = \pi r^2h$ $\quad(h)$
   (g) $V = \pi r^2h$ $\quad(r)$
   (h) $V = a(x + h)$ $\quad(x)$
   (i) $s = gt^2 - r$ $\quad(t)$
   (j) $t = 2\pi\sqrt{\dfrac{z}{g}}$ $\quad(z)$
   (k) $t = 2\pi\sqrt{\dfrac{z}{g}}$ $\quad(g)$
   (l) $S = 4\pi r^2$ $\quad(r)$
   (m) $y + ax = bx + c$ $\quad(x)$
   (n) $at - b = ct + d$ $\quad(t)$

## Worked exam question 4

(a) Expand the following expression, simplifying your answer as far as possible.

$$(3x - 1)(x + 2)$$

$(3x - 1)(x + 2) = (3x \times x) + (3x \times 2) - (1 \times x) - (1 \times 2)$ — **Do:** Multiply out the brackets

$= 3x^2 + 6x - x - 2$ — Collect the terms

$= 3x^2 + 5x - 2$

(b) Factorise the expression $4xy - 2y^2$

$4xy - 2y^2 = 2 \times 2 \times x \times y - 2 \times y \times y$ — **Do:** Work out the factors of both terms

$= 2y(2x - y)$ — Take all of the factors outside the brackets

(c) Make $c$ the subject of the formula

$$3c - 5b = a + c.$$

$$3c - 5b - c = a + c - c$$

**Do:**
Subtract c from both sides and note that $+c - c = 0$

$$2c - 5b = a$$

$$2c - 5b + 5b = a + 5b$$

Add 5b to both sides and note that $-5b + 5b = 0$

$$2c = a + 5b$$

$$c = \frac{a + 5b}{2}$$

**Don't:**
Forget to include 'c =' in your formula

(WJEC)

## Test yourself

**1.**

QUESTION    Multiply and simplify $3(x + 1) - 2(x - 3)$

ANSWER    $x + 9$    *If your answer is incorrect, review pages 196–198, Section 10.3, Examples 3, 4 and 5 on multiplying out expressions and pages 198–200, Section 10.4, Examples 6, 7, 8 and 9 on multiplying out expressions and collecting like terms*

**2.**

QUESTION    Expand and simplify $x(x - 3) - 2x(4 - x)$

ANSWER    $3x^2 - 11x$    *If your answer is incorrect, review pages 196–198, Sections 10.3, Examples 3, 4 and 5 on multiplying out expressions and pages 198–200, Section 10.4, Examples 6, 7, 8 and 9 on multiplying out expressions and collecting like terms*

**3.**

QUESTION    Factorise $8x - 20$

ANSWER    $4(2x - 5)$    *If your answer is incorrect, review page 201, Section 10.5, Examples 10, 11 and 12 on factorising expressions*

**4.**

QUESTION    Factorise $p^2x - px^2$

ANSWER    $px(p - x)$    *If your answer is incorrect, review page 201, Section 10.5, Examples 10, 11 and 12 on factorising expressions*

**5.**

QUESTION    Expand and simplify $(x + 2)(x - 5)$

ANSWER    $x^2 - 3x - 10$    *If your answer is incorrect, review pages 204–205, Section 10.6, Examples 13, 14 and 15 on quadratic expressions*

**6.**

QUESTION    Expand and simplify $(2x - 3)(x + 7)$

ANSWER    $2x^2 + 11x - 21$    *If your answer is incorrect, review pages 204–205, Section 10.6, Examples 13, 14 and 15 on quadratic expressions*

**7.**

**QUESTION**  Expand and simplify $(3x - 1)^2$

**ANSWER**  $9x^2 - 6x + 1$  *If your answer is incorrect, review pages 204–205, Section 10.6, Examples 13, 14 and 15 on quadratic expressions*

**8.**

**QUESTION**  Simplify $5p^2 \times 3p^3$

**ANSWER**  $15p^5$  *If your answer is incorrect, review page 207, Section 10.7, Example 16 on indices*

**9.**

**QUESTION**  Simplify $20x^3 \div 5x$

**ANSWER**  $4x^2$  *If your answer is incorrect, review page 207, Section 10.7, Example 16 on indices*

**10.**

**QUESTION**  Simplify $(3x^4)^2$

**ANSWER**  $9x^8$  *If your answer is incorrect, review page 207, Section 10.7, Example 16 on indices*

**11.**

**QUESTION**  Make $x$ the subject of the formula
$$y = 50 + 4x$$

**ANSWER**  $x = \dfrac{y - 50}{4}$  *If your answer is incorrect, review pages 209–210, Section 10.8, Examples 17, 18 and 19 on rearranging formulae*

**12.**

**QUESTION**  Make $x$ the subject of the formula
$$t = ax^2 - b$$

**ANSWER**  $x = \sqrt{\dfrac{t + b}{a}}$  *If your answer is incorrect, review pages 209–210, Section 10.8, Examples 17, 18 and 19 on rearranging formulae*

## Summary of key points to remember

1.  $2t$ is an **expression**, $y = 2t$ is a **formula**, $2t = 6$ is an **equation**.

2.  Multiplying out brackets:

$$3p(p + 4) = (3p \times p) + (3p \times 4)$$
$$= 3p^2 + 12p$$

3.  • $3x$ and $2x$ are 'like terms'
    so $3x + 2x$ is equal to $5x$

- $4x^2$ and $3x^2$ are 'like terms'

  so $4x^2 - 3x^2$ is equal to $1x^2$ or $x^2$

- $2x^2$ and $3x$ are '*not* like terms'

  so $2x^2 + 3x$ cannot be simplified to give one simple expression

4. Simplify $3x(x + 2) - x(x - 3)$ means 'multiply out the brackets and collect the terms'.

5. To factorise completely an expression such as $x^2 - 6x$, or $4x + 12y$, look for all the common factors and take them outside the bracket.

$$x^2 - 6x = x(x - 6)$$
$$4x + 12y = 4(x + 3y)$$

6. To multiply out and simplify quadratic expressions such as $(x + 3)(2x - 1)$ use one of these methods:

$$(x + 3)(2x - 1) = 2x^2 + (-1)x + 6x + 3(-1) \quad or \quad (x + 3)(2x - 1) = x(2x - 1) + 3(2x - 1)$$
$$= 2x^2 - x + 6x - 3 \qquad\qquad\qquad\qquad = 2x^2 - x + 6x - 3$$
$$= 2x^2 + 5x - 3 \qquad\qquad\qquad\qquad\quad = 2x^2 + 5x - 3$$

7. $(ax + b)^2 = (ax + b)(ax + b)$

8. $a^n \times a^m = a^{n+m}$
   $a^n \div a^m = a^{n-m}$
   $(a^n)^m = a^{nm}$
   $a^1 = a,\ a^0 = 1$

9. You can re-arrange formulae. To make $x$ the subject of the formula

$$y = 3x + 2$$

subtract 2 from both sides:

$$y - 2 = 3x + 2 - 2$$
$$y - 2 = 3x$$

divide both sides by 3:

$$\frac{y - 2}{3} = x$$

To make $x$ the subject of the formula $\quad t = 4x^2 + 1$

subtract 1 from both sides:

$$t - 1 = 4x^2 + 1 - 1$$
$$t - 1 = 4x^2$$

divide by 4:

$$\frac{t - 1}{4} = \frac{4x^2}{4}$$
$$\frac{t - 1}{4} = x^2$$

Take the square root

$$\sqrt{x^2} = x = \sqrt{\frac{t - 1}{4}}$$

# 11 Solving linear equations

## 11.1 Introduction

Equations occur in all areas of life and have applications for people in all walks of life. For example,

the scientist tracking rays bouncing off a satellite

or

the family deciding on the number of rolls needed to wallpaper the lounge.

They are both **solving** equations. They need to work out some unknown quantity.

This chapter initially looks at ways of solving **linear equations**, sometimes called simple equations. You will have seen how some of these equations are formed in Unit 8, Forming equations.

The key feature of linear equations is that the unknown quantity appears in the equation and is raised only to the power of 1. So, for example,

$$3x + 1 = 13$$
$$4x - 7y = 5$$

are both linear equations. In the first equation, $x$ is the unknown quantity. In the second equation, there are two unknown quantities, $x$ and $y$.

In a linear equation you will not see expressions in which the unknown is raised to a power greater than 1 or a negative power, such as:

$$x^2, \ 2y^3, \ \frac{4}{z}.$$

You will meet these sorts of expressions in other parts of this book.

Expressions such as $3x + 1$ are called linear because they are represented on graph by a straight line. In Unit 9, Straight line graphs, you saw that the graph of $y = 3x + 1$ is a straight line. So

$y = 3x + 1$       and       $3x + 1 = 13$
is a straight line            is a linear
graph                  equation.

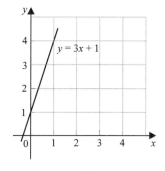

In addition to linear equations, this chapter also looks at solving **simultaneous equations** and **linear inequalities**.

The following sections take you through a number of examples of linear equations of differing degrees of difficulty.

## 11.2 Equations with the unknown quantity on one side

### Example 1

Solve       $x + 3 = 8$

In this equation, the unknown quantity, $x$, is present on one side of the equation only, to the left of the equals sign.

The key feature of all equations is that if you do to one side that which you do to the other side then you preserve the equality of the equation.

To solve this equation you need to isolate the unknown quantity, in this case $x$, i.e. get it on its own on one side of the equation.

So to solve

$$x + 3 = 8$$

subtract 3 from both sides

> Going from $x + 3 = 8$ to $x = 8 - 3$, gives rise to the saying 'change the side, change the sign'

$$x + 3 - 3 = 8 - 3$$

leaving $x = 8 - 3$

or $x = 5$

as the solution.

You can check the solution by substituting $x = 5$ into one side of the original equation. If $x = 5$,

$$x + 3 = 5 + 3 = 8$$

so $x = 5$ is correct.

## Exercise 11A

**1**. Solve these equations.

(a) $x + 5 = 7$   (b) $x - 3 = 8$   (c) $x + 1 = 13$   (d) $y - 6 = 3$   (e) $p + 8 = 17$

(f) $z - \frac{1}{2} = 2$   (g) $x + 6 = 4$   (h) $x + 11 = 5$   (i) $y - 3 = -7$

---

### *Example 2*

Solve:   $7 - x = 9$

At a first glance this equation might look a bit strange because it means

> '*Start with the number 7, take something away from it and end up with a number bigger than 7*'

How can you take something from 7 and end up with a result bigger than 7? The answer is that you take a negative number from 7.

It is easier to solve an equation if the term containing the unknown quantity is positive. So, to solve $7 - x = 9$, it helps if you first remove the term $-x$ by adding $x$ to both sides of the equation.

$$7 - x = 9$$

Add $x$ to both sides

$$7 - x + x = 9 + x$$
$$7 = 9 + x$$

Write this equation the other way round

$$9 + x = 7$$

since anything written as $A = B$ can also be written as $B = A$.

Now subtract 9 from both sides

$$9 + x - 9 = 7 - 9$$

Change the order on the left-hand side

$$9 - 9 + x = 7 - 9$$
$$0 + x = -2$$

so   $x = -2$

which is the solution.

It is useful to check your solution by substituting $x = -2$ into one side of the original equation.

$$7 - x = 7 - (-2) = 7 + 2 = 9$$

So $x = -2$ is correct.

### Exercise 11B

**1.** Solve these equations.

(a) $4 - x = 9$    (b) $2 - x = 10$    (c) $3 - y = 7$    (d) $\frac{1}{2} - x = 3\frac{1}{2}$    (e) $5 - z = 20$

(f) $8 - p = 21$    (g) $5 + x = 3$    (h) $11 + p = 2$    (i) $17 - y = 24$

*Example 3*

Solve:        $3x + 5 = 17$

There is more than one way of solving this type of equation.

**Method 1**

First, subtract 5 from both sides of the equation

$$3x + 5 - 5 = 17 - 5$$

so $3x \qquad = 12$

Then divide both sides by 3

$$\frac{3x}{3} = \frac{12}{3}$$

leaving $x = 4$

as the solution.

Check by substituting $x = 4$ into one side of the equation.

$$3x + 5 = 3 \times 4 + 5 = 12 + 5 = 17$$

**Method 2**

Solve:   $3x + 5 = 17$

This method involves using a **loop diagram**.

The left side of the equation, $3x + 5$ means

> *Start with x, multiply it by 3 and then add 5.*

These operations are shown in the top half of the loop diagram.
The $\updownarrow$ sign shows that there is equality at each stage.

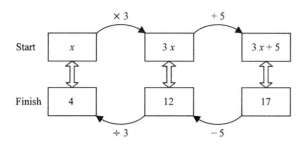

Continue the loop with the right-hand side of the equation, 17.
Then undo the loop by doing the inverse of each operation.

The inverse of $+5$ is $-5$ and the inverse of $\times 3$ is $\div 3$. So you end up with the solution $x = 4$.

A loop diagram helps you to understand how to solve equations.

---

## Exercise 11C

**1.** Solve these equations using two different methods.

(a) $4x + 3 = 23$      (b) $5x - 2 = 28$      (c) $2x + 3 = 12$      (d) $3x + 2 = 17$

(e) $5x - 7 = 23$      (f) $6x + 1 = 16$      (g) $\frac{1}{2}x + 1 = 4$      (h) $\frac{1}{4}x + 2 = 5$

(i) $\frac{1}{8}x - 3 = -1$      (j) $\frac{3}{4}x - 1 = 5$      (k) $\frac{2}{3}x - 2 = 4$      (l) $\frac{3}{4}x + 5 = 1$

---

### *Example 4*

Solve:      $5 - 4x = 19$

You can solve this equation using either method.

Add $4x$ to both sides to give

$$5 - 4x + 4x = 19 + 4x$$
$$5 = 19 + 4x$$

Change the sides

$$19 + 4x = 5$$

Subtract 19 from both sides

$$19 + 4x - 19 = 5 - 19$$
$$4x = -14$$

Divide both sides by 4

$$\frac{4x}{4} = \frac{-14}{4} = -\frac{7}{2}$$

So the solution is   $x = -3\frac{1}{2}$

Alternatively, you can use a loop diagram.

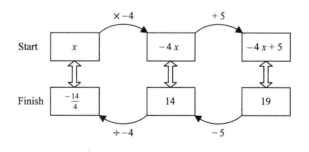

Then check the solution. If $x = -3\frac{1}{2}$

$$5 - 4x = 5 - 4 \times \left(-3\frac{1}{2}\right)$$
$$= 5 + 14$$
$$= 19$$

So $x = -3\frac{1}{2}$ is correct.

---

**Exercise 11D**

**1.** Solve the equations using either method from Example 4.

(a) $3 - 2x = 5$      (b) $4 - 3y = 10$      (c) $5 - 4x = 11$      (d) $4 - \frac{1}{2}x = 7$

(e) $5 - \frac{1}{4}x = 9$      (f) $2 - \frac{3}{4}x = -4$      (g) $3 - \frac{1}{2}x = 5$      (h) $2 - \frac{1}{4}y = -7$

(i) $-3 - \frac{1}{2}x = 5$      (j) $-4 - \frac{1}{4}x = 3$      (k) $\frac{1}{2} - 3x = 5$      (l) $4 - \frac{1}{2}x = 7$

---

## 11.3 Equations with brackets

In Unit 10 Manipulating algebra you saw how to manipulate algebraic expressions, and how to multiply out brackets. We will now apply these techniques to solving equations.

*Example 5*

Solve:      $3(x - 2) = 15$

First multiply out the bracket, giving

$$3x - 6 = 15$$

Then add 6 to both sides

$$3x - 6 + 6 = 15 + 6$$

so                  $3x = 21$

Now divide both sides by 3 to give

$$\frac{3x}{3} = \frac{21}{3}$$

or                 $x = 7$

as the solution.

Check $x = 7$ in the original equation

$$3(x - 2) = 3(7 - 2)$$
$$= 3(5) = 15$$

So $x = 7$ is correct.

*Example 6*

Solve:        $2(3x - 8) - 4(x - 3) = 5$

Multiply out the brackets

$$6x - 16 - 4x + 12 = 5$$

Rearrange the left-hand side to bring all the $x$ terms together.

$$6x - 4x - 16 + 12 = 5$$

so                      $2x - 4 = 5$

Then add 4 to both sides

$$2x - 4 + 4 = 5 + 4$$

$$2x = 9$$

Finally divide by 2 to give

$$x = 4\tfrac{1}{2}$$

Check the solution by substituting $x = 4\tfrac{1}{2}$ into the left-hand side of the original equation.

$$2(3x - 8) - 4(x - 3) = 2(3 \times 4\tfrac{1}{2} - 8) - 4(4\tfrac{1}{2} - 3)$$
$$= 2(5\tfrac{1}{2}) - 4(1\tfrac{1}{2})$$
$$= 11 - 6 = 5$$

This is the value on the right-hand side of the equation, so the equation is true for $x = -4\tfrac{1}{2}$, which is therefore the correct solution.

---

### Exercise 11E

**1.** Solve these equations.

(a) $3(x - 1) = 21$        (b) $4(x + 3) = 20$        (c) $2(3 - x) = 10$        (d) $4(2x + 1) = 28$
(e) $5(3x - 2) = 20$                    (f) $4(5 - 2x) = 48$                    (g) $3(2x + 1) + 4(x - 1) = 9$
(h) $4(x - 3) - 2(x - 1) = 2$        (i) $5(2 - 3x) + 4(2x - 1) = 11$        (j) $2(3 - 5x) - 3(4 - x) = 5$

---

## 11.4 Equations with the unknown quantity on both sides

This section looks at equations which have the unknown quantity on both sides.

*Example 7*

Solve:        $3x + 1 = 2x + 6$

As before, you need to get all the $x$ terms on one side of the equation.

First subtract 1 from both sides

$$3x + 1 - 1 = 2x + 6 - 1$$

so

$$3x = 2x + 5$$

then subtract $2x$ from both sides

$$3x - 2x = 2x + 5 - 2x$$

giving

$$x = 5$$

as the solution.

Check the solution in both sides of the original equation:

$$3x + 1 = 3 \times 5 + 1 = 16$$

and

$$2x + 6 = 2 \times 5 + 6 = 16$$

When $x = 5$ both sides of the equation are equal, so $x = 5$ is the correct solution.

> You could think of this in terms of rearranging the equation,
>
> $$3x + 1 = 2x + 6$$
>
> $$3x - 2x = 6 - 1$$
>
> remembering to reverse the operations or signs as you cross the equality.

### Example 8

Solve:      $3(2x - 1) = 4x + 6$

Multiply out the brackets to give

$$6x - 3 = 4x + 6$$

Add 3 to both sides

$$6x - 3 + 3 = 4x + 6 + 3$$

so

$$6x = 4x + 9$$

Subtract $4x$ from both sides

$$6x - 4x = 4x + 9 - 4x$$

so

$$2x = 9$$

Divide both sides by 2 to give the solution

$$x = 4\tfrac{1}{2}$$

You should check the solution in the same way as for Example 7 above.

---

### Exercise 11F

**1.** Solve the following equations.
   (a) $2x + 3 = x + 7$     (b) $5x - 4 = 3x + 8$     (c) $3 - 4x = 2x - 9$     (d) $3x + 1 = 2x - 5$
   (e) $4(3x - 2) = 2x + 12$     (f) $9x - 2 = 2(3x + 5)$     (g) $6(1 - \tfrac{1}{2}x) = 5 - 2x$
   (h) $4x - 7 = 7x - 4$     (i) $\tfrac{1}{2}(4 - 8x) = 5 - 3x$     (j) $3(4x - 5) = 7(x + 3)$

---

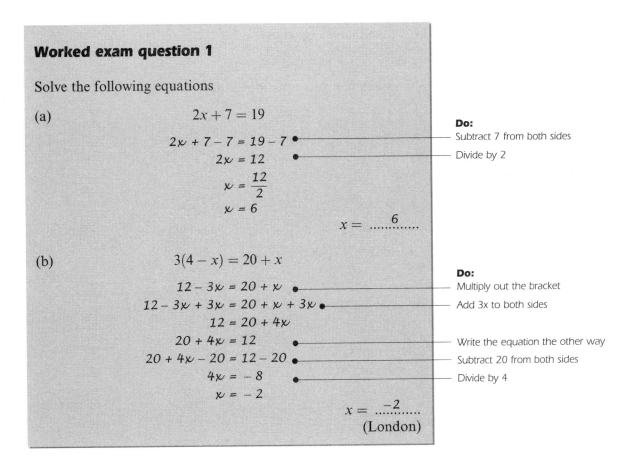

**Worked exam question 1**

Solve the following equations

(a)
$$2x + 7 = 19$$
$$2x + 7 - 7 = 19 - 7$$
$$2x = 12$$
$$x = \frac{12}{2}$$
$$x = 6$$

$$x = \underline{\phantom{xx}6\phantom{xx}}$$

**Do:**
Subtract 7 from both sides
Divide by 2

(b)
$$3(4 - x) = 20 + x$$
$$12 - 3x = 20 + x$$
$$12 - 3x + 3x = 20 + x + 3x$$
$$12 = 20 + 4x$$
$$20 + 4x = 12$$
$$20 + 4x - 20 = 12 - 20$$
$$4x = -8$$
$$x = -2$$

$$x = \underline{\phantom{xx}-2\phantom{xx}}$$
(London)

**Do:**
Multiply out the bracket
Add 3x to both sides

Write the equation the other way
Subtract 20 from both sides

Divide by 4

## 11.5 Simultaneous equations

In Unit 9, Straight line graphs, you were introduced to the idea of solving a pair of equations by using graphs. In the diagram below, the point P has coordinates $(2, 1)$ and lies *simultaneously* on the lines $2x + y = 5$ and $x - y = 1$.

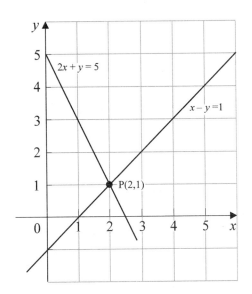

So $x = 2$, $y = 1$ is a solution of the **simultaneous equations**

$$2x + y = 5, \qquad x - y = 1$$

This section looks at ways of solving simultaneous equations using algebraic methods.

### Example 9

Solve the simultaneous equations:

$$2x + y = 5, \qquad x - y = 1$$

Label the first equation ① and the second equation ②.

This makes it easier to show your working. Write equation ② beneath equation ① i.e.

$$2x + y = 5 \qquad ①$$
$$x - y = 1 \qquad ②$$

If you add equation ① and ②, the $y$ terms cancel out, leaving an equation in $x$ only.

So **add** ① and ②

$$2x + y + x - y = 5 + 1$$
$$3x = 6$$

Then divide by 3 to give

$$x = 2$$

Substitute this value of $x = 2$ back into equation ② to give

$$2 - y = 1$$
$$y = 1$$

So the solution is $x = 2$, $y = 1$.

Check this in both equations

$$\text{Equation ①} : 2x + y = 2 \times 2 + 1 = 4 + 1 = 5$$

$$\text{Equation ②} : x - y = 2 - 1 = 1$$

which is correct.

### Example 10

Solve the simultaneous equations:

$$2x - 3y = 9, \qquad 5x + y = 14$$

Label $2x - 3y = 9$ equation ①.

Label $5x + y = 14$ equation ②.

As always, you need to eliminate one of the unknowns. In this example, you cannot just add or subtract the equations because neither the $x$ nor $y$ terms are the same in both equations.

First you need to multiply the equations by a number you choose which makes either the numbers of $x$ or the numbers of $y$ the same in each equation.

The easiest thing to do is:

- leave equation ① alone
- multiply equation ② by 3

Then:

$$2x - 3y = 9 \qquad ①$$
$$15x + 3y = 42 \qquad 3× ②$$

Now add these two equations which eliminates the terms in $y$

$$2x - 3y + 15x + 3y = 9 + 42$$
$$17x = 51$$

Then divide by 17 to give

$$\frac{17x}{17} = \frac{51}{17}$$

So
$$x = 3$$

Take this value of $x$ and substitute it into either ① or ②.

In equation ②, when $x = 3$

$$5x + y = 14$$
$$5 \times 3 + y = 14$$
$$15 + y = 14$$

Subtract 15 from both sides

$$y = 14 - 15$$

So
$$y = -1.$$

So the solution is $x = 3$, $y = -1$.

Check this solution in both equations

$$\text{Equation } ① : 2x - 3y = 2(3) - 3(-1) = 6 + 3 = 9$$

$$\text{Equation } ② : 5x + y = 5(3) + (-1) = 15 - 1 = 14$$

which is correct.

There is another way of doing this problem. You can write $y$ as an expression in terms of $x$ by rearranging equation ② as

$$y = 14 - 5x.$$

Then substitute the expression into equation ①.

$$2x - 3(14 - 5x) = 9$$
$$2x - 42 + 15x = 9$$
$$17x - 42 = 9$$
$$17x = 9 + 42$$
$$17x = 51$$
$$x = \frac{51}{17}$$
$$x = 3$$

Then continue as before to find $y$.

You might like to review work on lowest common multiples.

### Example 11

Solve the simultaneous equations

$$2x + 3y = 5 \qquad 5x + 4y = 2$$

As before, start by labelling the equations.

$$2x + 3y = 5 \quad \text{equation ①}$$
$$5x + 4y = 2 \quad \text{equation ②}$$

There is little to choose between whether to eliminate $x$ or $y$.

To eliminate $x$ you need to multiply ① by one number and ② by another number to get the same number of $x$, in each equation.

So multiply ① by 5 and ② by 2 to give

$$10x + 15y = 25 \qquad 5 \times ①$$
$$10x + 8y = 4 \qquad 2 \times ②$$

Now subtract equation ② from equation ① so that the two $10x$ terms cancel each other to leave

$$10x + 15y - 10x - 8y = 25 - 4$$
$$7y = 21$$

Then divide by 7 to give

$$y = 3$$

Now substitute this value for $y$ back into either ① or ②. In equation ① when $y = 3$

$$2x + 3y = 5$$

becomes $\quad 2x + 3 \times 3 = 5$

$$2x + 9 = 5$$

Subtract 9 from both sides

$$2x = 5 - 9$$
$$2x = -4$$
$$x = -2$$

So the solution is $x = -2$, $y = 3$

Unless you are really short of time in an examination, it is always useful to check that the solution works in both equations.

$2x + 3y$ gives $2 \times -2 + 3 \times 3 = -4 + 9 = 5$, which is correct.

$5x + 4y$ gives $5 \times -2 + 4 \times 3 = -10 + 12 = 2$, which is correct.

---

### Exercise 11G

**1**. Solve the simultaneous equations
$$2x + y = 7$$
$$x - y = 2$$
(a) algebraically
(b) by drawing the graphs of $2x + y = 7$ and $x - y = 2$.

**2**. Solve the simultaneous equations
$$x + y = 12$$
$$x - y = 1$$

**3**. Solve the simultaneous equations
$$3x - 2y = 7$$
$$4x + 3y = -2$$

**4**. Solve the simultaneous equations
$$3p + 4q = 2$$
$$5p + q = 9$$

**5**. Solve each pair of simultaneous equations
(a) $5x - 3y = -4$    $2x + y = 5$
(b) $4x + 5y = -1$    $7x + 4y = 3$
(c) $8x - 3y = 7$    $5x + 2y = 16$
(d) $\frac{1}{2}x + 3y = 4$    $3x + 2y = 8$
(e) $6x - 5y = 11$    $3x - y = 4$
(f) $3x - 2y = -4$    $7x - 5y = -11$
(g) $3x + 4y = 4$    $2y + x = 1$

---

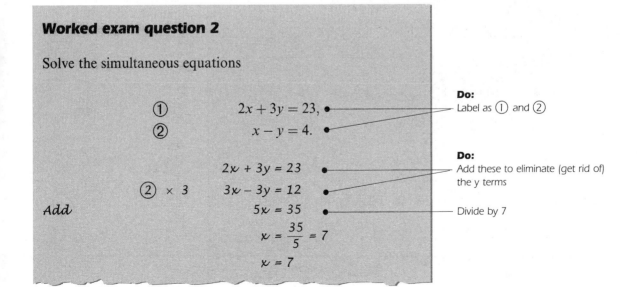

**Worked exam question 2**

Solve the simultaneous equations

① $\qquad 2x + 3y = 23,$ •————————— **Do:** Label as ① and ②
② $\qquad x - y = 4.$ •

$\qquad 2x + 3y = 23$ •————————— **Do:** Add these to eliminate (get rid of) the y terms
② $\times 3 \qquad 3x - 3y = 12$ •
*Add* $\qquad 5x = 35$ •————————— Divide by 7

$\qquad x = \dfrac{35}{5} = 7$

$\qquad x = 7$

Substitute $x = 7$ into ②

$$x - y = 4$$
$$7 - y = 4$$

So

$$y = 3$$

Check:

$$2x + 3y = 2 \times 7 + 3 \times 3$$
$$= 14 + 9 = 23$$

So the values of $x$ and $y$ are correct. ●————

**Do:**
Check the solution in ① if you have time

$$x = \underset{\overline{\quad\quad}}{7}$$

$$y = \underset{\overline{\quad\quad}}{3}$$

(MEG)

## Worked exam question 3

$$y = 2x + 28$$

$$5y = 9x + 150$$

(a) Solve the two simultaneous equations:

$$y = 2x + 28 \quad ① \;●————$$

**Do:**
Label as ①

$$5y = 9x + 150 \quad ② \;●————$$

Label as ②

$$5 \times ① \qquad 5y = 10x + 140$$

$$② \qquad 5y = 9x + 150$$

**Do:**
Subtract ② from $5 \times$ ①

Subtract $\quad 0 = x - 10 \;●————$

$$x - 10 = 0 \;●————$$

Add 10 to both sides

$$x = 10 \;●————$$

Substitute $x = 10$ into ① to find $y$

Substitute $x = 10$ into ① $\qquad y = 2x + 28$

$$y = 2 \times (10) + 28$$

$$y = 48$$

**Do:**
Check the solution in ② if you have time

Check $\qquad\qquad 5y = 5 \times 48 = 240$

$$9x + 150 = 9 \times 10 + 150 = 240$$

so the values of $x$ and $y$ are correct.

(b)   (i)   Write the equation $5y = 9x + 150$ in the form

$$y =$$

$$5y = 9x + 150$$

Divide by 5   $\dfrac{5y}{5} = \dfrac{9x}{5} + \dfrac{150}{5}$

$$y = 1.8x + 30$$

**Do:**
Divide each term by 5

## 11.6 Linear inequalities

In an **equation**, one side is equal to (or the same size as) the other side. For example, the equation $3x = 12$ means that $3x$ is equal to 12.

In a **strict inequality**, one side is not equal to the other side. It can be smaller than or bigger than the other side. For example, the inequality $2x < 7$ means that $2x$ is smaller than 7.

Sometimes in an inequality, one side can be smaller (or bigger) than or equal to the other side. For example, $4x \leqslant 20$ means that $4x$ is smaller than or equal to 20 and $2x \geqslant 6$ means that $2x$ is bigger than or equal to 6.

When dealing with linear inequalities most of the techniques used for linear equations can be applied.

For instance, to solve

$$3x + 5 < 17$$

simply subtract 5 from both sides

$$3x + 5 - 5 < 17 - 5$$

$$\text{so } 3x < 12$$

Divide by 3 to give

$$x < 4$$

which is the solution.

However you do need to be *very* careful when dealing with the multiplication and division of negative numbers in inequalities.

You know that $1 < 3$. If you multiply both sides by 2 you get $2 < 6$, which is a true statement. However if you multiply 1 by $-2$ you get $-2$ and if you multiply 3 by $-2$ you get $-6$. Clearly $-2$ is not less than $-6$ so the inequality is no longer true. In fact $-2 > -6$ so the inequality sign needs to be reversed.

So, whenever you are working with inequalities the best thing you can do is to avoid multiplying and dividing by negative numbers.

### *Example 12*

If $n$ is an integer and $-3 < n \leqslant 5$, write down the possible values of $n$.

The integers between $-3$ and $5$ are $-3, -2, -1, 0, 1, 2, 3, 4, 5$. But the first one has to be eliminated because $n$ must be greater than (and cannot be equal to) $-3$. So the values of $n$ are:

$$-2, -1, 0, 1, 2, 3, 4, 5$$

You can show the solution on a number line. The circle at $n = -3$ shows that $n$ *cannot* equal $-3$. The solid dot at $n = 5$ shows that $n$ *can* equal $5$.

> *An integer is a whole number. It can be positive, negative or zero.*

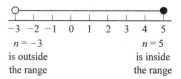

$n = -3$ is outside the range    $n = 5$ is inside the range

### *Example 13*

Solve the inequality: $\qquad 4x - 3 > 17$

Add 3 to both sides

$$4x - 3 + 3 > 17 + 3$$

So $\qquad\qquad\qquad 4x > 20$

Divide by 4 to give

$$x > 5$$

which is the solution.

### *Example 14*

Solve: $\qquad\qquad 2(5 - 3x) \leqslant -2$

Firstly multiply out the bracket

$$10 - 6x \leqslant -2$$

Then add $6x$ to both sides

$$10 - 6x + 6x \leqslant -2 + 6x$$

So $\qquad\qquad\qquad 10 \leqslant -2 + 6x$

Now add 2 to both sides

$$10 + 2 \leqslant -2 + 6x + 2$$

So $\qquad\qquad\qquad 12 \leqslant 6x$

Write this the other way round, but be careful with the inequality sign. It becomes

$$6x \geqslant 12$$

Divide by 2 to give

$$x \geqslant 2$$

which is the solution.

You could, if you wished, or were asked to do so, represent this on a number line.

The dot is solid to show that $x$ can equal 2.

## *Example 15*

Solve the inequality:

$$3x + 1 > 2x + 5$$

given that $x$ is an integer less than 10.

First subtract 1 from both sides to give

$$3x + 1 - 1 > 2x + 5 - 1$$

So $\qquad\qquad 3x > 2x + 4$

Now collect the $x$ terms on the side which has the biggest $x$ term by subtracting $2x$ from both sides to give

$$3x - 2x > 2x + 4 - 2x$$

So $\qquad\qquad x > 4$

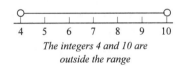

*The integers 4 and 10 are outside the range*

You can show this on a number line and since $x$ is an integer less than 10, the solution is $x = 5, 6, 7, 8, 9$.

## Exercise 11H

**1.** Write down all the integer values of $p$ for which
$$-5 \leqslant p < 3$$

**2.** Write down all the integer values of $n$ which satisfy the inequality
$$10 \geqslant n > -3$$

**3.** Solve each of these inequalities. Be careful to interpret the sign correctly in each case.
   (a) $3x - 7 \geqslant 23$
   (b) $4(3 - 2x) < 32$
   (c) $4x + 3 \leqslant 2x - 5$
   (d) $2x - 7 < 8$ given that $x$ is an integer greater than 0
   (e) $2(3x + 1) > 5x - 2$
   (f) $5(2x - 1) \leqslant 3(3x + 2)$

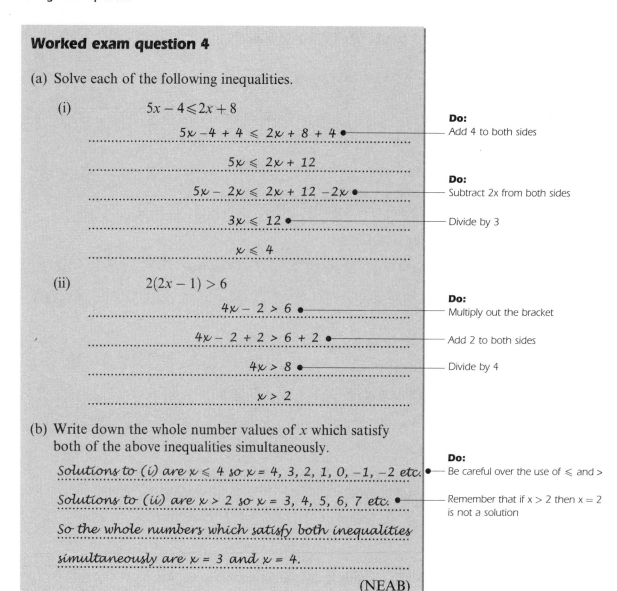

**Worked exam question 4**

(a) Solve each of the following inequalities.

(i)             $5x - 4 \leqslant 2x + 8$

$5x - 4 + 4 \leqslant 2x + 8 + 4$  ● ——————— **Do:** Add 4 to both sides

$5x \leqslant 2x + 12$

$5x - 2x \leqslant 2x + 12 - 2x$ ● ——————— **Do:** Subtract 2x from both sides

$3x \leqslant 12$ ● ——————— Divide by 3

$x \leqslant 4$

(ii)            $2(2x - 1) > 6$

$4x - 2 > 6$ ● ——————— **Do:** Multiply out the bracket

$4x - 2 + 2 > 6 + 2$ ● ——————— Add 2 to both sides

$4x > 8$ ● ——————— Divide by 4

$x > 2$

(b) Write down the whole number values of $x$ which satisfy both of the above inequalities simultaneously.

Solutions to (i) are $x \leqslant 4$ so $x = 4, 3, 2, 1, 0, -1, -2$ etc. ● — **Do:** Be careful over the use of $\leqslant$ and $>$

Solutions to (ii) are $x > 2$ so $x = 3, 4, 5, 6, 7$ etc. ● — Remember that if $x > 2$ then $x = 2$ is not a solution

So the whole numbers which satisfy both inequalities

simultaneously are $x = 3$ and $x = 4$.

(NEAB)

## Exercise 11I (Mixed questions)

**1.** Solve these equations:
(a) $x + 3 = 12$          (b) $3x + 1 = 16$
(c) $4x - 2 = 19$          (d) $7 - x = 10$
(e) $11 - 3x = 17$        (f) $8 - 5x = 15$
(g) $3x - 1 = 2x + 5$    (h) $4x - 3 = 2x - 11$
(i) $3(x - 1) = 2(x + 7)$    (j) $5(2 - x) = 3(x + 6)$

**2.** Solve the following equations:
(a) $\dfrac{x}{2} = 5$          (b) $4x - 2 = 10 - 2x$

**3.** Solve the following equation:
$3(x - 1) + x = 15$

**4.** Solve the simultaneous equations:
$2x - 3y = 14$
$3x + y = -1$

**5.** (a) Solve the equation   $9x + 6 = 36 - x$
(b) Solve the simultaneous equations:
$4p - q = 15$
$2p - q = 9$          [London]

**6.** List all the values of $x$, where $x$ is an integer such that
$-2 \leqslant x < 4$          [London]

**7.** Solve the inequality
$7x + 3 > 2x - 15$          [SEG]

**8.** $x$ is a positive integer and
$3x + 1 < 15$
Find all the possible values of $x$.

## Test yourself

| | |
|---|---|
| **QUESTION** | **1.** Solve the equation $4x + 3 = 27$ |
| **ANSWER** | $x = 6$ |

*If your answer is incorrect review page 216, Section 11.2 on equations with the unknown quantity on one side. Also check your arithmetic.*

| | |
|---|---|
| **QUESTION** | **2.** Solve the equation $19 + 3y = 9 - 2y$ |
| **ANSWER** | $y = -2$ |

*If your answer is incorrect review page 221, Section 11.4 on equations with the unknown quantity on both sides, Example 7. Also check your arithmetic.*

| | |
|---|---|
| **QUESTION** | **3.** Solve the simultaneous equations |

$$2x + 3y = 1$$
$$x + y = 2$$

| | |
|---|---|
| **ANSWER** | $x = 5, y = -3$ |

*If your answer is incorrect review page 223, Section 11.5 on simultaneous equations, particularly Example 11 on page 226.*

| | |
|---|---|
| **QUESTION** | **4.** Write down all the integer values for $x$ for which |

$$-6 < 2x \leqslant 10$$

| | |
|---|---|
| **ANSWER** | $x = -2, -1, 0, 1, 2, 3, 4, 5$ |

*If your answer is incorrect review page 229, Section 11.6 on linear inequalities, particularly up to and including Example 12 on page 230.*

| | |
|---|---|
| **QUESTION** | **5.** Solve the inequality |

$$3(x - 4) > 2x + 5$$

| | |
|---|---|
| **ANSWER** | $x > 17$ |

*If your answer is incorrect review page 229, Section 11.6 on linear inequalities, particularly Example 13 onwards on page 230.*

## Summary of key points to remember

1. In **linear equations** the unknown quantity (or quantities) is raised to the power 1.

   These are linear equations:

   $$x + 5 = 11$$
   $$7 - 4x = 2$$
   $$3(x - 5) = 2(x + 1)$$

   When solving linear equations

   - multiply out the brackets (if necessary)

- isolate the unknown on one side of the equation

- check your solution by substituting it into the original equation.

2. A pair of **simultaneous equations** has a solution which satisfies both equations.

The equations:

$3x - 2y = 19$
$5x + 3y = 11$

are simultaneous equations.

When solving simultaneous equations

- label the equations ① and ② and use these labels in your working

- add or subtract one equation from another to eliminate one unknown

- if necessary, choose numbers to multiply the equations by in order to eliminate the unknowns when you add or subtract the equations

- check that your solution works in both equations.

3. Expressions such as:

$x - 3 \leqslant 8$
$7 - 4x \geqslant 2$
$3(x - 7) < 9 + 4x$

are **linear inequalities**.

When solving linear inequalities, use the same techniques as for linear equations. Also

- avoid multiplying or dividing by negative numbers

- show your solution on a number line if this helps

- remember that:    $<$ means less than
$\leqslant$ means less than or equal to
$>$ means greater than
$\geqslant$ means greater than or equal to.

## 12.1 Introduction

Unit 9 was about straight-line graphs. This unit is about graphs that are not straight lines.

You should remember that the formula for a straight line can be written in the form:

$$y = mx + c$$

where

$m$ is the **gradient** of the straight line

and

$c$ is the **intercept** of the straight line with the $y$-axis.

In the formula of a straight-line graph, $x$ is raised to the power 1.

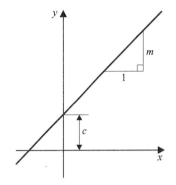

In this unit the graphs have expressions with $x^2$, $x^3$, $\frac{1}{x}$ and combinations of these.

You will learn to plot, draw or sketch graphs of the type:

$$y = Ax^3 + Bx^2 + Cx + D + \frac{E}{x}$$

but with the restriction that at least two of the numbers $A$, $B$, $C$, $D$ and $E$ are 0.

For example, you will plot, draw and use a graph such as

$$y = 2x^3 + 5x - \frac{3}{x}$$

## 12.2 The graph of $y = x^2$: the squared function

Construct a table of values for $y$ from $x = -4$ to 4

| $x$ | $-4$ | $-3$ | $-2$ | $-1$ | 0 | 1 | 2 | 3 | 4 |
|---|---|---|---|---|---|---|---|---|---|
| $y = x^2$ | 16 | 9 | 4 | 1 | 0 | 1 | 4 | 9 | 16 |

Then plot the graph, using these values.

On this graph we can use a one-to-one scale for each axis. It is not always possible to do so.

The graph should be a smooth curve. It should not have any kinks in it, and it should not be flattened off or pointed at the bottom.

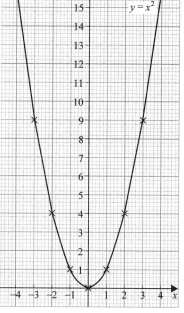

The graph of $y = x^2$:

- passes through the origin
- is symmetrical about the $y$-axis (vertical axis or line $x = 0$)

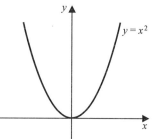

Using this information you can:

- sketch the graph of $y = x^2$
- sketch the graph of $y = x^2 + 3$

$y = x^2 + 3$ is the graph of $y = x^2$ translated $+3$ units, *up* the vertical axis.

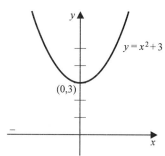

- sketch the graph of $y = x^2 - 5$

This is the graph of $y = x^2$ translated $-5$ units, *down* the vertical axis.

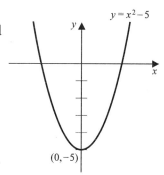

---

### Exercise 12A

1. (a) Copy and complete this table of values for
   $y = x^2 + 3$

| $x$ | $-4$ | $-3$ | $-2$ | $-1$ | 0 | 1 | 2 | 3 | 4 |
|---|---|---|---|---|---|---|---|---|---|
| $y$ | 19 | | 7 | | | | | 12 | |

   (b) Draw the graph of $y = x^2 + 3$ for values of $x$ from $-4$ to 4.

2. (a) Construct your own table of values for
      $y = x^2 - 3$
   (b) Draw the graph of $y = x^2 - 3$

3. *Sketch* the graphs of:
   (a) $y = x^2 - 1$     (b) $y = x^2 + 1$
   (c) $y = x^2 - 5$     (d) $y = x^2 + 5$
   (e) $y = x^2 + 2$     (f) $y = x^2 - 2$
   (g) $y = x^2 - 10$    (h) $y = x^2 + 8$
   (i) $y = x^2 - 8$     (j) $y = x^2 + 7$

## 12.3 The graph of y=x³: the cubic function

Construct a table of values for $y$ from $x = -4$ to 4.

*Remember*: $(-4)^3 = (-4) \times (-4) \times (-4) = -64$.

| $x$ | -4 | -3 | -2 | -1 | 0 | 1 | 2 | 3 | 4 |
|---|---|---|---|---|---|---|---|---|---|
| $y = x^3$ | -64 | -27 | -8 | -1 | 0 | 1 | 8 | 27 | 64 |

Then plot the graph using these values:

On this graph you cannot use a one-to-one scale on the $y$-axis because $x^3$ very quickly becomes too large.

The graph of $y = x^3$:

- passes through the origin

- is not symmetrical about the vertical axis

- has rotational symmetry of order 2 (if you rotate it through 180° it looks the same)

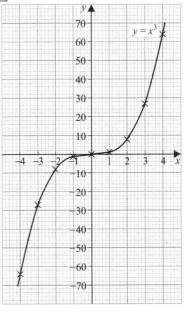

Using this information you can:

- sketch the graph of $y = x^3$

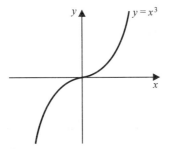

- sketch the graph of $y = x^3 + 2$

$y = x^3 + 2$ is the graph of $y = x^3$ translated $+2$ units, *up* the vertical axis.

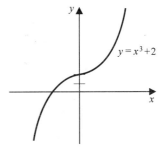

- sketch the graph of $y = x^3 - 4$

$y = x^3 - 4$ is the graph of $y = x^3$ translated $-4$ units, *down* the vertical axis.

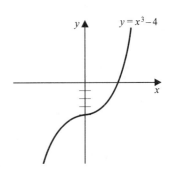

### Exercise 12B

1. (a) Copy and complete this table of values for
$y = x^3 + 2$

| $x$ | $-4$ | $-3$ | $-2$ | $-1$ | 0 | 1 | 2 | 3 | 4 |
|---|---|---|---|---|---|---|---|---|---|
| $y$ | $-62$ | | | | | | | 29 | |

(b) Draw the graph of $y = x^3 + 2$ for values of $x$ from $-4$ to 4.

2. Construct a table of values and draw the graph for these.
   (a) $y = x^3 - 2$   (b) $y = x^3 + 3$

(c) $y = x^3 - 4$   (d) $y = x^3 + 5$
(e) $y = x^3 + 1$   (f) $y = x^3 - 1$
Check your graphs with the sketches shown on page 236.

3. *Sketch* the graphs of:
   (a) $y = x^3 + 1$   (b) $y = x^3 + 2$
   (c) $y = x^3 - 1$   (d) $y = x^3 - 2$
   (e) $y = x^3 - 3$   (f) $y = x^3 + 3$
   (g) $y = x^3 + 5$   (h) $y = x^3 - 5$
   (i) $y = x^3 + k$ where $k$ is any constant number.
   (j) $y = x^3 - k$ where $k$ is any constant number.

## 12.4 The graph of $y = \dfrac{1}{x}$: the reciprocal function

Start by constructing a table of values of $y$ for values of $x$ from $x = -4$ to $x = 4$.

There is a problem when $x = 0$, because $\frac{1}{0}$ cannot be defined.

Instead of using $x = 0$ in the table you can choose two values close to $x = 0$, one positive and one negative.

For example, use $x = 0.2$ and $x = -0.2$.

| $x$ | $-4$ | $-3$ | $-2$ | $-1$ | $-0.2$ | 0.2 | 1 | 2 | 3 | 4 |
|---|---|---|---|---|---|---|---|---|---|---|
| $y = 1/x$ | $-0.25$ | $-0.33$ | $-0.5$ | $-1$ | $-5$ | 5 | 1 | 0.5 | 0.33 | 0.25 |

The graph is:

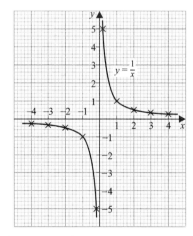

As $x$ crosses the boundary from being negative to being positive, the value of $y$ changes from negative to positive.

$$\frac{1}{\text{positive small number}} = \text{positive large number}$$

$$\frac{1}{\text{negative small number}} = \text{negative large number}$$

At $x = 0$ there is a **point of discontinuity**. In other words, there is a break in the curve at $x = 0$.

The graph of $y = \dfrac{1}{x}$:

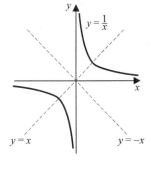

- has two separate branches, for positive and negative values of $x$. Neither branch passes through the origin.

- has two lines of symmetry, $y = x$ and $y = -x$

- When $x$ is close to 0 and positive then $y$ is very large and positive.

- When $x$ is close to 0 and negative then $y$ is very large and negative.

Using this information you can:

- sketch the graph of $y = \dfrac{1}{x}$

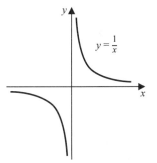

- sketch the graph of $y = \dfrac{1}{x} + 3$

$y = \dfrac{1}{x} + 3$ is the graph of $y = x$ translated $+3$ units, *up* the vertical axis.

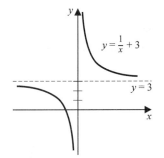

- sketch the graph of $y = \dfrac{1}{x} - 2$

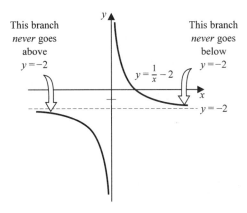

This branch *never* goes above $y = -2$

This branch *never* goes below $y = -2$

$y = \dfrac{1}{x} - 2$

$y = -2$

$y = \dfrac{1}{x} - 2$ is the graph of $y = \dfrac{1}{x}$ translated $-2$ units, *down* the vertical axis.

The line $y = -2$ is called an **asymptote**.

### Exercise 12C

1. (a) Copy and complete the table of values for
$$y = \frac{1}{x} + 2$$

| x | −4 | −3 | −2 | −1 | 1 | 2 | 3 | 4 |
|---|----|----|----|----|---|---|---|---|
| y | 1.75 | 1.67 | | | | | | 2.25 |

(b) Draw the graph of $y = \frac{1}{x} + 2$ for values of $x$ from −4 to 4.
(Be careful about what happens to the graph when $x$ is near to zero.)

2. Draw the graphs of:

(a) $y = \frac{1}{x} - 2$      (b) $y = \frac{1}{x} + 3$

(c) $y = \frac{1}{x} + 4$      (d) $y = \frac{1}{x} - 5$

(e) $y = \frac{1}{x} + 5$      (f) $y = \frac{1}{x} + 8$

3. *Sketch* the graphs of:

(a) $y = \frac{1}{x} + 6$      (b) $y = \frac{1}{x} - 6$

## 12.5 The graphs of $y = Ax^2$, $y = Ax^3$ and $y = \dfrac{A}{x}$

To draw the graph of $y = 3x^2$, first construct a table of values for $y = 3x^2$ for values of $x$ from −4 to 4.

| x | −4 | −3 | −2 | −1 | 0 | 1 | 2 | 3 | 4 |
|---|----|----|----|----|---|---|---|---|---|
| $y = 3x^2$ | 48 | 27 | 12 | 3 | 0 | 3 | 12 | 27 | 48 |

Then plot the graph using these values. Plot the graph of $y = x^2$ on the same axes.

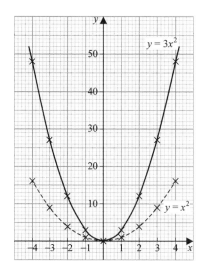

For every value of $x$, the $y$-value on $y = 3x^2$ is 3 times the $y$-value on the $y = x^2$ graph.

So $y = 3x^2$ is the same shape as $y = x^2$ but it is 3 times as steep.

*Example 1*

On the same axes, plot the graphs of $y = \dfrac{1}{x}$   and   $y = \dfrac{2}{x}$

for values of $x$ from $-4$ to 4.

Confirm that the graph of $y = \dfrac{2}{x}$ is two times as steep as $y = \dfrac{1}{x}$

The combined table of values is:

| $x$ | $-4$ | $-3$ | $-2$ | $-1$ | $-0.1$ | $0.1$ | $1$ | $2$ | $3$ | $4$ |
|---|---|---|---|---|---|---|---|---|---|---|
| $y = \frac{1}{x}$ | $-0.25$ | $-0.33$ | $-0.5$ | $-1$ | $-10$ | $10$ | $1$ | $0.5$ | $0.33$ | $0.25$ |
| $y = \frac{2}{x}$ | $-0.5$ | $-0.67$ | $-1$ | $-2$ | $-20$ | $20$ | $2$ | $1$ | $0.67$ | $0.5$ |

The graphs are:

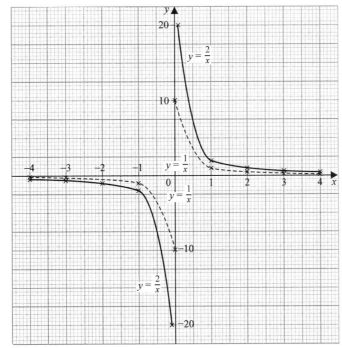

The $y$-values for $y = \dfrac{2}{x}$ are two times the corresponding $y$-values
for $y = \dfrac{1}{x}$

So $y = \dfrac{2}{x}$ is two times as steep as $y = \dfrac{1}{x}$

---

### Exercise 12D

1. On the same axes draw the graphs of
   $y = x^3$ and $y = 2x^3$ for values of $x$ from $-4$ to 4.
   Confirm that the graph of $y = 2x^3$ is two times
   as steep as the graph of $y = x^3$.

2. (a) Copy and complete the table of values
   opposite for $y = \frac{1}{2}x^3$

| $x$ | $-4$ | $-3$ | $-2$ | $-1$ | $0$ | $1$ | $2$ | $3$ | $4$ |
|---|---|---|---|---|---|---|---|---|---|
| $y$ | $-32$ | | | | | | | $13.5$ | |

(b) Draw the graph of $y = \frac{1}{2}x^3$
(c) Comment on the steepness of this graph
    compared with the steepness of the graph of
    $y = x^3$

3. (a) Copy and complete the table of values for $y = \dfrac{6}{x}$ for values of $x$ from 1 to 12.

(b) Draw the graph of $y = \dfrac{6}{x}$ for values of $x$ from 1 to 12.

(c) Comment on the steepness of this graph compared with the graph of $y = \dfrac{1}{x}$

| $x$ | 1 | 2 | 3 | 4 | 5 | 6 | 7 | 8 | 9 | 10 | 11 | 12 |
|---|---|---|---|---|---|---|---|---|---|---|---|---|
| $y$ | 6 | | | | | 1 | | | | 0.6 | | |

---

# 12.6 Sketch graphs of $y = Ax^2$, $y = Ax^3$ and $y = \dfrac{A}{x}$

You should now be able to sketch graphs of $y = Ax^2$, $y = Ax^3$ and $y = \dfrac{A}{x}$ where $A$ is any positive number.

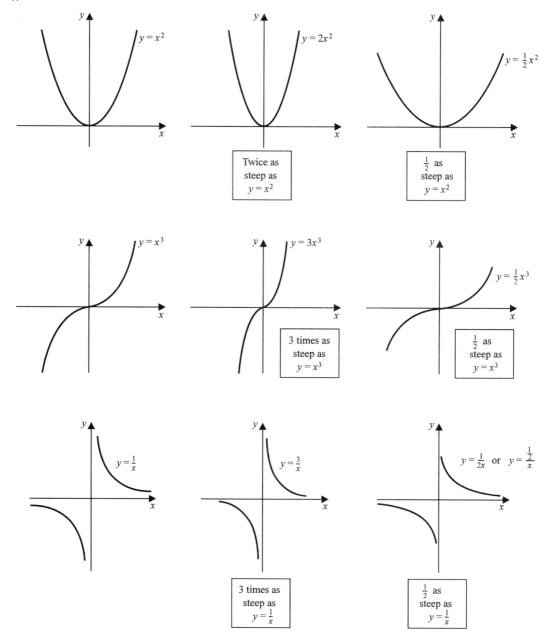

# 12.7 The graphs of $y = -x^2$, $y = -x^3$ and $y = \dfrac{-1}{x}$

We will look first at $y = -x^3$. You can construct a table of values for $y = -x^3$ for values of $x$ from $-4$ to $4$.

| $x$ | $-4$ | $-3$ | $-2$ | $-1$ | 0 | 1 | 2 | 3 | 4 |
|---|---|---|---|---|---|---|---|---|---|
| $y = -x^3$ | 64 | 27 | 8 | 1 | 0 | $-1$ | $-8$ | $-27$ | $-64$ |

Then you can plot the graph using these values. Plot the graph of $y = x^3$ on the same axes.

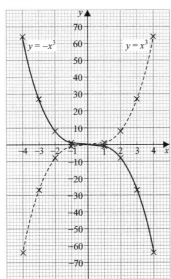

The graph of $y = -x^3$ is the same shape as the graph of $y = x^3$ but upside down.

More correctly, the graph of $y = -x^3$ is obtained by **reflecting** the graph of $y = x^3$ in the $x$-axis (the horizontal axis or the line $y = 0$).

| The graph of $y = -x^2$ is like this: | The graph of $y = x^2$ is like this: |
|---|---|

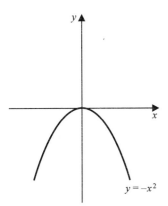

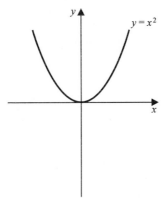

$y = -x^2$ is the reflection of $y = x^2$ in the $x$-axis.

The graph of
$$y = -\frac{1}{x}$$
is like this

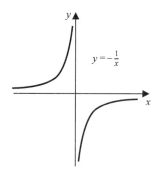

The graph of
$$y = \frac{1}{x}$$
is like this

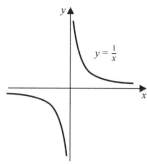

$y = -\dfrac{1}{x}$ is the reflection of $y = \dfrac{1}{x}$ in the $x$-axis.

### Worked exam question 1

Here are five equations:

1. $y = x^2 + 1$
2. $y = -x^2$
3. $y = \dfrac{2}{x}$
4. $y = 2$
5. $y = 1 - x$

Here are sketches of five graphs:

**A**

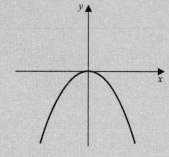

**B**

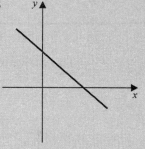

**C**

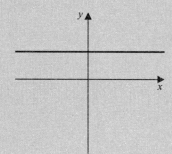

**D**

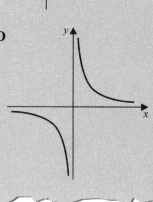

**Do:**

Look for the curves that pass through the origin

Look for the curves that have two branches

Look for the ones that are straight

**E**

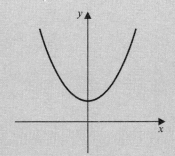

Match each sketch to the correct equation.

**Do:**

1. $E, y = x^2 + 1$ ● ─────────────────────────── Look for a curve not passing through the origin, quadratic shape

2. $A, y = -x^2$ ● ─────────────────────────── Look for a curve passing through the origin, quadratic shape, upside down

3. $D, y = \dfrac{2}{x}$ ● ─────────────────────────── Look for a graph with two branches

4. $C, y = 2$ ● ─────────────────────────── Look for a straight horizontal line

5. $B, y = 1 - x$ ● ─────────────────────────── Look for a straight line, not passing through the origin

## Worked exam question 2

Here is a sketch of the graph of $y = \dfrac{1}{x}$

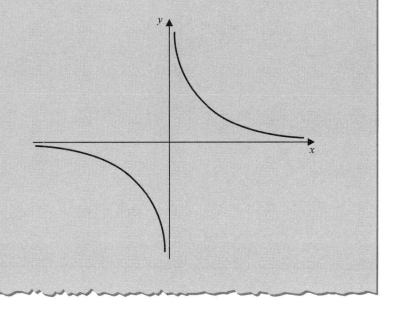

(i)   Sketch the graph of $y = \dfrac{-1}{x}$

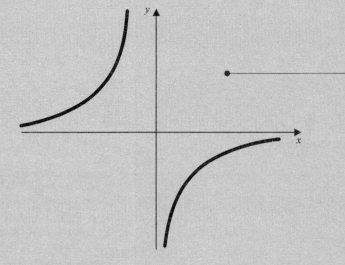

**Do:**
Remember that $y = \dfrac{-1}{x}$ is a reflection of $y = \dfrac{1}{x}$ in the horizontal axis

**Don't:**
Let a $\dfrac{1}{x}$-type graph go through $x = 0$

(ii)   Sketch the graph of $y = 2 + \dfrac{1}{x}$

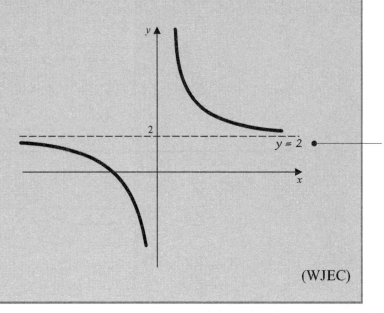

**Do:**
Remember that $y = 2 + \dfrac{1}{x}$ is $y = \dfrac{1}{x}$ moved 2 units up the y-axis. Mark in the 2 units

(WJEC)

## Exercise 12E

1. By drawing the graphs, confirm that:
   (a) the graph of $y = -x^2$ is a reflection of the graph of $y = x^2$ in the $x$-axis.
   (b) the graph of $y = -\dfrac{1}{x}$ is a reflection of the graph of $y = \dfrac{1}{x}$ in the $x$-axis.

2. (a) Copy and complete the table of values for $y = 1 - x^2$

| $x$ | $-4$ | $-3$ | $-2$ | $-1$ | 0 | 1 | 2 | 3 | 4 |
|---|---|---|---|---|---|---|---|---|---|
| $y$ | $-15$ | | | | 1 | | | $-8$ | |

   (b) Draw the graph of $y = 1 - x^2$ for values of $x$ from $-4$ to 4.

3. (a) Copy and complete the table of values for $y = 4 - x^3$

| $x$ | $-4$ | $-3$ | $-2$ | $-1$ | 0 | 1 | 2 | 3 | 4 |
|---|---|---|---|---|---|---|---|---|---|
| $y$ | | 31 | | | | | | | $-60$ |

   (b) Draw the graph of $y = 4 - x^3$ for values of $x$ from $-4$ to 4.

4. Draw the graph of $y = 6 - \frac{1}{x}$ for values of $x$ from $\frac{1}{2}$ to 4.

# 12.8 Quadratic graphs

An expression of the form $Ax^2 + Bx + C$, where $A$, $B$ and $C$ are numbers, is called a **quadratic expression**. Quadratic expressions always have an $x^2$ term. There is not always an $x$ term or a constant term. If $B = 0$ there is no $x$ term and if $C = 0$ there is no constant term.

You can draw a graph of a quadratic expression and use the graph to solve quadratic equations.

## *Example 2*

(a) Draw the graph of $y = 2x^2 - 13x + 15$ for values of $x$ from $-2$ to 7.

(b) Use your graph to find solutions to the equations:

   (i) $2x^2 - 13x + 15 = 0$

   (ii) $2x^2 - 13x + 15 = 5$

(a) Draw up a table of values for $y = 2x^2 - 13x + 15$.

   *Remember:*   $(-2)^2 = (-2) \times (-2) = 4$

   so   $2(-2)^2 = 2 \times 4 = 8$

| $x$ | $-2$ | $-1$ | 0 | 1 | 2 | 3 | 4 | 5 | 6 | 7 |
|---|---|---|---|---|---|---|---|---|---|---|
| $2x^2$ | 8 | 2 | 0 | 2 | 8 | 18 | 32 | 50 | 72 | 98 |
| $-13x$ | $+26$ | $+13$ | 0 | $-13$ | $-26$ | $-39$ | $-52$ | $-65$ | $-78$ | $-91$ |
| $+15$ | $+15$ | $+15$ | $+15$ | $+15$ | $+15$ | $+15$ | $+15$ | $+15$ | $+15$ | $+15$ |
| $y$ | 49 | 30 | 15 | 4 | $-3$ | $-6$ | $-5$ | 0 | 9 | 22 |

Now plot the points and draw the graph.

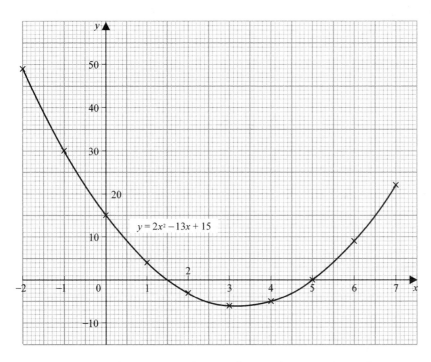

(b) To show you how to use the graph to solve equations the graph has been drawn again. You need not do this, usually, especially in an exam. It has been done here for your convenience.

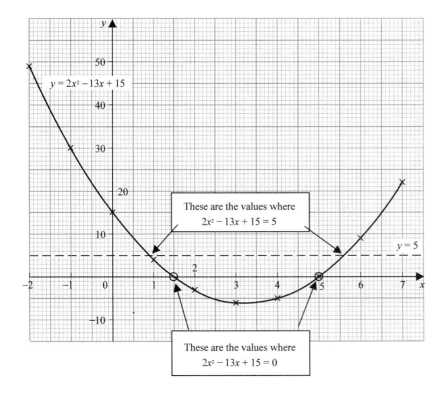

(i)  To solve the equation $2x^2 - 13x + 15 = 0$ using the graph
$y = 2x^2 - 13x + 15$, look at the graph where $y = 0$.

The $x$-values where the graph crosses the line $y = 0$ (the
horizontal axis) are the required values of $x$.

These $x$-values are $x = 1\frac{1}{2}$ and $x = 5$.

(ii)  To solve the equation $2x^2 - 13x + 15 = 5$ look at the
graph where $y = 5$.

Draw the line $y = 5$. Read off the values of $x$ where the
graph crosses this line.

The values of $x$ are $x = 0.9$ and $x = 5.6$ approximately.

Graphs of quadratic expressions are always similar in shape to a
graph of $x^2$.

When the $x^2$ term is positive:        When the $x^2$ term is negative:

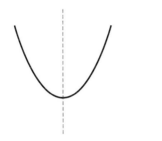    

Graphs of quadratic expressions have a vertical line of symmetry
and a minimum or maximum turning point.

In general a quadratic equation has two solutions. You can have
equations '$y = 0$' with:

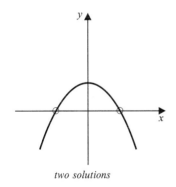        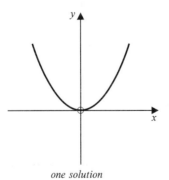        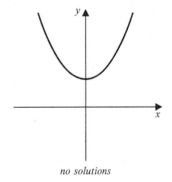

*two solutions*            *one solution*            *no solutions*

___

### Exercise 12F

**1.** (a) Copy and complete the table of values for
$y = x^2 - 8x + 15 = 0$

| $x$ | $-1$ | 0 | 1 | 2 | 3 | 4 | 5 | 6 | 7 |
|---|---|---|---|---|---|---|---|---|---|
| $y$ |  | 15 |  |  |  |  | 0 |  | 8 |

(b) Draw the graph of $y = x^2 - 8x + 15$
for values of $x$ from $-1$ to 7.

(c) Use your graph to solve the equations:
  (i)  $x^2 - 8x + 15 = 0$
  (ii) $x^2 - 8x + 15 = 5$

**2.** (a) Copy and complete the table of values for
$y = 2x^2 - 9x - 5$

| $x$ | −3 | −2 | −1 | 0 | 1 | 2 | 3 | 4 | 5 | 6 | 7 |
|---|---|---|---|---|---|---|---|---|---|---|---|
| $y$ | | | | | | | | | | | |

(b) Draw the graph of $y = 2x^2 - 9x - 5$ for values of $x$ from −3 to 7.

(c) Use your graph to solve the equations:
   (i) $2x^2 - 9x - 5 = 0$
   (ii) $2x^2 - 9x - 5 = -10$

## 12.9 Cubic graphs

An expression of the form $Ax^3 + Bx^2 + Cx + D$, where $A$, $B$, $C$ and $D$ are numbers is called a **cubic expression**. Cubic expressions always have an $x^3$ term. There is not always an $x^2$ term, an $x$ term or a constant term. If $B = 0$ there is no $x^2$ term, if $C = 0$ there is no $x$ term and if $D = 0$ there is no constant term.

You can draw a graph of a cubic expression, and use the graph to solve cubic equations.

### *Example 3*

(a) Draw the graph of

$$y = x^3 - 6x^2 + 3x + 11$$

for values of $x$ from −2 to 6.

(b) Use your graph to find solutions to the equations:
   (i) $x^3 - 6x^2 + 3x + 11 = 0$
   (ii) $x^3 - 6x^2 + 3x + 11 = 5$

(a) Draw up a table of values for $y = x^3 - 6x^2 + 3x + 11$.

*Remember :* $(-2)^3 = (-2) \times (-2) \times (-2)$
$= -8$

$-6(-2)^3 = (-6) \times (-8)$
$= 48$

| $x$ | −2 | −1 | 0 | 1 | 2 | 3 | 4 | 5 | 6 |
|---|---|---|---|---|---|---|---|---|---|
| $x^3$ | −8 | −1 | 0 | 1 | 8 | 27 | 64 | 125 | 216 |
| $-6x^2$ | −24 | −6 | 0 | −6 | −24 | −54 | −96 | −150 | −216 |
| $+3x$ | −6 | −3 | 0 | 3 | 6 | 9 | 12 | 15 | 18 |
| $+11$ | +11 | +11 | +11 | +11 | +11 | +11 | +11 | +11 | +11 |
| $y$ | −27 | 1 | 11 | 9 | 1 | −7 | −9 | 1 | 29 |

Now plot the points and draw the graph.

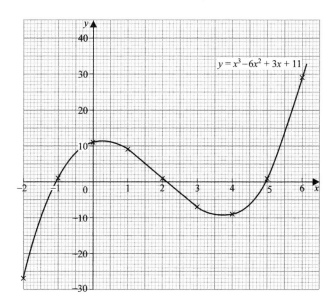

*Remember*: draw a smooth curve with no kinks, points or flat bits.

(b) (i) To solve the equation $x^3 - 6x^2 + 3x + 11 = 0$ look at the graph where $y = 0$, that is, where the graph crosses the horizontal axis.

The values of $x$ that satisfy the equation are $x = -1.1$, $x = 2.2$ and $x = 4.9$ approximately.

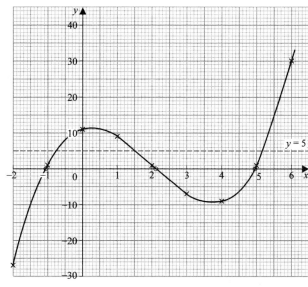

(ii) To solve the equation $x^3 - 6x^2 + 3x + 11 = 5$ look at the graph where $y = 5$. Draw the line $y = 5$. Read off the $x$-values where the graph crosses this line.

The values of $x$ are $x = -0.8$, $x = 1.5$ and $x = 5.2$ approximately.

Graphs of cubic expressions are always similar in shape to the graph of $x^3$.

When the $x^3$ term is positive:

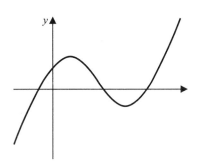

When the $x^3$ term is negative:

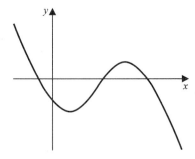

Graphs of cubic expressions usually have two turning points or bends, but some, like $y = x^3$ have only one turning point.

In general a cubic equation has three solutions. You can have equations '$y = 0$' with

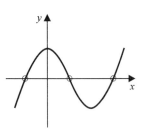

*three solutions*

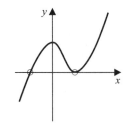

*two solutions*

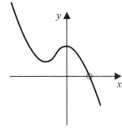

*one solution*

---

### Exercise 12G

1. (a) Copy and complete the table of values for
   $y = x^3 - 12x + 13$

   | x | −4 | −3 | −2 | −1 | 0 | 1 | 2 | 3 | 4 |
   |---|----|----|----|----|---|---|---|---|---|
   | y | −3 |    |    |    |   |   |   | 4 |   |

   (b) Draw the graph of $y = x^3 - 12x + 13$ for values of $x$ from −4 to 4.

   (c) Use your graph to find all of the solutions to the equations:

   (i) $x^3 - 12x + 13 = 0$
   (ii) $x^3 - 12x + 13 = 10$

2. Find all the solutions of the equation
   $x^3 - 18x = 20$

---

### Worked exam question 3

(a) Complete this table of values for $y = 5x^2$

| x | −3 | −2 | −1 | 0 | 1 | 2 | 3 |
|---|----|----|----|---|---|---|---|
| y | 45 | 20 | 5  | 0 | 5 | 20 | 45 |

**Do:**
Make sure you work out $5x^2$ as
$5 \times x \times x$ i.e. when x = 3,
$5x^2 = 5 \times 3 \times 3 = 5 \times 9 = 45$

(b) On the grid plot the points represented by the values in your table. Join them with a smooth curve.

(c) (i) The point with coordinates $(-3, 5)$ lies on the line with equation $y = 5x + 20$. Write down the coordinates of the point on the line with an $x$ coordinate of 3.

$$x = 3$$
$$y = 5 \times 3 + 20 \bullet$$
$$= 15 + 20$$
$$y = 35$$

$(3, \underset{\ldots\ldots}{35} )$

**Do:**
Work out $5x + 20$ when $x = 3$ as $(5 \times 3) + 20 = 15 + 20$

(ii) Plot the two points and join them with a straight line.

(d) (i) Which equation in $x$ is solved by writing down the $x$ coordinates of the points of intersection of the curve and the line?
Give your answer as simply as possible.

*Equation is*

$$5x^2 = 5x + 20$$

*Divide through by 5 to give*

$$\underset{\ldots\ldots\ldots\ldots}{x^2 = x + 4}$$

**Do:**
Remember that the points where the two graphs meet are the solutions

Divide every term by 5

(ii) Write down these values of $x$.
Give your answers correct to 1 decimal place.

*Solutions from the graph are*

$$x = \underset{\ldots\ldots\ldots\ldots}{-1.6} \text{ and } \underset{\ldots\ldots\ldots}{2.6}$$

**Do:**
Read off the graph as carefully and accurately as you can

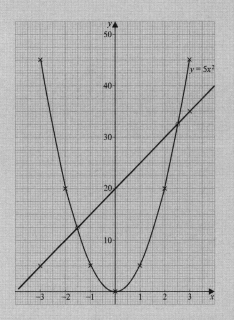

**Do:**
Draw a smooth curve draw the straight line between $(-3, 5)$ and $(3, 35)$

(London)

## Worked exam question 4

(a) Complete the table which gives the values of $y = x^2 + 2$ for values of $x$ ranging from $-2$ to $4$.

| $x$ | $-2$ | $-1$ | 0 | 1 | 2 | 3 | 4 |
|---|---|---|---|---|---|---|---|
| $y = x^2 + 2$ | 6 | 3 | 2 | 3 | 6 | 11 | 18 |

(b) On graph paper draw the graph of $y = x^2 + 2$ for values of $x$ between $-2$ and $4$.

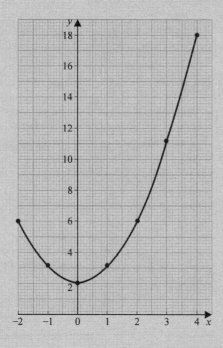

**Do:**
Draw a smooth curve

Remember $x^2$ means x multiplied by x

Remember that the graph is symmetrical

**Don't:**
Join the points with straight lines

(WJEC)

## Worked exam question 5

(a) Given that

$$y = \frac{x^2}{10} - \frac{1}{x}$$

complete the table below

| $x$ | 0.5 | 1 | 2 | 3 | 4 | 5 | 6 |
|---|---|---|---|---|---|---|---|
| $\frac{x^2}{10}$ | 0.02 | 0.1 | 0.4 | 0.9 | 1.6 | 2.5 | 3.6 |
| $-\frac{1}{x}$ | $-2$ | $-1$ | $-0.5$ | $-0.33$ | $-0.25$ | $-0.2$ | $-0.17$ |
| $y$ | $-1.98$ | $-0.9$ | $-0.1$ | 0.57 | 1.35 | 2.3 | 3.43 |

**Do:**
Work accurately
**Don't:**
Rush the arithmetic

(b) On a grid draw the graph of:

$$y = \frac{x^2}{10} - \frac{1}{x}$$

for values of $x$ from $x = 0.5$ to $x = 6$.

(c) (i) Explain clearly how you can find an estimate of $\sqrt[3]{10}$ from the graph.

$y = 0$ gives $\dfrac{x^2}{10} - \dfrac{1}{x} = 0$

i.e. $\dfrac{x^2}{10} = \dfrac{1}{x}$    $x^3 = 10$

................  so $x = \sqrt[3]{10}$

**Do:**
Remember that when the curve crosses the horizontal axis then $y = 0$. So $\frac{x^3}{10} - \frac{1}{x} = 0$ i.e. $\frac{x^3}{10} = \frac{1}{x}$
$\times$ by 10: $x^2 = \frac{10}{x}$
$\times$ by x: $x^3 = 10$
So $x = \sqrt[3]{10}$

(ii) Using your graph, find an estimate of $\sqrt[3]{10}$.

Where the graph crosses the horizontal axis
$x \simeq 2.1$

................  2.1

**Do:**
Read the x-value carefully

(d) Using the same axes and scales, draw the graph of

$$y = 3 - 2x$$

When $x = 0$,  $y = 3$
When $y = 0$,  $3 - 2x = 0$
$3 = 2x$
$x = 1\frac{1}{2}$

**Do:**
Remember that the graph of $y = 3 - 2x$ is a straight line. So you can plot it as soon as you have two points

(e) Write down the value of $x$ where the two graphs intersect.

*Graphs intersect where*

$$x \simeq 1.7$$

.....1.7.....

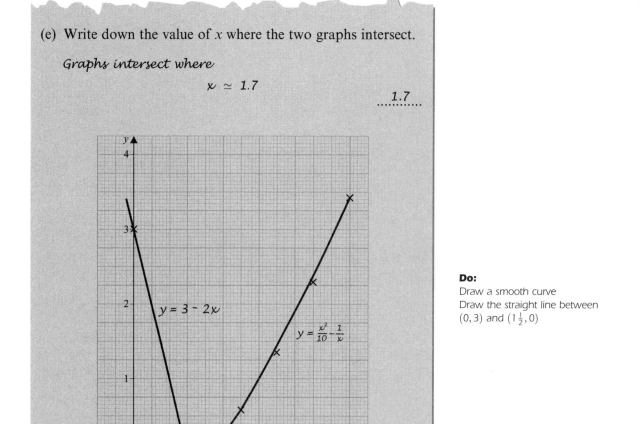

**Do:**
Draw a smooth curve
Draw the straight line between $(0, 3)$ and $(1\frac{1}{2}, 0)$

**Do:**
Read off the value of $x$ where the graphs intersect

(London)

---

### Exercise 12H (Mixed questions)

1. Sketch these graphs on a copy of the axes shown. Use a new set of axes for each graph.

   (a) $y = x^2 + 1$

   (b) $y = \dfrac{3}{x}$

   (c) $y = -x^3$

   (d) $y = 2 - x^2$

   (e) $y = x^3 - 1$

   (f) $y = \dfrac{1}{x} + 2$

2. (a) Draw the graph of $y = x^2 - 2x - 4$ for values of $x$ from $-3$ to $5$.

   (b) Use your graph to find approximate solutions to the equations:

   (i) $x^2 - 2x - 4 = 0$

   (ii) $x^2 - 2x - 4 = 3$

   (iii) $x^2 - 2x - 4 = -1$

3. (a) Draw the graphs of $y = \dfrac{12}{x}$ and $y = x + 4$ for values of $x$ from 1 to 6 on the same set of axes.

(b) Use your graphs to find a solution to the equation: $\frac{12}{x} = x + 4$

4. By drawing the graph of $y = 8x^2 - x^3 - 17x$ for values of $x$ from $-1$ to $5$, solve the equation $8x^2 - x^3 - 17x = -5$.

5. (a) Draw the graph of $y = 2x^2 - 3x + \frac{6}{x}$ for $0 < x \leqslant 6$

(b) Use your graph to find solutions to the equation $2x^2 - 3x + \frac{6}{x} = 20$

6. (a) Draw the graphs of $y = \frac{12}{x}$ and $y = 8x - x^2$ for values of $x$ from $0$ to $8$ on the same set of axes.

(b) Use your graphs to find approximate solutions to the equation
$$\frac{12}{x} = 8x - x^2$$

## Test yourself

**1.** The equation of a curve is

$$y = \frac{120}{x}$$

**QUESTION** (a) Complete the table for the equation

$$y = \frac{120}{x}$$

**ANSWER**

| $x$ | 3 | 4 | 5 | 8 | 12 | 20 | 24 | 30 |
|-----|----|----|----|----|----|----|----|----|
| $y$ | 40 | 30 | 24 | 15 | 10 | 6 | 5 | 4 |

*If you answer is incorrect check your arithmetic. You divide 120 by each x-value*

**QUESTION** (b) Draw the graph of

$$y = \frac{120}{x}$$

for the values of $x$ from 3 to 30.

**ANSWER**

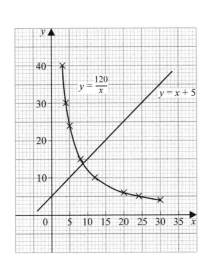

*If your graph is incorrect review page 238, Section 12.4 on the graph of $y = \frac{1}{x}$*

QUESTION (c) Use your graph to solve the equation

$$\frac{120}{x} = x + 5$$

ANSWER $x$ is approximately 8.8

*If your answer is incorrect review page 247 Section 12.8 on quadratic graphs onwards. Check that you used the graph of $y = x + 5$ to intersect $y = \frac{120}{x}$.*

---

QUESTION 2. (a) Draw the graphs of

$$y = 6x - x^2 \text{ and } y = \frac{x^3}{10}$$

for values of $x$ from 0 to 6 on the same set of axes.

ANSWER

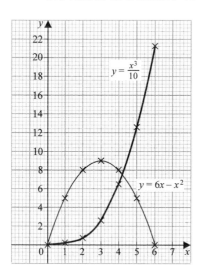

*If your graphs are incorrect review page 243, Section 12.7 on the graphs of $y = -x^2$, $y = -x^3$ and $y = \frac{-1}{x}$ and onwards. Check your table of values is*

| $x$ | 0 | 1 | 2 | 3 | 4 | 5 | 6 |
|---|---|---|---|---|---|---|---|
| $6x - x^2$ | 0 | 5 | 8 | 9 | 8 | 5 | 0 |
| $\frac{x^3}{10}$ | 0 | 0.1 | 0.8 | 2.7 | 6.4 | 12.5 | 21.6 |

---

QUESTION 2. (b) Use your graphs to solve the equation

$$\frac{x^3}{10} + x^2 - 6x = 0$$

ANSWER $x \simeq 4.2$ or 0

---

3. Here are six sketches of curves:

A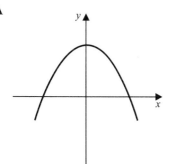

B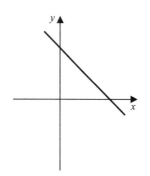

C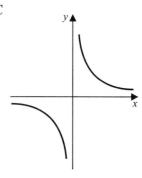

**D**

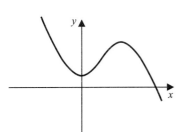

**E**

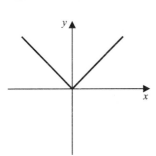

**F**

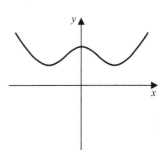

QUESTION    Write down the letter of the sketch which most closely fits these words:
(a)   a cubic graph                    ..............
(b)   the graph $y = 1 - x^2$          ..............
(c)   a reciprocal function            ..............

ANSWER      (a)   D                    *If your answers are incorrect review pages 235–247,*
(b)   A                    *Sections 12.2 to 12.7 inclusive*
(c)   C

## Summary of key points

**1.**

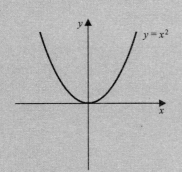

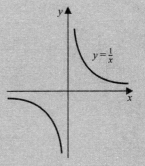

$y = x^2 + 1$ is the graph of $y = x^2$ translated $+1$ unit *up* the $y$-axis.

$y = -x^3$ is the graph of $y = x^3$ reflected in the $x$-axis.

$y = -\frac{1}{x}$ is the graph of $y = \frac{1}{x}$ reflected in the $x$-axis.

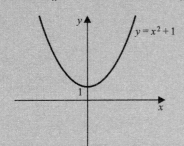

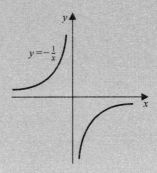

2. Graphs of quadratic expressions are similar in shape to the graph of $x^2$.

When the $x^2$ term   When the $x^2$ term
is positive:     is negative:

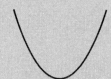 

3. In general a quadratic equation has two solutions, but might have one or none.

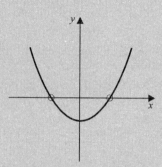

4. Graphs of cubic expressions are always similar in shape to the graph of $x^3$.

When the $x^3$ term    When the $x^3$ term
is positive:      is negative:

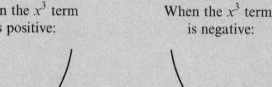

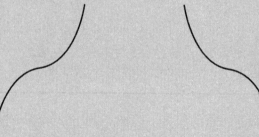

5. In general a cubic equation has three solutions, but might have two or one.

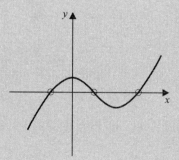

You should be able to draw graphs such as

$$y = x^3 + 2x - \frac{1}{x}$$

and use them to solve equations.

# 13 Trial and improvement

## 13.1 Introduction

In unit 11 you learned about ways of solving **linear equations**. These are equations of the type

$$3x + 1 = 13 \quad 4x - 3 = 2x + 5 \quad 5(3 - x) = 7$$

and so on.

The characteristic of all such equations is that they contain only expressions in $x$ and none in $x^2, x^3$ or any other powers of $x$.

You can always solve a linear equation by re-arranging the terms as you did in Equations 1.

In this unit you will learn ways of solving equations, usually known as **polynomial equations**, which do contain other powers of $x$. So you could have an equation such as

$$4x^3 - 3x^2 + 7x - 2 = 0$$

or

$$\frac{5}{x} + 3x - x^2 = 8$$

You will learn about a method called Trial and Improvement, which can be used to solve any equation, but only gives an approximate solution.

Later in the unit you will learn about a specific method of solving an equation such as

$$x^2 - 8x + 15 = 0$$

This equation is one of a type called quadratic equations. The main characteristic of any quadratic equation is that it contains an $x^2$ expression, an $x$ expression and a constant term.

You can solve a quadratic equation by trial and improvement and there are some exercises for you to try on this. However, there *will not* be any GCSE examination questions for you to do of this type. The method shown later in the unit gives *exact* answers and is therefore better than trial and improvement.

We start by looking at trial and improvement, mainly on cubic equations, that is equations that contain an expression in $x^3$ but no higher powers of $x$.

## 13.2 What is trial and improvement?

It is usually not possible to solve equations that are not linear or quadratic by rearranging terms. Indeed in some cases you can do no more than find an *approximate* solution by systematically substituting value into the equation until you get somewhere close to the solution. This method is called **trial and improvement**.

## 13.3 Finding an approximate solution using averages

Suppose you wish to solve the equation

$$x^3 + x = 20$$

The first thing you need to do is to find a very rough approximate solution.

To do this, write down a table of values, starting with $x = 0$.

| $x$ | $x^3 + x$ | Comment |
|:---:|:---:|:---:|
| **0** | $0^3 + 0 = 0$ | 0 is less than 20 |
| **1** | $1^3 + 1 = 1 + 1 = 2$ | 2 is less than 20 |
| **2** | $2^3 + 2 = 8 + 2 = 10$ | 10 is less than 20 |
| **3** | $3^3 + 3 = 27 + 3 = 30$ | 30 is greater than 20 |

You may also find it helpful to draw a diagram.

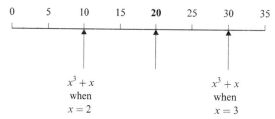

Since you are trying to solve the equation $x^3 + x = 20$ you can stop at this point because:

- when $x = 2$, $x^3 + x = 10$ which is *less* than 20.

- when $x = 3$, $x^3 + x = 30$ which is *greater* than 20.

So the solution to $x^3 + x = 20$ must be between $x = 2$ and $x = 3$.

You can now find a **first approximation** by taking $x$ to be the *average* of 2 and 3 so

$$x = \frac{2 + 3}{2} = \frac{5}{2} = 2.5$$

Now put $x = 2.5$ into the equation giving

$$x^3 + x = 2.5^3 + 2.5 = 18.125$$

This value of 18.125 is still less than the required value of 20.

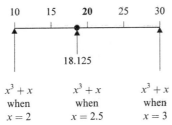

- When $x = 2.5$, $x^3 + x = 18.125$ which is less than 20

- When $x = 3$, $x^3 + x = 30$, which is greater than 20.

You can now see that the solution to $x^3 + x = 20$ lies between $x = 2.5$ and $x = 3$.

So next take $x$ to be the average of 2.5 and 3

$$x - \frac{2.5 + 3}{2} = \frac{5.5}{2} = 2.75$$

and put this value of $x$ into the left-hand side of the equation.

$$x^3 + x = 2.75^3 + 2.75 = 23.546\,875$$

This value of 23.546 875 is greater than our required value of 20.

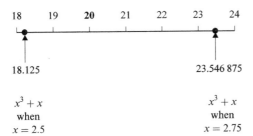

The diagram shows that $x = 2.5$ and $x = 2.75$ are now the closest approximations. So you can continue to refine your approximation by taking $x$ to be the average of these two values:

$$x = \frac{2.5 + 2.75}{2} = 2.625.$$

When $x = 2.625$, then

$$x^3 + x = 2.625^3 + 2.625 = 20.712\,890\,63.$$

We could just keep repeating this process, getting solutions closer and closer to the value of $x$.

---

### Exercise 13A

1. Find a solution to the equation $x^3 - x = 40$ using averages.
   *Note*: the solution lies between $x = 3$ and $x = 4$.

2. Find a solution to the equation $x^4 - 5x = 50$ using averages.
   *Note*: the solution lies between $x = 2$ and $x = 3$.

## 13.4 Finding an approximate solution without using averages

In the method in Section 13.3 you used the average of the previous two approximations to find the next one. This is systematic and effective, but not always very efficient.

The method that follows is probably the best one to use in an exam because time is precious.

When solving the equation

$$x^3 + x = 20$$

on page 263, you had reached the stage shown in the diagram.

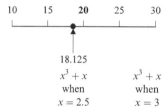

The next approximation was found by taking the average of 2.5 and 3.

But if you stop and study the diagram it should be clear that the solution is likely to be nearer to $x = 2.5$ than to $x = 3$ because 18.125 is closer to 20 than 30 is to 20.

So for this method you try a number closer to 2.5, say $x = 2.6$

When $x = 2.6$

$$x^3 + x = 2.6^3 + 2.6 = 20.176$$

So your diagram now looks like this:

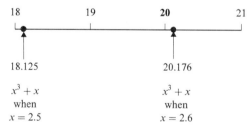

You can put this information in a table to help you.

| $x$ | $x^3 + x$ | Comment |
|-----|-----------|---------|
| 2.5 | 18.125 | $18.125 < 20$ |
| 2.6 | 20.176 | $20.176 > 20$ |

You can see that the answer must be less than $x = 2.6$ – so try $x = 2.59$.

When $x = 2.59$

$$x^3 + x = 2.59^3 + 2.59 = 19.963\,979$$

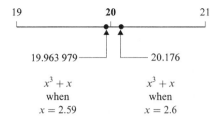

You could keep refining the approximation by trying any value between $x = 2.59$ and $x = 2.6$. But since the difference between 19.963 979 and 20 is less than the difference between 20.176 and 20, it will be more efficient to try a value closer to $x = 2.59$ than to $x = 2.6$. So you might choose $x = 2.592$, for example.

As with the method using averages, you could continue to improve your approximation for a very long time. The next section describes how you will know when to stop, depending on the degree of accuracy asked for in the question.

---

### Exercise 13B

**1.** $x^3 + 2x = 5$
  (a) Show that a solution of this equation lies between $x = 1$ and $x = 2$.
  (b) Use a method of trial and improvement to find a better solution to the equation.

---

## 13.5 When do you stop?

The trial and improvement process can continue indefinitely.

When engineers and scientists use trial and improvement methods to solve some very complex problems, they will usually use a computer and continue the process to the capability of the computer.

In your GCSE exam you will be told when to stop the trial and improvement process, either by giving your answer to a certain **degree of accuracy** or by doing a specified number of trials.

Exam questions are usually of one of these types:

- Solve the equation $x^3 + x = 20$ giving your solution correct to two decimal places.

- Show that a solution to the equation $x^3 + x = 20$ lies between $x = 2$ and $x = 3$.

  Given a first approximation of $x = 2.5$, use a trial and improvement method with three trials to improve this solution.

## 13.6 Looking at the problem

Let us look at the problem:

Solve the equation

$$x^3 + x = 20$$

giving your solution correct to two decimal places.

We looked at this equation in Section 13.3 and on page 262 we found that the solution lies between $x = 2.59$ and $x = 2.6$. So the solution correct to two decimal places will be either 2.59 or 2.60.

● When $x = 2.59$, $x^3 + x = 2.59^3 + 2.59 = 19.963\,979$

● When $x = 2.60$, $x^3 + x = 2.60^3 + 2.60 = 20.176$

$x = 2.59$ is the solution for which $x^3 + x$ is closest to 20.

So the solution correct to two decimal places is $x = 2.59$.

## 13.7 Doing a number of trials

In trial and improvement the process is:

● We have two approximate solutions.

● We use these two approximations to make a better one.

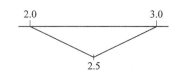

Each time you improve the approximation you are doing a **trial**.

Let us look at the problem:

Show that a solution to the equation

$$x^3 + x = 20$$

lies between $x = 2$ and $x = 3$

Given a first approximation of $x = 2.5$, use a trial and improvement method with three trials to improve this solution.

From Section 13.3, by the trial and improvement method using averages you saw that the first three trials were:

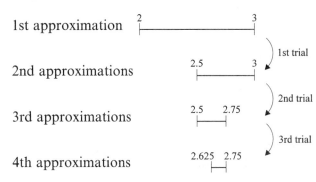

1st approximation

2nd approximations

3rd approximations

4th approximations

After 3 trials the improved solution is $x = 2.625$.

In a GCSE exam question you might be asked to carry out a particular number of trials – usually three or four. You usually get one mark for each trial done correctly.

### *Example 1*

(a) Show that a solution of the equation $3x^3 - 5x = 8$ lies between $x = 1$ and $x = 2$

(b) Using a trial and improvement method with four trials, solve the above equation.

(a) • When $x = 1$    $3x^3 - 5x = 3 - 5 = -2 < 8$

   • When $x = 2$    $3x^3 - 5x = 3(8) - 5(2) = 14 > 8$

So a solution lies between 1 and 2

(b) Try $x = 1.5$, then

$$3x^3 - 5x = 3(1.5)^3 - 5(1.5) = 10.125 - 7.5$$
$$= 2.625$$

and $2.625 < 8$

So try a solution between $x = 1.5$ and $x = 2$

Try $x = 1.8$, then

$$3x^3 - 5x = 3(1.8)^3 - 5(1.8) = 17.496 - 9.0 = 8.496$$

and $8.496 > 8$

So try a solution between 1.5 and 1.8, but very much closer to 1.8 than to 1.5

Try $x = 1.75$, then

$$3x^3 - 5x = 3(1.75)^3 - 5(1.75)$$
$$= 7.328\,125$$

• When $x = 1.8$, $3x^3 - 5x > 8$

• When $x = 1.75$, $3x^3 - 5x < 8$

So the solution is between 1.75 and 1.8

So for the 4th trial choose a value between 1.75 and 1.8

Try $x = 1.78$, then

$$3x^3 - 5x = 3(1.78)^3 - 5(1.78)$$
$$= 8.019\,256$$

(which is very close to 8)

So $3x^3 - 5x$ has an approximate solution of $x = 1.78$

### Exercise 13C

1. (a) Show that the equation $2x^3 + 3x = 15$ has a solution between $x = 1$ and $x = 2$.
   (b) Use a trial and improvement method with four trials to find an approximate solution of the above equation.

## 13.8 Using graphs

When you originally solved the equation $x^3 + x = 20$, it was quite easy to find out that the solution was between $x = 2$ and $x = 3$.

However, it is not always easy to find these two starting values. Sometimes you are given them in an exam question and sometimes you are asked to use a graph to find them, as in Example 2.

**Worked exam question 1**

There is a positive value of $x$ which satisfies the equation $x^2 + x = 18$.

Using a trial and improvement method find this value of $x$.

Give your answer correct to one decimal place

*First find a starting point by substituting a few values of x into the left-hand side of the equation, $x^2 + x = 18$*

*When x = 5, $x^2 + x = 30$ which is too big.*

*Start at x = 4 and work downwards.* ●————————

**Do:**
Be careful with your calculations

| $x$ | $x^2 + x$ | Comment |
|-----|-----------|---------|
| 4 | $4^2 + 4 = 20$ | greater than 18 |
| 3 | $3^2 + 3 = 12$ | less than 18 |
| 3.8 | $3.8^2 + 3.8$ $= 18.24$ | greater than 18 |
| 3.75 | $3.75^2 + 3.75$ $= 17.8125$ | less than 18 |

Use a table to show your working

Take a value of x closer to 4 than 3, because 20 is nearer to 18 than 12 is

*The solution is less than x = 3.8 but greater than x = 3.75, so to 1 decimal place the solution is x = 3.8.*

### Example 2

(a) Plot the graph of $y = x^3 - 5x + 1$ for values of $x$ from $-1$ to $2$.

(b) Use your graph to show that the equation $x^3 - 5x + 1 = 0$ has a solution between $x = 0$ and $x = 1$.

(c) Use a trial and improvement method to find, correct to 2 decimal places, the solution of the equation $x^3 - 5x + 1 = 0$ which lies between $x = 0$ and $x = 1$.

(a) First, work out a table of values for $y$, using values of $x$ from $-1$ to $2$.

*Remember:* $(-1)^3 = -1 \times -1 \times -1$
$$= -1$$

and $-5(-1) = -5 \times -1$
$$= +5$$

| $x$ | $-1$ | $0$ | $1$ | $2$ |
|---|---|---|---|---|
| $x^3$ | $-1$ | $0$ | $1$ | $8$ |
| $-5x$ | $+5$ | $0$ | $-5$ | $-10$ |
| $+1$ | $+1$ | $+1$ | $+1$ | $+1$ |
| $y$ | $5$ | $1$ | $-3$ | $-1$ |

Then plot the graph.

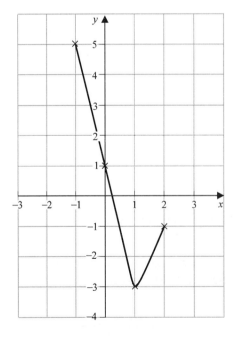

(a) The solution to the equation $x^3 - 5x + 1 = 0$ occurs when the curve crosses the horizontal axis, that is when $y = 0$. (You looked at similar problems in Unit 12 on page 235.)

(b) You can see from the graph that the solution looks to be nearer to $x = 0$ than $x = 1$, so try a first approximation which is less than $x = 0.5$.

If $x = 0.3$,

$$x^3 - 5x + 1 = 0.3^3 - 5(0.3) + 1$$
$$= 0.027 - 1.5 + 1$$
$$= -0.473$$

Now you can see that:

- when $x = 0$, $x^3 - 5x + 1 = 1$ which is greater than 0 and
- when $x = 0.3$, $x^3 - 5x + 1 = -0.473$ which is less than 0.

So the solution to the equation lies between 0 and 0.3.

So now try $x = 0.2$

$$x^3 - 5x + 1 = 0.2^3 - 5(0.2) + 1 = 0.008$$

- When $x = 0.2$, $x^3 - 5x + 1 = 0.008 > 0$
- When $x = 0.3$, $x^3 - 5x + 1 = -0.473 < 0$

This suggests that the solution will be very close to $x = 0.2$, because 0.008 is very close to 0. So try putting $x = 0.21$ into the equation,

$$x^3 - 5x + 1 = 0.021^3 - 5(0.21) + 1 = -0.040\,739$$

- When $x = 0.2$,    $x^3 - 5x + 1 = 0.008 > 0$
- When $x = 0.21$,   $x^3 - 5x + 1 = -0.040\,739 < 0$

The solution must lie between $x = 0.2$ and $x = 0.21$

Substituting $x = 0.205$ into the equation gives

$$x^3 - 5x + 1 = 0.205^3 - 5(0.205) + 1 = -0.016\,384\,875$$

- When $x = 0.2$,    $x^3 - 5x + 1 = 0.008 > 0$
- When $x = 0.205$, $x^3 - 5x + 1 = -0.016\,384\,875 < 0$

So $x = 0.2$ gives a result for $x^3 - 5x + 1$ which is closer to 0 than the result given by $x = 0.205$

So to three decimal places the solution must be either 0.200, 0.201, 0.202, 0.203 or 0.204. Each of these rounds down to 0.20 correct to two decimal places so the answer is $x = 0.20$.

---

### Exercise 13D

1. Use a trial and improvement method, with *three* trials, to find an approximate solution of the equation $x^3 + 2x = 100$

2. Use a trial and improvement method to find a solution of the equation $x^2 - 2x = 6$ Give your answer correct to two decimal places.

3. (a) Plot the graph of $y = x^3 - 12x + 1$ for values of $x$ from 1 to 4.
   (b) Use your graph to find a first approximation to the solution of the equation $x^3 - 12x + 1 = 0$
   (c) Use trial and improvement to obtain the solution correct to two decimal places.

# 13.9 Strengths and weaknesses

The major strength of trial and improvement is that it will always work – it always gives a solution.

The method has two weaknesses:

- it only gives approximate solutions

- it can be time-consuming

Time is important in an exam. A question on trial and improvement is usually straightforward and worth about 4 marks. It is important that you work through the question quickly, clearly and accurately **showing all of your working** to maximise the number of marks you get for a correct method.

---

**Worked exam question 2**

(a) Find a value of $x^3 + 5x$ when $x = 3.7$

(b) Use trial and improvement to solve the equation

$$x^3 + 5x = 60$$

Give the value of $x$ correct to two decimal places.

(a) When $x = 3.7$

$$x^3 + 5x = 3.7^3 + 5(3.7)$$
$$= 50.653 + 18.5$$
$$= 69.153$$

**Do:**
Be careful working out $3.7^3 + 5(3.7)$

(b) Start with $x = 3.7$ and work down.

Work down because $69.153 > 60$

**Do:**
Put your results in a table

| $x$ | $x^3 + 5x$ | Comment |
|---|---|---|
| 3.7 | 69.153 | greater than 60 |
| 3.6 | $3.6^3 + 5(3.6) = 64.656$ | greater than 60 |
| 3.5 | $3.5^3 + 5(3.5) = 60.375$ | greater than 60 |
| 3.4 | $3.4^3 + 5(3.4) = 56.306$ | less than 60 |
| 3.48 | $3.48^3 + 5(3.48) = 59.544192$ | less than 60 |
| 3.49 | $3.49^3 + 5(3.49) = 59.958549$ | less than 60 |
| 3.495 | $3.495^3 + 5(3.495) = 60.1665$ | greater than 60 |

Solution must lie between 3.5 and 3.4

too small

too small

Solution must lie between 3.49 and 3.495

**Don't**
Add $x^3 + 5x$ to make $5x^4$
This is a serious error

**Do:**
Give your answer correct to 2 d.p.

The solution correct to two decimal places is $x = 3.49$.

## 13.10 Solving quadratic equations using factors

**Quadratic equations** are equations with expressions containing powers *no greater* than $x^2$. You could use trial and improvement to solve a quadratic equation such as

$$x^2 + 2x = 120$$

But trial and improvement is really no more than a method of sophisticated guesswork. For quadratic equations there are other ways of finding the solution. Remember from Unit 12, Graphs of curves, that a quadratic graph is this shape:

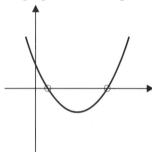

and in general a quadratic equation has two solutions.

## 13.11 Spotting a solution

Look at the equation

$$x^2 + 2x = 120 \quad (\text{or } x^2 + 2x - 120 = 0)$$

We can factorise the left-hand side to give

$$x(x + 2) = 120$$

This now reads:

> (a number) multiplied by (that number plus 2)
> gives us 120.

and you might be able to spot that $x = 10$ works, because $10 \times 12 = 120$.

You might also spot (but it is harder) that $x = -12$ also works, because $-12 \times (-12 + 2) = -12 \times (-10) = 120$.

So the two solutions to

$$x^2 + 2x = 120$$

are $x = 10$ and $x = -12$

You can check these solutions by substituting the values of $x$ into the original equation.

Spotting solutions is really a matter of guesswork.

*Example 3*

Solve the equation

$$x^2 - 3x - 70 = 0$$

We can write the equation as:

$$x^2 - 3x = 70$$
$$x(x - 3) = 70$$

(a number) $\times$ (that number $-3$) gives 70

You may spot that

$$10 \times 7 = 70$$

So $x = 10$ is a solution and also

$$-7 \times (-7 - 3) = -7 \times (-10) = 70$$

so $x = -7$ is a solution

---

## Exercise 13E

**1.** Try to spot the solutions to:

    (a) $x^2 + x = 20$       (b) $x^2 - 2x = 120$       (c) $x^2 + 5x = 50$

---

## 13.12 Confirming solutions

In an exam question you may be told a solution or pair of solutions of an equation and asked to confirm them. You do this by substituting the given values into the original equation.

*Example 4*

Confirm that $x = 5$ and $x = 3$ are solutions of the equation

$$x^2 - 8x + 15 = 0$$

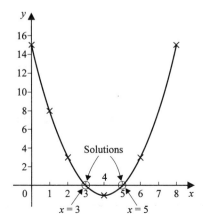

When $x = 5$ we have

$$\begin{aligned} x^2 - 8x + 15 &= 5^2 - (8 \times 5) + 15 \\ &= 25 - 40 + 15 \\ &= 0 \end{aligned}$$

So $x = 5$ is a solution.

When $x = 3$ we have

$$\begin{aligned} x^2 - 8x + 15 &= 3^2 - (8 \times 3) + 15 \\ &= 9 - 24 + 15 \\ &= 0 \end{aligned}$$

So $x = 3$ is a solution.

## Example 5

Confirm that $x = 7$ and $x = 2$ are solutions of the equation

$$x^2 - 9x + 14 = 0$$

When $x = 7$ we have

$$\begin{aligned} x^2 - 9x + 14 &= 7^2 - (9 \times 7) + 14 \\ &= 49 - 63 + 14 \\ &= 0 \end{aligned}$$

So $x = 7$ is a solution.

When $x = 2$ we have

$$\begin{aligned} x^2 - 9x + 14 &= 2^2 - (9 \times 2) + 14 \\ &= 4 - 18 + 14 \\ &= 0 \end{aligned}$$

So $x = 2$ is a solution.

---

### Exercise 13F

1. For each of these equations, confirm the solutions given.
   (a) $x^2 - 6x + 8 = 0$    $x = 4$    $x = 2$
   (b) $x^2 - 11x + 30 = 0$   $x = 5$    $x = 6$
   (c) $x^2 + 2x - 15 = 0$    $x = 3$    $x = -5$
   (d) $x^2 - 4x - 21 = 0$    $x = 7$    $x = -3$

2. Draw the graph of $y = x^2 - 6x + 8$ from $x = 0$ to $x = 6$ to confirm the solutions in 1(a).

## 13.13 Finding a rule for solving quadratic equations

So far we have spotted or confirmed the solutions to eight quadratic equations. These equations and their solutions are written in this table.

| Equation | Solution | Sum of solutions (add) | Product of solutions (multiply) |
|---|---|---|---|
| $x^2 + 2x - 120 = 0$ | $x = 10, -12$ | $-2$ | $-120$ |
| $x^2 - 3x - 70 = 0$ | $x = 10, -7$ | $3$ | $-70$ |
| $x^2 - 8x + 15 = 0$ | $x = 5, 3$ | $8$ | $15$ |
| $x^2 - 9x + 14 = 0$ | $x = 7, 2$ | $9$ | $14$ |
| $x^2 - 6x + 8 = 0$ | $x = 4, 2$ | $6$ | $8$ |
| $x^2 - 11x + 30 = 0$ | $x = 5, 6$ | $11$ | $30$ |
| $x^2 + 2x - 15 = 0$ | $x = 3, -5$ | $-2$ | $-15$ |
| $x^2 - 4x - 21 = 0$ | $x = 7, -3$ | $4$ | $-21$ |

Compare the 'sum' and 'product' columns with the equations.

Can you see what happens?

Look at the 3rd equation:

$$x^2 - 8x + 15 = 0$$

It has solutions $x = 5$ and $x = 3$. The equation is

$$x^2 - \left(\begin{array}{c}\text{add the}\\\text{solutions}\end{array}\right)x + \left(\begin{array}{c}\text{multiply}\\\text{the solutions}\end{array}\right) = 0$$

or

$$x^2 - (\text{sum})x + (\text{product}) = 0$$

The same thing works in all eight quadratic equations. The equation is always:

$$x^2 - \left(\begin{array}{c}\text{sum of}\\\text{solutions}\end{array}\right)x + \left(\begin{array}{c}\text{product of}\\\text{solutions}\end{array}\right) = 0$$

Check this with the 1st equation:

$$x^2 + 2x - 120 = 0$$

The solutions are $\quad x = 10$ and $x = -12$

Sum of solutions is $\quad 10 + (-12) = -2$

Product of solutions is $\quad 10 \times (-12) = -120$

So the equation is

$$x^2 - \begin{pmatrix} \text{sum of} \\ \text{solutions} \end{pmatrix} x + \begin{pmatrix} \text{product of} \\ \text{solutions} \end{pmatrix} = 0$$
$$x^2 - (-2)x + (-120) = 0$$
$$x^2 + 2x - 120 = 0$$

which is correct.

## 13.14 The general rule

To solve a quadratic equation

$$x^2 + bx + c = 0$$

you need to find two numbers $n$ and $m$ such that

- $n \times m = c$
- $n + m = -b$

Then the solutions are $x = n$ and $x = m$

In other words adding the solutions gives the negative of the number in front of $x$. Multiplying the solutions gives the constant term.

### Example 6

Solve $x^2 - 7x + 10 = 0$

We need two numbers $n$, $m$ such that

$$\left. \begin{array}{l} n \times m = 10 \\ n + m = -(-7) = 7 \end{array} \right\} \begin{array}{l} \text{two numbers which multiply to} \\ \text{give 10 and add to give 7} \end{array}$$

Think of all the factors of 10. You can see that these numbers must be 5 and 2.

So the solution is $x = 5$, $x = 2$.

### Exercise 13G

1. Solve these quadratic equations.
   (a) $x^2 - 12x + 32 = 0$
   (b) $x^2 - 7x + 12 = 0$
   (c) $x^2 - 9x + 20 = 0$
   (d) $x^2 - 9x + 18 = 0$
   (e) $x^2 + 8x + 15 = 0$
   (f) $x^2 + 15x + 56 = 0$
   (g) $x^2 + 7x + 12 = 0$
   (h) $x^2 + 2x - 15 = 0$
   (i) $x^2 + 3x - 18 = 0$
   (j) $x^2 - 6x - 7 = 0$
   (k) $x^2 + 5x - 24 = 0$
   (l) $x^2 - 15x + 26 = 0$
   (m) $x^2 + 5x - 14 = 0$
   (n) $x^2 - 5x - 14 = 0$
   (o) $x^2 - 6x + 9 = 0$
   (p) $x^2 - 8x + 16 = 0$
   (q) $x^2 - 4x - 21 = 0$
   (r) $x^2 - 3x - 28 = 0$
   (s) $x^2 - 7x - 18 = 0$
   (t) $x^2 - x - 2 = 0$

## 13.15 Formal solution using factors

Until now all the methods you have used to solve quadratic equations have involved some element of guesswork. This section shows you how to find the formal solution using factors.

In Unit 10, Manipulating algebra on pages 202–205 you looked at ways of multiplying expressions such as

$$(x + 3)(x + 5) \text{ to obtain } x^2 + 8x + 15$$

The solution was shown in a diagram:

$$(x + 3)(x + 5) = x^2 + 8x + 15$$

you could write this in reverse as

$$x^2 + 8x + 15 = (x + 3)(x + 5)$$

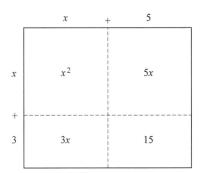

This reverse process is called factorising. We can use the same idea to solve an equation such as

$$x^2 + 8x + 15 = 0$$

Factorising gives

$$(x + 3)(x + 5) = 0$$

So  *either* $x + 3 = 0, \quad x = -3$

 or   $x + 5 = 0, \quad x = -5$

So the solutions to $x^2 + 8x + 15 = 0$ are $x = -3$ or $x = -5$

### Example 7

Solve $x^2 - 7x + 10 = 0$

Factorising gives

$$x^2 - 7x + 10 = 0$$
$$(x - 2)(x - 5) = 0$$

So  *either* $x - 2 = 0$ i.e. $x = 2$

 or   $x - 5 = 0$ i.e. $x = 5$

The solutions are $x = 2$ or $x = 5$

### Example 8

Solve $x^2 - 2x - 15 = 0$

$$x^2 - 2x - 15 = 0$$
$$(x + 3)(x - 5) = 0$$

So  *either* $x + 3 = 0, \quad x = -3$

 *or*   $x - 5 = 0, \quad x = 5$

The solutions are $x = -3$ or $x = 5$

## Exercise 13H

1. Solve (by factorising):
    (a) $x^2 + 7x + 12 = 0$  (b) $x^2 - 7x + 12 = 0$  (c) $x^2 - 11x + 30 = 0$  (d) $x^2 - 8x + 12 = 0$
    (e) $x^2 - 3x - 28 = 0$  (f) $x^2 + 5x - 24 = 0$  (g) $x^2 - 5x + 6 = 0$  (h) $x^2 - 13x + 30 = 0$
    (i) $x^2 + 5x - 6 = 0$  (j) $x^2 - 6x + 5 = 0$  (k) $x^2 + x - 2 = 0$  (l) $x^2 - x - 6 = 0$

2. Repeat Exercise 13G question 1 using factorising.

---

### Worked exam question 3

Solve the equation

$$x^2 + 4x - 21 = 0$$

Factorising $x^2 + 4x - 21 = 0$

gives      $(x - 3)(x + 7) = 0,$

So either  $x - 3 = 0,$
               $x = 3$

or            $x + 7 = 0$
               $x = -7$

The solutions are $x = 3$ or $x = -7$

**Do:**
Look for 2 numbers which multiply to give $-21$ and add to give 4

Multiply out the brackets to see that your factorisation is correct

**Don't:**
Write $x = 7$ as an answer

Only give one answer

### Worked exam question 4

(a) Expand and simplify $(x + 5)(x - 3)$.

$$(x + 5)(x - 3) = x^2 - 3x + 5x - 15$$
$$= x^2 + 2x - 15$$
$$x^2 + 2x - 15$$

**Do:**
Be careful over the signs

**Don't:**
Think that $-3x + 5x$ is $-8x$ or $-2x$

(b) Solve $x^2 - 5x - 14 = 0$

$x^2 - 5x - 14 = (x - 7)(x + 2)$

So  $x - 7 = 0$  i.e. $x = 7$

or  $x + 2 = 0$  i.e. $x = -2$

$$x = 7 \text{ or } x = -2$$

(London)

**Do:**
Remember that $-7 \times +2 = -14$

Check by your brackets

**Don't:**
Only write one answer

---

## Exercise 13I (Mixed questions)

1. Use a method of trial and improvement to find the positive solution of $x^2 + x = 175$
    Give your answer correct to one decimal place.

2. Use a method of trial and improvement to find the solution of $x^3 + 4x = 60$
    Give your answer correct to three significant figures.

3. Solve the equation $x^4 - x = 10$ by using the method of trial and improvement with four trials.

4. (a) Show that the equation $x^3 + 2x = 20$ has a solution between $x = 2$ and $x = 3$.
   (b) Use a method of trial and improvement, with four trials, to find a solution of the above equation.

5. (a) Plot the graph of $y = x^3 + x - 5$ for values of $x$ from $-1$ to $2$.
   (b) Use your graph to find a first approximation to the solution of the equation $x^3 + x - 5 = 0$
   (c) Use trial and improvement to obtain this solution correct to two decimal places.

6. Solve these quadratic equations.
   (a) $x^2 - 7x + 12 = 0$       (b) $x^2 + 13x + 42 = 0$
   (c) $x^2 + 4x - 21 = 0$       (d) $x^2 - 4x - 21 = 0$
   (e) $x^2 - x - 6 = 0$         (f) $x^2 + 5x - 6 = 0$
   (g) $x^2 - 5x - 6 = 0$        (h) $x^2 + 5x - 24 = 0$
   (i) $x^2 - 5x - 24 = 0$       (j) $x^2 + 4x - 12 = 0$

## Test yourself

**QUESTION**    1. Work out the value of $x^3 + 4x$ when $x = 4.7$.

**ANSWER**    122.623    *If your answer is incorrect check that you have worked out $4.7 \times 4.7 \times 4.7$ and added this to $4 \times 4.7$*

**QUESTION**    2. Use trial and improvement to solve $x^3 + 4x = 120$. Give your answer correct to two decimal places.

**ANSWER**    4.66    *If your answer is incorrect first check your working again – you may have made an arithmetical error. Then, review pages 262–268, Sections 13.3 to 13.8 on solving equations by trial and improvement.*

**QUESTION**    3. Solve $x^2 + 2x - 24 = 0$

**ANSWER**    $x = 4$ or $x = -6$    *If your answer is incorrect review page 276, Section 13.14 on the general rule, and page 277, Section 13.15 on formal solution using factors.*

**QUESTION**    4. (a)  Expand and simplify $(x - 3)(x + 7)$
             (b)  Solve $x^2 + 6x - 16 = 0$

**ANSWER**    (a)  $x^2 + 4x - 21$    *If your answer is incorrect review page 275, Section 13.13 on solving quadratic equations by factors*
             (b)  $x = 2$ or $x = -8$

## Summary of key points to remember

1. Trial and improvement is used to solve equations containing powers of $x$ such as $x^3$ and $x^2$.

2. The trial and improvement method gives approximate solutions to polynomial equations.

3. You need to find a first approximation if you are not given one, either using a graph or by substituting some values into the equation.

4. Work through the process carefully showing all of your working. Use a table.

5. Do not stop until you have reached the degree of accuracy required or performed the number of trials asked for in the question.

6. Sometimes you can spot a solution to a quadratic equation.

7. To solve a quadratic equation

$$x^2 + bx + c = 0$$

you need to find two numbers $n$ and $m$ such that

- $n \times m = c$
- $n + m = -b$

The two solutions are $x = n$ and $x = m$.

8. You should be able to solve a quadratic equation such as

$$x^2 - 8x + 15 = 0$$

by factorising.

# 14 Properties of shapes

## 14.1 Man-made and natural shapes

*Triangular shapes make the structure of this bridge strong.*

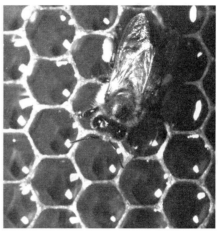

*Bees lay their eggs in wax chambers like these. The hexagonal shape is very strong.*

Architects, engineers and designers need to know about different shapes and how to use their properties to solve problems.

The topics covered in this unit include: the geometrical language that you need to know to describe various mathematical shapes and their properties; how to represent 3-D shapes with 2-D diagrams and how to draw nets of 3-D shapes.

## 14.2 Geometrical language

- A straight line is **one-dimensional** (1-D). It only has a *length*.

- Squares and circles are **two-dimensional** (2-D) shapes. They have *area*. All the points of a 2-D shape are in the same **plane** (or *flat surface*).

- Cuboids and tennis balls are **three-dimensional** (3-D) objects. They have *volumes* (or *capacities*).

- An **angle** is a measure of **turn** (or *change of direction*).

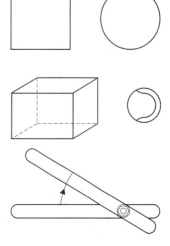

- Two lines are **parallel** if they are *in the same direction*. You can show that two lines in a diagram are parallel by drawing arrows on the lines.

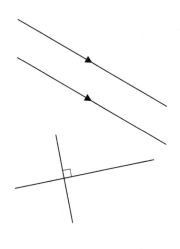

- Two lines are **perpendicular** if they are *at right angles* to each other. You can show that two lines in a diagram are perpendicular to each other by drawing a square sign where the lines meet.

- A **horizontal** line and a **vertical** line are *perpendicular to each other*.

- The sides of a 3-D shape are sometimes called **edges**. You can show that sides of a shape on a diagram are equal by drawing a dash mark across each of the equal sides. If there is more than one set of equal sides, you can use a two-dash mark for the next set, a three-dash mark for the next set, and so on.

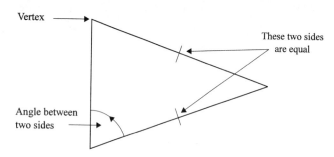

- A point at which two sides meet is called a **corner** or **vertex**. The plural of vertex is **vertices**.

- The **angle** at a vertex is a measure of the turn between the two sides that meet there. Angles are usually measured in **degrees**. A right angle is an angle of 90°.

- The length round the edge of a circle is called the **circumference** of the circle.

  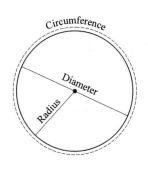

  A straight line going from a point on the circumference of a circle through the centre of the circle to the opposite point on the circumference is called a **diameter**.

  A straight line from the centre of the circle to a point on the circumference is called a **radius** of the circle.

  A diameter of a circle is **twice** the length of a radius of the circle.

- A part of the circumference of a circle is called an **arc**. A straight line between one point on the circumference and another, when the line does not pass through the centre of the circle, is called a **chord** of the circle.

  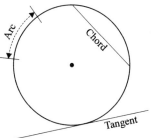

A straight line that touches a circle is called a **tangent** to the circle.

- A chord divides a circle into two parts, called **segments** of a circle. The smaller (or minor) segment and the larger (or major) segment together make up the whole circle.

- When a radius is drawn at each end of an arc of a circle the shape that is formed is called a **sector** of the circle.

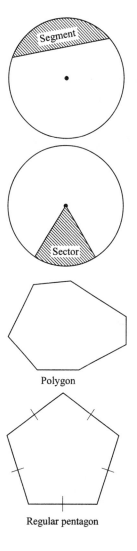

## 14.3 Naming 2-D shapes

A **polygon** is a 2-D shape that has any number of straight sides.

A polygon is **regular** if all its sides and all its angles are *equal*.

This table shows the special names used for polygons with different numbers of sides.

| Name of polygon | Number of sides |
| --- | --- |
| triangle | 3 |
| quadrilateral | 4 |
| pentagon | 5 |
| hexagon | 6 |
| heptagon | 7 |
| octagon | 8 |
| nonagon | 9 |
| decagon | 10 |
| dodecagon | 12 |

Polygon

Regular pentagon

## 14.4 Types of triangle

An **isosceles** triangle has *two equal sides*.

An **equilateral** triangle has *three equal sides*. The three angles are each 60°.

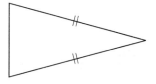

A **right-angled** triangle has a
*right angle* as one of its angles.

A **scalene** triangle has
*no sides and no angles equal.*

## 14.5 Classifying quadrilaterals

Special quadrilaterals are shown below. The ones further down the
diagram have more special properties.

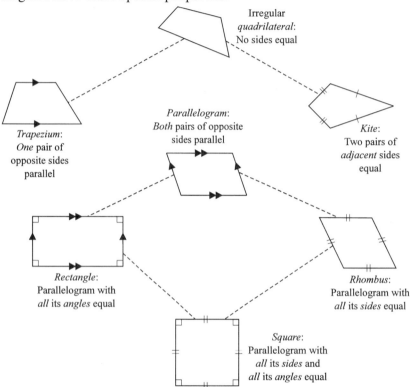

*Irregular
quadrilateral*:
No sides equal

*Trapezium*:
*One* pair of
opposite sides
parallel

*Parallelogram*:
*Both* pairs of opposite
sides parallel

*Kite*:
Two pairs of
*adjacent* sides
equal

*Rectangle*:
Parallelogram with
*all* its *angles* equal

*Rhombus*:
Parallelogram with
*all* its *sides* equal

*Square*:
Parallelogram with
*all* its *sides* and
*all* its *angles* equal

---

### Worked exam question 1

Here are the names of some quadrilaterals.

Square
Rectangle
Rhombus
Parallelogram
Trapezium
Kite

(a) Write down the names of the quadrilaterals which have
two pairs of parallel sides.

*Square, rectangle, rhombus, parallelogram*

**Do:**
Remember that
a trapezium has only one pair of
parallel sides a kite has no parallel
sides

(b) Write down the names of the quadrilaterals which must have two pairs of equal sides.

*Square, rectangle, rhombus, parallelogram, kite*

(London)

## Exercise 14A

1. Here is a list of names of shapes:

| | | |
|---|---|---|
| equilateral triangle | square | kite |
| right-angled triangle | rectangle | trapezium |
| parallelogram | octagon | pentagon |
| isosceles triangle | hexagon | rhombus |

Use the list to help you write down the names of the shapes below.

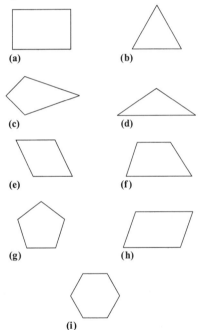

2. Write down the special names of these shapes:
   (a) a triangle with two equal sides,
   (b) a polygon with five sides,
   (c) a triangle with all its sides equal,
   (d) a polygon with six vertices,
   (e) a polygon with eight equal sides and eight equal angles.

3. Write down the name of a quadrilateral in which:
   (a) all the sides and all the angles are equal,
   (b) there is only one pair of parallel sides.

4. Write down the names of all the types of quadrilateral that have:
   (a) two pairs of parallel sides,
   (b) all their angles equal,
   (c) all their sides equal,
   (d) two pairs of equal sides.

## 14.6 Congruent shapes

Shapes that are **congruent** are *exactly the same shape* and the *same size* as each other. This means that they are identical. If you draw them on paper and cut them out, they will fit exactly over each other. You might need to turn over the cut out shape to make it fit.

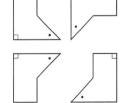

All the corresponding angles are equal.

All the corresponding lengths are equal.

## Example 1

Look at the shapes below. Find two pairs of congruent shapes.

Measure the sides carefully.

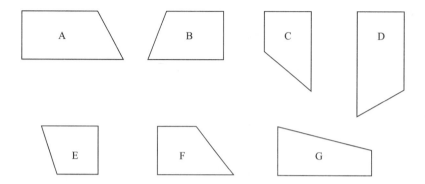

Shapes **A** and **D** are congruent. Shapes **C** and **F** are congruent.

They are exactly the same size and shape.

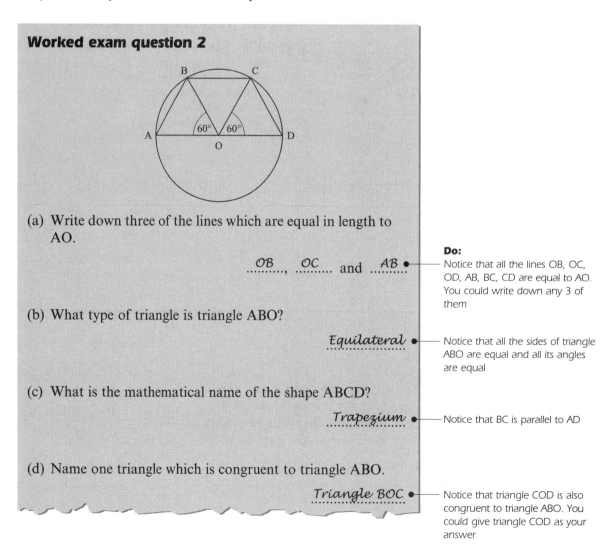

**Worked exam question 2**

(a) Write down three of the lines which are equal in length to AO.

 ...OB..., ...OC... and ...AB...

(b) What type of triangle is triangle ABO?

*Equilateral*

(c) What is the mathematical name of the shape ABCD?

*Trapezium*

(d) Name one triangle which is congruent to triangle ABO.

*Triangle BOC*

**Do:**

Notice that all the lines OB, OC, OD, AB, BC, CD are equal to AO. You could write down any 3 of them

Notice that all the sides of triangle ABO are equal and all its angles are equal

Notice that BC is parallel to AD

Notice that triangle COD is also congruent to triangle ABO. You could give triangle COD as your answer

(e) Some pairs of lines in the figure are parallel to each other. Write down one pair of parallel lines.

.........*AB*.... and ....*OC*.... •———— Notice that BC and AD, BO and CD are also pairs of parallel lines

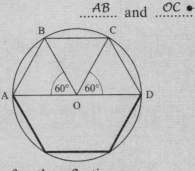

Shape ABCD is to be reflected in line AD.

(f) Sketch the image of ABCD after the reflection.

(g) What is the mathematical name of the shape formed by ABCD together with its reflection in the line AD?

*A regular hexagon* •

(London)

**Do:**
Remember that a polygon with 6 sides is called a hexagon. It is regular because all the sides and all the angles are equal

---

## Exercise 14B

You will need a ruler, a protractor and squared paper for this exercise.

**1**. Find three pairs of congruent shapes from the shapes below. (Measure the lengths and angles of the shapes carefully.)

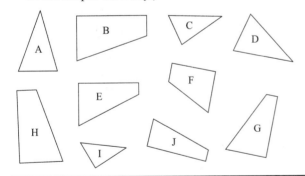

**2.** Copy this shape on to squared paper.

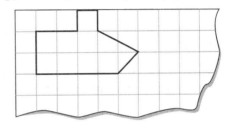

On the same paper, draw two shapes that are congruent to the given one, but turned round into a different position, or turned over.

---

## 14.7 Naming 3-D objects

● **A cuboid** has *eight vertices* (corners). It has *12 edges* and *six faces*.

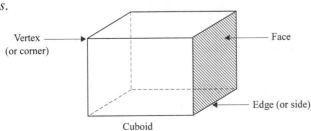

Vertex (or corner) ———→      Face

Edge (or side)

Cuboid

- A **prism** is a 3-D shape that has the *same cross-section* along its whole length or height. If a 'slice' is cut across the length of a prism and parallel to its end face, the shape of the 'slice' is the same shape and size as the end face. The shape is called the **cross section** of the prism.

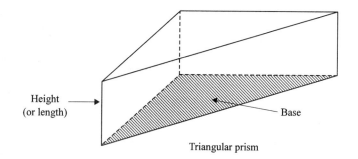

Triangular prism

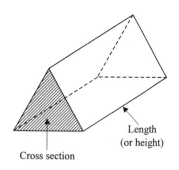

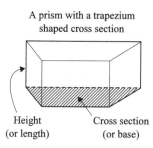

A prism with a trapezium shaped cross section

At *GCSE level* prisms are usually **right** prisms. The length (or height) of the prism is at *right angles* to the cross-section (or base).

A **cylinder** is a prism whose cross section is a *circle*.

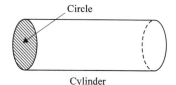

Cylinder

- A **pyramid** is a 3-D shape on a *base* that has other faces that meet at a *point*.

At *GCSE level*, pyramids are usually **right** pyramids. The height from the point of the pyramid is at *right angles* to its base.

The base of a **square pyramid** is a *square*.

A **cone** is a pyramid whose base is a *circle*.

- A **sphere** is a 3D shape like a round *ball*.

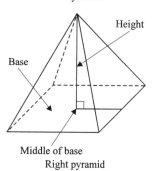

Right pyramid

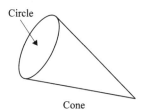

Cone

# 14.8 2-D representation of 3-D objects

All the faces of a cuboid are rectangles. When you draw a cuboid, some of the faces do not look like rectangles in the drawing.

When you **represent** a **3-D object** by a **2-D shape**, you always represent *vertical lines* by vertical lines.

*Parallel lines* should always look parallel. You can draw a *horizontal line* of the object in any direction except vertically.

This is one of the ways in which you can represent a cuboid:

*Step 1*: Start with a rectangle

*Step 2*: Draw an identical rectangle just above and to the right.

Step 3: Join up the corners. Use broken lines for the hidden edges.

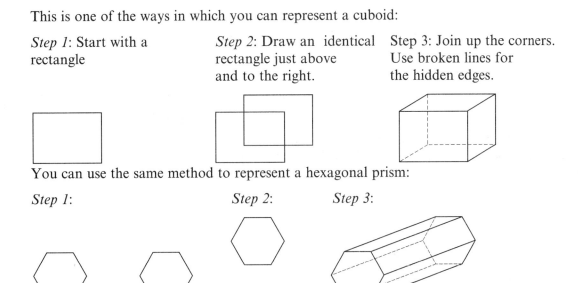

You can use the same method to represent a hexagonal prism:

*Step 1*:　　　　　　　*Step 2*:　　　　*Step 3*:

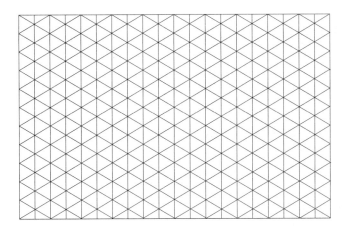

You can also represent 3-D shapes on **isometric** paper or dotty isometric paper. Isometric paper has a grid of lines that form equilateral triangles. One set of these lines is vertical.

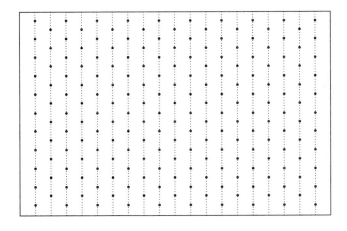

Dotty isometric paper has dots where the lines on isometric paper meet.

On isometric paper lengths in three perpendicular directions are drawn to the same scale, but faces do not appear as their true shape.

*Example 2*

On isometric paper draw a diagram of a prism with this cross section:

Draw the edges of the cross section shape along the lines of the isometric paper. Use the vertical lines of the grid for the vertical lines of the shape.

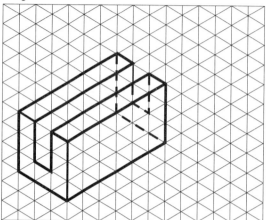

The height of the shape is three sides of the small triangle on the grid. From each vertex of the U draw the length of the prism along the grid lines. In this diagram the length is six triangle sides, but it could be any number of sides.

Draw the cross-section shape at the other end of the prism. Make the parallel lines look parallel. Join the corresponding points to form the remaining edges.

## Worked exam question 3

1.  The diagram shows an incomplete drawing of a triangular prism OABCDE

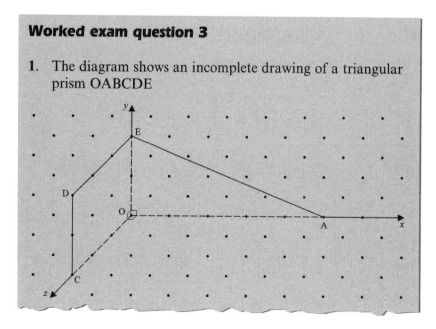

(a) Complete the drawing of the prism, and label the point *B*.

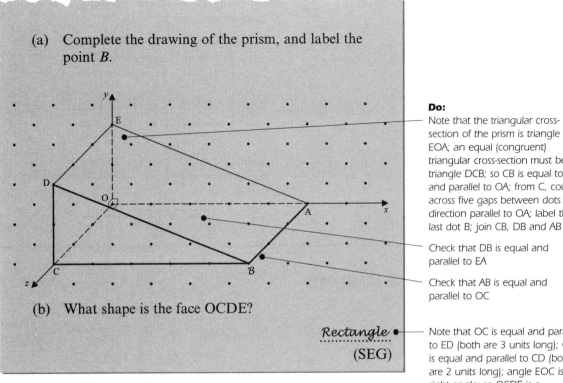

**Do:**
Note that the triangular cross-section of the prism is triangle EOA; an equal (congruent) triangular cross-section must be triangle DCB; so CB is equal to and parallel to OA; from C, count across five gaps between dots in a direction parallel to OA; label the last dot B; join CB, DB and AB

Check that DB is equal and parallel to EA

Check that AB is equal and parallel to OC

(b) What shape is the face OCDE?

*Rectangle*

(SEG)

Note that OC is equal and parallel to ED (both are 3 units long); OE is equal and parallel to CD (both are 2 units long); angle EOC is a right angle; so OCDE is a rectangle

You can also represent 3-D objects on squared paper.

In this square-based right pyramid, the edges AD and BC are drawn along the diagonals of the grid squares. In the 3-D pyramid AB is perpendicular to AD and BC. The vertex E is vertically above the centre of the base.

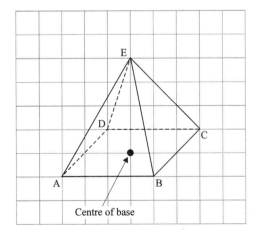

Centre of base

---

## Exercise 14C

You will need squared and isometric paper for this exercise.
1. On ordinary paper draw diagrams of prisms with these cross-sections:

(a)

(b)

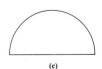
(c)

2. On isometric paper draw diagrams of:
   (a) a cube
   (b) a cuboid
   (c) a prism with an L-shaped cross-section
   (d) a prism with a T-shaped cross-section

3. On squared paper draw diagrams of prisms with these cross-sections:

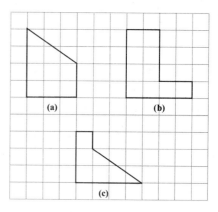

# 14.9 Drawing nets of 3-D objects

*Example 3*

Draw a net of a cuboid.

- *Step 1*: Find an empty packet that is a cuboid.

- *Step 2*: Cut along one edge (shown by the bold broken line in the diagram).

- *Step 3*: Open out the packet so that it lies flat.

- *Step 4*: Cut off the tabs (shown shaded in the diagram).

- *Step 5*: Draw the opened out shape on ordinary paper.

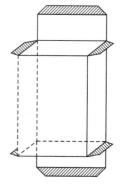

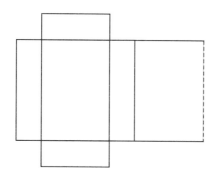

This shape is called the **net** of the cuboid.

The **net of a 3-D object** is the 2-D shape that can be folded to make the 3-D object.

## *Example 4*

Draw a full-size net of this triangular prism.

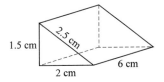

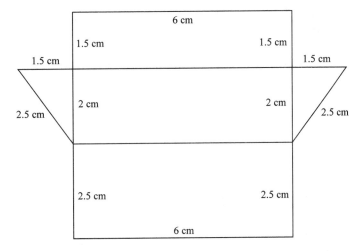

---

## Exercise 14D

You will need a ruler, a protractor and compasses for this exercise.

**1**. Draw full-size nets of these 3-D shapes:
   (a) Cuboid

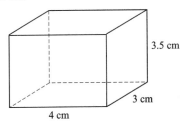

   (b) Right pyramid with rectangular base

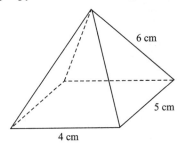

(c) Prism with triangular cross-section

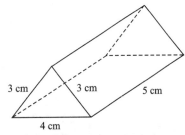

(d) Pyramid with triangular base and all edges 6 cm.

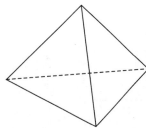

**2**. The base of a pyramid is a square with sides of 4 cm. The sloping edges are all 5 cm long.
   (a) On paper or card draw a full size net of the pyramid.
      Add tabs to your net.
   (b) Fold your net and stick the edges to make the pyramid.

## Worked exam question 4

This diagram shows part of the net of a triangular prism. It is drawn accurately, full size.

One face GHIJ of the prism is missing from the net.

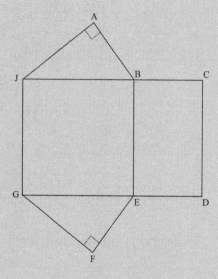

(a) Draw, accurately, the face GHIJ on the diagram.

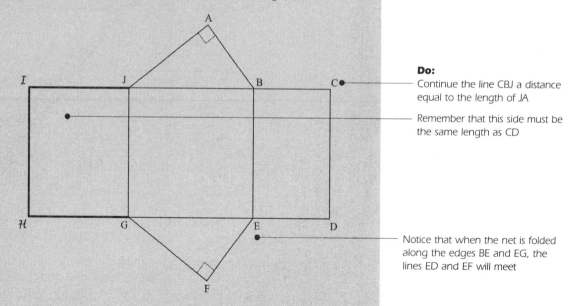

**Do:**
Continue the line CBJ a distance equal to the length of JA

Remember that this side must be the same length as CD

Notice that when the net is folded along the edges BE and EG, the lines ED and EF will meet

(b) When the net is made into a prism, which line joins ED?

.............. EF ..............

(WJEC)

## Exercise 14E (Mixed questions)

You will need a ruler, compasses, squared and isometric paper for this exercise.

**1.** From the shapes in the diagram write down the letters of three pairs of congruent shapes.

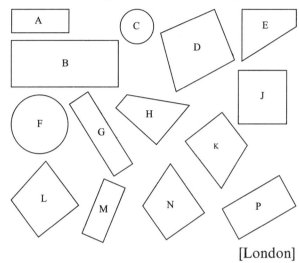

[London]

**2.** Write down the special names of these shapes:
   (a) a quadrilateral that has all its angles equal but not all its sides equal,
   (b) a triangle that has two equal angles,
   (c) a polygon that has ten sides,
   (d) a triangle with none of its sides equal,
   (e) a quadrilateral with one pair of parallel sides,
   (f) all the quadrilaterals which have all their sides equal.

**3.** The base of this prism is a regular hexagon with sides of 2 cm. The length of the prism is 6 cm.
   (a) On paper or card draw a full-size net of the prism.
      Add tabs to your net.

   (b) Fold your net and stick the edges to make the prism.

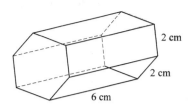

**4.** The first shape below represents a side view of a cottage and the second diagram below represents the front view of the same cottage.

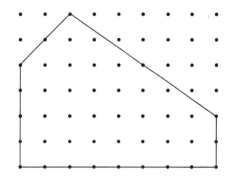

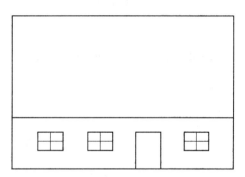

Draw a sketch which represents a three dimensional (3-D) view of the cottage. Show the windows and the door in your sketch.

[MEG]

## Test yourself

**1.** A prism has a cross-section that is a regular pentagon.

**QUESTION**  Draw a diagram to represent the prism on ordinary paper. Use your diagram to find out how many vertices the prism has.

**ANSWER**    10

*If your answer is incorrect, review page 283, Section 14.3 on Naming 2-D shapes; page 287, Section 14.7 on Naming 3-D objects and page 288, Section 14.8 on 2-D representation of 3-D objects.*

**2.** A quadrilateral has two pairs of equal sides, but none of its sides are parallel to each other.

**QUESTION**   Write down the special name of the quadrilateral.

**ANSWER**   kite                                    *If your answer is incorrect review page 284, Section 14.5 on Classifying quadrilaterals.*

**3.**

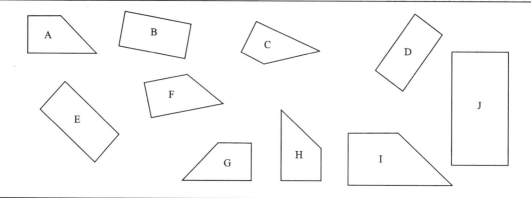

**QUESTION**   Find two pairs of congruent shapes in the diagram above.

**ANSWER**   A and G, B and D                        *If your answer is incorrect, review page 286, Section 14.6 on Congruent shapes, Example 1.*

**4.** The diagram below shows the net of a 3-D shape.

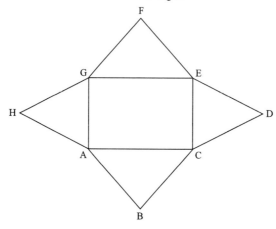

**QUESTION**   (a)   What is the name of the 3-D object that has this net?

**ANSWER**   Pyramid                                 *If your answer is incorrect, review pages 292–293, Section 14.9 on Drawing nets of 3-D objects, Examples 3 and 4.*

**QUESTION**   (b)   When the net is made into a 3-D object, which line is joined to HG?

**ANSWER**   FG                                      *If your answer is incorrect review pages 292–293, Section 14.9 on Drawing nets of 3-D objects, Examples 3 and 4.*

# Summary of key points to remember

1. Two lines are **parallel** if they are *in the same direction.*
   You can show that two lines in a diagram are parallel
   by drawing arrows on the lines.

2. Two lines are **perpendicular** if they are *at right angles* to
   each other. You can show that two lines in a diagram are
   perpendicular to each other by drawing a square sign where
   the lines meet.

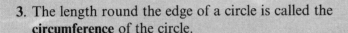

3. The length round the edge of a circle is called the
   **circumference** of the circle.

   A straight line going from a point on the circumference
   of a circle through the centre of the circle to the opposite
   point on the circumference is called a **diameter** of the circle.

   A straight line from the centre of the circle to a point on
   the circumference is called a **radius** of the circle.

   A diameter of a circle is **twice** the length of a radius of the circle.

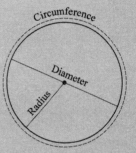

4. A part of the circumference of a circle is called an **arc**.

   A straight line between one point on the circumference
   and another, when the line does not pass through the
   centre of the circle, is called a **chord**.

   A straight line that touches a circle is called a **tangent** to
   the circle.

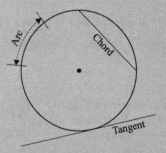

5. A **polygon** is a 2-D shape that has any number of straight
   sides (edges).

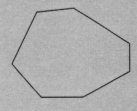

6. A **polygon** is **regular** if all its sides and all its angles are
   equal.

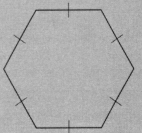

7. • An **isosceles triangle** has *two equal sides*, and two
equal angles.

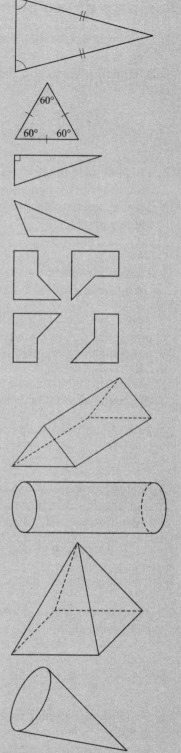

   • An **equilateral triangle** has *three equal sides*. Each of the
three angles is 60°.

   • A **right-angled triangle** has a *right-angle* as one of its
angles.

   • A **scalene triangle** has *no sides and no angles equal.*

8. **Congruent** shapes are exactly the *same shape* and the *same
size*. This means that they are identical.

All the corresponding angles are equal.

All the corresponding lengths are equal.

9. A **prism** is a **3-D shape** that has the *same cross-section*
along the whole of its length.

10. A **cylinder** is a **prism** whose cross-section is a circle.

11. A **pyramid** is a 3-D shape on a **base** that has other faces
that meet at a **point**.

The base of a square pyramid is a square.

A **cone** is a pyramid whose base is a circle.

12. A **sphere** is a 3-D shape that is like a round ball.

13. When you **represent** a **3-D object** by a **2-D shape**, you
always represent **vertical lines** by vertical lines. **Parallel
lines** should always look parallel. You can draw a **horizontal
line** of the object in any direction except vertically.

14. The **net** of a 3-D object is the 2-D shape that can be folded
to make the 3-D object.

# 15 Position and movement

**Coordinates** are numbers or letters used to describe the position of a point in space.

You can use coordinates to describe the position of a landmark on a map. They are also used in navigation, satellite tracking, television and a host of other situations.

*TV companies use coordinates when they bounce TV signals off satellite to bring you live television from around the world*

## 15.1 The coordinate system

The coordinate system we use today was invented over 350 years ago by a brilliant Frenchman called René Descartes. He created a way of using numbers and lines called axes to identify the positions of points in two-dimensional space. Here's how:

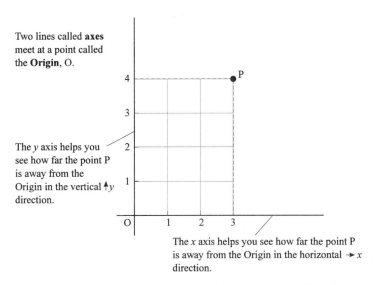

Two lines called **axes** meet at a point called the **Origin**, O.

The $y$ axis helps you see how far the point P is away from the Origin in the vertical $y$ direction.

The $x$ axis helps you see how far the point P is away from the Origin in the horizontal $x$ direction.

The point marked P is 3 units to the right of O. It is 3 units in the positive direction of $x$ from O.

P is also 4 units up from O. It is 4 units in the positive direction of $y$ from O.

The **coordinates** of P are (3, 4)

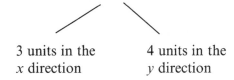

3 units in the $x$ direction

4 units in the $y$ direction

The coordinates of the Origin O are (0, 0)

These are sometimes called **Cartesian coordinates**, after DesCartes.

You can extend the axes in the negative directions of $x$ and $y$. You then have four **quadrants**.

Here are the coordinates of 4 different points, one in each of the four **quadrants**:

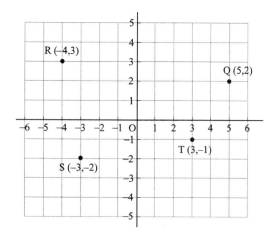
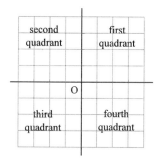

## Example 1

(a) Write down the coordinates of each of the four points labelled A, B, C and D.

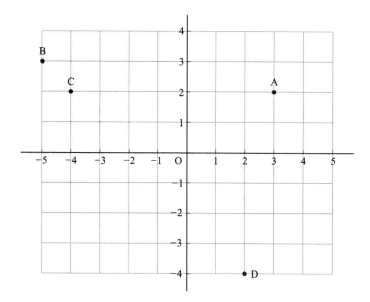

(b) M is the midpoint of CD. Write down the coordinates of M.

(a) A = (3, 2);
B = (−5, 3);
C = (−4, 2);
D = (2, −4).

(b) You draw the line from C to D, and mark approximately the position of M.

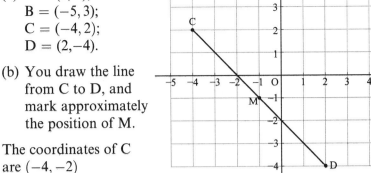

The coordinates of C are (−4, −2)

The coordinates of D are (2, −4):

The coordinates of M are therefore $(\frac{1}{2}(-4+2), \frac{1}{2}(-2+(-4)))$

The coordinates of M are (−1, −3)

You can write a general rule about the midpoint of a line PQ:

If P is the point $(a,b)$ and Q is the point $(c,d)$ then the coordinates of the midpoint of PQ are $(\frac{1}{2}(a+c), \frac{1}{2}(b+d))$

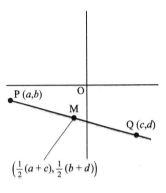

### *Example 2*

(a) Draw a pair of axes and label the points A (2, 1) and B (8, 4).

(b) The point P lies on AB and is nearer to A than to B: it divides the line AB in the ratio 1:2. Write down the coordinates of P.

(a) You draw the axes, and mark A and B like this:

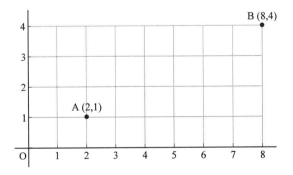

(b) Since P divides AB in the ratio 1:2 we have

$$PB = 2PA$$

So we can mark P on the line AB like this.

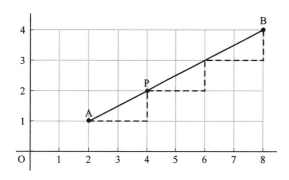

Then the coordinates of P are (4, 2).

### Example 3

(a) Draw a pair of axes and mark on the points P (3, 1), Q (4, 3), R (8, 3) and S (7, 1).

Draw straight lines from P to Q, from Q to R, from R to S and from S to P to create a quadrilateral PQRS.

(b) What is the name of this type of quadrilateral?

(c) Draw the diagonals PR and QS. Write down the coordinates of the point of intersection of these two diagonals.

> **Note:**
> *The phrases 'name', 'special name' or ' geometrical name' all mean the same thing.*

The diagram is like this.

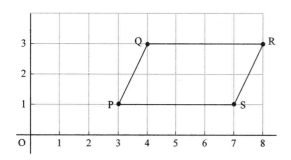

(b) PQRS is a parallelogram.

(c) The two diagonals, PR and QS, intersect at their midpoints. Both of these midpoints have coordinates $(5\frac{1}{2}, 2)$.

### Exercise 15A

1. Using the grid at the top of page 303,
   (a) Write down the coordinates of the points A, B and C.
   (b) Find the coordinates of the midpoint of AC.

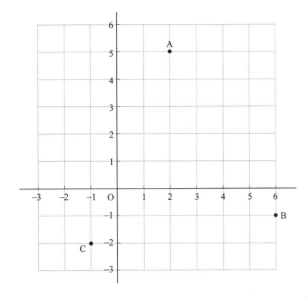

**2.** Points P, Q, R and S are the points (3, 0), (4, 0), (4, 6) and (3, 6).
(a) Draw a pair of axes and plot these four points: P(3, 0), Q(4, 0), R(4, 6) and S(3, 6).

(b) Draw straight lines from P to Q, from Q to R, from R to S and from S to P to form the quadrilateral PQRS. Write down the geometrical name of the quadrilateral PQRS.

**3.** The points A, B, C and D are the four vertices of a square. The coordinates of A are $(-4, 3)$, those of B are $(1, 5)$ and those of C are $(3, 0)$. Find the coordinates of the point D.

**4.** PQRS is a parallelogram. The coordinates of P are $(-5, 2)$, those of Q are $(2, 4)$ and those of S are $(-2, -2)$. Find the coordinates of R.

**5.** (a) On a pair of axes mark the points A $(-6, 2)$, and B $(7, 10)$.
(b) Write down the coordinates of the midpoint of AB.
(c) A point P lies on AB and is nearer to A than it is to B. The point P divides AB in the ratio 1 : 3. Find the coordinates of P.

**6.** The centre of a square is at (2, 2). One of the vertices of the square is at (5, 4). Find the

## 15.2 Finding areas using coordinates

Here is an example to show how the topics of coordinates and area can be combined in examination problems.

### Worked examination question 1

**(a)** On the same axes, plot and label the four points A (3,3), B (5,0), C $(-2, -2)$ and D $(-4, 1)$.

**(b)** Draw the line AB, BC, CD and DA
Write down the geometrical name of the quadrilateral ABCD.

**(c)** Calculate the area of the quadilateral ABCD.

For **(a)** the diagram is

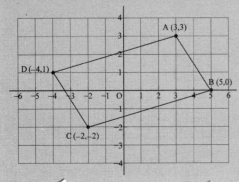

For **(b)**
The quadrilateral ABCD is a parallelogram.

For **(c)** there are three ways we can work out the area of ABCD. In an examination you will only need to use one method, unless told otherwise.

**Method 1:**

Enclose ABCD in the rectangle PQRS, like this.

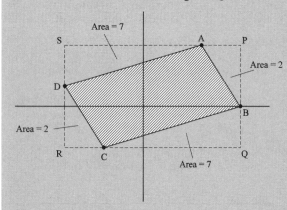

ABCD = area PQRS – areas of 4 triangles on the outside
Area of triangle APB = area of triangle CRD = $1/2 \times 2 \times 3$ = 3 square units.
Area of triangle BQC = area of triangle DSA = $1/2 \times 2 \times 7$ = 7 square units.
Area of PQRS = $9 \times 5 = 45$

**So:**
**Area ABCD = $45 - (3 + 7 + 3 + 7)$.**
**Area ABCD = $45 - 20 = 25$ square units.**

**Method 2:**
Split the rectangle ABCD into 4 right-angled triangles and a rectangle.

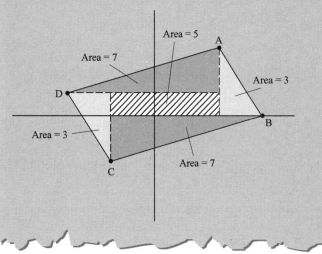

The area of each triangle is
$1/2 \times 2 \times 7 = 7$ square units.

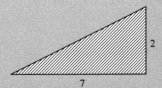

2

7

The area of each triangle is
$1/2 \times 2 \times 3 = 3$ square units.

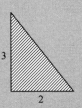

3

2

The area of each triangle is
$1 \times 5 = 5$ square units.

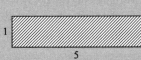

1

5

**So:**
**Area ABCD $= 7 + 3 + 7 + 3 = 25$ square units.**

**Method 3:**
This formula could be used:

$$\text{Area of a parallelogram} = \text{Base} \times \text{Height}$$

To be able to use this formula the length of *BC* and the
perpendicular distance between the sides *BC* and *AD* need to
be worked out. This can be done using Pythagoras' theorem.
There is more about Pythagoras' Theorem in unit 19.

---

### Exercise 15B

1. (a) Plot the four points A (2, 3), B (5, 4), C (4,
7) and D (1, 6) on a single pair of axes.
   (b) Write down the geometrical name of the
quadrilateral ABCD.
   (c) Calculate the area of the quadrilateral
ABCD.

2. The vertices of a triangle ABC are at the points
A $(-3, 2)$, B (6, 0) and C (4, 1).
Calculate the area of ABC.

3. (a) Plot and label the points
A (4, 3), B (4, 0), C $(-3, -2)$ and D $(-3, 1)$.
   (b) Draw the lines AB, BC, CD and DA.
Write down the special name of the
quadrilateral ABCD
   (c) Draw the line AC.
Calculate the area, in square units, of
triangle ABC.

---

## 15.3 The locus (path) of a moving point

Imagine a cyclist moving along a straight horizontal road.

The path taken by the centre of the rear wheel of the cycle will be like the dashed line in the picture below.

This dashed line is called the **locus** of the midpoint of the wheel.

In more general terms, the **locus** of a point is the path taken by the point as it moves according to some rule. We can also say that the locus is the set of all points that the moving point can occupy.

### Example 4

A ship leaves a harbour H and travels due North to a lighthouse L. At L the ship turns and travels due East to a marker buoy, B. At B the ship turns again and travels back to H in a straight line.

Sketch the path taken by the ship.

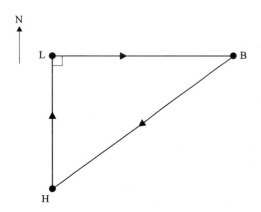

This is the sketch of the path taken by the ship. It is also the locus of the ship.

### Example 5

In the diagram below A and B are fixed points.

A
•                                    B
                                    •

A point P moves such that

$$PA = PB$$

Sketch the locus of P.

The first, obvious position for P is exactly halfway between A and B.

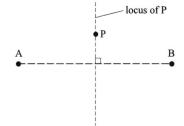

locus of P

A          P          B

But P can actually occupy any position along the line which **bisects** AB and is **perpendicular** to AB. Its locus is therefore the **perpendicular bisector** of AB.

---

### Exercise 15C

**1.** Two straight lines meet at a point as shown in the diagram. A point P moves such that it is an equal perpendicular distance from both lines. Copy the diagram to sketch the locus of P as a dashed line.

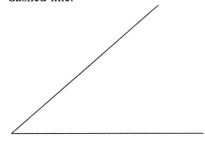

Sketch the locus of P.

**2.** A point P moves such that its distance from a fixed point A is always 5 cm.
  (a) Sketch the locus of P.
  (b) Write down the geometrical name for this locus.

**3.** A yacht leaves a port P and travels for 40 km on a bearing of 060° to reach a marker buoy B. At B the yacht turns and travels for a further 50 km due East to reach a lighthouse L. At L the yacht turns again and travels back to P in a straight line.
  (a) Using a scale of 1 cm to represent 10 km, make an accurate scale drawing of the locus of the yacht.
  (b) Using your scale drawing, find the actual distance between the lighthouse and the port.

**4.** The line AB is 6 cm long. A point P moves such that the shortest distance from P to the line AB is always 2 cm.
  (a) Make an accurate drawing of the locus of P.
  (b) Calculate the total length of this locus.

**5.** The diagram shows a cycle wheel with a valve at V.

A                                                      B

The wheel rolls for two complete revolutions along the straight horizontal track AB. Sketch the locus of the valve.

---

## 15.4 Loci (paths) that are regions

A locus does not always have to be a line or a point it can also be a **region**.

### Example 6

Point P can move such that it is always within 3 m of point A. Its locus is the circular region, radius 3 m, with A as centre.

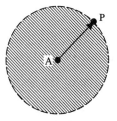

PA ≤ 3

*Example 7*

This is a plan of Mr Jenkins garden.

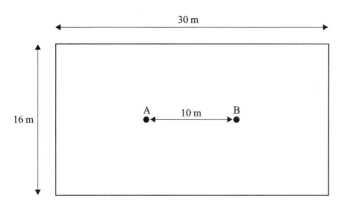

Apple trees are positioned at points A and B. Mr Jenkins wishes to plant a third apple Tree. He is advised that to promote pollination the third apple tree should be placed no more than 5 metres from the tree at A and no more than 8 metres from the tree at B.

Make an accurate drawing to show the region in which Mr Jenkins should plant the third apple tree.

We will use a scale of 1 cm to represent 2 m.

We draw a circle, centre A, of radius 2.5 cm and another circle, centre B, of radius 4 cm.

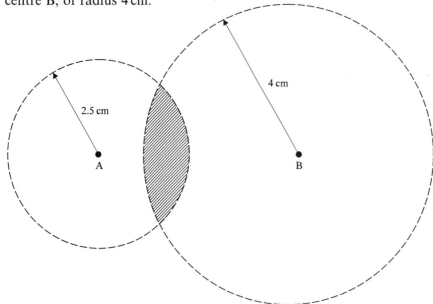

The inside of the first circle shows all the points less than 5 m from A

The inside of the second circle shows the points less than 8 m from B.

The shaded regions within the required distance of both A and B, so this is where the third tree should be planted.

## Exercise 15D

**1.** In the plan of Mrs Khan's garden below, the line AB represents the wall of her house and the point P represents a pear tree.

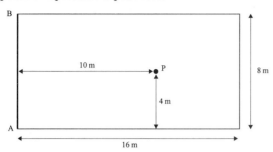

Mrs Khan wishes to plant a walnut tree. She is advised that the walnut tree should be at least 6 metres from the wall AB and more than 5 metres from the pear tree P.
Using a scale of 1 cm to represent 1 metre, make an accurate sketch to show the region in which Mrs Khan should plant the walnut tree.

**2.** The diagram opposite shows a garage and a driveway. There is a car on the driveway and a security light at L.

The diagram is drawn to scale: 2 cm represents 1 metre.
The security light has a sensor which switches on the light when anything moves within its range. Its range is 2 metres.

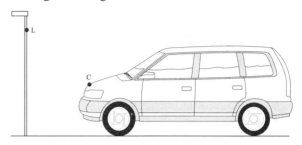

(a) Copy the diagram and draw the boundary of the sensor's range.
(b) The top C of the front of the car is 1 metre above the ground. Draw the locus of the point C as the car is driven towards the garage.
(c) How far is the front of the car from the garage door when light senses it and turns on?                [NEAB]

---

## Worked exam question 2

Jason has to sail his ship between two rocks so that the ship is always the same distance from the point A on the first rock and the point B on the second rock.

The diagram shows the rocks.

Copy the diagram and construct accurately the path along which Jason must sail his ship.

*This locus is the perpendicular bisector to the line AB.*

*So the path of Jason's ship is the dotted line.*

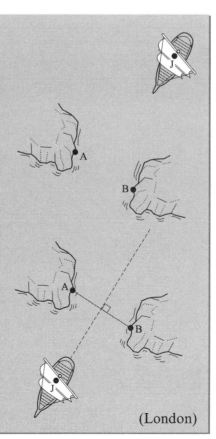

(London)

**Do:**
Realise that you are being asked to draw the locus of the point J (for Jason's ship) which moves such that JA = JB.

**Do:**
Draw AB, find the mid-point of AB. Then use a protractor to measure a 90° angle.

### Exercise 15E (Mixed questions)

1. The vertices of a triangle ABC are at the points A (3, 0), B (−5, 2) and C (−4, 5).
   (a) Plot the points A, B and C and draw the triangle ABC
   (b) Calculate the area of triangle ABC.

2. (a) Plot the points A (5, 0) and B (−1, 0).
   (b) Draw the locus of the point P which moves subject to the rule PA = PB.
   (c) Write down the equation of the locus of P.

3. The point A has coordinates (4, 3). The point B has coordinates (−5, 6).
   A third point P lies no more than 6 units from A and no more than 8 units from B.
   Make an accurate drawing to show all the possible positions of the point P.

4. PQRS is a rectangle.

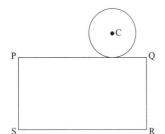

The circle, centre C, rolls around the outside edges ABCD.
Draw the locus of C as the circle rolls around the complete rectangle.

5. A and B are two fixed points which are 6 cm apart.

A ●◄─ ─ ─ ─ 6 cm ─ ─ ─ ►● B

A point P moves so that PA = 3PB
Draw the locus of P.

6. A man sets out from his home, H, and walks 4 km due North to a point P. At P he turns onto a bearing of 300° and walks for a further 6 km to reach a point Q. At Q he turns again and walks in a straight line back to H.
   (a) Make a scale drawing of the man's path.
   (b) Find the total distance he walks.

---

## Test yourself

1. The coordinates of the vertices A, B, and C of a triangle are
   A (−5, 2), B (3, 4) and C (0, −6).

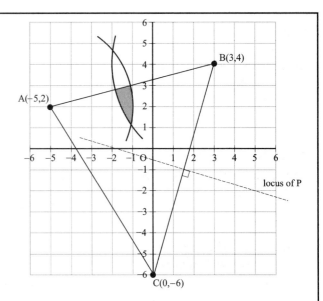

---

**QUESTION** (a) Plot the points A, B and C.

**ANSWER** Check A, B and C on the diagram above.

*If your answer is incorrect review page 299, Section 15.1 on the coordinate system.*

| | |
|---|---|
| QUESTION | (b)  Work out the area of the triangle ABC. |
| ANSWER | Area of ABC = 37 square units | *If your answer is incorrect review page 303, Section 15.2 on finding areas using coordinates.* |

---

**2.**  A variable point P moves such that the distances from P to B and P to C are equal.

---

| | |
|---|---|
| QUESTION | Draw the locus of P. |
| ANSWER | The locus of P is the perpendicular bisector of the line BC. | *If your answer is incorrect review page 305, Section 15.3 on the locus of a moving point.* |

---

**3.**  A point Q lies inside the triangle ABC. It must be no more than 4 units from A and no more than 5 units from B.

---

| | |
|---|---|
| QUESTION | Shade in the possible region within which Q must lie. |
| ANSWER | | *If you have difficulty in answering this review page 307, Section 15.4 on loci that are regions.* |

## Summary of key points to remember

**1.**  The two axes are called:
   ***x* axis (horizontal)**
   ***y* axis (vertical).**
   They meet at the **origin**.

**2.**  The **coordinates** of the origin are $(0,0)$.

**3.**  For a general point with coordinates (a,b):
   • a is the distance from the vertical axis.
   • b is the distance from the horizontal axis.

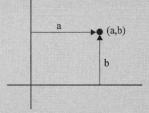

**4.**  The convention for **positive** and **negative** numbers is:

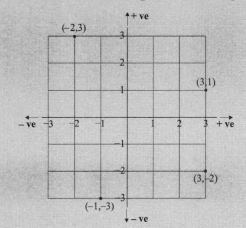

**5.**  The locus of a moving point is the **path taken by that point as it moves according to some rule**. Or the locus is the **set of all points that the moving point can occupy, given a rule**.

# 16 Symmetry and angles

This unit introduces line symmetry and rotational symmetry and shows you how to draw planes of symmetry of 3-D shapes. It includes facts about angles of intersecting straight lines, triangles, quadrilaterals, polygons, and considers tessellations and parallel lines.

## 16.1 Why is symmetry important?

Many shapes in nature, such as flowers, animals and snowflakes, are symmetrical. Shapes that are symmetrical balance well, both visually and physically. Designers use symmetry to make their designs attractive and practical.

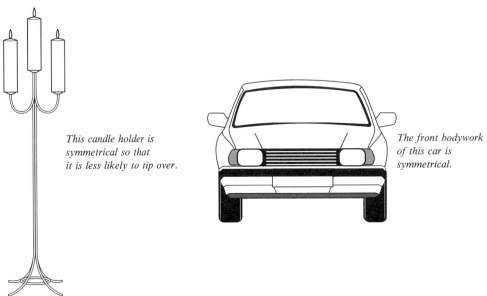

*This candle holder is symmetrical so that it is less likely to tip over.*

*The front bodywork of this car is symmetrical.*

## 16.2 Recognising line symmetry

This shape is **symmetrical** about the broken line.

The shape has one **line of symmetry** (or **axis of symmetry**). One half of the shape is the mirror image of the other half. One half of the shape is congruent to the other half, so corresponding lengths are equal and corresponding angles are equal.

A line of symmetry is sometimes called a mirror line.

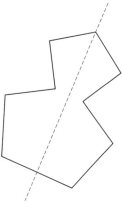

This shape has four lines of symmetry.

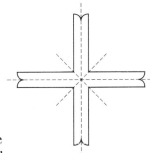

A 2-D shape has a **line of symmetry** if the line divides the shape into two halves and one half is the mirror image of the other half.

The mirror image of a point is the same distance from the line of symmetry as the original point.

The line joining a point to its mirror image is at right angles to the line of symmetry.

A point on the line of symmetry is its own mirror image.

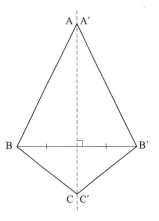

### *Example 1*

Complete this drawing so that the dotted line is the line of symmetry.

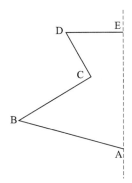

First mark the mirror images of B, C at D at B′, C′ and D′. Then join the points A′B′C′D′E′.

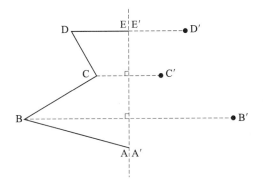

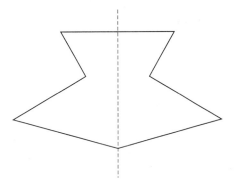

This is the completed shape.

### Exercise 16A

You can use tracing paper to copy the shapes and check the symmetry in this exercise.

1. Copy these shapes and draw in all the lines of symmetry, if any. Use dotted lines.

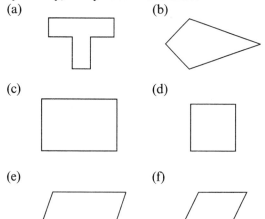

(a)　　　　　　　　　　(b)

(c)　　　　　　　　　　(d)

(e)　　　　　　　　　　(f)

2. The arrowhead shape LMNO is a type of kite. LO = ON and LM = MN. Copy the diagram and draw any lines of symmetry.

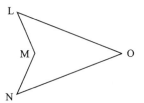

3. Draw a shape with only one line of symmetry. Show the line of symmetry with a dotted line.

4. Draw a shape that has four lines of symmetry. Show the lines of symmetry with dotted lines.

## 16.3 Recognising rotational symmetry

This shape can be **turned** (rotated), holding the centre point P fixed. If the point A is at any of the *four* positions A, B, C or D the shape will look exactly the same.

The shape has **rotational symmetry of order 4**.

The point P is called the **centre of rotation**.

A 2-D shape has **rotational symmetry** if it fits onto itself two or more times in one turn.

The number of times a shape fits onto itself in one turn is the **order of rotational symmetry**.

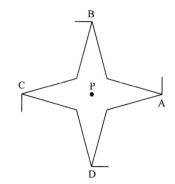

*Example 2*

Write down the order of rotational symmetry of this shape.

Suppose the shape is turned, holding the centre point fixed. If the point *Q* is at any of the *three* positions Q, R or S the shape will look exactly the same.

The shape has rotational symmetry of order 3.

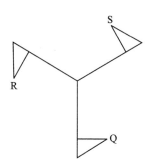

*Example 3*

This drawing has been torn in half.

Complete the drawing so that the
 whole shape has rotational symmetry
of order 2.

This is the completed shape.

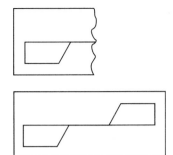

## Exercise 16B

You can use tracing paper to check the symmetry
 in this exercise.

**1**. Write down the order of rotational symmetry,
 if any, of these shapes.

(a)    (b)    (c)

(d)    (e)    (f)

(g)      (h)

**2**. Draw a shape that has rotational symmetry of
 order:
 (a) 2  (b) 4  (c) 3  (d) 8

# 16.4 Drawing planes of symmetry

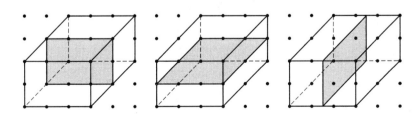

This cuboid is symmetrical about each of the shaded planes. It has
**3 planes of symmetry**.

A 3-D shape has a **plane of symmetry** if the plane divides the
shape into two halves and one half is the mirror image of the other
half.

## *Example 4*

The cross-section of this prism is a semicircle. Copy the shape onto squared paper. Draw all its planes of symmetry on separate diagrams.

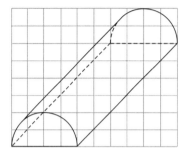

There are two planes of symmetry:

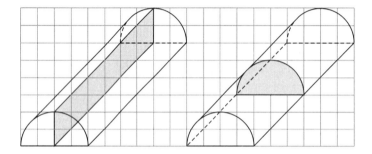

## Exercise 16C

You will need squared paper and dotty isometric paper for this exercise.

**1.**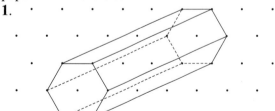

Copy this hexagonal prism twice. On each of your diagrams draw a different plane of symmetry of the prism.

**2.** Copy the shapes opposite that represent 3-D objects. Draw all their planes of symmetry on separate diagrams.

(a)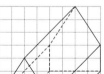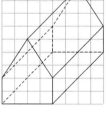

(b)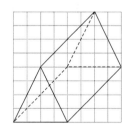

(c)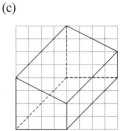

(d)

*The base is a square.*

# 16.5 Geometrical language about angles

An **angle** is a measure of **turn** (or change of direction).

An object can turn through an angle. One point on the object remains still and the object rotates around that point. The turn can be **clockwise** (the same direction as the hands of a clock move) or **anticlockwise** (the opposite direction to the hands of a clock).

A **whole turn** is a turn through 4 right angles. A **half turn** is a turn through 2 right angles. A **quarter turn** is a turn through 1 right angle.

The angle at a **vertex** (or corner) of a 2-D shape is measured between the two sides that meet there.

Angles are usually measured in **degrees** (°) and 90° equals one **right angle**.

**Acute angles** are smaller than one right angle.

**Obtuse angles** are bigger than one right angle and smaller than two right angles.

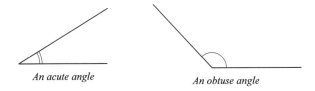

An acute angle     An obtuse angle

**Reflex angles** are bigger than two right angles.

Two angles are called **supplementary** when they add up to two right angles (180°)

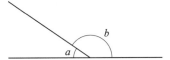

A reflex angle

$a$ and $b$ are supplementary angles because $a + b = 180°$

Angles of 62° and 118° are supplementary angles
$(62° + 118° = 180°)$

The angle marked at the corner Q in the drawing is called angle Q, angle PQR or angle RQP.

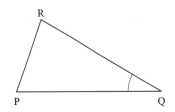

Sometimes you are asked to find the angle marked $x$ in a diagram. Here $x$ is the size of the angle.

Sometimes Greek letters are used to label angles. The most usual one is $\theta$ (pronounced theta).

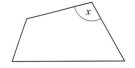

## 16.6 Angles in triangles and quadrilaterals

 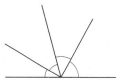

If you place two right angles together they make a straight line.

A right angle equals 90°, so the angles making a straight line
$= 2 \times 90° = 180°$.

Any number of angles placed together to make a straight line add
up to 180°.

If you place four right angles at a point they make an angle of
$4 \times 90° = 360°$.

Any number of angles placed at a point add up to 360°.

Where the two straight lines meet:

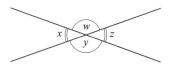

$w + x = 180°$   (angles on a straight line)
$w + z = 180°$   (angles on a straight line)
so   $x = z$

The angles $x$ and $z$ are called **vertically opposite angles**.

The angles $w$ and $y$ are also vertically opposite angles and

$$w = y$$

*Example 5*

*Step 1*: draw any triangle on paper and cut it out

*Step 2*: colour each angle of the triangle with a different colour

*Step 3*: draw a straight line on paper

*Step 4*: tear each angle from the triangle and place the angles
together against the straight line

*Step 5*: write down what you notice.

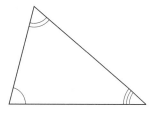 

The angles placed together make a straight line so they add up to 180°.

The sum of the angles of a triangle is 180°.

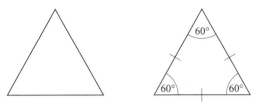

An equilateral triangle has rotational symmetry of order 3 so its angles are all equal.

The angles add up to 180°, so each angle equals 180° ÷ 3 or 60°.

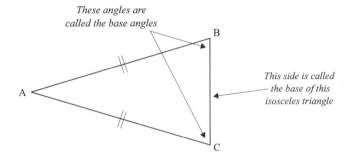

*These angles are called the base angles*

*This side is called the base of this isosceles triangle*

An **isosceles triangle** has two equal sides. The third side (the unequal one) is called the **base** of the triangle.

The two dashes drawn on the sides **AB** and **AC** show that the two sides are equal.

The **height** of an isosceles triangle is drawn from the point where the **equal sides meet** (A here) and is **perpendicular** to the third side (BC here).

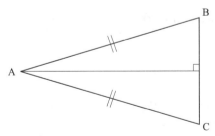

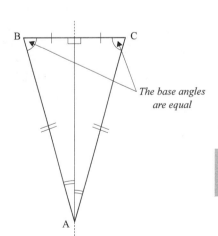

*The base angles are equal*

The height of an isosceles triangle is a line of symmetry so:

- the height **bisects** the base.
- the height is perpendicular to the base.
- **the two base angles are equal**.
- the height bisects the third angle.

**Bisects** means divides exactly into two equal parts.

A **diagonal** of a quadrilateral is a straight line drawn from one vertex to the opposite vertex.

A **quadrilateral** can be divided into two triangles by drawing one of its diagonals. The angles of the two triangles put together make the angles of the quadrilateral.

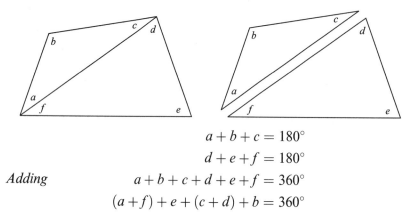

$$a + b + c = 180°$$
$$d + e + f = 180°$$

*Adding*    $$a + b + c + d + e + f = 360°$$
$$(a + f) + e + (c + d) + b = 360°$$

The sum of the angles of a quadrilateral is 360°.

### Example 6

Work out the named angles, giving reasons.

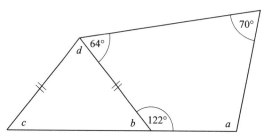

$$a + 122° + 64° + 70° = 360° \text{ (sum of angles of quadrilateral)}$$
$$a + 256° = 360°$$
$$a = 360° - 256° = 104°$$
$$b = 180° - 122° \text{ (angles on a straight line)}$$
$$b = 58°$$
$$c = 58° \text{ (base angles of isosceles triangle)}$$
$$d = 180° - (58° + 58°) \text{ (sum of angles of triangle)}$$
$$d = 180° - 116°$$
$$d = 64°$$

**Exercise 16D**

**1**. Work out the named angles, giving reasons.

(a)

(b)

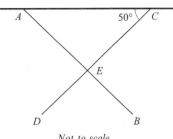

(c)

(d)

(e)

(f)

(g)

(h)

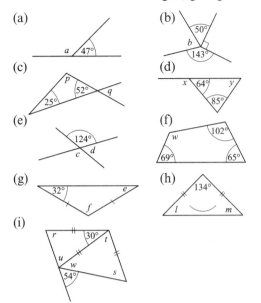

(i)

**2**. Diagram NOT accurately drawn.

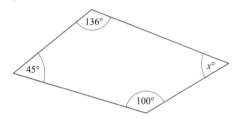

Work out the value of $x$.          [London]

**3**. A workbench is standing on a horizontal floor. The side view of the workbench is shown.

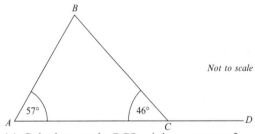

*Not to scale*

The legs $AB$ and $CD$ are equal in length and joined at $E$. $AE = EC$. Angle $ACD = 50°$.
(a) Work out the size of angle $BAC$ giving a reason for your answer.
(b) Work out the size of angle $AEC$ giving a reason for your answer.          [SEG]

**4**.

*Not to scale*

(a) Calculate angle $BCD$, giving a reason for your answer.
(b) Calculate angle $ABC$, giving a reason for your answer.          [MEG]

## 16.7 Using symmetry to discover properties of quadrilaterals and circles

One diagonal of a **kite** is the line of symmetry of the kite so:

• this diagonal bisects the angles between the equal sides.

• this diagonal bisects the other diagonal.

• the diagonals meet at right angles.

A **parallelogram** has rotational symmetry of order 2 so:

• the opposite sides are equal.

• the opposite angles are equal.

• the diagonals bisect each other.

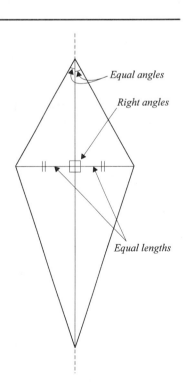

*Equal angles*

*Right angles*

*Equal lengths*

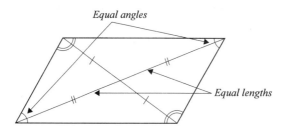

*Equal angles*

*Equal lengths*

A **rectangle** is a special parallelogram with four equal angles. It has two lines of symmetry so, in addition to the properties of a parallelogram:

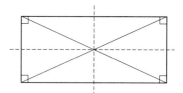

- the diagonals are equal.

A **rhombus** is another special parallelogram, with four equal sides. Its diagonals are lines of symmetry so, in addition to the properties of a parallelogram:

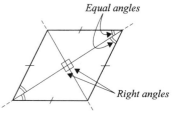

*Equal angles*

- the diagonals bisect each other at right angles.

- the diagonals bisect the angles at the vertices.

*Right angles*

A **square** is a special parallelogram, rectangle and rhombus so it has all their individual properties.

In the diagram a line is drawn from the centre of the circle to the middle point of a chord.

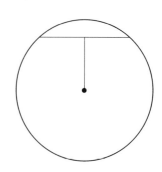

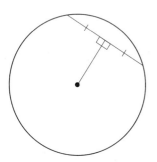

The line is a line of symmetry so it is perpendicular to the chord.

The perpendicular bisector of a chord of a circle passes through the centre of the circle.

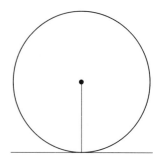

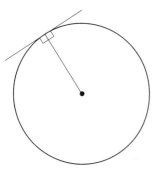

In this diagram a radius is drawn to the point where a tangent touches the circle.

The radius is a line of symmetry so it is perpendicular to the tangent.

In this diagram OC is a line of symmetry. So angle AOC and angle BOC are equal.

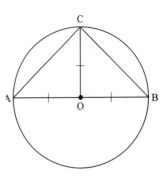

Angle AOC + angle BOC = 180° (angles on a straight line)
so angle AOC = angle BOC = 90°.

Triangle AOC and triangle BOC are isosceles (AO, OC and OB are equal radii) so their base angles are equal.

The angles of a triangle add up to 180° so each base angle equals 45°.

Angle ACB = 45° + 45° = 90°.

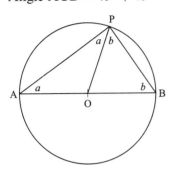

In this diagram AOB is a diameter of the circle.

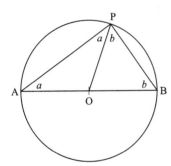

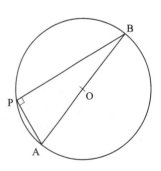

P is any point on the circumference of the circle. AO = OP (equal radiuses).

So angle OAP = angle OPA = $a$ (base angles of isosceles triangle)
BO = OP (equal radiuses)
so angle OBP = angle OPB = $b$ (base angles of isosceles triangle)

In triangle ABP, $a + a + b + b = 180°$ (sum of the angles of a triangle)
$$2a + 2b = 180°$$
Dividing by 2         $a + b = 90°$
or                   angle    APB = 90°

This useful fact about angles in circles is sometimes written:

**The angle on a diameter is a right angle**

*or*

**the angle in a semicircle is a right angle**.

## Worked exam question 1

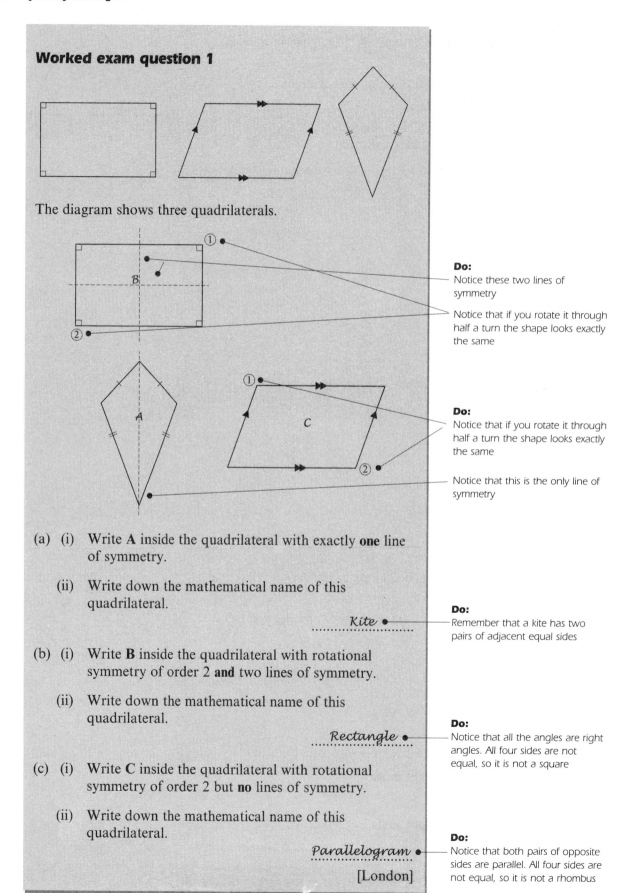

The diagram shows three quadrilaterals.

**Do:**
Notice these two lines of symmetry

Notice that if you rotate it through half a turn the shape looks exactly the same

**Do:**
Notice that if you rotate it through half a turn the shape looks exactly the same

Notice that this is the only line of symmetry

(a) (i) Write **A** inside the quadrilateral with exactly **one** line of symmetry.

(ii) Write down the mathematical name of this quadrilateral.

..........*Kite*..........

**Do:**
Remember that a kite has two pairs of adjacent equal sides

(b) (i) Write **B** inside the quadrilateral with rotational symmetry of order 2 **and** two lines of symmetry.

(ii) Write down the mathematical name of this quadrilateral.

..........*Rectangle*..........

**Do:**
Notice that all the angles are right angles. All four sides are not equal, so it is not a square

(c) (i) Write **C** inside the quadrilateral with rotational symmetry of order 2 but **no** lines of symmetry.

(ii) Write down the mathematical name of this quadrilateral.

..........*Parallelogram*..........

[London]

**Do:**
Notice that both pairs of opposite sides are parallel. All four sides are not equal, so it is not a rhombus

## Exercise 16E

**1.** Write down the names of all the quadrilaterals that have:
  (a) all angles equal
  (b) both pairs of opposite sides equal
  (c) all the sides equal
  (d) both pairs of opposite angles equal
  (e) the diagonals equal
  (f) the diagonals bisecting each other
  (g) the diagonals meeting right
  (h) the diagonals angles bisecting each at other at right angles
  (i) at least one pair of opposite sides parallel.

**2.** In the parallelogram:
  (a) write down the value of *a*
  (b) calculate:
  (i) *b*   (ii) *c*

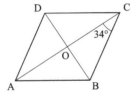

**3.** In the kite PQRS angle QPR = 63°.
Calculate:
  (a) angle PQS
  (b) angle PQR

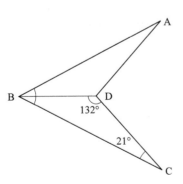

**4.** In the rhombus ABCD angle ACB = 34°. The diagonals cross at O.
Work out:
  (a) angle OBC
  (b) angle ABC

**5.** The arrowhead shape ABCD is a type of kite.
AB = BC and AD = DC. Angle BDC = 132° and angle BCD = 21°.
Calculate angle ABC.

**6.** O is the centre of the circle. M is the middle point of the chord PQ. Angle OQM = 47°. Calculate the size of angle MOQ.

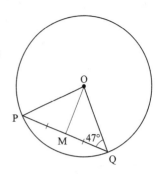

**7.** AB is a diameter of the circle. Angle BAC = 41°.
  (a) Write down the size of angle ACB.

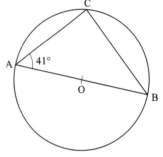

**8.** AB is a diameter of the circle with centre O. ST is the tangent at A to the circle.
  (a) angle BCA
  (b) angle BAC
  (c) angle CAS.

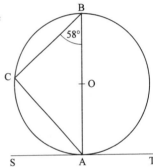

# 16.8 Angles in polygons

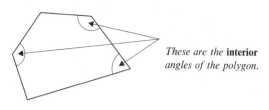

*These are the **interior** angles of the polygon.*

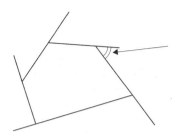

*This is an **exterior** angle of the polygon. It is formed by continuing the side of the polygon.*

At a vertex of a polygon the sum of the interior angle and the exterior angle is 180° (angles on a straight line).

### Example 7

*Step 1*: draw a polygon (with each angle less than 180°) on a piece of paper.

*Step 2*: continue each side of the polygon to form the exterior angles.

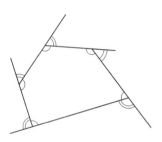

*Step 3*: label each exterior angle with a different letter.

*Step 4*: cut out the exterior angles with some adjoining paper.

*Step 5*: place the angles together at a point.

*Step 6*: write down what you notice.

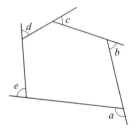    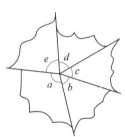

The exterior angles fit together at a point with no gaps, so they add up to 360°.

Try this yourself with a polygon with a different number of sides.

The sum of the exterior angles of any polygon is 360°.

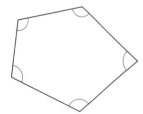    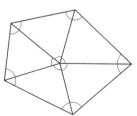

In this pentagon the five vertices are joined to a point inside to make five triangles. The sum of the interior angles of a pentagon and the five angles at the point inside equals the sum of the angles of five triangles.

The sum of the interior angles of a pentagon $+360° = 5 \times 180°$
$$= 900°$$

so the sum of the interior angles of a pentagon $= 900° - 360°$
$$= 540°$$

To find the sum of the interior angles of a polygon with $n$ sides join all the vertices to a point in the centre to make $n$ triangles.

The sum of the interior angles of a polygon with $n$ sides equals

$$n \times 180° - 360°$$

This result is sometimes given as '**($2n$–4) right angles**' because $n \times 180° - 360° = 90°(2n - 4) = (2n - 4)$ right angles. The result can also be given as **($n$–2) $\times$ 180°** because

$$n \times 180° - 360° = 180°(n - 2) = (n - 2) \times 180°$$

If the polygon is regular (all its sides and all its angles are equal) each interior angle is the sum of all the interior angles divided by the number of sides.

So the size of each interior angle of a regular pentagon is

$$540° \div 5 = 108°$$

***Example 8***

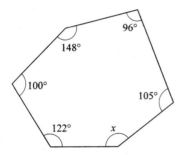

Calculate $x$.

**First method, using exterior angles**

Five of the exterior angles are

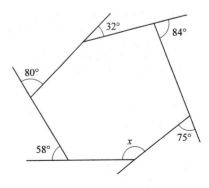

$180° - 122° = 58°$
$180° - 100° = 80°$
$180° - 148° = 32°$
$180° - 96° \quad = 84°$
$180° - 105° = 75°$   (*angles on a straight line*)

These five angles add up to $329°$.

All the exterior angles add up to $360°$.

So the exterior angle at $x$ is $360° - 329° = 31°$

So $x = 180° - 31 = 149°$ (*angles on a straight line*)

### Second method, using interior angles

Join all the vertices to a point inside the polygon to make six triangles.

Sum of all the angles in six triangles $= 6 \times 180° = 1080°$

This includes $360°$ at the central point.

So the sum of all the interior angles $= 1080° - 360° = 720°$

The sum of the five known angles is

$$122° + 100° + 148° + 96° + 105° = 571°$$

so $x = 720° - 571° = 149°$

---

### Exercise 16F

1. Calculate the named angles, giving reasons.
   (a)

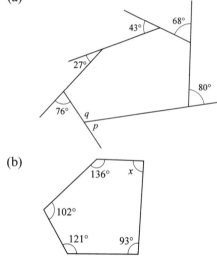

   (b)

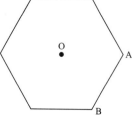

2. Work out the size of one interior angle of a regular nonagon (a polygon with 9 sides).

3. Each interior angle of a regular polygon is $144°$.
   (a) Calculate the number of sides of this polygon.
   (b) Calculate the **sum** of the interior angles, in degrees, of a polygon which has 7 sides.
   [London]

4. The diagram shows a regular hexagon. O is the point at the centre of the hexagon. A and B are two vertices.
   (a) Write down the order of rotational symmetry of the regular hexagon.

   (b) Copy the diagram. Draw the lines from O to A and from O to B.
      (i) Write down the size of angle AOB.
      (ii) Write down the mathematical name for triangle AOB. [London]

5. The tables at a conference centre are all of the same shape and size.
   Each table has four sides.
   The long side of each table is twice the length of each of the shorter sides.
   For meetings the tables are arranged together to form different worktops. Two arrangements of the tables are shown.

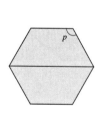 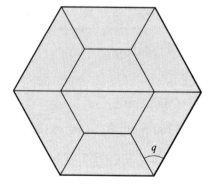

   *Arrangement A*          *Arrangement B*

   (a) Both arrangements are in the shape of a regular polygon. What mathematical name is given to this polygon?
   (b) What is the size of the angle marked $p$?
   (c) What is the size of the angle marked $q$?
   (d) Express, in the form $1 : n$ the ratio of the length of the outside edge of arrangement $A$ to the length of the outside edge of arrangement $B$. [SEG]

# 16.9 Tessellations

This pattern of tiles is made from two basic tiles; squares (black) and equilateral triangles (white). When the tiles completely cover the space with no gaps the pattern is called a **tessellation**.

It can be shown that there are only 17 different ways in which a basic pattern can be repeated. These repeating patterns are often found on furnishing fabrics, dress materials, wallpapers and tiled floors and walls.

In the thirteenth century the Arabs used all 17 methods to decorate the tiled walls and floors of the Alhambra Palace in Granada, Spain.

This tessellation is made from different arrangements of the same triangle.

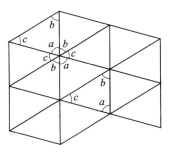

At each point where six triangles meet there are two of each of the different angles of the triangle.

$$a + b + c = 180°  \text{ (sum of angles of a triangle)}$$

so $a + b + c + a + b + c = 360°$

This tessellation is made from different arrangements of the same quadrilateral.

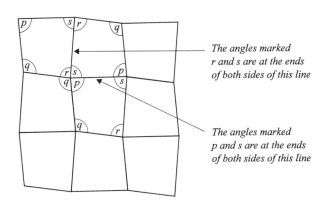

*The angles marked r and s are at the ends of both sides of this line*

*The angles marked p and s are at the ends of both sides of this line*

At each point where four quadrilaterals meet there is one each of the four different angles of the quadrilateral.

$$p + q + r + s = 360° \quad \text{(sum of angles of a quadrilateral)}$$

For shapes to tessellate it must be possible to arrange the shapes so that the sum of the angles meeting at a point is 360°.

When drawing tessellations it is a good idea to cut out the shape (or shapes) in card and draw round the outline (or outlines).

### Example 9

Draw a tessellation using this shape as the basic unit:

*Step 1*: trace the shape on to card and cut it out.

*Step 2*: draw an outline of the shape on paper.

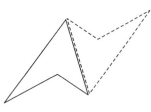

*Step 3*: rotate the card shape and place it next to your first drawing so that two equal sides are against each other. Draw round the outline of the shape.

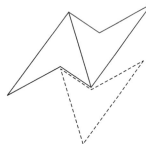

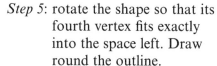

*Step 4*: repeat step 3 using two other equal sides

*Step 5*: rotate the shape so that its fourth vertex fits exactly into the space left. Draw round the outline.

*Step 6*: continue in the same way until you have filled up the space on your paper.

Not all shapes will tessellate. The size of one interior angle of a regular octagon is 135°. If two regular octagons are placed together, as in the diagram, the two adjacent interior angles add to 270°. So the angle in the gap is 360° − 270° = 90°. This is too small for another octagon corner angle of 135°.

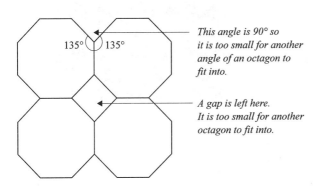

135°  135°

*This angle is 90° so it is too small for another angle of an octagon to fit into.*

*A gap is left here. It is too small for another octagon to fit into.*

## Exercise 16G

You will need graph paper, squared paper and isometric paper for this exercise.

**1.** Draw a tessellation using as the basic shape:

(a)                    (b)

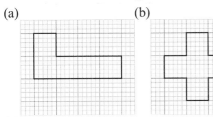

(c)

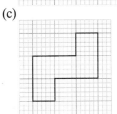

**2.** Write down the letters of the shapes which will tessellate.

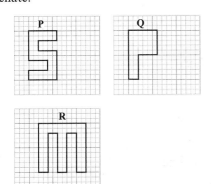

**3.** Draw a different tessellation using the black squares and the white equilateral triangles used for the pattern at the beginning of this section.

**4.** (a) Write down the geometrical name of the quadrilateral shown in the diagram.

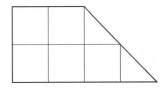

Draw a grid with 8 squares across and 6 squares down, inside a rectangle.

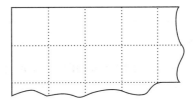

Quadrilaterials identical to the one in (a) are to be used to tessellate the inside of the rectangle.
(b) Show how the tessellation can be drawn on your grid.

[London]

**5.** ABCDE is a regular pentagon. O is the centre of the pentagon.

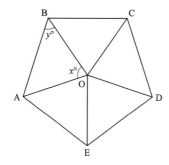

(a) Work out the value of
 (i) $x$,    (ii) $y$.

Diagram NOT accurately drawn

Copy the hexagon on to isometric paper.

(b) On the grid show how regular hexagons tessellate. One hexagon has been drawn.

(c) Explain why regular pentagons will not tessellate.

[London]

**6.** Make a tessellation using a suitable shape or shapes.

**7.** Write down the names of the three regular polygons which are used to make this tessellation.

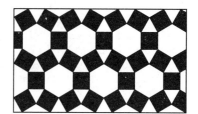

---

## 16.10 Angles at parallel lines

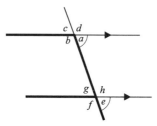

Remember: two lines are parallel if they run in exactly the same direction.

The arrows show that the lines are parallel.

If you cut out angle $e$ it will fit exactly over angle $a$.

So angle $a$ = angle $e$

They are called **corresponding angles**.

Also angle $b$ = angle $f$, angle $c$ = angle $g$ and angle $d$ = angle $h$.

These are three other pairs of corresponding angles.

These angles are called corresponding angles because they are on corresponding sides of the parallel lines and the intersecting line.

Sometimes they are called **F** angles because the shape of the lines makes the letter **F**.

Corresponding angles are equal.

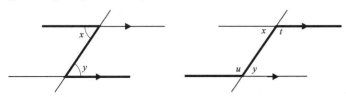

If this drawing is rotated angle $x$ will fit exactly over angle $y$.

So angle $x =$ angle $y$

They are called **alternate angles**.

Also angle $t =$ angle $u$ because they are alternate angles. These angles are called alternate angles because they are on alternate sides of the parallel lines and the intersecting line.

Sometimes they are called **Z** angles because the shape of the lines makes a letter **Z**.

Alternate angles are equal.

### *Example 10*

Calculate $p$, $q$ and $r$, giving reasons.

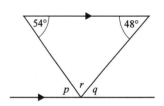

$p = 54°$ (*alternate angles*)

$q = 48°$ (*alternate angles*)

$54° + 48° + r = 180°$ (*sum of angles of triangle*)

$\qquad 102° + r = 180°$

So $\qquad r = 180° - 102° = 78°$

---

## Worked exam question 2

In the diagram, AB equals AC.

BA and CD are parallel.

Angle CAD is 90° and angle ADC is 40°.

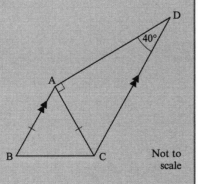

Not to scale

(a) Calculate angle DCA.

$\underline{Angle\ DCA = 180° - (90° + 40°)}$ •────────

$\qquad\quad \underline{= 180° - 130°}$

$\qquad\quad\quad \underline{= 50°}$

$\qquad\qquad\qquad\quad \underline{50} \ldots\ldots\ldots$ degrees

**Do:**
Use the fact that the three angles in triangle ADC add up to 180°

(b)  (i)   Write down another angle equal to DCA.

*Angle BAC*

**Do:**
Look again at the information given

(ii)   Give a reason for your answer.

*BA is parallel to CD so angle DCA and*

*angle BAC are equal alternate angles*

(c)  Calculate angle ABC.

*Angle ABC + angle ACB = 180° − 50° = 130°*

*so angle ABC = 130° ÷ 2* •

*= 65°*

**Do:**
Use the fact that angle ABC and angle ACB are equal base angles of isosceles triangle ABC

..........65...... degrees

(SEG)

---

## Exercise 16H

**1.** Calculate the named angles, giving reasons.

(a)

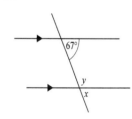

(b)

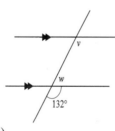

(c)

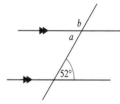

(d)

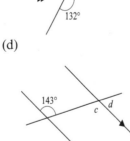

(e)

(f)

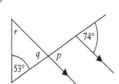

**2.** The diagram has two pairs of parallel lines.

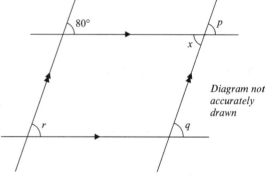

*Diagram not accurately drawn*

Angles marked *p* and *q* are equal.
(a) What geometrical name is given to this type of equal angles?
(b) Write down the size of angle *r*.
(c) (i) Write down the size of angle *x*.
    (ii) What geometrical name is given to the pair of angles *x* and *q*?          [London]

3. The diagram shows the following information:

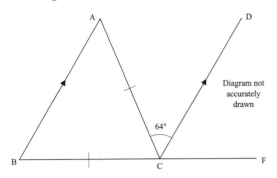

Diagram not accurately drawn

BA is parallel to CD, CA = CB, angle
ACD = 64°. Find the size of:
(a) angle BAC,
(b) angle BCA.                    [London]

4. Ajit is painting a ceiling. He uses two step
ladders, ABC and PQR, and a plank, XY, as
shown.

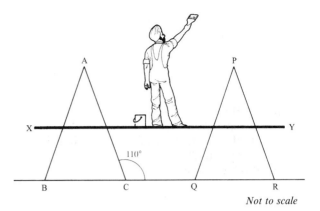

*Not to scale*

XY is parallel to BCQR. ABC and PQR are
congruent isosceles triangles. Angle ACQ is 110°
(a) What is the size of the angle PRQ?
(b) What is the size of the angle BAC?    [SEG]

---

## Exercise 16I (Mixed questions)

You will need a protractor, squared paper and
dotty squared paper for this exercise.

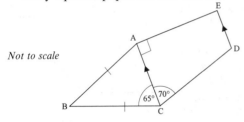

*Not to scale*

1. The pentagon ABCDE is the frame for
Ibrahim's mountain bike.
ABC is an isosceles triangle in which AB = BC
and
angle BCA = 65°.
In the quadrilateral ACDE, angle ACD = 70°,
angle CAE = 90° and AC is parallel to ED.
(a) Calculate angle ABC, giving a reason for
each step of your working.
(b) Calculate angle CDE, giving a reason for
your answer.
                                          [MEG]

2. PR = QR and angle PRQ = 54°.

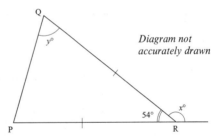

*Diagram not accurately drawn*

(a) Work out the value of x.
Triangle PQR is a special type of triangle.
(b) Write down the mathematical name of this
type of triangle.
(c) Work out the value of y.          [London]

3. The diagram shows a
quadrilateral ABCD.
Lengths AB and AD are
each 5 m. Lengths CB and
CD are each 10 m.
Angle DAB = 60°. Angle
ADC = 136°.
(a) Write down the length
of BD.
(b) What is the
mathematical name
for this quadrilateral?
(c) Calculate the value of
angle x.          [SEG]

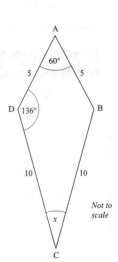

*Not to scale*

**4.**

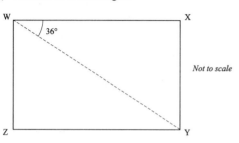

*Square*                    *Rectangle*

(a) (i) How many lines of symmetry has the square?
    (ii) How many lines of symmetry has the rectangle?

(b) WXYZ is a rectangle.

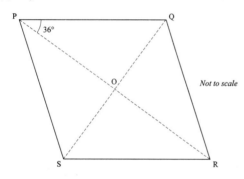

*Not to scale*

Angle XWY = 36°.
Work out the size of angle WYZ, giving a reason for your answer.

(c) PQRS is a rhombus.

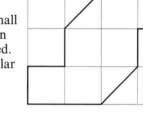

*Not to scale*

Angle QPR = 36°.
The diagonals PR and QS cross at O.
Working out the size of angle PQS, giving a reason for your answer.              [SEG]

**5.**

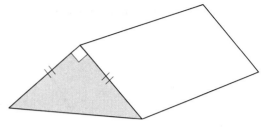

The diagram represents a prism.
The cross-section (shaded region) of the prism is a right-angled isosceles triangle.
Sketch the diagram.
Draw one plane of symmetry of the prism.                                [London]

**6.** A regular octagon, drawn on the right, has eight sides. One side of the octagon has been extended to form angle *p*.

(a) Work out the size of angle *p*.
(b) Work out the size of angle *q*.                                    [SEG]

**7.** Tina is designing a pattern.
She draws the small design which then has to be enlarged.
Draw a rectangular grid 12 squares across and 9 squares down.

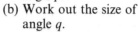

On your grid draw an enlargement of the small shape so that its edges lie along the edges of the rectangle.  [SEG]

---

# Test yourself

**1.**    **A**           **B**           **C**           **D**           **E**

   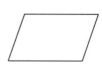 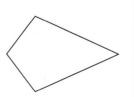

**QUESTION**   (a)   Write down the letters of the shapes that have
      (i)   one line of symmetry
      (ii)   two lines of symmetry
      (iii)   three lines of symmetry.

**ANSWER**   (i) B, E (ii) A (iii) C    *If your answer is incorrect review page 312, Section 16.2 on recognising line symmetry*

**QUESTION**   (b)   Write down the letters of the shapes that have rotational symmetry of order
      (i)   2
      (ii)   3

**ANSWER**   (i) A, D (ii) C    *If your answer is incorrect review page 314, Section 16.3 on recognising rotational symmetry*

---

**2.**

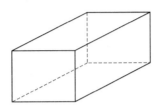

**QUESTION**   The diagram represents a cuboid
How many planes of symmetry does the cuboid have?

**ANSWER**   3    *If your answer is incorrect review page 315, Section 16.4 on planes of symmetry*

---

**3.**   In the diagram PQ is parallel to SR, QR equals SR and angle QSR is 62°.

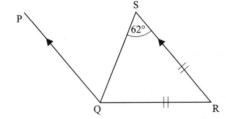

**QUESTION**   (a)   Write down the size of angle PQS.

**ANSWER**   62°    *If your answer is incorrect review page 332, Section 16.10 on angles at parallel lines*

**QUESTION**   (b)   Calculate the size of angle QRS.

**ANSWER**   56°    *If your answer is incorrect review page 318, Section 16.6 on angles in triangles*

---

**4.**

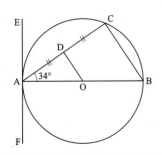

AB is a diameter of the circle and O is the centre of the circle. D is the middle point of the chord AC.
EAF is the tangent at A to the circle. Angle BAC = 34°.

QUESTION   Calculate the size of
(a) angle EAD   (b) angle ADO   (c) angle AOD
(d) angle ACB   (e) angle ABC

ANSWER   (a) 56°   (b) 90°   (c) 56°       *If your answer is incorrect review page 321, Section*
(d) 90°   (e) 56°                          *16.7 on properties of quadrilaterals and circles*

---

5.   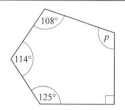   Four of the angles of a pentagon
are 125°, 114°, 108° and 90°.

QUESTION   Calculate the angle marked *p* in the diagram

ANSWER   103°       *If your answer is incorrect review page 326, Section*
*16.8 on angles in polygons*

---

6.       **A**               **B**               **C**               **D**               **E**

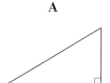   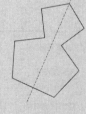 

QUESTION   Write down the letters of the shapes which will tessellate.

ANSWER   A, C and D       *If your answer is incorrect review page 329, Section*
*16.9 on tessellations*

# Summary of key points to remember

1. A 2-D shape has a **line of symmetry** if the line divides the shape into two
   halves and one half is the mirror image of the other half.

   A 2-D shape has **rotational symmetry** if it fits onto itself two or more
   times in one turn.

   The number of times a shape fits onto itself in one turn is the **order of
   rotational symmetry**.

   A 3-D shape has a **plane of symmetry** if the plane divides the
   shape into two halves and one half is the mirror image of the
   other half.

2. An angle is a measure of **turn** (or **change of direction**). **Acute**
   angles are smaller than one right angle. **Obtuse** angles are bigger
   than one right angle and smaller than two right angles. **Reflex**
   angles are bigger than two right angles. Two angles are called
   **supplementary** when they add up to two right angles (180°).

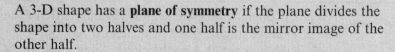
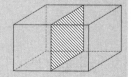

**3.** Angles on a straight line add up to 180°.

Angles at a point add up to 360°.

Vertically opposite angles are equal.

**4.** The sum of the angles of a triangle is 180°.

Each angle of an equilateral triangle equals 60°.

The base angles of an isosceles triangle are equal.

The sum of the angles of a quadrilateral is 360°.

**5.** The perpendicular bisector of a chord of a circle passes through the centre of the circle.

A radius drawn to the point where a tangent touches a circle is perpendicular to the tangent.

The angle in a semicircle is a right angle.

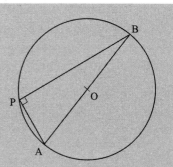

6. At a vertex of a polygon, the sum of the interior angle and the exterior angle is 180°.

The sum of the exterior angles of any polygon is 360°.

The sum of the interior angles of a polygon with $n$ sides equals $n \times 180° - 360°$.

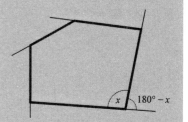

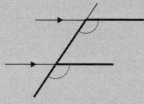

7. Angles at parallel lines:

Corresponding angles are equal.

Alternate angles are equal.

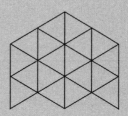

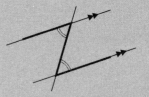

8. A **tessellation** is an arrangement of a shape or set of shapes on a flat surface so that all the space is filled with no gaps and no overlaps.

For shapes to tessellate it must be possible to arrange the shapes so that the total of the angles meeting at a point is 360°.

# 17 Transformations

## 17.1 Introduction

This unit covers four types of transformations: translations, reflections, rotations and enlargements. The study of enlargements leads to the ideas of mathematical similarity and congruence.

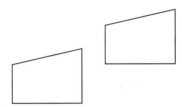

This trapezium has been moved across the page. Each point on the shape has moved the same distance in the same direction. Changes in the shape, size or position of an object are called **transformations**.

For your GCSE exam you need to know about four types of transformation: translations, reflections, rotations and enlargements.

## 17.2 Translations

In mathematics the original shape is called the **object**. The transformed shape is called the **image**.

A transformation where each point on the object moves the same distance in the same direction is called a **translation**.

To describe a translation fully you need to give the *distance* moved and the *direction* of the movement. One way of doing this is to write down the **column vector** of the translation.

Triangle **P** is translated to **Q**. All the points on **P** are moved a distance $-4$ units parallel to the $x$-axis followed by 2 units parallel to the $y$-axis.

This is a translation by the **column vector** $\begin{pmatrix} -4 \\ 2 \end{pmatrix}$.

A column vector is a way of describing a movement (displacement). The column vector $\begin{pmatrix} 3 \\ -2 \end{pmatrix}$ means the movement of a point by adding 3 onto the $x$-coordinate of the point and subtracting 2 from the $y$-coordinate of the point.

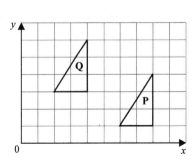

Here are some displacements and their column vectors.

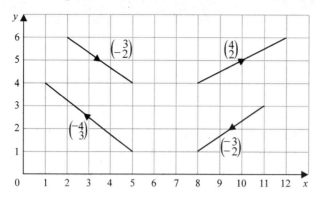

### Example 1

The shape EFGH is shown on the grid. EFGH is translated to RSTU so that R(2, 3) is the image of E. Plot R and draw RSTU, the image of EFGH.

E(−3, 5) is translated to R(2, 3). The x-coordinate has been moved from −3 to 2, so 5 has been added to the x-coordinate.

The y-coordinate has been moved from 5 to 3, so 2 has been subtracted from the y-coordinate. S is the image of F(−1, 5) so the coordinates of S are (−1 + 5, 5 − 2). S = (4, 3).

In the same way T = (−1 + 5, 1 − 2) = (4, −1) and U = (−3 + 5, 4 − 2) = (2, 2).

Join the points in order, to make the image RSTU.

Note: You could say that the column vector of the translation is $\begin{pmatrix} 5 \\ -2 \end{pmatrix}$.

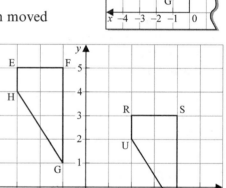

### Exercise 17A

You will need isometric and squared paper for this exercise. Tracing paper could be useful.

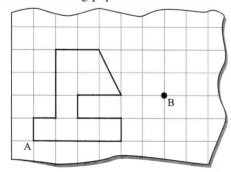

1. Copy this shape onto squared paper.

The point B is the image of point A after a translation. Draw the whole shape following the translation.

2. Shape **L** is shown on the grid.
   L is translated using this rule:
   Move all points +3 units parallel to the x-axis followed by +2 units parallel to the y-axis. (Move them by the vector $\begin{pmatrix} 3 \\ 2 \end{pmatrix}$.)

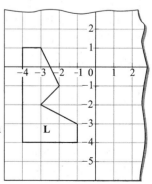

**2.** On squared paper draw a set of coordinate axes with $x$ and $y$ both going from $-5$ to $5$.
   (a) Draw the image of **L** after the translation and label it **M**.
   (b) Write down the coordinates of the corners of shape **M**.

**3.** On squared paper draw a set of coordinate axes with $x$ and $y$ both going from $-5$ to $5$.
   The corners of triangle ABC are A$(-3, 1)$, B$(-3, 4)$ and C$(0, 3)$.
   (a) Draw triangle ABC on your grid.
   Triangle ABC is translated to triangle A$'$B$'$C$'$ by the vector $\begin{pmatrix} 4 \\ -3 \end{pmatrix}$.
   (b) Work out the coordinates of A$'$, B$'$ and C$'$.
   (c) Draw triangle A$'$B$'$C$'$ on your grid.

**4.** Describe fully the transformation which maps shape **P** onto shape **Q**.

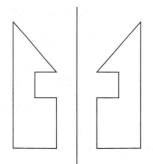

**5.** Make a pattern using repeated translations. You may use one, two or more shapes.

---

## 17.3 Reflections

A reflection is something like a mirror image. The 'mirror' is called a **mirror line** or a **line of reflection**.

The point A is reflected in a mirror.

The image of A (labelled A$'$) is behind the mirror.

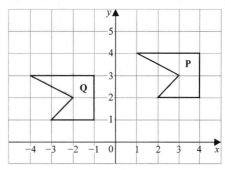

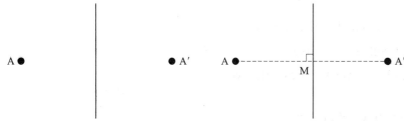

If you draw a line from A to A$'$ to cross the mirror at M

$$AM = A'M$$

and  AA$'$ is at right angles to the mirror.

You can draw the reflection of a shape by using these facts to find the images of different points of the shape.

*Hint*: if the mirror line is at an angle it is easier to draw a reflection if you turn the paper until the mirror line is 'vertical'.

### Example 2

The shape ABCD is reflected in the line MN.

Draw the image of the shape and label it A$'$B$'$C$'$D$'$.

Draw a line from A at right angles to MN. Continue the line to a point the same distance the other side and label the point A$'$.

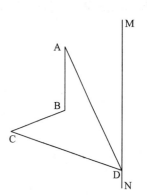

Repeat this for the points B, C and D.

Join the points to make the reflected shape.

*Note*: a point on the mirror line is its own image.

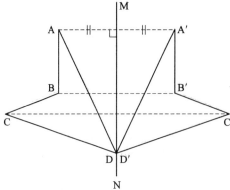

You can use tracing paper to draw a reflection.

*Step 1*: draw a shape and a mirror line.

*Step 2*: trace the shape and the mirror line.

*Step 3*: turn the tracing paper over and place the tracing so that the mirror lines are over each other.

*Step 4*: transfer the image shape to your drawing.

The shape ABCD in Example 2 maps onto the shape A′B′C′D′ after the reflection.

The vertices of shape ABCD are labelled anticlockwise.

The vertices of A′B′C′D′ are labelled clockwise.

If ABCD were cut out it would turn over to fit exactly over A′B′C′D′.

- A transformation where the image of an object is like a mirror image is called a **reflection**. The image is the *same shape and size* as the original shape, but it is *'turned over'*.

The shape **P** is reflected to **Q**.

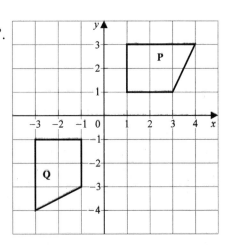

This is how the mirror line is drawn:

Draw a line from a point on **P** to its corresponding point on **Q** (shown by a broken line on the diagram).

Find the middle point of the line.

Repeat for another point on **P** and its corresponding point on **Q**.

Join the two middle points to give the **mirror line**.

The equation of the mirror line is $y = -x$.

To describe a reflection fully you need to say which line is the mirror line.

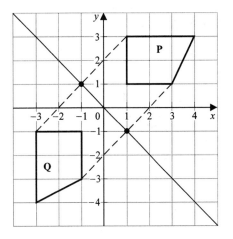

## Example 3

Describe fully the transformation that maps shape **A** onto shape **B**.

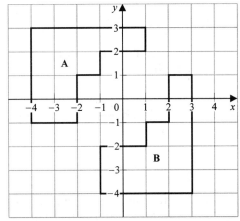

The image **B** is the same shape and size as the original shape **A**, but it is 'turned over'. So the transformation is a reflection. First draw the mirror line.

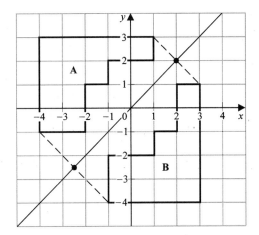

The equation of the mirror line is $y = x$. So A maps onto B after a reflection in the line $y = x$.

(Read about the equations of straight lines in Unit 9.)

## Exercise 17B

You will need squared or graph paper and tracing paper for this exercise.

1. Copy the shape **A** and the line MR. Draw the image of shape **A** after a reflection in the line MR.

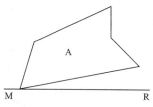

2. Copy this shape and the line MN onto squared paper. Draw the image of the shape after a reflection in the line MN.

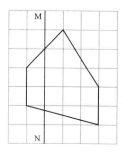

3. Copy the grid and the shaded shape.
   Draw the line whose equation is $x = 1$.
   Draw the image of the shape after a reflection in the line $x = 1$.

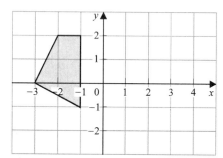

4. Copy triangle PQR and the line ML onto squared paper.
   Draw the image of triangle PQR after it is reflected in the line ML.
   The image of the point P has been found for you.
   *Hint*: turn the page so that ML is 'vertical'.

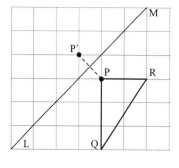

5. Draw a pair of axes with both $x$ and $y$ going from $-6$ to 6.
   (a) Plot the points A$(-4, 2)$, B$(0, 1)$, C$(1, 0)$, D$(3, 4)$ and E$(-2, 4)$ and join them in order to form the closed shape ABCDE.
   (b) Draw the image of ABCDE after a reflection in the $x$-axis.

6. Draw a set of coordinate axes with $x$ from $-4$ to 10 and $y$ from 0 to 7.
   (a) Plot the points $(-2, 1)$, $(1, 3)$ and $(0, 5)$. Join them and label the triangle **A**.
   The triangle **A** is reflected in a line **M**. The image points of two of the vertices have coordinates $(5, 3)$ and $(6, 5)$.
   (b) Write down the coordinates of the image of the third vertex of **A**.
   (c) Work out the equation of **M**, the line of reflection.

7. Describe fully the transformation that maps **A** onto **B**.

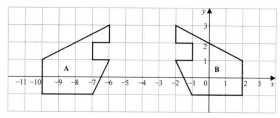

8. Use tracing paper to draw a pattern by making repeated reflections of a shape.

## 17.4 Rotations

The minute hand of a clock **rotates** (turns) about a fixed point near one of its ends. You can also say that it *turns through an angle* about a fixed point.

A transformation where an object turns through an angle about a fixed point is called a **rotation**.

The fixed point is called the **centre of rotation**.

The image is the *same shape and size* as the original object.

You can use tracing paper to rotate a shape.

*Step 1*: make a tracing of the shape and mark the centre of rotation with a dot. Go over the outline on the back of the tracing paper with pencil.

*Step 2*: place your tracing over the shape and keep the dot fixed. *Hint*: you could use the point of a pair of compasses for this.

*Step 3*: rotate the tracing paper through the angle given.

*Step 4*: transfer the image to your drawing by scribbling over the tracing paper.

### Example 4

Rotate the shape half a turn about the point marked with a dot.

The shape rotated half a turn.

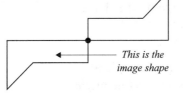

*This is the image shape*

### Exercise 17C

You will need tracing paper and a protractor for this exercise.

1. Copy the shapes. Use tracing paper to rotate each shape half a turn about the point marked with a dot.
   (a)          (b)          (c)

2. Rotate each of the shapes in question **1** a quarter turn anticlockwise about the point marked with a dot.

3. Copy the shape. Draw the image after a rotation about the point R of:
   (a) a quarter turn anticlockwise
   (b) a half turn
   (c) a quarter turn clockwise.

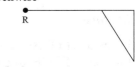

4. Copy the shape. Draw the image after a rotation about the dot of:
   (a) 120° anticlockwise
   (b) 240° anticlockwise
   (c) 120° clockwise
   *Hint*: use a protractor to make sure the turn is exactly 120°.

## 17.5 Using squared or isometric paper to rotate shapes

You can use squared paper to rotate shapes.

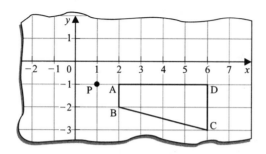

To draw the image of the shape ABCD after a quarter turn anticlockwise about the point P(1, −1), work out the image of each point on the shape and join up the individual points to form the image shape. Use the lines on the grid to help you.

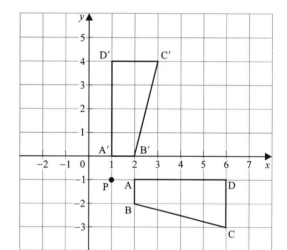

Rotate A about P through a quarter of a turn (90°) anticlockwise and it ends up at (1, 0).

Rotate B about P through a quarter of a turn (90°) anticlockwise and it ends up at (2, 0). D goes to (1, 4).

You do not have to find all the image points. Here you have enough information to draw the shape without finding the coordinates of C′.

When a shape is rotated through a given angle all the lines in the shape rotate through the same angle.

The distance of an image point from the centre of rotation is the same as the distance of the original point from the centre of rotation.

### Example 5

Draw a set of axes with $x$ from −3 to 8 and $y$ from −2 to 6. Copy the shape EFGH and draw its image after a half turn about the point P(2, 2).

Rotate H about P through half a turn (180°) and its image is H′(1, 3). Rotate E about P and its image is E′(1, 5). The image of F is F′(0, 5) and the image of G is G′(−3, 3). Join the points E′F′G′H′ to form the image of EFGH.

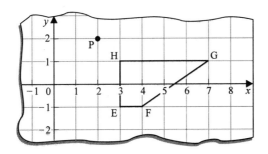

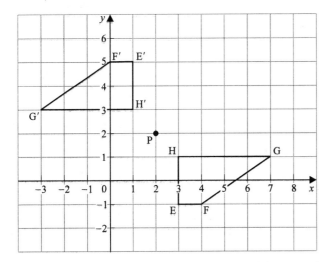

In an exam you may be asked to describe fully the transformation which maps shape **P** onto shape **Q**.

In the diagram each side of **Q** is at right angles to the corresponding side of **P** so P has made a quarter turn anticlockwise to get to **Q**.

To describe the rotation fully you need to say which point is the centre of rotation.

You can find the centre of rotation geometrically. It is at the same distance from each point and its image. So the centre is on the perpendicular bisector of the line joining each point to its image.

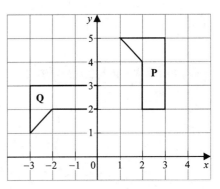

On the diagram join two corresponding points on **P** and **Q** with a line. Draw the perpendicular bisector of the line. Repeat this for another pair of corresponding points on **P** and **Q**. The centre of the rotation is where the two perpendicular bisectors cross. The centre of this rotation is $(1, 1)$.

To describe a rotation fully you need to give the angle of turn (and whether it is clockwise or anticlockwise) and give the centre of rotation.

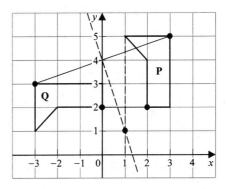

*Example 6*

Describe fully the transformation that maps shape **A** onto shape **B**.

Each side of **B** is at right angles to the corresponding side of **A** so **A** has made a quarter turn clockwise to get to **B**. By drawing the perpendicular bisectors of lines joining corresponding points, the centre of rotation is found to be $(2, 1)$.

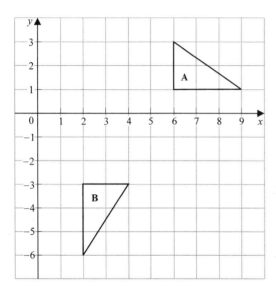

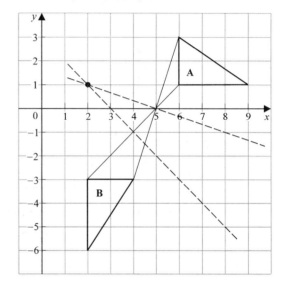

So the transformation that maps **A** onto **B** is a quarter turn clockwise about the point $(2, 1)$.

## Worked exam question 1

The diagram shows an equilateral triangle *ABC*.

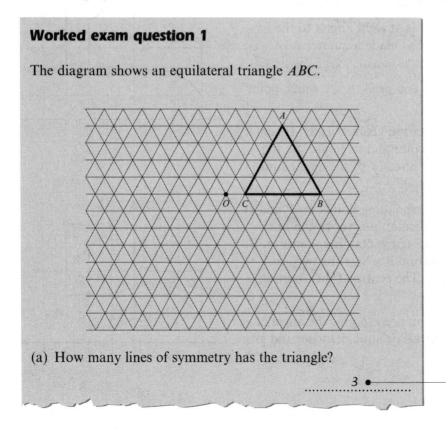

(a) How many lines of symmetry has the triangle?

.................................... 3

**Do:**
Remember that a line of symmetry can be drawn from each vertex to the middle point of the opposite side

(b) What is the size of angle *ACB*?

Give a reason for your answer.

...............60............... degrees

Reason *The sum of the angles of a triangle is 180°.* •

*All the angles of an equilateral triangle are equal* •

*so angle ACB = 180° ÷ 3 = 60°*

**Do:**
Use the fact that the angles of a triangle add up to 180°

Use the fact that an equilateral triangle has 3 equal angles

(c) The triangle is rotated 180° about *O*.

Draw and label the new position of the triangle.

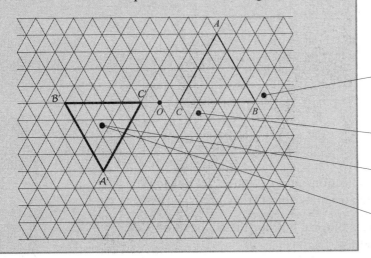

**Do:**
Use the fact that COC' is a straight line, because angle COC' = 180°. Also BOB' and AOA' are straight lines

Use the fact that OC' = OC, OB' = OB and OA' = OA

Check that each of the sides of triangle ABC has been rotated through 180°

Check that triangle A'B'C' is the same shape and size as triangle ABC.

## Exercise 17D

You will need squared or graph paper for this exercise.

**1.** Draw a grid with *x* and *y* going from −6 to 6. Copy the shape **A**. Draw the image of **A** after:
(a) a half turn about the origin O(0,0). Label the image **B**.
(b) a quarter turn clockwise about the origin. Label the image **C**.
(c) a quarter turn anticlockwise about the origin. Label the image **D**.

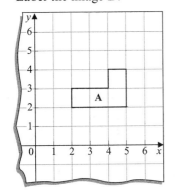

**2.** Draw coordinate axes on graph paper with *x* and *y* from −8 to 8. Copy the shape **R**. Draw the image of **R** after:
(a) a half turn about the point P(0,2). Label the image **S**.
(b) a quarter turn clockwise about the point P(0,2). Label the image **T**.
(c) a quarter turn anticlockwise about the point P(0,2). Label the image **U**.

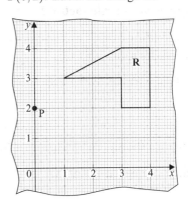

**3.**

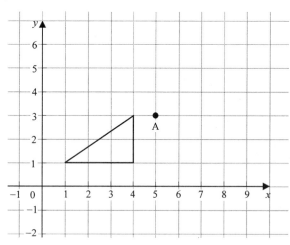

Rotate the triangle through 180° about centre A.
On a copy of the grid draw the new position of
the triangle.                    [London]

**4.** Describe fully the transformation which maps
shape **A** onto shape **B**.

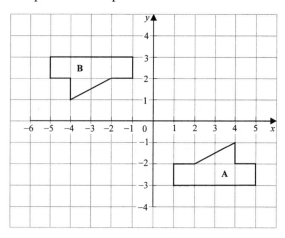

---

# 17.6 Enlargements

When you use translations, reflections and rotations the image is
the same size and shape as the original object (they are congruent).

A transformation that changes the size but not the shape of an
object is called an enlargement.

The quantity which multiplies the original lengths to get the image
lengths is called the **scale factor of the enlargement**.

To work out the scale factor of an enlargement you divide a length
of the image by the corresponding length of the original shape.

In the diagram, **B** is an enlargement of **A**. The scale factor is
$4 \div 2 = 2$.

The sides of shape **B** are all 2 times the length of the
corresponding sides of shape **A**. You can say that **B** is an
enlargement of **A** with **scale factor 2**.

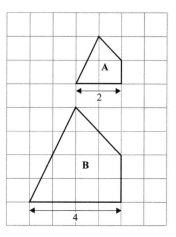

All the corresponding angles are equal so **A** and **B** are the same
shape. They are the same way up.

Each side of **B** is parallel to the corresponding side of **A**.

### Example 7

On a grid, enlarge the shaded shape by a scale factor of 3.

Start your enlargement at point B.

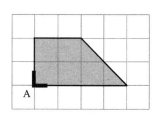

The sides of the image must be parallel to the corresponding sides of the original shape and three times as long.

The vertical line at A is 2 units long so the vertical line at B is $2 \times 3 = 6$ units long.

The horizontal line at A is 4 units long so the horizontal line at B is $4 \times 3 = 12$ units long. Draw in that line at B.

All the other sides of B are 3 times the length of the corresponding sides of A so you can complete the enlarged shape.

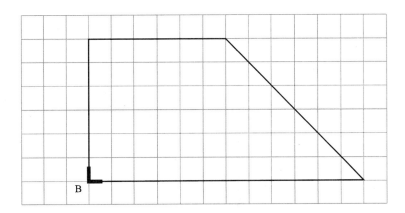

*Remember*: check that the corresponding lines are parallel.

---

### Exercise 17E

You will need squared paper for this exercise.

1. Copy the shaded shape onto squared paper. On the same paper draw enlargements of the shaded shape with scale factor:
   (a) 2  (b) 3  (c) 4.

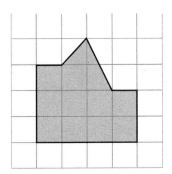

2. On the grid, enlarge the shaded shape by a scale factor of 3. Start your enlargement at point B.

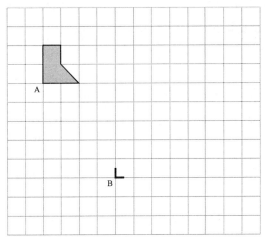

[London]

3. Copy Grid **A** and the shaded shape onto
   squared paper. Then draw Grid **B** on the same
   paper with 11 squares across and 10 squares
   down.
   (a) Draw a line of symmetry of the shaded shape
       on Grid **A**.
   (b) On Grid **B** draw an enlargement, scale factor
       3, of the shaded shape.                [London]

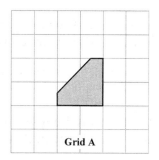

**Grid A**

## 17.7 Centre of enlargement

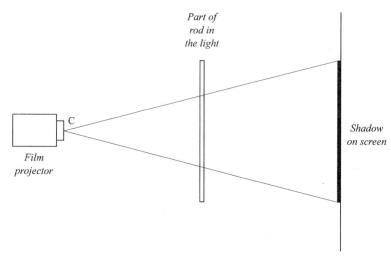

*Part of
rod in
the light*

C

*Film
projector*

*Shadow
on screen*

When a rod is held vertically in the light beam from a film
projector at C a shadow of part of the rod appears on the screen.

In the diagram the distance from C to the screen is twice the
distance from the rod to the screen.

The shadow on the screen is twice as large as the part of the rod in
the light beam. The scale factor of the enlargement is 2.

C is called the **centre of enlargement**.

*Example 8*

Copy triangle PQR and the point C.

(a) Construct accurately the image of triangle PQR after an
    enlargement by a scale factor of 3, using C as the centre of
    enlargement.

(b)  (i)  Measure the lengths P'Q' and PQ and work out $\dfrac{P'Q'}{PQ}$.

     (ii)  Measure the lengths P'R' and PR and work out $\dfrac{P'R'}{PR}$.

     (iii)  Measure the lengths R'Q' and RQ and work out $\dfrac{R'Q'}{RQ}$.

R

C

P          Q

(c) What do you notice about your answers to part (b)?

(a) Draw a line from C to P and continue it to P′ so that CP′ is 3 times CP.

   *Hint*: use compasses to mark off three lengths equal to CP.

   Join CR and continue it to R′ so that CR′ is 3 times CR.

   Join CQ and continue it to Q′ so that CQ′ is 3 times CQ.

   Join the points P′, Q′ and R′ to form the image triangle P′Q′R′.

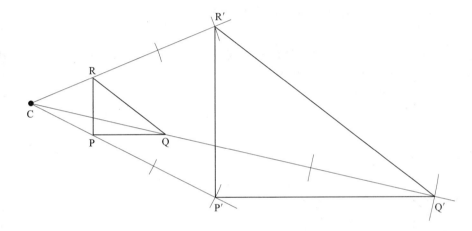

(b)  (i)  P′Q′ = 6 cm, PQ = 2 cm        so $\dfrac{PQ'}{PQ} = \dfrac{6}{2} = 3$

   (ii)  P′R′ = 4.5 cm, PR = 1.5 cm    so $\dfrac{P'R'}{PR} = \dfrac{4.5}{1.5} = 3$

   (iii)  R′Q′ = 7.5 cm, RQ = 2.5 cm   so $\dfrac{R'Q'}{RQ} = \dfrac{7.5}{2.5} = 3$

(c) The ratio of the length of a side of the image to the length of the corresponding side of the object is always the same. It is equal to the scale factor of the enlargement.

### Example 9

Copy triangle PQR and the point C *inside* the triangle.

Construct the image of triangle PQR after an enlargement by the scale factor of 3, using C as the centre of enlargement.

Use the same method as Example 8.

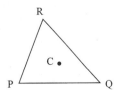

The enlargement looks like this:

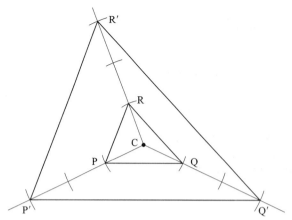

You will sometimes need to describe fully the transformation that maps one shape onto its enlargement.

In the diagram PQRS is the same shape as ABCD. The sides of PQRS are all 2 times the length of the corresponding sides of ABCD, so the transformation is an enlargement by a scale factor of 2.

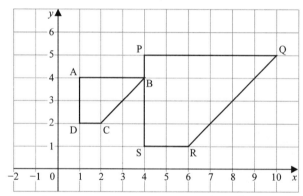

To describe the transformation fully you need to give the centre of enlargement. To find the centre of enlargement you reverse the method used in Example 8. Join P to A and continue the line. Join Q to B and continue the line. In the same way join R to C and S to D and continue the lines.

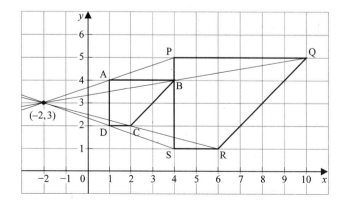

The lines all pass through the same point $(-2, 3)$ so this is the centre of enlargement. The transformation is an enlargement by scale factor 2 with centre of enlargement $(-2, 3)$.

To describe an enlargement fully you need to give the scale factor and the centre of enlargement.

### *Example 10*

Describe fully the transformation that makes shape **M** the image of shape **L**.

**M** is the same shape as **L**, but the sides of **M** are all 3 times the corresponding sides of **L**. So the transformation is an enlargement with scale factor 3.

Join pairs of corresponding points with lines and extend the lines. The lines meet at the point $(7, 0)$.

So the transformation is an enlargement, scale factor 3, centre $(7, 0)$.

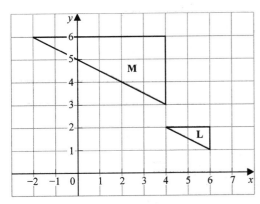
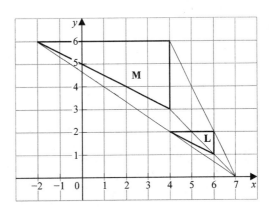

If you start with shape **M** from Example 10 and transform it to shape **L** the shape remains the same, but the size is changed, so the transformation is an enlargement.

The sides of **L** are all $\frac{1}{3}$ the length of the corresponding side of **M**. So the transformation that maps M on to L is an enlargement by a scale factor of $\frac{1}{3}$ with centre $(7, 0)$.

### *Example 11*

Draw the image of the shape DEFG after an enlargement by a scale factor of $\frac{1}{3}$ with centre C.

Label the image $D'E'F'G'$.

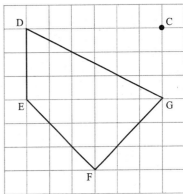

Join CD. CD = 6 units.

The scale factor is $\frac{1}{3}$ so $CD' = \frac{1}{3} \times 6 = 2$ units.

Mark the point D' 2 units from C along CD.

In the same way mark E' where $CE' = \frac{1}{3}CE$, F' where $CF' = \frac{1}{3}CF$ and G' where $CG' = \frac{1}{3}CG$.

*Hint*: use the squares of the grid so that you can do this without a ruler.

Join D'E'F'G' to form the image.

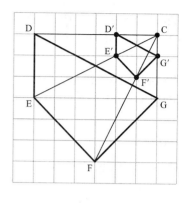

## Worked exam question 2

The diagram shows a quadrilateral *OABC*.

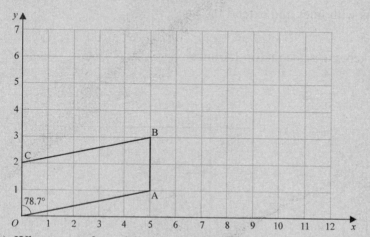

(a) What type of quadrilateral is *OABC*?

*Parallelogram*

**Do:**
Remember that a parallelogram has both pairs of opposite sides parallel

(b) The quadrilateral *OABC* is enlarged, with centre *O* and scale factor 2, to give *O'A'B'C'*. Draw the quadrilateral *O'A'B'C'*.

**Do:**
Mark
A' so that OA' is two times OA,
C' so that OC' is two times OC
and
B' so that OB' is two times OB

Check that A'B' is two times AB and that corresponding sides are parallel.

(c) (i) Angle $AOC = 78.7°$. Write down the size of angle *OCB*.

**Do:**
Remember that angle AOC and BCC′ are corresponding angles

*angle BCC′ = 78.7°*

*so angle OCB = 180° − 78.7° = 101.3*

.......101.3...... degrees

(ii) Mark with a *Z* on the diagram an angle that is equal to angle *AOC*.

Mark **one** of the angles shown with a Z on the diagram

(d) On the diagram below mark a new point, *E*, so that the quadrilateral *OAEC* is a kite.

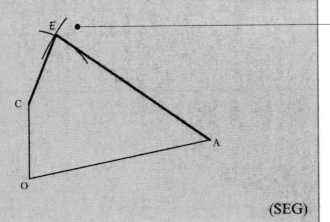

**Do:**
Remember that OC equals EC and OA equals EA if OAEC is a kite

Use compasses with a radius equal to OC. With centre C draw an arc
Use compasses with a radius equal to OA. With centre A draw an arc. E is where the two arcs meet

(SEG)

---

## Exercise 17F

You will need squared paper and graph paper for this exercise.

1. Copy the shape opposite and the dot marked C onto squared paper.
   Construct accurately the enlargement of the shape by scale factor 4 using the point C as the centre of enlargement.

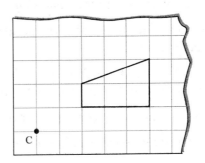

2. Draw a grid on squared paper with the $x$-axis from $-10$ to $10$ and the $y$-axis from $-14$ to $4$.
   (a) Plot the points $A(3, 1)$, $B(2, -4)$ and $C(-3, 1)$ and join them to form triangle ABC.
   (b) Draw the enlargement of triangle ABC by the scale factor 3, using the origin $(0, 0)$ as the centre of enlargement.
   (c) Write down the coordinates of the vertices of the image.

3. The triangle **Q** is an enlargement of the triangle **P**.
   (a) Write down the scale factor of the enlargement.
   (b) Work out the coordinates of the centre of enlargement.

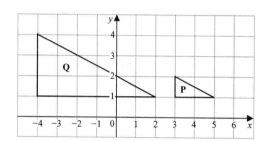

4. (a) Describe fully the transformation that maps the shape **A** onto the shape **B**.

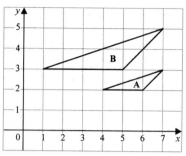

   (b) Describe fully the transformation that maps the shape **B** onto the shape **A**.

5. Draw the image of the shaded shape after an enlargement by scale factor $\frac{1}{4}$ with C as the centre of enlargement.

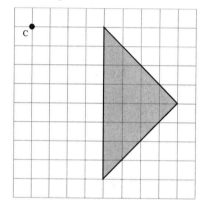

## 17.8 Similar shapes

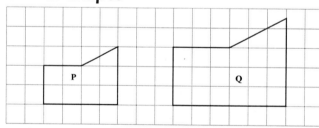

All the angles in shape **Q** are equal to the corresponding angles in shape **P**, so **P** and **Q** are the *same shape*.

The sides opposite the equal corresponding angles are called corresponding sides.

The sides of shape **Q** are all $1\frac{1}{2}$ times the corresponding sides of shape **P**, so **Q** is an enlargement of **P** with scale factor $1\frac{1}{2}$.

You can say that **P** and **Q** are **similar** (they are the **same shape**).

Two shapes are mathematically **similar** when:

● one shape is an enlargement of the other shape

- all the corresponding angles are equal
- all the corresponding lengths are in the same ratio.

Two similar shapes are exactly the *same shape*.

You can investigate similarity in Example 12.

### Example 12

(a) On graph paper copy shape RSTU.

Draw the enlargement of RSTU with centre Q and scale factor 3. Label the enlargement CDEF.

(b) Measure all the angles of CDEF.

(c) Measure all the corresponding angles of RSTU.

(d) Write down what you notice about your answers to (b) and (c).

(e) Write down what you notice about the lengths of the sides of CDEF and the corresponding sides of RSTU.

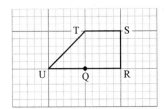

(a) QR = 1 cm, so QC = 1 × 3 = 3 cm.
QU = 1 cm, so QF = 1 × 3 = 3 cm and so on. Join C, D, E and F.

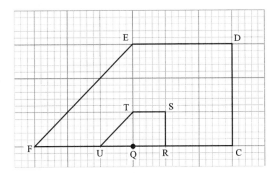

(b) Angle C = 90°, D = 90°, E = 135° and F = 45°.

(c) Angle R = 90°, S = 90°, T = 135° and U = 45°.

(d) Angle C = R, D = S, E = T, F = U.

(e) All the sides of CDEF are 3 times the corresponding sides of RSTU.

When a shape is transformed by an enlargement, the original shape and its *image after an enlargement* are **similar** to each other.

You can explain that triangle ABC and triangle DEF are similar by making one of these statements:

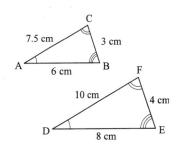

*Either* • Triangle DEF is an enlargement of triangle ABC with scale factor $\frac{4}{3}$.

*or*    • Triangle ABC is an enlargement of triangle DEF with scale factor $\frac{3}{4}$.

*or*    • The angles of triangle ABC are equal to the corresponding angles of triangle DEF
Angle A = angle D, angle B = angle E and angle C = angle F.

*or*    • The ratios of the sides of triangle ABC to the corresponding sides of triangle DEF are equal.

$$\frac{AB}{DE} = \frac{6}{8} = \frac{3}{4}, \frac{BC}{EF} = \frac{3}{4}, \frac{AC}{DF} = \frac{7.5}{10} = \frac{75}{100} = \frac{3}{4}$$

## *Example 13*

In the diagram EB is parallel to DC.

(a) Write down the size of angle AEB.

(b) Work out the length of AB.

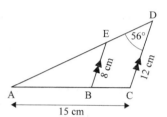

(a) Angle AEB = angle ADC = 56° (*corresponding angles of the parallel lines* EB *and* DC)

(b) Triangle AEB is an enlargement of triangle ADC as all the corresponding angles are equal.

The ratio of corresponding sides $= \frac{EB}{DC} = \frac{8}{12} = \frac{2}{3}$

So AB $= \frac{2}{3} \times$ AC $= \frac{2}{3} \times 15$ cm $= 10$ cm

Notice that if triangle AEB is an enlargement of triangle ADC with scale factor $\frac{2}{3}$, then triangle ADC is an enlargement of triangle AEB with scale factor $\frac{3}{2}$ (which is $\frac{2}{3}$ inverted).

---

## **Exercise 17G**

**1.** Calculate the length of OY.

Diagram NOT accurately drawn

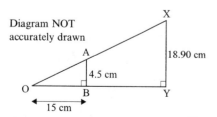

[London]

**2.** Triangle PQR is similar to triangle XYZ, PR = 8 cm. PQ = 16 cm, XZ = 4 cm and angle QPR = 60°.

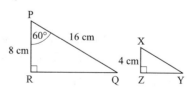

(a) Write down the size of angle YXZ.
(b) Work out the length of XY.

3. In each pair of similar figures calculate the lengths marked:

(a)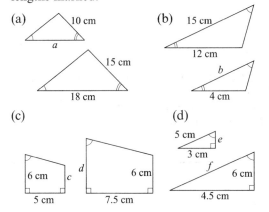

(b)

(c)

(d)

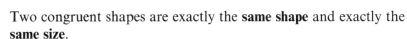

4. The height of a cone is 18 cm and the diameter of the base is 10.8 cm.
   The cone is cut parallel to its base to make a smaller cone. The height of the smaller cone is 12 cm.
   Calculate the diameter of the smaller cone.

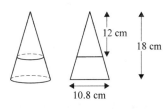

## 17.9 Congruent shapes

Two shapes are **congruent** when:

● one shape is an enlargement of the other with scale factor 1 or

● all the corresponding angles are equal and all the corresponding lengths are equal.

Two congruent shapes are exactly the **same shape** and exactly the **same size**.

### Exercise 17H

You will need a ruler and protractor for this exercise.

1.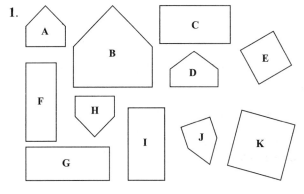

Write down the letters of two pairs of congruent shapes.
*Hint*: measure the lengths and the angles carefully.

2. Triangle ABC is congruent to triangle EDC.
   AB = 6 cm, AC = 4 cm and DC = 5 cm.

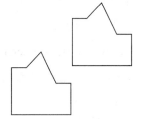

   (a) Write down the length of:
       (i) DE    (ii) CE    (iii) BC.
   (b) Write down an angle equal to angle BAC.
   (c) What geometrical property is true about the sides AB and DE?

3. PQRS is a kite with PS = PQ and QR = RS. The diagonals meet at O.

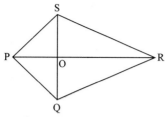

Write down three pairs of congruent triangles from the diagram.

4.

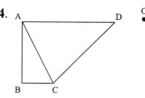
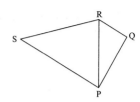

PQRS is the image of ABCD after a rotation about O.
Write down two pairs of congruent triangles from the diagram.

## 17.10 Combining transformations

A     B     C

This pattern is made by repeated reflections of a shape:

**A** is reflected to the image **B** and **B** is reflected to the image **C**.

**C** is the image of **A** after two reflections.

**C** is also the image of **A** after a single translation.

So the combination of the two reflections can be equivalent to a single translation.

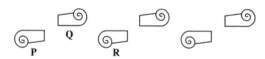

This pattern has been made by repeated 180° rotations:

**P** has been rotated to the image **Q**.

**Q** has been rotated to the image **R**.

**R** is the image of **P** after two rotations.

**R** is also the image of **P** after a single translation.

So the combination of two 180° rotations is equivalent to a single translation.

These examples show that one transformation followed by another can be equivalent to a single transformation.

### Example 14

On squared paper draw coordinate axes with $x$ and $y$ from $-6$ to $6$.

(a) Plot the points $(2, -4)$, $(2, -1)$, $(6, -1)$ and $(4, -4)$.

    Join them in order and label the shape **P**.

(b) Reflect **P** in the *x*-axis. Label the reflection **Q**.

(c) Rotate **Q** through 180° about the point $(0, 0)$. Label this image **R**.

(d) Describe fully the single transformation which maps **P** onto **R**.

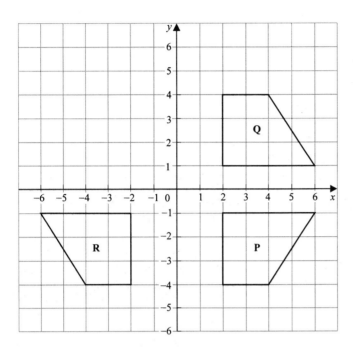

(a) The points are plotted and the shape labelled **P**.

(b) Reflect each point in the *x*-axis in turn. The point $(6, -1)$ reflects to $(6, 1)$.

(c) Rotate each point of **Q** through 180°. The point $(6, 1)$ rotates to $(-6, -1)$.

(d) R is the same shape and size as **P**, but it has been turned over.

So the single transformation which maps **P** onto **R** is a reflection in the *y*-axis.

---

### Exercise 17I

You will need squared paper for this exercise.

**1.** Draw a grid for *x* from −9 to 9 and *y* from −5 to 5.
Copy the shape **L**, shown opposite, onto your grid.
  (a) Reflect the shape **L** in the *y*-axis. Label the image **M**.
  (b) Reflect the shape **M** in the *x*-axis. Label the image **N**.
  (c) Describe fully the *single* transformation which maps the shape **L** onto the shape **N**.

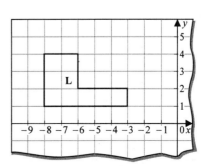

2. Draw a grid for $x$ from $-7$ to 10 and $y$ from $-6$ to 6. Copy shape **F** onto your grid.

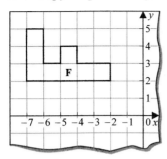

(a) Rotate **F** through $180°$ about $(0, 0)$. Label the image **G**.
(b) Rotate **G** through $180°$ about $(5, -1)$. Label the image **H**.
(c) Describe fully the *single* transformation which makes **H** the image of **F**.

3. Copy this diagram onto squared paper.

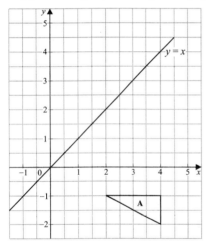

(a) Reflect the triangle **A** in the $x$-axis. Label the reflection **B**.
(b) Reflect the triangle **B** in the line $y = x$. Label the reflection **C**.
(c) Describe fully the transformation which maps the triangle **A** onto the triangle **C**.    [London]

4. Copy the diagram onto squared paper.

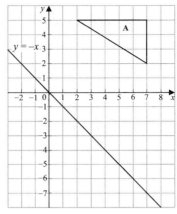

(a) Rotate triangle **A** clockwise through $90°$ about $(0, 0)$. Label the image **B**.
(b) Draw the image of **B** after a reflection in the line $y = -x$. Label the reflection **C**.
(c) Describe fully the single transformation which maps triangle **A** onto triangle **C**.

5. Draw a set of coordinate axes with $x$ from $-8$ to 8 and $y$ from $-7$ to 7.
(a) Plot the points $(2, 1)$, $(6, 1)$ and $(6, 4)$. Join them up and label the triangle **A**.
(b) Reflect **A** in the $y$-axis. Label the reflection **B**.
(c) Draw the line $y = x$.
(d) Reflect **B** in the line $y = x$. Label the reflection **C**.
(e) Describe fully the *single* transformation which maps **A** onto **C**.

6. (a) Copy the grid below. Draw the image of the shaded shape after a reflection in the $y$-axis. Label the image **A**.

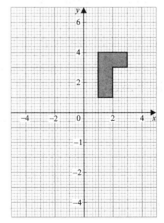

(b) On the same grid draw the image of the shaded shape after a quarter turn clockwise about the origin $(0, 0)$. Label this image **B**.
(c) Describe fully the *single* transformation which maps **A** onto **B**.    [London]

## Exercise 17J (Mixed questions)

**1.** The diagram shows a shaded rectangle ABCD and the new positions of the rectangle under two different transformations.

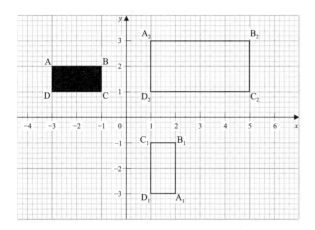

(a) Describe fully the single transformation which maps ABCD onto $A_1B_1C_1D_1$.

(b) Describe fully the single transformation which maps ABCD onto $A_2B_2C_2D_2$.    [SEG]

**2.** The parallelogram ABCD has vertices $(6, 3)$, $(9, 3)$, $(12, 9)$ and $(9, 9)$ respectively.

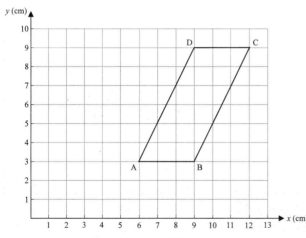

Copy the grid and the parallelogram.
An enlargement scale factor $\frac{1}{3}$ and centre $(0, 0)$ transforms parallelogram ABCD onto parallelogram $A'B'C'D'$.

(a) (i) Draw the parallelogram $A'B'C'D'$.
   (ii) Calculate the area of parallelogram $A'B'C'D'$.

(b) The side AB has length $3\,cm$. The original shape ABCD is now enlarged with a scale factor of $\frac{2}{5}$ to give $A''B''C''D''$.
Calculate the length of the side $A''B''$.
    [SEG]

**3.** A tessellation is made by reflecting a design as shown.

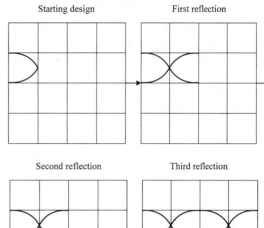

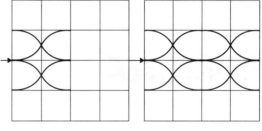

(a) Copy the grid and the shape below. Use the same method to make another tessellation. Reflect the new design in lines **a**, **b** and **c**.

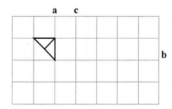

(b) A pattern for some wallpaper is made from identical quadrilaterals which form a tessellation.

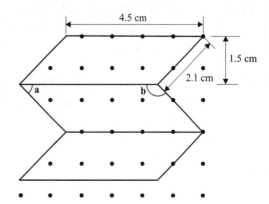

3. (i) What is the mathematical name for one of these quadrilaterals?
   (ii) Angle **a** = 46.2°.
       Calculate the value of angle **b**.
   (iii) One sheet of wallpaper has an area of 40 000 cm².
       Calculate approximately the number of quadrilaterals printed on one sheet.
   (iv) A shape from the pattern is drawn opposite.
       On dotty squared paper draw an enlargement of this shape with centre A and scale factor 3.

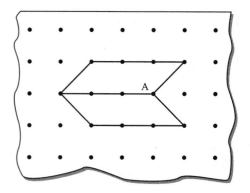

## Test yourself

**1.**

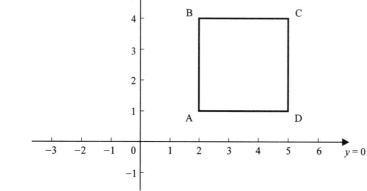

*Notice: the line with the equation x = 0 is the y-axis. The line with the equation y = 0 is the x-axis.*

---

**QUESTION**  (a)  The square ABCD is reflected in the line $x = 1$.
What are the new coordinates of C?

**ANSWER**  $(-3, 4)$  *If your answer is incorrect review page 343, Section 17.3 on reflections.*

**QUESTION**  (b)  The square ABCD is rotated about the centre $(2, 0)$ until $B$ is at $(-2, 0)$.
What are the new coordinates of C?

**ANSWER**  $(-2, 3)$  *If your answer is incorrect review page 347, Section 17.4 on rotations.*

---

**2.**

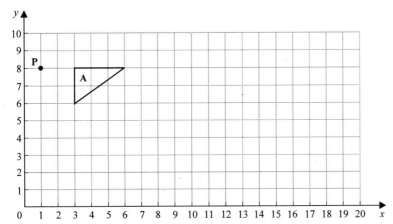

QUESTION Copy the axes and the triangle **A** onto squared paper.
Draw the image of **A** after an enlargement with centre P $(1, 8)$ and scale factor 3.
Write down the coordinates of the vertices of the image.

ANSWER $(7, 8)$, $(16, 8)$ and $(7, 2)$       *If your answer is incorrect review page 352, Section 17.6 on enlargements*

**3.** In the diagram NO $= 5.1$ cm, PL $= 4.5$ cm, LM $= 4$ cm and MN $= 6$ cm

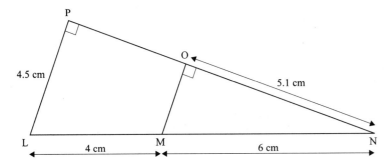

QUESTION Calculate the length of
(a)  PN     (b)  OM

ANSWER (a)  8.5 cm  (b)  2.7 cm      *If your answer is incorrect review page 360, Section 17.8 on similar shapes.*

**4.** F, G and H are the mid points of OB, OC and OD.

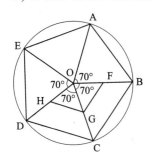

**QUESTION**    (a)    Write down all the triangles that are congruent to triangle OBC.

**ANSWER**    (a)    Triangle OAB, triangle OCD and triangle ODE and OEA    *If your answer is incorrect review page 363, Section 17.9 on congruent shapes.*

**QUESTION**    (b)    Write down all the triangles that are similar but not congruent to triangle OBC.

**ANSWER**    (b)    Triangle OFG and triangle OGH    *If your answer is incorrect review page 360, Section 17.8 on similar shapes.*

---

**5.**

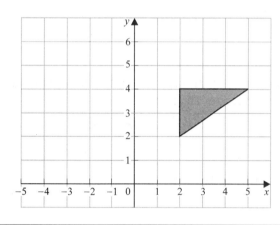

**QUESTION**    Copy the grid and the shaded triangle.

(a)    Draw the image of the shaded triangle after a rotation through an angle of 90° anticlockwise about the origin $(0, 0)$. Label the image **S**.

**ANSWER**    Your triangle S should have its vertices at the points $(-2, 2)$, $(-4, 2)$ and $(-4, 5)$.    *If your answer is incorrect check that you have rotated the shaded triangle anticlockwise and through 90°, then review page 347, Section 17.4 on rotations.*

**QUESTION**    (b)    Draw the image of the shaded triangle after a rotation through an angle of 90° anticlockwise about the point $(2, 1)$. Label the image **T**.

**ANSWER**    Your triangle T should have vertices at the points $(1, 1)$, $(-1, 1)$ and $(-1, 4)$.    *If your answer is incorrect check that you have rotated the shaded shape and not **S**, that you have rotated it about the point $(2, 1)$ and not $(0, 0)$, and through 90° anticlockwise. Then review page 347, Section 17.4 on rotations*

**QUESTION**    (c)    Describe fully the single transformation which maps **S** onto **T**.

**ANSWER**    A translation by the vector $\begin{pmatrix} 3 \\ -1 \end{pmatrix}$    *If your answer is incorrect review page 341, Section 17.2 on translations and page 363, Section 17.9 on combining transformations.*

# Summary of key points to remember

1. Changes in the shape, size or position of an object are called **transformations**.

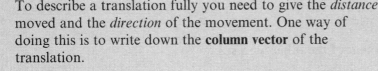

2. A transformation where each point on the object moves the same distance in the same direction is called a **translation**.

   To describe a translation fully you need to give the *distance* moved and the *direction* of the movement. One way of doing this is to write down the **column vector** of the translation.

3. A transformation where the image of an object is like a mirror image is called a **reflection**. The image is the *same shape and size* as the original shape, but it is '*turned over*'.

   To describe a reflection fully you need to say which line is the mirror line.

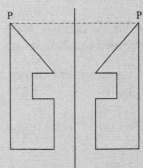

4. A transformation where an object turns through an angle about a fixed point is called a **rotation**.

   The fixed point is called the **centre of rotation**.

   The image is the *same shape and size* as the original object.

   When a shape is rotated through a given angle all the lines in the shape rotate through the same angle.

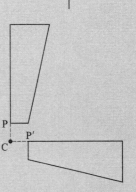

   The distance of an image point from the centre of rotation is the same as the distance of the original point from the centre of rotation.

   To describe a rotation fully you need to give the angle of the turn (and say whether it is clockwise or anticlockwise) and give the centre of rotation.

5. A transformation that changes the size but not the shape of an object is called an **enlargement**.

   The quantity which multiplies the original lengths to get the image lengths is called the **scale factor** of the enlargement.

   To describe an enlargement fully you need to give the scale factor and the centre of enlargement.

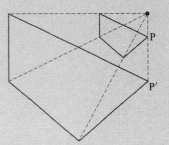

6. Two shapes are mathematically **similar** when:

   - one shape is an enlargement of the other shape

   - all the corresponding angles are equal

   - all the corresponding lengths are in the same ratio.

   Two shapes are similar if one is an enlargement of the other.

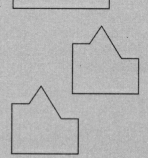

7. Two shapes are **congruent** when:

   - one shape is an enlargement of the other with scale factor 1 or

   - all the corresponding angles are equal and all the corresponding lengths are equal.

   Two congruent shapes are exactly the **same shape** and the **same size**.

8. One transformation followed by another can be equivalent to a single transformation.

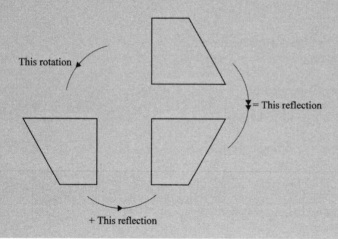

This rotation

= This reflection

+ This reflection

# 18 Length, area and volume

## 18.1 Introduction

In this unit you will discover and use formulae to find lengths and areas of two-dimensional shapes, and surface areas and volumes of three-dimensional shapes. The section on dimension theory shows you a way of checking that the formula you are using in a calculation will give you a sensible result.

## 18.2 Two-dimensional shapes

The total length around the edges of a two-dimensional shape is called the **perimeter** of the shape.

The perimeter of this rectangle is 10 cm.

$$\text{Perimeter} = 2 + 3 + 2 + 3 = 10 \text{ cm}$$

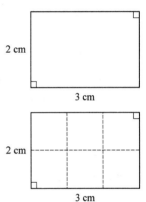

The amount of two-dimensional space occupied (or covered) by a two-dimensional shape is called the **area** of the shape.

This rectangle occupies 6 centimetre squares, so the area of the rectangle is 6 square centimetres, or $6 \text{ cm}^2$.

Perimeter and area are used in many real situations. An international running track has a perimeter of 400 metres.

When Estate Agents sell a house they sometimes advertise the total floor space or area of the inside of the building.

For your GCSE examination you will need to know how to calculate the perimeter and area of common two-dimensional shapes.

**HOUSE FOR SALE**
£105, 000

200 square metres
of floor space

## 18.3 Rectangles

The perimeter of a rectangle is found by adding the lengths of the four sides together.

$$\text{Perimeter} = a + b + a + b = 2(a + b)$$

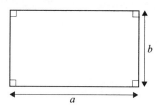

The area of a rectangle is found by multiplying the length by the width

$$\text{Area} = a \times b = ab$$

A **square** is a special rectangle. In a square, the width is equal to the length, or $a = b$.

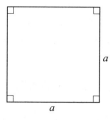

$$\text{perimeter of square} = 2(a + a) = 2 \times 2a = 4a$$

$$\text{area of square} = a \times a = a^2$$

### Example 1

In the diagram, ABCD represents a rectangular carpet.
$AB = DC = 6\,\text{m}$ and $BC = AD = 4\,\text{m}$

Calculate:

(a) the perimeter of the carpet

(b) the area of the carpet.

(a) Perimeter $= 2(6 + 4) = 2 \times 10 = 20\,\text{m}$

(b) Area $= 6 \times 4 = 24\,\text{m}^2$

### Example 2

The diagram shows a rectangle PQRS. $PQ = SR = 8\,\text{cm}$.

The perimeter of PQRS is 26 cm. Calculate:

(a) the length of QR  (b) the area of PQRS

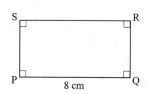

(a) Let $QR = w\,\text{cm}$, then

$$\text{perimeter} = 2(8 + w)$$

But the perimeter is 26 cm so

$$2(8 + w) = 26$$
$$8 + w = 13$$

$$w = 13 - 8 = 5\,\text{cm}$$

So:  $QR = 5\,\text{cm}$

We could also find QR by saying:

$$\text{perimeter} = 8 + QR + 8 + SP = 26\,\text{cm}$$

$$16 + QR + SP = 26\,\text{cm}$$

So: $\qquad\qquad QR + SP = 10\,\text{cm}$

and since $\qquad\qquad QR = SP$

$$QR = \tfrac{1}{2} \times 10\,\text{cm} = 5\,\text{cm}$$

(b) Area = length × width

$\qquad = 8 \times 5$

$\qquad = 40\,\text{cm}^2$

## *Example 3*

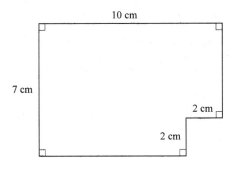

This is a
7 cm by 10 cm
rectangle with a
2 cm square
cut off

For the shape shown, calculate:

(a) the perimeter  (b) the area.

(a) Label the missing lengths in the diagram. Add the lengths
of the six sides to find the perimeter

$$7 + 10 + 5 + 2 + 2 + 8 = 34\,\text{cm}$$

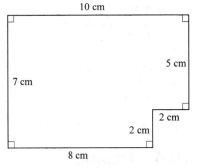

(b) *Method 1*

Split the shape up into two rectangles.

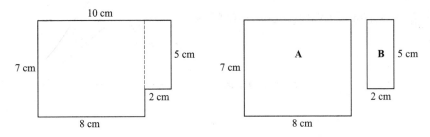

Area of rectangle **A** $= 8 \times 7 = 56\,\text{cm}^2$

Area of rectangle **B** $= 2 \times 5 = 10\,\text{cm}^2$

So the total area $= 56 + 10 = 66\,\text{cm}^2$

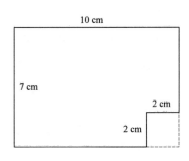

*Method 2*

Subtract the area of the 2 cm square from the area of the whole rectangle. So:

$$\text{Area} = (7 \times 10) - (2 \times 2)$$
$$= 70 - 4$$
$$= 66 \, \text{cm}^2$$

---

### Exercise 18A

1. In the diagrams below the lengths are in centimetres unless otherwise marked. Calculate the perimeters and areas of each shape.

   (a)
   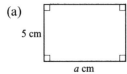

   (b)
   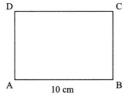

   (c)

2. ABCD is a rectangle. The length AB is 10 cm. The perimeter of ABCD is 28 cm. Calculate:
   (a) the length of BC
   (b) the area of ABCD.

3. A farmer uses exactly 2000 metres of fencing to fence off a square field. Calculate the area of the field.

4. The price of a new carpet is £6 per square metre. Mrs Abbot buys a new carpet which is rectangular and measures 4 metres by 3 metres. Calculate the cost of her new carpet.

5. A rectangle measures 9 cm by 4 cm. Square **A** has an area equal to the area of the rectangle **A**. Calculate the length of a side of the square.

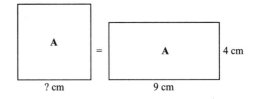

6. A square has sides of length 8 cm.
   (a) Calculate the perimeter of the square.
   (b) Find the lengths and widths of four rectangles which have a perimeter equal to that of the square.
   (c) Show that of all these shapes, it is the square which has the greatest area.

---

## 18.4  Triangles

The perimeter of any triangle can be found by adding together the lengths of its three sides.

So perimeter $= a + b + c$

To find the formula for the area of any triangle, look at a right-angled triangle first.

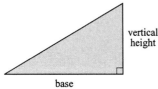

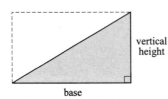

The area of this triangle    is    half the area of this rectangle

So the area of a right-angled triangle is
half the length of the base × vertical height.

Here is a triangle which is not right-angled.

The area of this triangle is again half the area of the rectangle
shown in the diagram.

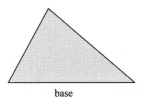
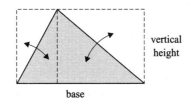

base                base        vertical height

Indeed, all of these triangles have an equal area because their base
length and vertical height are the same.

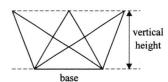

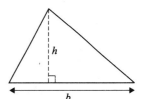

So the formula for the area of a triangle is:

$$\textbf{Area} = \tfrac{1}{2} \times \textbf{base length} \times \textbf{vertical height}$$

or:          $\textbf{Area} = \tfrac{1}{2}\textbf{bh}$

## Example 4

Calculate the area of each of these triangles.

(a)             (b)               (c)

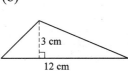
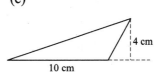

(a) Area $= \tfrac{1}{2} \times$ base $\times$ vertical height
$= \tfrac{1}{2} \times 8 \times 5 = 4 \times 5 = 20\,\text{cm}^2$

(b) Base $= 12\,\text{cm}$ and vertical height $= 3\,\text{cm}$, so:

$$\text{Area} = \tfrac{1}{2} \times 12 \times 3 = 18\,\text{cm}^2$$

(c) Base $= 10\,\text{cm}$ and vertical height $= 4\,\text{cm}$, so:

$$\text{Area} = \tfrac{1}{2} \times 10 \times 4 = 20\,\text{cm}^2$$

## Example 5

The diagram opposite shows a triangle ABC.

The point M is on BC. The angle $AMB = 90°$ and $BC = 10\,\text{cm}$

The area of ABC is $20\,\text{cm}^2$

Calculate the length of AM.

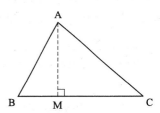

AM is the vertical height of the triangle. So:

$$\text{Area of ABC} = \tfrac{1}{2} \times \text{BC} \times \text{AM}$$
$$= \tfrac{1}{2} \times 10 \times \text{AM}$$
$$= 5 \times \text{AM}$$

But the area of ABC is $20\,\text{cm}^2$, so:

$$5 \times \text{AM} = 20$$
$$\text{AM} = 20 \div 5 = 4\,\text{cm}$$

### Exercise 18B

**1.** Calculate the area of each of these triangles.

(a)

(b)

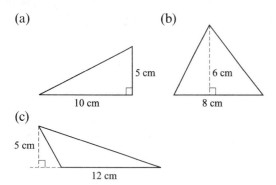

5 cm

10 cm

6 cm

8 cm

(c)

5 cm

12 cm

**2.** A builder marks out a triangular building plot, PQR. The length of PQ is 30 metres. The perpendicular distance from R to PQ is 24 metres. Calculate the area of the plot.

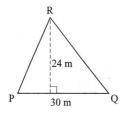

R

24 m

P     30 m     Q

**3.** The area of the triangle ABC is $42\,\text{cm}^2$. The length of BC is 14 cm. Calculate the distance AM.

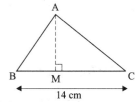

A

B     M     C

14 cm

**4.** (a) Write down an expression for the perimeter of this triangle.
   (b) If the actual perimeter of the triangle is 30 cm, find the value of $x$.

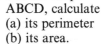

2x

$x+2$

$x$

**5.** For the shape ABCD, calculate
   (a) its perimeter
   (b) its area.

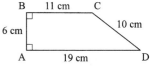

B     11 cm     C

6 cm                    10 cm

A     19 cm     D

*Hint*: to find the area, split the shape into a rectangle and a right-angled triangle.

## 18.5 Parallelograms

The diagram shows a quadrilateral (four-sided figure) ABCD. It is a **parallelogram**. This means that the sides AB and DC are parallel and the sides AD and BC are also **parallel**.

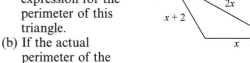

Also, length DC = AB and length AD = BC

To work out the perimeter of the parallelogram, you just add together the lengths of the four sides.

$$\text{perimeter} = a + b + a + b = 2(a + b)$$

To find a formula for the area of a parallelogram, draw a line from B to meet DC at 90°. This creates the shaded triangle shown in the diagram.

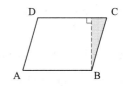

Now imagine cutting off this shaded triangle and moving it so that it fits on to the other end of the parallelogram.

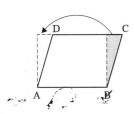 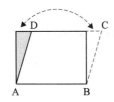

This makes a rectangle which has an area equal to the area of the parallelogram.

The area of the rectangle is the length AB × the width. The width is the perpendicular distance between the parallel lines AB and DC.

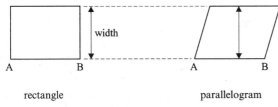

rectangle                    parallelogram

So the area of a parallelogram is

**length of base × perpendicular distance between the parallel lines**

or          **Area = $b \times h = bh$**

A **rhombus** is a special kind of parallelogram which has all four sides of equal length.

perimeter = $4b$
area = $bh$

### *Example 6*

The diagram shows a parallelogram PQRS.

PQ = SR = 12 cm and PS = QR = 8 cm. The perpendicular distance between PQ and SR = 5 cm.

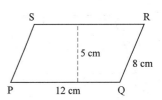

Calculate:

(a) the area of the parallelogram

(b) the perpendicular distance between QR and PS.

(a) Area = base length × perpendicular distance between PQ and
SR

Area = $12 \times 5 = 60\,\text{cm}^2$.

(b) Rotate the parallelogram so that QR is horizontal.

Label the perpendicular distance between QR and PS as $p$.

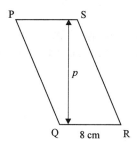

Then :     Area = QR × perpendicular distance between QR
and PS

= QR × $p$

= $8 \times p$

From part (a) the area is $60\,\text{cm}^2$.

So:

$$8 \times p = 60$$
$$p = 60 \div 8$$
$$p = 7.5\,\text{cm}$$

---

### Exercise 18C

**1.** Calculate the area of each of these
parallelograms.

(a)

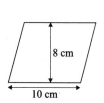

10 cm

(b)

5 cm

(c)

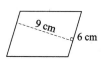

**2.** ABCD is a parallelogram. AB = DC = 12 cm.
The area of ABCD is 48 cm². Calculate the
distance between the parallel lines AB and DC.

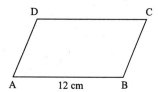

**3.** UVWT is a parallelogram. UV = TW = 9 cm
and UT = VW = 5 cm. The perpendicular
distance between UV and TW is 4 cm.

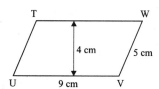

Calculate:
(a) the area of the parallelogram
(b) the perpendicular distance between VW and
UT.

**4.** A square has area equal to the area of the
parallelogram ABCD. Calculate the perimeter of
the square.

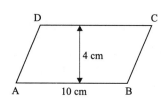

# 18.6 Trapeziums

The diagram shows a quadrilateral ABCD. This quadrilateral is called a **trapezium**.

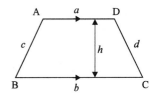

In a trapezium one pair of sides is parallel. In this case AD and BC are parallel.

The perimeter of a trapezium is found by adding together the lengths of the four sides. So

$$\text{perimeter} = a + b + c + d$$

To find a formula for the area of a trapezium start with ABCD.

Mark the midpoint of AB as M.

Mark the midpoint of DC as N.

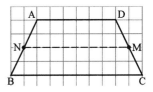

By counting the squares on the grid you can see that

$$\text{length NM} = \text{average of AD and BC}$$
$$= \tfrac{1}{2}(\text{AD} + \text{BC})$$
$$= \tfrac{1}{2}(a + b)$$

Then draw the lines from M and N to BC which meet BC at 90°.

This creates the two shaded triangles shown in the diagram.

Now imagine cutting off those two triangles and rotating them 180° so that they fit alongside AN and DM to create a rectangle.

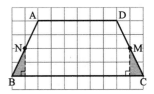

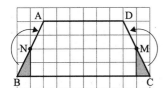 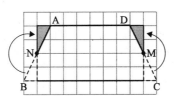

The rectangle has the same area as the trapezium ABCD.

The area of the rectangle $= \text{length} \times \text{width}$
$\qquad\qquad\qquad\quad = \text{NM} \times \text{distance between AD and BC}$

So for the trapezium ABCD

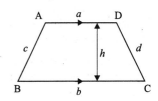

$$\text{Area} = \text{NM} \times \text{distance between the parallel sides}$$
$$\text{Area} = \tfrac{1}{2}(a + b) \times h = \tfrac{1}{2}(a + b)h$$

*Example 7*

A building plot is in the shape of a trapezium PQRS.

PQ = 30 metres. SR = 18 metres and the distance between the parallel sides PQ and SR is 20 metres.

(a) Calculate the area of the building plot.

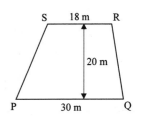

A second building plot is to have the same area as the first plot.
The second plot is to be a square.

(b) Calculate the length of a side of the square, giving your answer
correct to the nearest metre.

(a) Area of PQRS $= \frac{1}{2}(a + b) \times h$

$$= \frac{1}{2}(30 + 18) \times 20$$

$$= \frac{1}{2} \times 48 \times 20$$

$$= 24 \times 20$$

$$= 480 \, \text{m}^2$$

(b) Let the length of a side of the square be $y$ metres.

Then the area of the square $= y \times y = y^2$

But the area of the square must be $480 \, \text{m}^2$

So        $y^2 = 480$

$$y = \sqrt{480}$$

$$= 21.91 \, \text{m}$$

So $y$ is $22 \, \text{m}$, correct to the nearest metre.

*Hint*: you can use the  $\boxed{\sqrt{x}}$  key on your calculator.

---

### Exercise 18D

1. In Exercise 18B, Question 5, you were asked to
calculate the area of this shape by breaking it
down into a rectangle and a triangle.

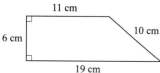

Now calculate the area of this shape by treating
it as a trapezium.

2. The diagram represents an architect's draft
sketch of the cross-section of a new house.

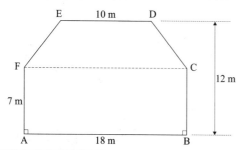

The cross-section is made up of a rectangle
ABCF and a trapezium CDEF. Calculate the
area of the cross-section.

3. The diagram shows the cross-section of a ramp
for motor vehicles.

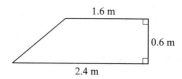

Calculate the area of the cross-section.

# 18.7 Circles

In the shapes you have studied so far – rectangles, triangles, parallelograms and trapeziums – you have been shown how to find the formulae for area and perimeter.

To find the formulae for area and perimeter of a circle requires mathematics beyond GCSE level, so in this section the formulae are given without proof.

The work covered in this section is a very important part of mathematics and always appears in GCSE exams.

The distance around the outside, or outer edge, of a circle is called the **circumference** of the circle.

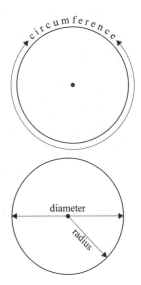

The formula for the circumference is given by

$$\text{circumference} = \pi d$$

or          $$\text{circumference} = 2\pi r$$

where:

$d =$ the diameter of the circle

$r =$ the radius of the circle $= \frac{1}{2}d$

and $\pi = 3.14$ (approximately). A more exact value can be obtained by using the $\pi$ button on your calculator.

Although we do not prove the formula here, you can check it using the following method. You will need some centimetre cubes.

Use a pair of compasses to draw circles with different diameters on a sheet of paper.

Draw in the diameter of each circle and mark its length in centimetres.

Place centimetre cubes side by side around the circumference of each circle.

For each circle you should find that the number of centimetre cubes needed to go round the circumference is just over 3 times the diameter of the circle.

This confirms that circumference is approximately 3 × diameter.

The area of a circle is given by the formula

$$\text{area} = \frac{\pi d^2}{4}$$

or          $$\text{area} = \pi r^2$$

You can check this formula using the following method.

Draw a circle of any diameter. Then draw the square whose sides just touch the circle. The length of one side of the square is $d$, the diameter of the circle.

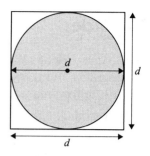

The area of the square is $d \times d = d^2$

You should be able to see that:

the area of the circle is less than the area of the square

the area of the circle is more than half the area of the square

So a reasonable estimate for the area of the circle is approximately $\frac{3}{4}$ of the area of the square, since $\frac{1}{2} < \frac{3}{4} < 1$. So the area of the circle is approximately $\frac{3}{4}d^2$.

Compare this with the formula for the area of a circle:

$$\text{area of a circle} = \frac{\pi d^2}{4}$$

and $\dfrac{\pi}{4}$ is $\dfrac{3.14}{4}$ (approximately), which is close to $\frac{3}{4}$.

This confirms that the area of the circle is approximately $\frac{3}{4}d^2$.

You will need to know the formulae for the area and circumference of a circle. They are not given on the formulae sheet that you are given with the examination papers.

### *Example 8*

Mrs. Jones has an ornamental pond in her garden. The pond is in the shape of a circle of radius 2.5 m.

Calculate:

(a) the circumference of the pond

(b) the area of the surface of the pond.

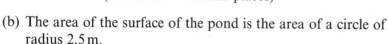

(a) The circumference is given by

$$C = 2\pi r$$
$$= 2 \times \pi \times 2.5 = 15.71 \text{ m}$$
$$\text{(correct to 2 decimal places)}$$

(b) The area of the surface of the pond is the area of a circle of radius 2.5 m.

The area is given by

$$A = \pi r^2$$
$$= \pi \times (2.5)^2 = \pi \times 6.25 = 19.63 \text{ m}^2$$
$$\text{(correct to 2 decimal places)}$$

## Example 9

Calculate the area of a circle which has a circumference of 20 cm.

To do this question you must first find the diameter or radius of the circle. The formula for the circumference is

$$C = \pi d$$

so:     $20 = \pi \times d$

$d = 20 \div \pi$

$d = 6.37\,\text{cm}$ (correct to 2 decimal places)

Then the area is given by

$$A = \frac{\pi d^2}{4} = \frac{\pi \times 6.37 \times 6.37}{4}$$

$A = 31.87\,\text{cm}^2$ (correct to 2 decimal places)

We could also use $C = 2\pi r$

Then     $20 = 2 \times \pi \times r$

$r = 20 \div (2 \times \pi)$

$= 3.183$

Using this value in Area $= \pi r^2$

$$A = \pi \times 3.183 \times 3.183$$

$$A = 31.83\,\text{cm}^2$$

## Exercise 18E

1. Calculate the circumference and area of a circle
   (a) of radius 5 cm        (b) of radius 7.2 cm
   (c) of diameter 8 cm      (d) of diameter 18.8 cm.

2. Calculate the area of a circle which has a circumference of 25 cm.

3. Calculate the circumference of a circle of area 100 cm².

4. In his garden, Mr. Assad has a circular fish pond of radius 1.8 m.
   Mr. Assad decides to put a protective fence around the edge of the pond. He also decides to cover the surface of the pond with wire mesh.
   Calculate:
   (a) the minimum length of fencing he will require
   (b) the minimum area of wire mesh he will require.

5. George cuts a circle of diameter 6 cm from a sheet of card. The card is a rectangle measuring 10 cm by 8 cm.
   Calculate the area of the card that will be left over after George has cut out the circle.

6. The diagram shows a thin sheet of metal. The sheet of metal consists of a rectangle with a semi-circular end piece.
   Calculate:
   (a) the perimeter of the sheet of metal
   (b) the area of the sheet of metal.

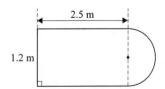

## Worked exam question 1

This is a sketch of the walls of part of a French Chateau.

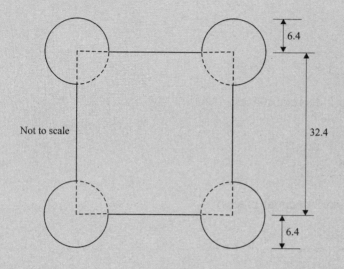

The plan has order 4 rotation symmetry. The tower at each corner is circular, with centre at the corner of the square. The lengths marked are in metres.

(a) Find the area of one of the complete circles.

$A = \pi r^2$ •——————————————————————————

$A = \pi \times (6.4)^2$ •————————————————————

$A = 128.68$ [2 d.p.]

(a) $\underline{128.68\ m^2}$

**Do:**
Recall the formula

Substitute correctly

Use the $\pi$ button on your calculator or $\pi = 3.14$

**Don't:**
Treat $\pi r^2$ as $(\pi r)^2$

(b) Find the total area shown on the plan within the walls. Include the towers.

Total area = area of square + area of 4 towers

$= (32.4 \times 32.4) + 4 \times (\frac{3}{4}$ of $128.68)$

$= 1435.8\ m^2$

(b) $\underline{1435.8\ m^2}$

**Do:**
Show the working

The calculations in the correct order

**Don't:**
Rush through the arithmetic

# 18.8 Three-dimensional shapes

As well as working out perimeters and areas of two-dimensional shapes, you will also need to know how to work out surface areas and volumes of three-dimensional shapes.

The **surface area** is the area of the entire surface of the shape. The **volume** of a shape is the amount of three-dimensional space that it occupies.

## 18.9 Cuboids

A **cuboid** is the correct mathematical name for the shape we usually call a box.

The diagram shows some centimetre cubes laid out in the shape of a 3 by 4 rectangle.

It is a cuboid 1 cm high.

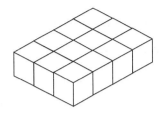

Now suppose that more centimetre cubes are added to this cuboid until it is 5 cm high.

This is now a cuboid which is 3 cm wide by 4 cm long by 5 cm high.

The total number of centimetre cubes used to make the cuboid is $3 \times 4 \times 5 = 60$.

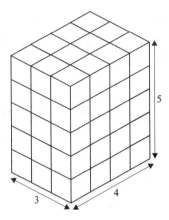

The volume of a cuboid is the amount of three-dimensional space it occupies.

The volume of this cuboid is 60 cubic centimetres or $60 \, \text{cm}^3$.

So you can find the volume of a cuboid by using the formula

$$\textbf{volume} = \textbf{width} \times \textbf{length} \times \textbf{height}$$

or $\qquad\qquad v = wlh$

The surface area of a cuboid is found by adding together the areas of each of its six faces.

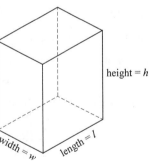

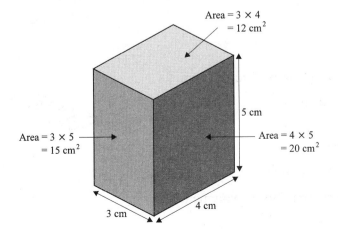

So the total surface area of this 3 cm by 4 cm by 5 cm cuboid is

$$
\begin{aligned}
\text{Surface area} &= 2(3 \times 4) + 2(3 \times 5) + 2(4 \times 5) \\
&= 2(12) + 2(15) + 2(20) \\
&= 2(12 + 15 + 20) \\
&= 2 \times 47 \\
&= 94 \, \text{cm}^2
\end{aligned}
$$

In the general case

$$
\begin{aligned}
\text{Surface area} = 2(&\text{width} \times \text{length} + \text{width} \times \text{height} \\
&+ \text{length} \times \text{height})
\end{aligned}
$$

or          **surface area $= 2(wl + wh + lh)$**

A **cube** is a special case of a cuboid which has its width, length and height all equal to each other. So if the length of any edge of a cube is $x$ units, then

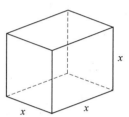

**volume of a cube $= x^3$**

**surface area of a cube $= 6x^2$**

### *Example 10*

Calculate:

(a) the volume          (b)   the surface area

of a cuboid measuring 5 cm by 7 cm by 10 cm.

(a) Volume $= w \times l \times h$
$$= 5 \times 7 \times 10 = 350 \, \text{cm}^3$$

(b) Surface area $=$ total area of the six faces
$$
\begin{aligned}
&= 2(5 \times 7) + 2(5 \times 10) + 2(7 \times 10) \\
&= 2(35) + 2(50) + 2(70) \\
&= 2(35 + 50 + 70) \\
&= 2 \times 155 \\
&= 310 \, \text{cm}^2
\end{aligned}
$$

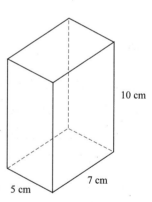

### *Example 11*

A gold bar is in the shape of a cuboid 12 cm by 8 cm by 5 cm.

The gold bar is melted down and made into a cube. During this process none of the gold is lost.

Calculate the length of a side of the cube.

Volume of the gold bar $= 12 \times 8 \times 5 = 480 \, \text{cm}^3$

Let the length of a side of the cube be $x$ cm. So the volume of the cube is $x^3$.

But the volume of the cube has to equal the volume of the cuboid.
So:

$$x^3 = 480$$

$$x = \sqrt[3]{480}$$

$$x = 7.83 \, \text{cm (correct to 2 decimal places)}$$

---

### Exercise 18F

1. A cuboid measures 6 cm by 9 cm by 12 cm.
   Calculate:
   (a) the volume of the cuboid
   (b) the surface area of the cuboid.

2. A fish pond is in the shape of a cuboid. The
   pond measures 3.2 m by 2.4 m. When the pond
   is full, the depth of
   the water is 30 cm.
   Calculate the
   volume of water in
   the pond when the
   pond is full.

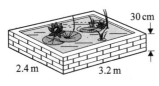

3. The diagram shows
   the net of an open-
   topped box. The
   box, when made, is
   in the shape of a
   cuboid. Calculate:
   (a) the volume of
   the cuboid

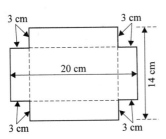

(b) the surface area of the box.

4. A bar of silver is in the shape of a cuboid
   measuring 15 cm by 10 cm by 6 cm. It is melted
   down and turned into a cube. During this
   process none of the silver is lost.

Calculate the length of a side of the cube.

5. The volume of a cube in cubic centimetres is
   numerically equal to the surface area of the cube
   in square centimetres.
   Calculate the length of a side of the cube.

---

## 18.10 Prisms

A **prism** is a three-dimensional shape which has a flat top and a
flat base which are identical. The base and the top are joined by
straight edges. A cuboid is a special case of a prism.

Here are some examples of prisms.

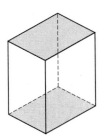
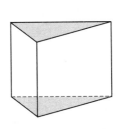
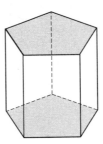

*Rectangular based*      *Triangular based*      *Pentagonal based*

The volume of a prism can be found by using the rule

$$\text{Volume of prism} = \text{area of base} \times \text{vertical height}$$

This rule can be confirmed for a cuboid. The volume of a cuboid is

$$\text{volume} = \text{width} \times \text{length} \times \text{height}$$

but width × length is actually the area of the rectangular base of the cuboid. So, for a cuboid

$$\text{Volume} = \text{area of base} \times \text{vertical height}$$

This does not prove the rule for the volume of a prism, it merely confirms that the rule works in the case of a cuboid.

There is no special formula for the surface area of a prism. You have to add together the areas of each of the faces.

## Example 12

Calculate the volume of the triangular based prism ABCDEF.

AB = 5 cm  BC = 12 cm  AE = 8 cm and the angle ABC = 90°.

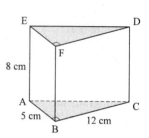

The base of the prism is the right-angled triangle ABC. The area of this triangle is

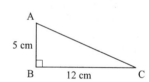

$$\tfrac{1}{2} \times \text{base} \times \text{height} = \tfrac{1}{2} \times 5 \times 12 = 30 \, \text{cm}^2$$

The volume of the prism = area of base × vertical height. So

$$\text{volume} = \text{area of base} \times \text{AE}$$
$$= 30 \times 8 = 240 \, \text{cm}^3$$

## Example 13

The base of a prism is the L-shape ABCDEF.

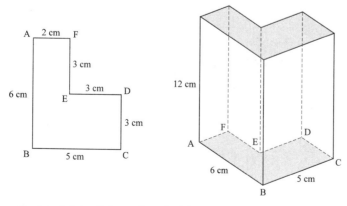

The vertical height of the prism is 12 cm.

Calculate:

(a) the volume of the prism

(b) the surface area of the prism.

(a) Area of the base $= (6 \times 5) - (3 \times 3)$
$$= 30 - 9$$
$$= 21\,\text{cm}^2$$

Volume $=$ area of base $\times$ vertical height
$$= 21 \times 12 = 252\,\text{cm}^3$$

(b) To work out the surface area of this prism, calculate the areas of the 6 rectangular faces.

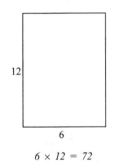     

| 12 | 12 | 12 | 12 | 12 | 12 |
| 6 | 5 | 3 | 3 | 3 | 2 |
| $6 \times 12 = 72$ | $5 \times 12 = 60$ | $3 \times 12 = 36$ | $3 \times 12 = 36$ | $3 \times 12 = 36$ | $2 \times 12 = 24$ |

Then add the area of the base and the top, which are both $21\,\text{cm}^2$.

So the surface area $= 72 + 60 + 36 + 36 + 36 + 24 + 21 + 21$
$$= 306\,\text{cm}^2.$$

## Exercise 18G

**1.** Calculate the volume of each of these prisms.

(a)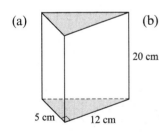

5 cm   12 cm

(b)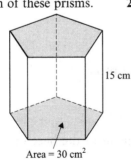

20 cm

15 cm

Area = 30 cm²

(c)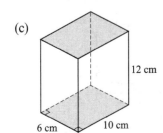

12 cm

6 cm   10 cm

**2.** The diagram shows a wedge ABCDEF. The horizontal base BCDE is a rectangle. BC = 8 cm and CD = 14 cm. The vertical face ABEF is also a rectangle. AB = FE = 5 cm. The vertical faces ABC and FED are right-angled triangles.

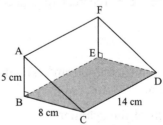

F

A   E

5 cm   D

B   14 cm

8 cm   C

(a) Calculate the volume of the wedge ABCDEF.

The wedge is solid and made of gold. It is melted down and re-cast in the shape of a cube. During this process none of the gold is lost.

(b) Calculate the length of an edge of the cube.

3. The trapezium ABCD opposite is the base of a prism of height 15 cm.
   (a) Calculate the volume of the prism.
   (b) Calculate the surface area of a cube whose volume is equal to the volume of the prism.

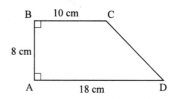

## 18.11 Cylinders

A cylinder is a prism with a circular top and base.

The volume of a prism is given by

$$\text{Volume} = \text{area of base} \times \text{vertical height}$$

So the volume of a cylinder of vertical height $h$, with a circular base of radius $r$ is given by

$$\textbf{Volume} = \textbf{area of circle} \times \textbf{vertical height}$$
$$= \boldsymbol{\pi r^2 h}$$

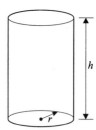

### Example 14

A tin of beans is in the shape of a cylinder.

The circular base has a radius of 4 cm. The height of the tin is 10 cm.

Calculate the volume of the tin of beans.

The volume is given by

$$V = \pi r^2 h$$

and in this case $r = 4$ and $h = 10$, so:

$$V = \pi \times 4^2 \times 10$$
$$V = \pi \times 16 \times 10$$
$$V = 502.7 \, \text{cm}^3 \text{ (correct to 1 decimal place)}$$

### Example 15

The volume of a cylinder is 2400 cm³. The diameter of the base of the cylinder is 16 cm.

Calculate the height of the cylinder.

Since the diameter of the base is 16 cm then the radius is 8 cm.

Using the formula:

$$V = \pi r^2 h$$
$$V = \pi \times 8^2 \times h$$

But:   $$V = 2400$$

so :   $\pi \times 8^2 \times h = 2400$

$\pi \times 64 \times h = 2400$

$h = \dfrac{2400}{\pi \times 64}$

$= 11.94 \, \text{cm}$ (correct to 2 decimal places)

---

### Exercise 18H

1. Calculate the volume of a cylinder
   (a) of radius 5 cm and height 13 cm
   (b) of diameter 12 cm and height 15 cm.

2. A metal rod is in the form of a cylinder. The rod has a diameter of 6 cm and is 75 cm long.

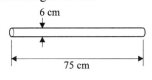

6 cm

75 cm

   (a) Calculate the volume of the metal rod.
   The rod is melted down and re-cast as a cube. During this process none of the metal is lost.
   (b) Calculate the length of an edge of the cube.

3. A cylinder has volume 2000 cm$^3$ and height 8 cm.
   Calculate the radius of the base of the cylinder.

---

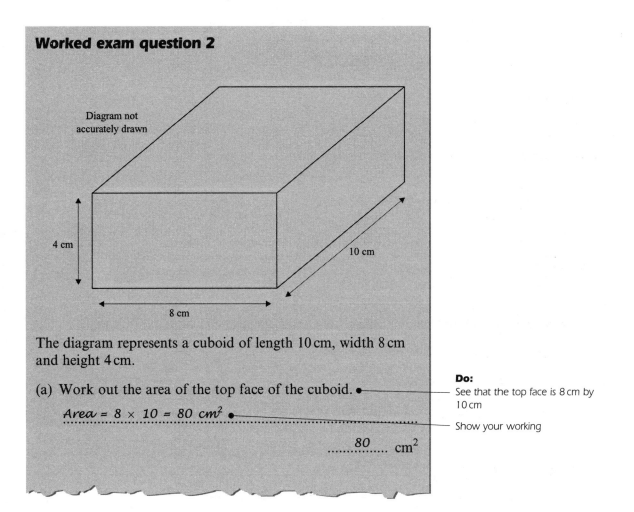

### Worked exam question 2

Diagram not accurately drawn

4 cm

10 cm

8 cm

The diagram represents a cuboid of length 10 cm, width 8 cm and height 4 cm.

(a) Work out the area of the top face of the cuboid.

*Area = 8 × 10 = 80 cm²*

............................................................

80 ....... cm$^2$

**Do:**
See that the top face is 8 cm by 10 cm

Show your working

(b) Work out the volume of the cuboid.

$$Volume = 4 \times 8 \times 10$$
$$= 32 \times 10$$
$$= 320 \ cm^3$$

............ cm$^3$ .......320......

**Do:**
Show your working

## Worked exam question 3

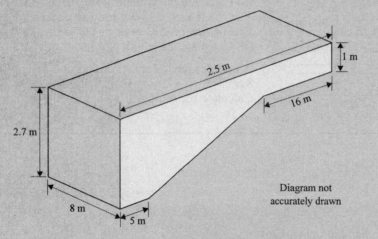

2.5 m
1 m
16 m
2.7 m
8 m
5 m

Diagram not
accurately drawn

The diagram represents a swimming pool.

The pool has vertical sides.

The pool is 8 m wide.

(a) Calculate the area of the shaded cross section.

25
1
9
1
16
1.7
5

$$Area = (25 \times 1) + \left(\frac{9+5}{2}\right) \times 1.7$$
$$= 25 + 7 \times 1.7$$
$$= 25 + 11.9$$
$$= 36.9$$

.......36.9...... m$^2$

**Do:**
Show your working

Read your formulae sheet

Check your answer
**Don't:**
Rush your work

The swimming pool is completely filled with water.

(b) Calculate the volume of water in the pool.

$$Volume = Area \ of \ cross \ section \times width$$
$$= 36.9 \times 8$$
$$= 295.2$$

.......295.2...... m$^3$

**Do:**
Show your method

64 m$^3$ of water leaks out of the pool.

(c) Calculate the distance by which the water level falls.

level drops $y$ metres

So $25 \times y \times 8 = 64 \text{ m}^3$

$200 y = 64$

$y = \dfrac{64}{200}$

$y = 0.32 \text{ m}$

**Do:**
Show your method

.......0.32....... m

## 18.12 Dimension theory

Throughout this unit you have been learning to use formulae to find areas and volumes. When using these formulae it is easy to make a mistake, to confuse one formula with another or to use the wrong formula. For example, it would be easy to use $2\pi r$ for the area of a circle instead of $\pi r^2$.

**Dimension theory** is a way of helping you to check that the formula you are using produces a sensible answer.

For example, the formula for the volume of a cuboid is

$$V = wlh$$

and the formula for the volume of a cylinder is

$$V = \pi r^2 h$$

These two formulae do not look alike, but they have a common feature.

In the formula for the volume of a cuboid, the letters $w$, $l$ and $h$ all represent distances or lengths.

- $w$ represents the width of the cuboid

- $l$ represents the length of the cuboid

- $h$ represents the height of the cuboid

Anything which represents a **length** (or distance) is said to have a **dimension of 1**.

So $w$, $l$ and $h$ all have a dimension of 1.

In the formula for the volume of a cuboid $V = wlh$

$$w \quad \times \quad l \quad \times \quad h \quad = \quad V$$

$$\begin{pmatrix} \text{dimension} \\ \text{of } 1 \end{pmatrix} \begin{pmatrix} \text{dimension} \\ \text{of } 1 \end{pmatrix} \begin{pmatrix} \text{dimension} \\ \text{of } 1 \end{pmatrix} \begin{pmatrix} \text{dimension} \\ \text{of } 3 \end{pmatrix}$$

You *add* the dimensions $1 + 1 + 1 = 3$

Any formula that represents a **volume** has a **dimension of 3**.
Similarly, any formula that represents an **area** has a **dimension of 2**.

In the formula for the volume of a cylinder $V = \pi r^2 h$

- $\pi$ is a **number**, so it is dimensionless or has a **dimension of 0**.

- $r$ is the radius, it is a length, so it has a dimension of 1.

$$r^2 = r \times r$$

so
$$\underset{\text{dimension 1}}{r} \quad \times \quad \underset{\text{dimension 1}}{r} \quad = \quad \underset{\text{dimension 2}}{r^2}$$

- $h$ is the height, it is a length, so it has a dimension of 1.

So
$$\underset{\substack{\text{dimension} \\ \text{of 0}}}{\pi} \quad \times \quad \underset{\substack{\text{dimension} \\ \text{of 2}}}{r^2} \quad \times \quad \underset{\substack{\text{dimension} \\ \text{of 1}}}{h} \quad = \quad \underset{\substack{\text{dimension} \\ \text{of 3}}}{V}$$

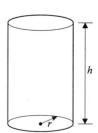

This shows that the expressions $wlh$ (for a cuboid) and $\pi r^2 h$ (for a cylinder) both have a dimension of 3 – which is correct as they are expressions for volumes.

### Example 16

Check that the formula

$$A = \pi r^2$$

for the area of a circle, is dimensionally correct.

In the formula

$\pi$ is a number, so it is dimensionless

$r$ is the radius, it is a length so it has dimension of 1 and $r^2$ has a dimension of 2.

So $\pi r^2$ has a dimension of 2. Any expression representing an area must have a dimension of 2, so the formula is dimensionally correct.

### Example 17

In the expression $2\lambda ab^2$, 2 and $\lambda$ (the Greek letter 'lambda') are dimensionless whilst $a$ and $b$ represent lengths. What is the dimension of this expression.

2 and $\lambda$ have a dimension of 0, $a$ has dimension of 1 and $b^2$ has a dimension of 2. So the dimension of the expression is $1 + 2 = 3$.

---

### Exercise 18I

1. Sarah is doing a science experiment. She needs to be able to work out the volume and the surface area of a sphere. She has a formula sheet, but unfortunately there is an ink blot over part of the formulae for a sphere.

   Explain which of these expressions will be the one for the volume and which will be the one for the surface area of a sphere.

   $$\blacksquare = 4\pi r^2$$
   $$\blacksquare = \frac{4\pi r^3}{3}$$

2. In these expressions, the numbers and the Greek letters all represent dimensionless quantities. The other letters represent lengths.

$$3\mu x^3, \quad 2\lambda(a+b), \quad a^2b, \quad \alpha b^2 + 2c^2,$$

$$\sqrt{\pi r^2}, \quad \frac{abc}{h}$$

Explain which of these expressions could represent either a length, an area, or a volume.

3. Carl claims that the formula for the surface area of a cylinder is

$$\text{Surface area} = 2\pi r^2 + 2\pi rh$$

Check to see if this formula is dimensionally correct.

4. In his Design and Technology coursework, Jaswant has to do some work with an ellipse. He remembers the formula $\pi ab$, knowing that this gives either the circumference or the area of the ellipse.

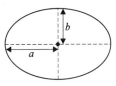

Explain whether the expression gives the circumference or area.

---

## Worked exam question 4

The expressions shown in the table below can be used to calculate lengths, areas or volumes of various shapes.

$\pi$, 2, 4 and $\frac{1}{2}$ are numbers which have no dimensions. The letters $r$, $l$, $b$ and h represent lengths.

Put a tick in the box underneath those expressions that can be used to calculate a volume.

| $2\pi r$ | $4\pi r^2$ | $\pi r^2 h$ | $\pi r^2$ | $lbh$ | $\frac{1}{2}bh$ |
|---|---|---|---|---|---|
| | | ✔ | | ✔ | |

**Do:**
Remember that volume has dimension 3

**Count** the index numbers in each case for $\pi r^2h$ – count of index numbers is $2 + 1 = 3$

**Don't:**
Multiply the index numbers

Think that the number $\pi$ has dimensions of length

---

## Exercise 18J (Mixed questions)

1. The radius of a circle is 9 cm. Work out:
   (i) the circumference of the circle
   (ii) the area of the circle.  [London]

2. A jeweller buys a gold bar. The bar is a prism.

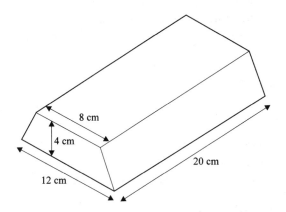

The cross-section of the prism is a trapezium.
The parallel sides are 8 cm and 12 cm long.
The distance between the parallel sides is 4 cm.
The bar is 20 cm long.
Calculate the volume of the gold bar  [WJEC]

3. A gold rod is in the shape of a cylinder. It has a diameter of 12 cm and is 16 cm long.
   (a) Calculate the volume of the gold rod.
   The rod is melted down and re-cast as a cube.
   No gold is lost during this process.
   (b) Calculate the length of an edge of the cube.

4. Here is a list of expressions which could represent the lengths, areas or volumes of various shapes.

$$3\mu a \quad \lambda a^2 b \quad 2\pi r \quad \pi r^2 h \quad \lambda^2 h$$

$$\frac{\mu a^2 b^2}{h} \quad \pi(a^2b + ab^2)$$

4. In the expressions, the Greek letters $\pi$, $\lambda$ (lambda), $\mu$ (mu), and the numbers 2, 3 and $\frac{1}{2}$ are dimensionless. The other letters represent lengths.
   List the expressions that could represent a volume.

5. The cross-section of a tunnel is a semi-circle of radius 4 metres.

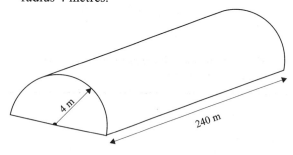

The tunnel is 240 metres long.
(a) Calculate the area of the cross-section of the tunnel.
(b) Calculate the volume of the inside of the tunnel.

6. A sheet of card is in the shape of the parallelogram ABCD.
   A circle of radius 3 cm is cut from the card.
   Calculate the area of the card remaining after the circle has been cut out.

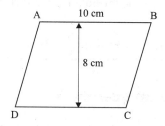

## Test yourself

1. A solid shape has a cross-section which is a trapezium with a semi-circle attached. The dimensions of the shape are shown in the diagram.

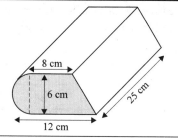

QUESTION    Calculate the area of the cross-section

ANSWER      75.14 cm² 

If your answer is incorrect review page 381, Section 18.6 on trapeziums and page 383 Section 18.7, on circles

QUESTION    Calculate the volume of the shape.

ANSWER      1853.5 cm³ 

If your answer is incorrect review page 389, Section 18.10 on prisms and page 392, Section 18.11 on cylinders. The shape is a prism so volume = area of cross-section × length

The shape is made of metal. It is melted down and re-cast as a cube. During this process none of the metal is lost.

QUESTION    Calulate the length of an edge of the cube

ANSWER      12.28 cm 

If your answer is incorrect first check that you took the cube root of your answer to (b) to work out the length of the edge of the cube. Then review page 387, Section 18.9 on cuboids, especially Example 11

2. One of the formulae in the list below can be used to calculate the area of material needed to make the curved surface of the lampshade in the diagram.

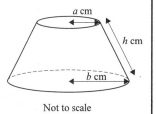

Not to scale

(i) $\pi h(a + b)^2$

(ii) $\pi h^2(a + b)$

(iii) $\pi h(a + b)$

(iv) $\pi h^2(a + b)^2$

---

**QUESTION**    State which formula is correct. Give a reason for your answer.

**ANSWER**    $\pi h(a + b)$ because formula (iii) has dimension 2 which is the dimension of area. Formulae (i) and (ii) have dimension 3 and formula (iv) has dimension 4    *If your answer is incorrect review page 395, Section 18.12 on dimension theory*

## Summary of key points to remember

1. For two-dimensional shapes you need to know and be able to use these formulae.

Check the formulae sheet on page 596 to see which ones are given in the GSCE exam and which ones you need to memorise.

| Shape | Perimeter | Area |
|---|---|---|
| Rectangle | $2(a + b)$ | $ab$ |
| Triangle | $a + b + c$ | $\frac{1}{2}bh$ |
| Parallelogram | $2(a + b)$ | $bh$ |
| Trapezium | $a + c + d + b$ | $\frac{1}{2}(a + b)h$ |

| Circle | Circumference | Area |
|---|---|---|
|  | $\pi d$ | $\dfrac{\pi d^2}{4}$ |
| | $2\pi r$ | $\pi r^2$ |

2. For three-dimensional shapes you need to know and be able to apply these formulae.

Check the formulae sheet on page 596 to see which ones are given in the GCSE exam and which ones you need to memorise.

| **Shape** | **Volume** |
|---|---|
| Cuboid | $wlh$ |

| Prism | Area of base × height |
|---|---|

| Cylinder | $\pi r^2 h$ |
|---|---|

3. You should be able to use dimension theory to check that the formula you are using is sensible.

- numbers are dimensionless

- lengths have a dimension of 1

- area has a dimension of 2

$$\underset{\text{(dimension 1)}}{\text{length}} \times \underset{\text{(dimension 1)}}{\text{length}} = \underset{\text{(dimension 2)}}{\text{area}}$$

- volume has a dimension of 3

$$\underset{\text{(dimension 1)}}{\text{length}} \times \underset{\text{(dimension 1)}}{\text{length}} \times \underset{\text{(dimension 1)}}{\text{length}} = \underset{\text{(dimension 3)}}{\text{Volume}}$$

*Remember*: you *add* the dimensions.

# 19 Pythagoras' theorem

## 19.1 Why is Pythagoras' theorem useful?

Pythagoras' theorem was proved by the Pythagorean school, which was founded by Pythagoras, a Greek philosopher and mathematician who lived in the sixth century BC.

If you know the lengths of two sides of a right-angled triangle, you can use Pythagoras' theorem to calculate the length of the third side.

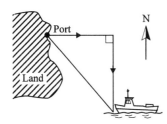

*When a boat sails a certain distance due east from a port, and then sails another distance due south, you can work out how far the boat is from the port.*

If you know that the three sides of a triangle obey Pythagoras' theorem, you know that one angle of the triangle is a right angle.

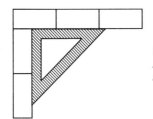

*The triangle can be made of wood. A builder can use it to make sure that two walls are at right angles.*

Pythagoras' theorem is used by builders, architects, engineers and others. It is always tested in GCSE examinations.

In this unit you will investigate Pythagoras' theorem and use it to calculate the lengths of sides of right-angled triangles.

## 19.2 Squares and square roots

When you use Pythagoras' theorem, you need to be able to work out squares and square roots of numbers. This section reminds you how to do this.

$4^2$ means 4 squared, and its value is $4 \times 4$, which equals 16.

Sometimes you can work out the square of a number in your head, but often you need to use a calculator.

*Example 1*

Work out $15.3^2$.

Press these keys on your calculator:

$$\boxed{1}\ \boxed{5}\ \boxed{\cdot}\ \boxed{3}\ \boxed{\times}\ \boxed{1}\ \boxed{5}\ \boxed{\cdot}\ \boxed{3}\ \boxed{=}$$

The answer displayed shouuld be $234.09$

Instead, you could press these keys on your calculator:

$$\boxed{1}\ \boxed{5}\ \boxed{\cdot}\ \boxed{3}\ \boxed{\text{SHIFT}}\ \overset{x^2}{\boxed{\ \ }}$$

The answer displayed should again be $234.09$

Some calculators work in a different way. If you get a different answer, look in your calculator instruction booklet.

$\sqrt{36}$ means the square root of 36. When the square root of 36 is multiplied by itself, the answer is 36. You know that $6 \times 6 = 36$, and so $\sqrt{36} = 6$

Often, you will need to use a calculator to work out square roots.

*Example 2*

Work out $\sqrt{3.24}$

Press these keys on your calculator:

$$\boxed{3}\ \boxed{\cdot}\ \boxed{2}\ \boxed{4}\ \boxed{\sqrt{}}$$

The answer displayed should be $1.8$

Sometimes, the answer has many digits after the decimal point. Unless you are told otherwise, it is best to write down the first four figures from your calculator display.

On some calculators, the square root key has to be pressed *before* the number. If your answer is not 1.8, look in your calculator instruction booklet.

*Example 3*

Work out $\sqrt{368}$

Press these keys on your calculator:

$$\boxed{3}\ \boxed{6}\ \boxed{8}\ \boxed{\sqrt{}}$$

The answer displayed should be $19.183326$. An answer that is correct to four significant figures is usually accurate enough (19.18 in this case).

## Example 4

Work out $\sqrt{1\,552\,517}$ and give your answer correct to three significant figures.

Press these keys on your calculator:

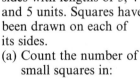

The answer displayed should be $1246.0004$. (Write down the uncorrected value.)

The value correct to three significant figures is 1250. Remember to include the 0 in the 1250. Without it, the answer is just over 100, but it should be just over 1000.

---

### Exercise 19A

1. Use your calculator to work out:
   (a) $4^2$     (b) $3.5^2$     (c) $20^2$
   (d) $9.7^2$     (e) $18.6^2$     (f) $36.4^2$

2. Use your calculator to work out:
   (a) $\sqrt{49}$     (b) $\sqrt{225}$     (c) $\sqrt{1.69}$
   (d) $\sqrt{33.64}$     (e) $\sqrt{0.81}$     (f) $\sqrt{297}$

3. Use your calculator to work out the values of these expressions. Give your answers correct to 3 s.f.
   (a) $\sqrt{254}$     (b) $\sqrt{2341}$     (c) $\sqrt{18.3}$
   (d) $\sqrt{29.44}$     (e) $\sqrt{8476}$     (f) $\sqrt{1\,825\,963}$

---

# 19.3 Finding out about Pythagoras' theorem

### Exercise 19B

1. The triangle PQR has sides with lengths of 3, 4 and 5 units. Squares have been drawn on each of its sides.
   (a) Count the number of small squares in:
      (i) the square PQUV
      (ii) the square QRST
      (iii) the square PWXR.
   (b) Add your answers for parts (a)(i) and (ii) together.
   (c) Write down what you notice about your answers to parts (a) and (b).

2. The right-angled triangle ABC, shown opposite, has sides with lengths of 3.5, 12 and 12.5 units. Squares have been drawn on each side of the triangle.
   (a) Count the numbers of small squares in:
      (i) the square CBFG     (ii) the square ACHI
      (iii) the square ADEB.
   (b) Add your answers for parts (a)(i) and (ii) together.
   (c) Write down what you notice about your answers to parts (a) and (b).

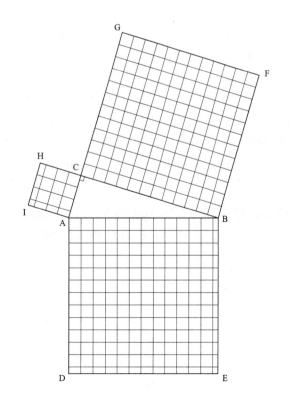

## 19.4 Pythagoras' theorem

The longest side of a right-angled triangle is the one opposite the right angle. It is called the **hypotenuse**. In question **2** of Exercise 19B, the hypotenuse is AB.

Another way to find the results you discovered in Exercise 19B is to calculate the areas of the squares.

In *triangle* PQR, the area of the square on the hypotenuse is

$$PR^2 = 5^2 = \mathbf{25}$$

The sum of the areas of the squares on the other two sides is

$$QR^2 + PQ^2 = 3^2 + 4^2 = 9 + 16 = \mathbf{25}$$
$$5^2 = 3^2 + 4^2$$

(5 squared = 3 squared + 4 squared), and so

$$PR^2 = QR^2 + PQ^2$$

In *triangle ABC*, the area of the square on the hypotenuse is

$$AB^2 = 12.5^2 = \mathbf{156.25}$$

The sum of the areas of the squares on the other two sides is

$$AC^2 + BC^2 = 12^2 + 3.5^2 = 144 + 12.25 = \mathbf{156.25}$$
$$12.5^2 = 12^2 + 3.5^2$$

(12.5 squared = 12 squared + 3.5 squared), and so

$$AB^2 = AC^2 + BC^2$$

These are particular cases of the theorem known as Pythagoras' theorem.

**Pythagoras' theorem**: In a right-angled triangle, the square on the hypotenuse is equal to the sum of the squares on the other two sides.

If a triangle has a *right angle*, you can use Pythagoras' theorem to calculate the length of one of its sides.

Use the formula $a^2 + b^2 = c^2$ to calculate the length of the hypotenuse.

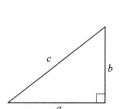

## 19.5 Using Pythagoras' theorem to calculate the length of the hypotenuse

*Example 5*

Calculate the length $x$ in this triangle:

$$a^2 + b^2 = c^2$$
$$8^2 + 6^2 = x^2$$
$$x^2 = 64 + 36$$
$$= 100$$

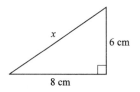

So: $x = \sqrt{100} = 10\,\text{cm}$

## *Example 6*

A boat leaves Morecambe and sails due west for 5.6 km. The boat then changes course and sails due south for 4.3 km.

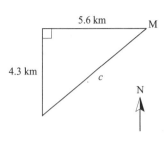

Calculate the final distance of the boat from Morecambe, giving your answer correct to one decimal place.

$$a^2 + b^2 = c^2$$
$$c^2 = 5.6^2 + 4.3^2$$
$$= 31.36 + 18.49$$
$$= 49.85$$

So:
$$c = \sqrt{49.85}$$
$$= 7.0604\ldots\,\text{km}$$

The boat is 7.1 km from Morecambe correct to 1 d.p.

---

## Exercise 19C

**1.** Calculate the lengths $a$, $b$, $c$ and $d$ in the following triangles.

(a)
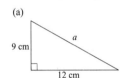

(b)

(c)
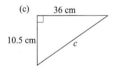

(d)
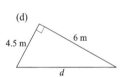

**2.** Find the following lengths. Give your answers correct to one decimal place.
(a) Find AC.

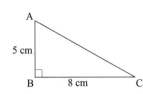

(b) Find GH.

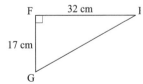

(c) Find LN.
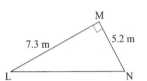

(d) Find PR.
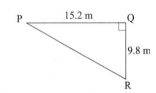

**3.** A shelf bracket is made in the shape of triangle DEF with a right angle at E. DE = 15 cm and EF = 8 cm.

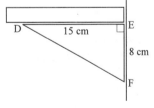

Calculate the length of the sloping side DF.

**4.** Alice Springs is 1800 km due west of Curtis Island, which is off the coast of Queensland, Australia. Sydney is 1150 km due south of Curtis Island.
Calculate the distance between Alice Springs and Sydney. Give your answer correct to the nearest 10 km.

# 19.6 Using Pythagoras' theorem to calculate one of the shorter sides of a triangle

Using the formula $a^2 + b^2 = c^2$, you can calculate the longest side $c$ of a right-angled triangle. If you need to find one of the shorter sides ($a$, for example), it is easier to change the formula so that $a^2$ is its subject.

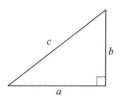

Pythagoras' theorem states that

$$a^2 + b^2 = c^2$$

Subtract $b^2$ from both sides of the equation:

$$a^2 + b^2 - b^2 = c^2 - b^2$$
$$a^2 = c^2 - b^2$$

Use the formula $\boldsymbol{a^2 = c^2 - b^2}$ to calculate the length of a shorter side of a right-angled triangle.

### Example 7

An isosceles triangle XYZ has XY = 13.8 cm, YZ = 13.8 cm and XZ = 8.4 cm.

Calculate the height of the triangle.

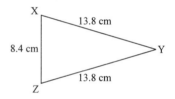

The **height** of an isosceles triangle is the length of the line that is perpendicular to the unequal side of the triangle (XZ here) and that meets the point at which the equal sides meet (Y here). The unequal side of the triangle is called the **base** of the triangle.

YW is the height of the triangle. YW is a line of symmetry, and so XW = ZW

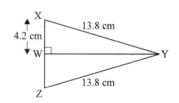

$$XW = \tfrac{1}{2} \times 8.4 = 4.2 \text{ cm}$$

Triangle YXW has a right angle at W, and so you can use Pythagoras' theorem to calculate the height of triangle XYZ.

$$a^2 = c^2 - b^2$$

$$YW^2 = 13.8^2 - 4.2^2$$
$$= 190.44 - 17.64$$
$$= 172.8$$

So:

$$YW = \sqrt{172.8}$$
$$= 13.145\ldots$$

The height of the triangle is 13.1 cm, correct to 1 d.p.

## Example 8

A ladder is 2.6 m long. It leans against a wall with one end on the ground 1 m (horizontally) from the wall. The other end of the ladder just reaches a ledge.

Calculate the height of the ledge above the ground.

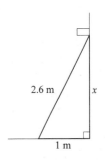

$$a^2 = c^2 - b^2$$
$$x^2 = 2.6^2 - 1^2$$
$$= 6.76 - 1$$
$$= 5.76$$

So:

$$x = \sqrt{5.76}$$
$$= 2.4\,\text{m}$$

The ledge is 2.4 m above the ground. (Check that this length is shorter than the hypotenuse.)

## Exercise 19D

**1.** Calculate the lengths $a$, $b$, $c$ and $d$ in the following triangles.

(a)

(b)

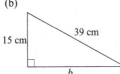

(c)

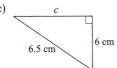

(d)

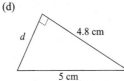

(c) Find LM.

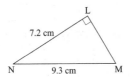

(d) Find PQ.

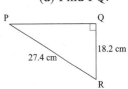

**3.** The height of a loft window frame is 105 cm. The window is kept open by a metal stay. The stay is at right angles to the window and is attached to the window 85 cm from the hinge.

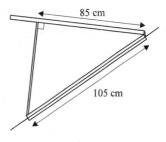

Calculate the length of the stay.

**2.** Calculate the following lengths. Give your answers correct to one decimal place.
(a) Find AB.

(b) Find DE.

## Worked exam question

A pawnbroker's sign consists of a right-angled triangular frame attached to a vertical wall as shown. The horizontal bar of the frame is 3 m above the ground and is 0.75 m long. The hypotenuse of the triangle is 2 m long.

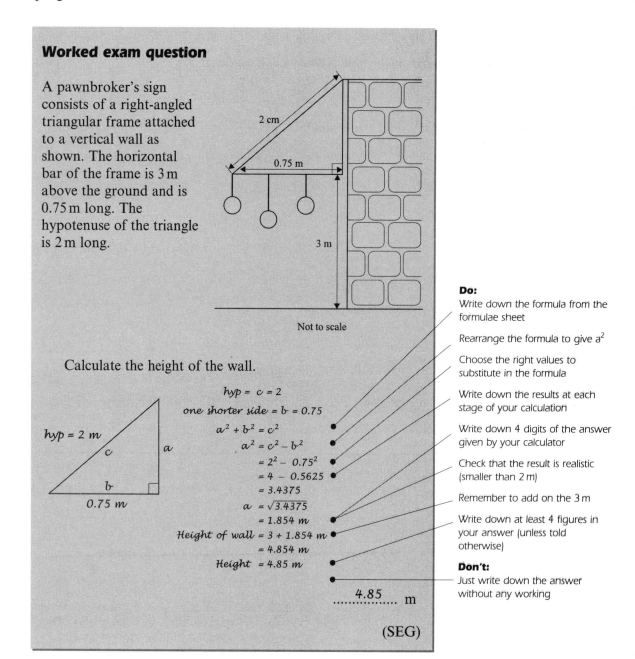

Not to scale

Calculate the height of the wall.

$hyp = c = 2$

one shorter side $= b = 0.75$

$a^2 + b^2 = c^2$

$a^2 = c^2 - b^2$

$= 2^2 - 0.75^2$

$= 4 - 0.5625$

$= 3.4375$

$a = \sqrt{3.4375}$

$= 1.854\ m$

Height of wall $= 3 + 1.854\ m$

$= 4.854\ m$

Height $= 4.85\ m$

................ 4.85 ........ m

**Do:**

Write down the formula from the formulae sheet

Rearrange the formula to give $a^2$

Choose the right values to substitute in the formula

Write down the results at each stage of your calculation

Write down 4 digits of the answer given by your calculator

Check that the result is realistic (smaller than 2 m)

Remember to add on the 3 m

Write down at least 4 figures in your answer (unless told otherwise)

**Don't:**

Just write down the answer without any working

(SEG)

## Exercise 19E (Mixed questions)

1. A rectangle is 12 cm long and 7 cm wide. Work out the length of a diagonal of the rectangle.

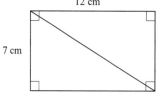

2. A boat takes part in a race round the Hulin Rocks in the Irish Sea. The boat leaves Larne and sails due north for 12.8 km. The boat then changes course and sails due east for 11.2 km.

Calculate the distance the boat must then travel in a straight line back to Larne, giving your answer correct to one decimal place.

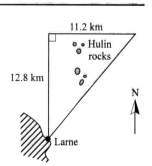

**3.** A tent pole is 2.7 m high. A guy rope goes from the top T of the tent pole to a peg P on the ground. The guy rope is 3.2 m long.

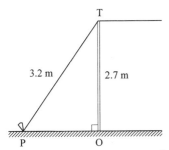

Calculate the distance OP of the peg from the bottom of the tent pole.

**4.** An isosceles triangle ABC has AB = 8.7 cm and BC = 8.7 cm. The height of the triangle is BD, and BD = 6.3 cm.

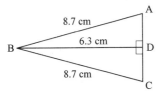

Work out the length of AC.

**5.** In an isosceles triangle LMN, LM = 39 cm, NL = 39 cm and MN = 27 cm.
Calculate the height of the triangle LMN.

**6.** ABC is a right-angled triangle. AB is of length 4 m and BC is of length 13 m.

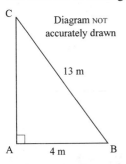

Calculate the length of AC.                    [London]

**7.** Work out the length, in metres, of side AB of the triangle.                    [London]

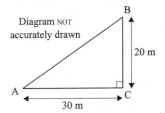

**8.**

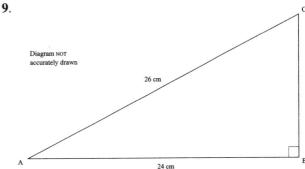

The diagram shows three places, which are on the same horizontal plane.
Windy Cragg is 5.2 km due north of Hill Top.
Walton Scree is 6.8 km due east of Hill Top.
Calculate the distance from Walton Scree to Windy Cragg.
Give your answer correct to 1 decimal place.
                    [London]

**9.**

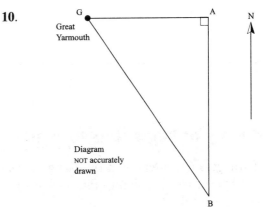

In the diagram, triangle ABC is right-angled at B. AB = 24 cm and AC = 26 cm.
Calculate the length of BC.                    [London]

**10.**

A boat sails due east from Great Yarmouth for 14.7 km to a position A. The boat then changes course and sails due south for 19.8 km to a position B.
Calculate the distance, in km, of B from Great Yarmouth.                    [London]

# Test yourself

1.  Davinda leaves Gatwick airport in her helicopter and flies due west for 19 km to Ewhurst. A passenger boards the helicopter and Davinda flies due north for 35 km to Heathrow airport.

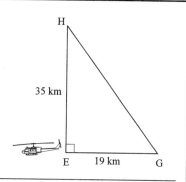

**QUESTION**   Calculate the distance in a straight line between the airports at Gatwick and Heathrow.

**ANSWER**   39.82 km (or 40 km to the nearest km)   *If your answer is incorrect, review pages 404–405, Section 19.5, Examples 5 and 6.*

2.  A wire TA is 13 m long. It is one of the supports for a vertical radio mast. The wire is attached to the mast at T and to the ground at A. The distance AM from A to the base of the mast is 4.8 m.

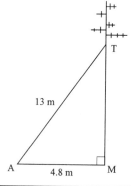

**QUESTION**   Calculate the length TM.

**ANSWER**   12.08 m   *If your answer is incorrect, review page 407, Section 19.6, Example 8.*

# Summary of key points to remember

1.  **Pythagoras' theorem**: in a right-angled triangle, the square on the hypotenuse is equal to the sum of the squares on the other two sides.

2.  If a triangle has a **right angle**, you can use **Pythagoras' theorem** to calculate the length of one of its sides.

3.  Use the formula $a^2 + b^2 = c^2$ to calculate the length of the hypotenuse.

4.  Use the formula $a^2 = c^2 - b^2$ to calculate the length of a shorter side.

# 20 Trigonometry in 2-D

## 20.1 Why was trigonometry 'invented'?

Trigonometry is an area of mathematics in which we study lengths and angles, usually as related to triangles.

Two of the problems which led to the development of trigonometry were:

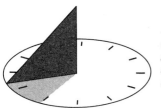

*... creating a means of telling the time using shadows which vary according to the time of day.*

*... working out the relationship between the width of a channel in a harbour and the range of a cannon-ball.*

*This surveyor's sighting equipment performs trigonometric calculations automatically*

Today, trigonometry is used by surveyors, architects, engineers and others. It is a very important branch of mathematics – as well as being one that is **always tested at GCSE level**.

## 20.2 Naming the sides of a right-angled triangle

You need to be able to identify the sides of right-angled triangles.

Draw two right-angled triangles like these on thin card and cut them out.

*Mark the right angle on each side of your cards like this.*

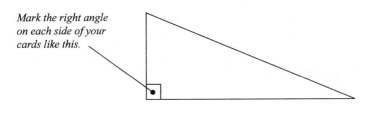

*Shade the larger angle of one triangle.*

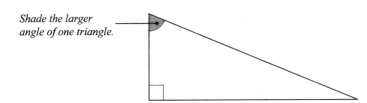

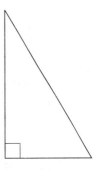

*Shade the smaller angle of the other triangle.*

Do this on both sides of each card.

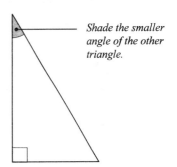

Label the sides of your triangle like this:

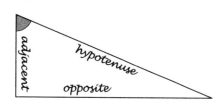

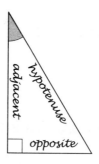

The side across from the right-angle is called the **hypotenuse**.

The hypotenuse is always the longest side of a right-angled triangle.

The side across from, or opposite, the shaded angled is called the **opposite**.

The side next to the shaded angle is called the **adjacent**.

The shaded angle is between the adjacent side and the hypotenuse.

## Exercise 20A

1. Each of the triangles below has a shaded angle. The sides are marked with the lengths or letters. For each triangle work out which side is the hypotenuse, opposite or adjacent to the shaded angle. Record the lengths and letters in a table like this:

| triangle | hypotenuse | opposite | adjacent |
|----------|------------|----------|----------|
| (a)      | 5 cm       | 3 cm     | 4 cm     |
| (b)      |            |          |          |
| (c)      |            |          |          |

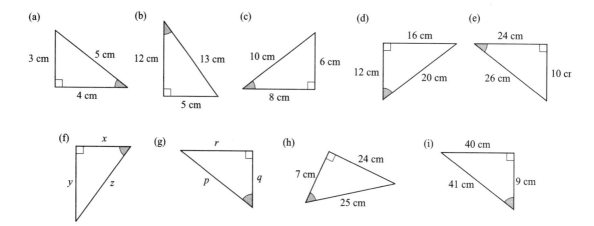

## 20.3   The trigonometric ratios

Here is a right-angled triangle with one of its angles labelled $\theta$.

The sides have been labelled as hypotenuse, opposite and adjacent.

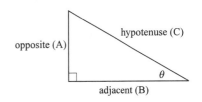

There are three basic triognometric ratios for the triangle. These are the ratios of the different sides to each other. The three trigonometric ratios are defined as:

$$\text{Sine }\theta = \frac{\text{opposite}}{\text{hypotenuse}} \qquad \text{Cosine }\theta = \frac{\text{adjacent}}{\text{hypotenuse}} \qquad \text{Tangent }\theta = \frac{\text{opposite}}{\text{adjacent}}$$

These are often abbreviated to:

$$\text{Sin }\theta = \frac{\text{opp}}{\text{hyp}} \qquad \text{Cos }\theta = \frac{\text{adj}}{\text{hyp}} \qquad \text{Tan }\theta = \frac{\text{opp}}{\text{adj}}$$

Some people use this mnemonic to help remember the ratios:

| **SOH** | **CAH** | **TOA** |
| --- | --- | --- |
| Silly **O**ld **H**ens | Cackle **A**nd **H**ail | Till **O**ld **A**ge |

## 20.4  Using a calculator to find trigonometric ratios

Scientific calculators are designed to work out the trigonometric ratios for any angle.

Here is how to work out Cosine 53°:

> input   **53**
>
> press   [COS]
>
> read off the result   $0.6018I5023$

It is usually sufficient to give the result correct to 4 decimal places, so Cosine 53° = 0.6018

You can also work out an angle given one of its trigonometric ratios.

Suppose you were given that Tan $x$ = 0.6713

Here is how to find the value of $x$:

> input   **0.6713**
>
> press   [INV] or [2nd]
>
> press   [TAN]
>
> read off the result   $33.87346I95$

Answers like this one are usually quoted correct to the second decimal place or some given degree of accuracy, so if:

$$\text{Tan}\, x = 0.6713 \quad \text{then} \quad x = 33.87°, \text{ correct to 2 d.p.}$$

### Exercise 20B

**1.** Use your calculator to help you complete this table of values:

| Angle in degrees | Sine | Cosine | Tangent |
|---|---|---|---|
| 0 | | | |
| 10 | | | |
| 15 | | | |
| 20 | | | |
| 33 | | | |
| 45 | | | |
| 52 | | | |
| 60 | | | |
| 75 | | | |
| 80 | | | |
| 88 | | | |

**2.** Use your calculator to find the angle $x$ in each of the cases. Give your answers correct to 2 d.p.
(a) Tan $x = 0.4817$
(b) Sin $x = 0.8283$
(c) Sin $x = 0.4555$
(d) Cos $x = 0.7771$
(e) Tan $x = 2.3$
(f) Tan $x = 53$
(g) Cos $x = 0.1234$
(h) Sin $x = 0.0456$
(i) Cos $x = 0.9945$

## 20.5 How to work out an angle, given two sides of a triangle

### *Example 1*

Calculate the size of the angle marked $x°$.

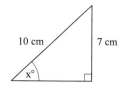

The hypotenuse is 10 cm and the side opposite $x$ is 7 cm.

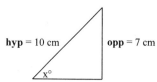

The three trigonometric ratios are:

$$\text{Sin}\, \theta = \frac{\text{opp}}{\text{hyp}} \qquad \text{Cos}\, \theta = \frac{\text{adj}}{\text{hyp}} \qquad \text{Tan}\, \theta = \frac{\text{opp}}{\text{adj}}$$

As you know opp and hyp you can ignore the Cos $\theta$ and Tan $\theta$ ratios and just use

$$\text{Sin}\, \theta = \frac{\text{opp}}{\text{hyp}}$$

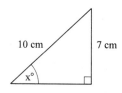

So:

$$\text{Sin}\,\theta = \frac{\text{opp}}{\text{hyp}}$$

$$\text{Sin}\,\theta = \frac{7}{10}$$

$$\text{Sin}\,\theta = 0.7 \quad \text{and} \quad \theta = 44.43°$$

## *Example 2*

Calculate the size of the angle marked $y$.

In this picture

$$\text{opp} = 5 \text{ and adj} = 12$$

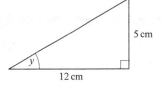

Because you know opp and adj and do not know hyp you use the ratio

$$\text{Tan}\,y = \frac{\text{opp}}{\text{adj}}$$

So:

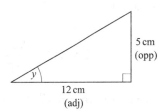

$$\text{Tan}\,y = \frac{5}{12}$$

$$\text{Tan}\,y = 0.4167 \quad \text{and} \quad y = 22.62°$$

## Exercise 20C

**1.** Work out each of the angles marked with a letter.

(a)

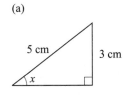

(b)

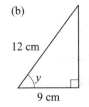

(c)

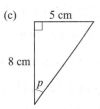

(d)

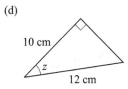

(e)

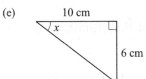

(f)

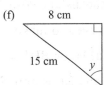

(g)

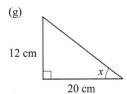

(h)

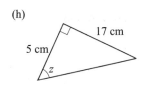

(i)

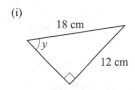

## 20.6 How to work out an unknown length given one length and an angle of a right-angled triangle

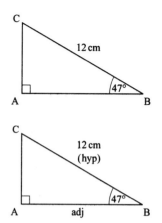

### *Example 3*

Calculate the length of AB

You know that the angle at B is 47°.

You also know that the hypotenuse is 12 cm, or hyp = 12.

You want to work out AB, the side which is adjacent to the known angle.

So because you know the angle and hyp and want adj you use the Cosine ratio

$$\text{Cos}\,47° = \frac{\text{adj}}{\text{hyp}} \quad \text{or} \quad \text{adj} = \text{hyp} \times \text{Cos}\,47°$$

and it is more sensible to use the second of these

$$\text{adj} = \text{hyp} \times \text{Cos}\,47$$
$$\text{AB} = 12 \times \text{Cos}\,47$$
$$\text{AB} = 12 \times 0.6820 \quad \text{so} \quad \text{AB} = 8.18\,\text{cm (correct to 2 d.p.)}$$

### *Example 4*

A ship sets sail from a harbour H.

The ship travels due North to reach a marker buoy B.

At B it turns and travels due East to a light house L.

The bearing of L from H is 058° and LH = 38 km.

Calculate the distance from B to L

Firstly you need to make a sketch of this situation

The angle at H, or BHL = 58°

LH is hyp and BL is opp. So you use the Sine ratio

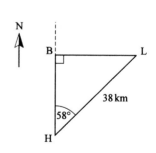

$$\text{Sin}\,58 = \frac{\text{opp}}{\text{hyp}} \quad \text{or} \quad \text{opp} = \text{hyp} \times \text{Sin}\,58$$

so, opp = hyp × Sin 58

or BL = 38 × 0.8480

BL = 32.23 km

## Example 5

The angle of elevation of the Sun is 37°

A vertical pole casts a shadow of length 19.9 metres on horizontal ground.

Calculate the height of the pole.

Again you need to draw a sketch of the situation.

To do this you need to know the meaning of the term angle of elevation of the Sun.

This is the angle between the horizontal ground and the Sun, or the angle through which you would need to turn your eyes to look at the sun.

In the diagram the height of the pole is labelled h.

You have the angle = 37° and the adj = 19.9

You want opp

So you use the Tangent ratio, in the form

$$opp = adj \times Tan\,37$$

So:

$$h = 19.9 \times Tan\,37 \text{ or } h = 19.9 \times 0.7536$$

$$h = 15.00 \text{ metres (correct to 2 significant figures)}$$

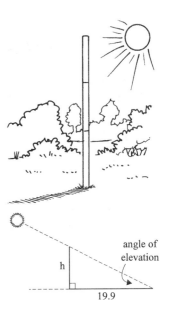

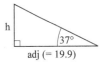

## Exercise 20D

**1.** Work out each of the lengths marked with a letter

(a)

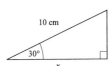

(b)

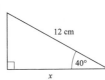

(c)

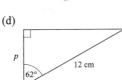

(d)

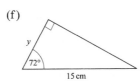

(e)

(f)

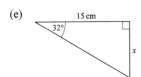

**2.** The angle of elevation of the Sun is 46°
A vertical mast casts a shadow of length 240 metres on horizontal ground.
Calculate the height of the mast.

**3.** A man sets off from a point P and walks due East to a point Q. At Q he turns and walks for a further 12 km on a bearing of 301° from Q until he reaches a point R.
The point R is due North of P.
Calculate the distance PQ.

# Worked exam question 1

In this problem give at least three significant figures in each of your answers.

In the diagram, AB represents a ladder leaning against a wall of a house.

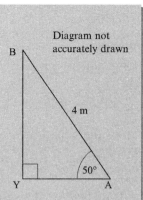

Diagram not accurately drawn

The ladder is 4 m long.

The angle between the ladder and the horizontal ground is 50°.

Calculate in metres:

(a)    the height, **BY**, of the top of the ladder above the ground,

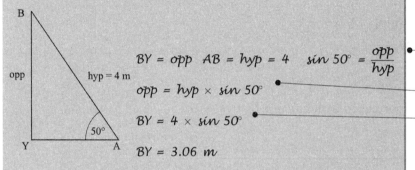

$BY = opp$   $AB = hyp = 4$   $sin\ 50° = \dfrac{opp}{hyp}$

$opp = hyp \times sin\ 50°$

$BY = 4 \times sin\ 50°$

$BY = 3.06\ m$

**Do:**
Use Sine

Write down the formula from the formulae sheet

Rearrange formula to give opp

Choose the right values to substitute in the formula
check that the answer is realistic

$$BY = 3.06 \text{ m}$$

(b)    the distance, **AY**, of the foot of the ladder from the wall of the house.

$AY = adj$        $4 = hyp$

$adj = hyp \times cos\ 50°$   $cos\ 50° = \dfrac{adj}{hyp}$

$AY = 4 \times cos\ 50°$

$AY = 4 \times 0.64279$

$AY = 2.57\ m$

**Do:**
Use Cos

**Don't**
Just write down the answer without any working

$$AY = 2.57 \text{ m}$$

Part (b) of the last example could also have been done by using Pythagoras' theorem of Unit 19. How this relates to problems of trigonometry is shown in the next example.

## Worked exam question 2

ABC is a right-angled triangle

AB is of length 4 cm and BC is of length 13 cm

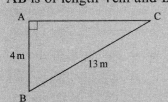

Diagram NOT accurately drawn

(a)    Calculate the length of AC

$$AC^2 = 13^2 - 4^2$$

$$AC^2 = 169 - 16$$

$$AC^2 = 153$$

$$AC = \sqrt{153}$$

so AC = 12.37 correct to 2 d.p.

$BC^2 = AC^2 + AB^2$ [Pythagoras]

so

$AC^2 = BC^2 - AB^2$

(b)    Calculate the size of the angle ABC

4 = adj     13 = hyp

So use the Cosine ratio

$$\text{Cos } \theta = \frac{\text{adj}}{\text{hyp}}$$

So Cos B = $\dfrac{4}{13}$

Cos B = 0.3077

B = 72.08°    (correct to 2 d.p.)

$A\hat{B}C = \theta$

AB = adj

BC = hyp

(London)

---

## Exercise 20E (Mixed questions)

These problems are designed to be of the type you are likely to encounter in your GCSE examinations. As well as showing your knowledge of trigonometry you may well need to show your knowledge of Pythagoras's theorem, bearings and angle work in the same questions.

**1.** The diagram shows a ladder resting between a horizontal floor and a vertical wall.
The top of the ladder is 6 metres above the floor.

The bottom of the ladder is 2.5 metres from the base of the wall.

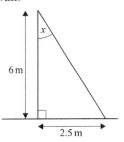

Calculate:
(a) the length of the ladder
(b) the angle, $x$, between the ladder and the wall.

2. A cubical box PQRS is held on a trailer by a tight rope. The rope passes over the box and is secured at two points A and B.

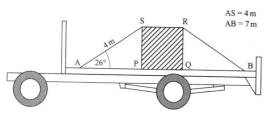

AS = 4 m
AB = 7 m

Calculate:
(a) the height of the box    (b) the length RB
(c) the angle QRB

3. (a) Calculate the size of the angle QPR

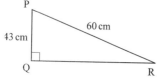

60 cm

43 cm

(b) Calculate the length of the side AB

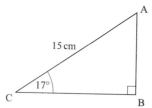

15 cm

17°

(c) Calculate the length of the side XY

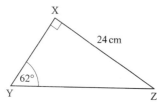

24 cm

62°

4. The diagram shows the cross-section of a swimming pool 33 m long. It is 4 m deep at the deep end and this deepest part of the pool is 8 m long.

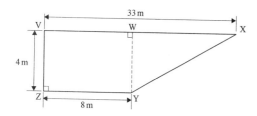

(a) Calculate the length of the sloping bottom of the pool XY
(b) Calculate the angle VXY

5. State why it would be impossible to draw a triangle with sides and angle as shown below.

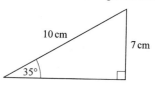

10 cm

7 cm

35°

6. John wishes to estimate the height, *h*, of a vertical wall.

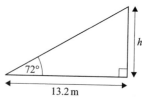

72°

13.2 m

He stands in a position 13.2 metres from the base of the wall.
He measures the angle of elevation of the top of the wall to be 72°
Calculate the height of the wall.

7. The diagram shows a step-ladder, ABC, standing on horizontal ground.

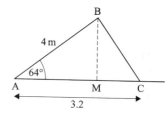

4 m

64°

3.2

AB = 4 m, angle CAB = 64° and AC = 3.2 m.
The point M is vertically below B. Calculate:
(a) the height MB     (b) the angle BCM

8. Calculate each of the sides marked with a letter

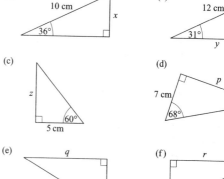

(a)

10 cm

*x*

36°

(b)

12 cm

31°

*y*

(c)

*z*

5 cm

60°

(d)

*p*

7 cm

68°

(e)

*q*

12 cm

51°

(f)

*r*

22°

12 cm

(g)

*s*

10 cm

72°

(h)

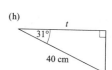

*t*

31°

40 cm

9. A ship sets sail from a harbour H and travels for 24 km along a bearing of 070° until it reaches a point due East of a marker buoy B. Calculate the distance between the ship and the marker buoy.

10. The diagram shows a ladder, LD, of length 8 metres resting against a vertical wall. The ladder makes an angle of 23° with the wall. Calculate the distance BL, from the base of the wall to the bottom end of the ladder.

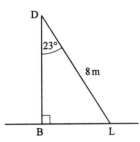

11. The diagram below shows a vertical television aerial AT standing on horizontal ground. The height of the aerial is 15 metres. The aerial casts a shadow AP on the horizontal ground. The angle of elevation of the sun is 13°. Calculate the length of the shadow AP of the aerial.

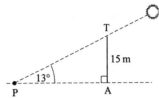

## Test yourself

1. This is the plan for a slide to be built in a children's play area.
It is in the shape of a triangle ABC.
AB is to be the horizontal base.
The vertex C is vertically above point M which is on AB.
The distance AC is to be 4.5 metres.
The distance AB is to be 12 metres.
The angle MAC = 43°.

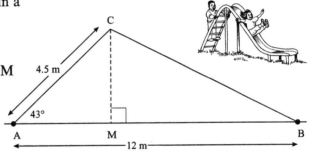

**QUESTION**  (a)  Calculate the height CM

**ANSWER**   3.07 m

*If your answer is incorrect review page 416, Section 20.6 to make sure you used the correct ratio, which should be for Sine 43° as in Example 4.*

**QUESTION**  (b)  Calculate the angle MBC

**ANSWER**   19.41°

*If your answer is incorrect review page 418, Worked Exam Question on Pythagoras' theorem to find the length AM.*
*Then find MB. Check page 416, Section 20.6 for the correct use of the Tangent ratio as in Example 5.*

2. A ship sets sail from a harbour H and sails due East. After travelling for 15.7 km it reaches a point P. At P the ship turns and heads due South to reach a point S, where it stops. The distance from P to S is 20.8 km.

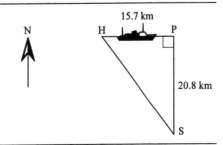

QUESTION  (a)  Calculate the distance, in km from H to S.

ANSWER  26.06 km  *If your answer is incorrect review page 417, Section 20.6.*

---

QUESTION  (b)  Calculate the bearing of H from S.

ANSWER  323° (to the nearest degree)  *If your answer is incorrect review page 414, Section 20.5 for the use of trigonometric ratios. You could use any of the three because you know all sides. Check also: Bearings on page 445. The 323° is:*
$$360° - angle\ PSH$$
$$360° - 37° = 323°$$

## Summary of key points to remember

1.  In your exam you will be given a formulae sheet with these trigonometric ratios, but remember them if you can.

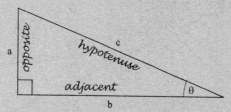

There are three basic trigonometric ratios for the triangle. These are the ratios of the different sides to each other. The three trigonometric ratios are defined as:

$$Sin\ \theta = \frac{opposite}{hypotenuse} \qquad Cosine\ \theta = \frac{adjacent}{hypotenuse} \qquad Tangent\ \theta = \frac{opposite}{adjacent}$$

These are often abbreviated to:

$$Sin\ \theta = \frac{opp}{hyp}\ or\ Sine = \frac{a}{c} \qquad Cos\ \theta = \frac{adj}{hyp}\ or\ Cosine = \frac{b}{c} \qquad Tan\ \theta = \frac{opp}{adj}\ or\ Tangent = \frac{a}{b}$$

Some people use this mnemonic to help remember them:

| **SOH** | **CAH** | **TOA** |
|---|---|---|
| Silly Old Hens | Cackle And Hail | Till Old Age |

2.  You may also need to use **bearings** in these questions, so remember that a bearing is an angle measured clockwise from due North.

3. You may need to use terms such as **Angle of elevation of the Sun**.

   This is the angle between the Sun and the horizontal ground.

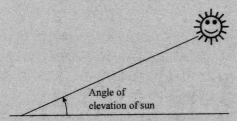

Angle of
elevation of sun

4. It is **essential** that you **show all your workings** when you answer examination questions on trigonometry.

# 21 Using appropriate measures

## 21.1 Introduction

It is difficult to imagine living in the real world without coming into contact with **measures**. When you tell someone your age, look at your watch, try on a dress or coat, put petrol in your car, look at the record charts, or read the football results, you think in terms of measures.

In this unit you will start by learning about the difference between what are called discrete measures – such as the price of a coat, and continuous measures – such as the length of a car. You will also learn about the standard units of length, capacity, mass and time and the metric and imperial systems of units. The last section looks at compound measures such as density, which is mass (one measure) divided by volume (a second measure).

## 21.2 Discrete measures and continuous measures

In October 1995, England played Wales in the semi-final of the Rugby League World Cup. England won the match by 25 points to 10 points. The number of points scored in the match was 35. 35 was the **measure** of the number of points scored in the match.

This is an example of a **discrete measure**. It is discrete because the number of points must be a whole number. In a match there can be 34 points, 35 points, 36 points, etc. but the number of points cannot be a value in between 35 and 36; for example, 34.2, 36.7, etc. are *not* possible scores. The measures are a set of **distinct** numbers.

In ice skating, the judges give the skaters scores out of 6. These scores are given to one decimal place, for example 5.6, 5.8, 5.6 and 5.7. Although these scores are not whole numbers, they are still discrete. The judges can give scores such as 5.6 or 5.7, but not values between these scores, such as 5.63, 5.75, etc. The numbers are still distinct.

The type of measure is different when Liz states on a job application form that she is 17. 17 is a measure of Liz's age. However, there is no way in which she can state her age **exactly**. If she stated that she was 17 years, five months, two weeks, four days, three hours, 37 minutes and 12 seconds old, she would still not necessarily be being precisely accurate (this might be her age to the nearest second).

Time is a **continuous measure**. It is continuous because, between any two times, there can be an infinite number of times. The value can be **any** number on the continuous number line.

The most commonly used continuous measures are those of length, area, volume, temperature, time, weight (or mass), speed, and acceleration. These are discussed later in this unit.

---

### Exercise 21A

1. Decide whether each of these is a **discrete** measure or a **continuous** measure.
   (a) your height
   (b) the volume of a bottle
   (c) the size of a pair of shoes
   (d) the number of CDs in a shop
   (e) the number of pages in a book
   (f) the length of a new road
   (g) the top speed of a new car
   (h) the attendance at a concert
   (i) the area of a field
   (j) the cost of a new house.

---

## 21.3 Approximating continuous measures

It is impossible to measure the exact height of a person. All that we can do is to make the measurement to a certain degree of accuracy. This degree of accuracy will depend on the accuracy of the instrument used to make the measurement.

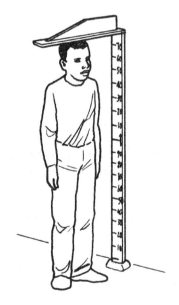

For instance, someone's height may be recorded as 178 cm. This height may be measured correct to the nearest centimetre, using a tape measure. This would mean that the actual height was rounded up or down to 178 cm.

If a height of 178 cm is correct to the nearest centimetre this means that

$$177.5\,\text{cm} \leqslant \text{height} \leqslant 178.5\,\text{cm.}$$

The actual height is anywhere between half a centimetre above or half a centimetre below the recorded height. For example, '178 cm correct to the nearest centimetre' means that the height could have any value from 177.5 cm to 178.5 cm inclusive.

You could use an instrument that is more accurate than a tape measure to measure the height. Suppose this gives a recorded height of 177.7 cm correct to the nearest millimetre.
177.7 cm = 1777 mm, and so the actual height could be anywhere in the range from half a millimetre below to half a millimetre above the recorded height.

$$1776.5\,\text{mm} \leqslant \text{height} \leqslant 1777.5\,\text{mm}$$

or    $$177.65\,\text{cm} \leqslant \text{height} \leqslant 177.75\,\text{cm}$$

More loosely, we would say that 'the actual height is between 1776.5 and 1777.5 millimetres', or that 'the height is between 177.65 and 177.75 centimetres'.

In the example above the lowest possible value of the height is 177.65 cm, and the greatest possible value of the height is 177.75 cm. In other words, the **lower bound** for the height is 177.65 cm, and the **upper bound** is 177.75 cm.

The **tolerance** of a measure is the **difference between its upper bound and its lower bound**. In this case, the tolerance of the height is $177.75 - 177.65 = 0.10$ cm.

### Example 1

In 1954 Roger Bannister was the first man to run one mile in under 4 minutes. His time for the race was recorded as 3 min 59.4 s correct to the nearest tenth of a second.

Work out:

(a) his fastest possible time.

(b) his slowest possible time.

(a) The time is recorded correct to the nearest tenth of a second. Half of one tenth of a second is 0.05 s. His fastest possible time is the lower bound of the time

$$3 \text{ min } 59.4 \text{ s} - 0.05 \text{ s} = 3 \text{ min } 59.35 \text{ s}$$

(b) His slowest possible time is the upper bound of the time. To find this, add 0.05 s to the recorded time. This slowest possible time is:

$$3 \text{ min } 59.4 \text{ s} + 0.05 \text{ s} = 3 \text{ min } 59.45 \text{ s}$$

### Exercise 21B

1. Maxine measures the thickness of a sheet of metal using a gauge. The reading is 5.96 mm correct to the nearest hundredth of a millimetre.
   (a) What is the maximum possible thickness of the sheet of metal?
   (b) What is the minimum possible thickness of the sheet of metal?

2. In 1995, the Derby was won in record time by a horse called *Lammtarra*. The time for the race was recorded as 2 min 32.31 s, correct to the nearest hundredth of a second.
   (a) What is the longest possible time that *Lammtarra* could have taken to run the Derby?
   (b) What is the shortest possible time that *Lammtarra* could have taken?

# 21.4 Standard units of length

In the UK, in everyday life, we currently use a mixture of **metric units** and **imperial units**, although we are increasingly moving towards using only metric units in commerce and industry.

The **standard metric unit** of **length** is the **metre**.

The metre was first defined in relation to the distance around the Earth. This is its history.

A **meridian** is an imaginary circle around the Earth which passes through the North Pole and the South Pole. The **prime meridian** is the meridian which passes through Greenwich in London. In 1795, France created a decimal system for measuring length and mass. In this system, the standard unit of length was defined by dividing one-quarter of a meridian into 10 000 000 equal parts. The length of one of these parts was called a metre. This length was calculated and then marked on a bar of platinum, which was kept in a vault in Paris.

Later, the metre was defined in terms of a wavelength on the electromagentic spectrum. It is now defined in terms of the speed of light, which is $3.0 \times 10^8$ m/s.

Parts or multiples of a metre (m) which are used as metric units are:

$$1 \text{ millimetre } (1 \text{ mm}) = \frac{1}{1000} \text{ m} \qquad 1 \text{ m} = 1000 \text{ mm}$$

$$1 \text{ centimetre } (1 \text{ cm}) = \frac{1}{100} \text{ m} \qquad 1 \text{ m} = 100 \text{ cm}$$

$$1 \text{ kilometre } (1 \text{ km}) = 1000 \text{ m} \qquad 1 \text{ m} = \frac{1}{1000} \text{ km}$$

It sometimes helps you to get a feel for these measures if you can use a visual image:

- The door to a room is usually about 2 m high.

- A football pitch is about 100 m long.

- The length of ten football pitches laid end to end is about 1 km.

- The base of an adult male finger is about 2 cm (or 20 mm) wide.

*Example 2*

Wasim's height is 1.85 m.

Calculate his height (a) in centimetres (b) in millimetres.

(a) 1 m = 100 cm

and so:

1.85 m = 1.85 × 100 = 185 cm

Wasim's height is 185 cm.

(b) 1 m = 1000 mm

and so:

1.85 m = 1.85 × 1000 = 1850 mm

Wasim's height is 1850 mm.

---

## Exercise 21C

1. (a) What is 1500 m in kilometres?
   (b) What is 25 cm in millimetres?
   (c) What is 3 km in metres?
   (d) What is 1 000 000 mm in metres?

2. Estimate:
   (a) the height of a room in metres,
   (b) the length of a family car in metres,
   (c) the thickness of a book in centimetres,
   (d) your height in
       (i) centimetres
       (ii) metres
       (iii) millimetres,

   (e) the length of this line

   ---

       (i) in centimetres
       (ii) in millimetres.
   (f) the height of your house in metres,
   (g) the length of a diagonal of a page of this book in centimetres.

3. Which one of these is a sensible estimate of the distance from London to Manchester? Explain your answer.
   (a) 3 km     (b) 3000 km     (c) 300 km
   (d) 300 mm    (e) 30 cm      (f) 300 cm

---

### Worked exam question 1

On the way to Chester Zoo, a bus driver takes a short cut.
They come to a low bridge with maximum headroom 4 metres.

1 metre = 39 inches
12 inches = 1 foot

The driver knows his bus is 13 feet 1 inch high.

Can the bus go under the bridge?

Show all your working.

*bridge height = 4 m = 4 × 39 in = 156 in*

*bus height = 13 ft 1 in = (13 × 12 + 1) in = 157 in* ●────

*the bridge is too low for the bus to go under.*

**Do:**
Work out the height of the bus and the height of the bridge in the same units

(NEAB)

# 21.5 Standard units of capacity

The capacity of an object is its **volume**. The **standard metric unit** of **capacity** is the **litre**.

The standard UK milk bottle has a capacity of just over half a litre.

**1 litre = 1000 cubic centimetres = 1000 cm$^3$**

Imagine a cube that measures 10 cm × 10 cm × 10 cm.

The cube has a volume (or capacity) of $10 \times 10 \times 10 = 1000 \, \text{cm}^3$, or 1 litre.

**1 litre = 1000 cubic centimetres (cm$^3$)**
**= 1000 millilitres (ml)**

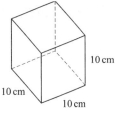

So:

**1 millilitre = 1 cubic centimetre**
**1 ml = 1 cm$^3$**

Also:

**1 litre = 100 centilitres (cl)**

- Petrol is sold by the litre.

- A standard-size carton of orange juice has a capacity of 1 litre.

- The capacity of a wine bottle is 75 cl. This means that the volume of wine in the bottle is $75 \, \text{cl} = 75 \, \text{cm}^3 = 0.75$ litres.

## *Example 3*

Sue and Terry are going to a party. They decide that they will both take the same volume of wine. Sue buys a 3 litre wine pack. Terry buys some 75 cl bottles of wine.

How many bottles must Terry buy to ensure that he has the same volume of wine as Sue?

Sue buys 3 litres, which is $3 \times 100 = 300 \, \text{cl}$ of wine.

Terry's bottles each contain 75 cl of wine, and so

2 bottles contain $2 \times 75 = 150 \, \text{cl}$
4 bottles contain $4 \times 75 = 300 \, \text{cl}$

So Terry has to buy 4 bottles of wine.

### Exercise 21D

1. (a) What is 3 litres in millilitres?
   (b) What is 500 cl in litres?
   (c) What is 1500 cl in litres?
   (d) What is 10 litres in millilitres?

2. The volume of a cuboid is given by:
   volume = length × width × height
   A cuboid measures 30 cm × 10 cm × 40 cm.

(a) Calculate the volume of the cuboid, giving
    your answer in
    (i) cubic centimetres    (ii) litres
    (iii) centilitres         (iv) millilitres.
(b) Calculate the number of 75 cl bottles which
    together have a capacity equal to the
    capacity of the cuboid.

## 21.6 Standard units of mass

The **mass** of an object is the quantity of matter in that object.
People often confuse **mass** with **weight**. The mass of an object is
the same on Earth or out in space. The **weight** of an object is
affected by the pull of gravity on that object.

The pull of gravity on the moon is far smaller than the pull of
gravity on Earth. Therefore, an astronaut's weight is much lower
on the moon than it is on Earth. However, the astronaut's mass on
the moon is the same as it is on Earth.

On Earth, for everyday purposes, we assume that the pull of
gravity is the same all over the surface of the Earth, and we use
the units of mass as units of weight. That is why we so often say
that a bag of potatoes weighs 5 kilograms when what we really
mean is that the mass of the potatoes is 5 kilograms.

The standard unit of mass in the metric system is the **kilogram**
(kg).

- The cornflakes in a standard-size packet have mass $\frac{1}{2}$ kg.

- The sugar in a standard-size bag weighs (has a mass of) 1 kg.

The other metric units of mass based on the kilogram are the
**gram**, the **milligram** and the **tonne**.

**1 gram (1 g)**        $= \dfrac{1}{1000}$ **kg**        **1 kg = 1000 g**

**1 milligram (1 mg)** $= \dfrac{1}{1000}$ **g**        **1 g = 1000 mg**

**1 tonne (1 t)**        **= 1000 kg**

Solid fuel, concrete and logs are usually sold in tonnes.

Solid fuel for a
central heating
system

Concrete for
a drive

Logs for an
open fire

Food is usually sold in kilograms or grams. For instance, the weight of the contents of a standard-size tin of baked beans is 424 g.

## Example 4

A bottle of paracetamol tablets contains 100 tablets. Each tablet weighs 500 mg.

(a) Calculate the total mass (weight) of the tablets in milligrams, and in grams.

(b) Calculate the number of tablets in 1 kilogram.

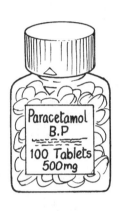

(a) Total mass $= 100 \times 500 = 50\,000$ mg

To change milligrams into grams, you need to divide by 1000, so

$$50\,000\,\text{mg} = \frac{50\,000}{1000}\,\text{g} = 50\,\text{g}$$

(b) Each tablet weighs 500 mg

500 mg = 0.5 g.

1 kg = 1000 g.

So the number of tablets in 1 kg of tablets is

$$\frac{1000}{0.5} = 2000\,\text{tablets}$$

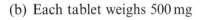

## Exercise 21E

1. Convert these measures into the units given.
   (a) 3 kg to grams          (b) 4 t to kilograms
   (c) 4 t to grams           (d) 5400 g to kilograms
   (e) 300 mg to grams        (f) 3.2 g to milligrams
   (g) 1 t to grams           (h) 2 t to milligrams

2. The contents of a standard-size tin of baked beans weigh 424 g. The tins are delivered to shops in packs of 24 tins.

(a) Calculate the mass of the beans in one of these packs of 24 tins, giving your answer
   (i) in grams       (ii) in kilograms
(b) How many tins of beans contain a total of 1 tonne of beans?

3. Convert a mass of 3 tonnes to milligrams. Express your answer as a number in standard form.

### Worked exam question 2

(a) The length of a school hall, correct to the nearest metre, is 27 m. Write down the least and greatest possible values of the length of the hall.

(a) *Least is 26.5 m; Greatest is 27.5 m*

**Do:**
Remember to subtract or add half a unit

(b) Square carpet tiles have a length of 38 cm correct to the nearest cm. Write down the least and greatest possible values for the length of the sides.

(b) *Least is 37.5 cm, Greatest is 38.5 cm*

(c) One row of tiles is laid side by side along the length of the hall. Neglecting any gaps between the tiles, explain why 69 tiles is the least possible number of tiles needed to do this.

(c) *69 × 38.5 cm = 26.565 m*

Show some working

*So, need to be sure you have enough of greatest*

*length of tile to exceed 26.5 m.*

(WJEC)

### Worked exam question 3

Rachel weighs 45 kg and her sister Carys weighs 85 pounds. Use the fact that 1 kg is about 2.2 pounds to calculate which of them is heavier and by how many pounds

**Do:**
Multiply 45 by 2.2

Show your working

*Rachel weighs 45 × 2.2 = 99 pounds*

*So, Rachel is the heavier by 99 − 85 = 14 pounds*

(WJEC)

## 21.7 Standard units of time

You need to know these standard units of time.

- 1 **year** is the amount of time that it takes the Earth to make one circuit around the Sun.

- 1 **day** is the amount of time that it takes the Earth to spin once on its own axis.

- 1 **year** = **365 days** (366 days in a **leap year**)

- 1 **week** = **7 days**
  1 **day**  = **24 h**
  1 **h**    = **60 min**
  1 **min**  = **60 s**

The month is a non-standard unit of time.

**1 lunar month = 4 weeks**

The length of 1 calendar month depends on the month:

● February has 28 days (29 in a leap year)

● April, June, September and November have 30 days

● January, March, May, July, August, October and December have 31 days.

*Example 5*

Old Lol died on his 84th birthday. Estimate the length of his life, giving your answer in

(a) days   (b) weeks   (c) hours   (d)   minutes   (e)   seconds

(a) 84 years  $= 84 \times 365 + 21$ days
$= 30\,681$ days

(There are 21 leap years in 84 years)

(b) 84 years  $= \dfrac{30\,681}{7}$ weeks

$= 4383$ weeks

(c) 84 years  $= 30\,681 \times 24$ hours
$= 736\,344$ hours

(d) 84 years  $= 736\,344 \times 60$ min
$= 44\,180\,640$ min

(e) 84 years  $= 44\,180\,640 \times 60$ seconds
$= 2\,650\,838\,400$ s

---

**Exercise 21F**

1. The winning time in a women's marathon race is 2 h 28 min 17 s. What is this time in seconds?

2. Calculate the number of minutes in the month of August.

3. Sarah makes a telephone call lasting 200 seconds. Convert this time to minutes and seconds.

4. Tinka the cat was born on 8 May 1976. He died on 6 October 1994. Estimate the length of his life
(a) in years to the nearest year
(b) in days to the nearest day.

5. Calculate the number of minutes between the times of 10.50 and 13.15 on the same day.

6. The instructions for cooking a turkey are 'Cook for 45 minutes per kilogram, and then add a further 30 minutes'.
Ms Dean buys a turkey weighing 6.4 kg.
(a) Calculate the amount of time needed to cook this turkey, giving your answer
(i) in minutes   (ii) in hours and minutes.
(b) Ms Dean wants to serve the turkey for lunch at 13.00. What is the latest time she can start to cook the turkey?

## 21.8 Imperial units

The metric system of units is used in most of the countries, including the UK. However, some non-metric units are still in use in the UK. These units are called **Imperial units**.

Here are some Imperial units that are still in regular use, with their metric equivalents.

- **Length**
  1 inch (1 in)  = 2.54 cm = 25.4 mm    1 metre = 39.37 in
  1 foot (1 ft)  = 12 in = 12 × 2.54 cm
             = 30.48 cm
  1 yard (1 yd) = 3 ft = 0.4144 m
  1 mile        = 1.6 km    1 km = $\frac{5}{8}$ mile
  5 miles       = 8 km

- **Capacity**
  1 gallon   = 4.55 litres    1 litre = 0.22 gallons
  1 pint     = $\frac{1}{8}$ gallon = 0.57 litres    1 litre is
                                approximately 1.75
                                pints

Garages sell petrol by the litre, but some people still ask for their petrol in gallons. Garages often display a chart that shows the conversion between litres and gallons, and they usually quote the conversion as

  5 litres = 1.1 gallons

- **Mass**
  outside restaurants and pubs, you will sometimes see '8 oz steak' written on the menu.

  1 ounce (1 oz)  = 28.35 g    100 g is approximately $3\frac{1}{2}$ oz
  1 pound (1 lb) = 16 oz = 454 g    1 kg = 2.2 lb

*Example 6*

Mary buys a 3 litre wine box.

Find the capacity of the wine box approximately in pints.

1 litre is approximately 1.75 pints so 3 litres is approximately
3 × 1.75 = 5.25 pints

*Example 7*

A signpost shows that the distance between two cities is 600 km. What is this distance in miles?

8 km = 5 miles
1 km = $\frac{5}{8}$ mile

So:        600 km = $\frac{5}{8}$ × 600 miles = 375 miles.

## Exercise 21G

1. A turkey weighs 6.4 kg.
   (a) What is the weight of the turkey in pounds, correct to two decimal places?
   (b) What is the weight of the turkey in pounds and ounces, correct to the nearest ounce?

2. In 1995, Jonathan Edwards set a world record for the triple jump of 18.29 metres.
   Convert this distance to feet and inches, correct to nearest tenth of an inch.

3. The Corner Stop garage sells unleaded petrol at 56.7 p per litre.
   Calculate the price of 1 gallon of this petrol, giving your answer correct to the nearest penny.

4. The distance from the Earth to the Sun is approximately 93 000 000 miles. Convert this distance to kilometres.

---

### Worked exam question 4

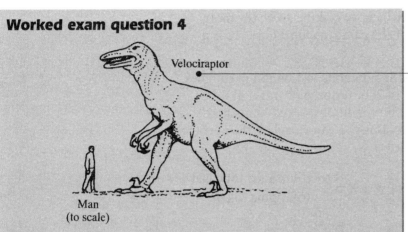

Velociraptor

Man
(to scale)

**Do:**
Estimate the height of the dinosaur in relation to the height of the man in the scale diagram

The scale diagram shows a man and a dinosaur called a velociraptor.

The man is 6 feet tall.

Estimate the height of the velociraptor.

(i) in feet,

> *velociraptor's height = 3 × man's height*
> *= 3 × 6 ft*
> *= 18 ft*

..........18.......... feet

(ii) in metres.

> *18 ft = 216 in*
> *= 216 × 2.54 cm*
> *= 548.64 cm*
> *= 5.5*
> *to one decimal place.*

**Do:**
Show your working

..........5.5.......... metres

(London)

## 21.9 Compound measures

Sometimes we can calculate a form of measure by multiplying or dividing two different forms of measure. For example, a car travels a certain distance in a certain time. *Distance* (or length) and *time* are two forms of measure.

When we divide them as $\dfrac{\text{distance travelled by the car}}{\text{time taken to travel}}$

or $\dfrac{\text{distance}}{\text{time}}$

we calculate a third measure, which we call the *speed* (or more correctly, the *average speed*) of the car. This third measure is a **compound measure**.

The coach journey from Bury St Edmunds to London is 80 miles. The coach makes the journey in $2\frac{1}{2}$ h. It does not travel at a constant speed, because of traffic conditions, speed limits and stopping to pick up passengers. But you can calculate the average speed of the coach on this journey.

$$\text{average speed of coach} = \frac{\text{total distance travelled}}{\text{total time taken}}$$
$$= \frac{80}{2.5}$$
$$= 32 \text{ miles per hour}$$

*Example 8*

The *Flying Scotsman* was a famous steam train that used to run between London and Edinburgh. The journey from London to Edinburgh was 393 miles, and the *Flying Scotsman* did this journey in 7 h 15 min.

Calculate the average speed of the *Flying Scotsman* on this journey, giving your answer in (a) miles per hour (b) kilometres per hour.

(a) average speed $= \dfrac{\text{distance}}{\text{time}}$

$$= \frac{393}{7.25} = 54.21 \text{ miles per hour (mph)}$$

correct to two decimal places.

(b) 1 mile = 1.6 km, and so 393 miles = 393 × 1.6 km = 628.8 km.

average speed $= \dfrac{\text{distance}}{\text{time}}$

$$= \frac{628.8}{7.25} = 86.73 \text{ kilometres per hour (km\,h}^{-1})$$

correct to two decimal places.

*Example 9*

Mary travels 180 km on her moped, which uses 6.75 litres of petrol during the trip.

Calculate the fuel consumption of the moped in kilometres per litre.

$$\text{fuel consumption} = \frac{\text{distance travelled}}{\text{amount of petrol used}}$$

$$= \frac{180}{6.75}$$

$$= 26.67 \text{ km per litre}$$

correct to two decimal places.

*Example 10*

The density of a substance is its mass per unit volume. That is,

$$\text{density} = \frac{\text{mass}}{\text{volume}}$$

A block of lead is a cube. The length of a side of the cube is 3 cm. The mass of the cube is 308 g.

Calculate the density of the lead.

The volume of the cube is $3 \times 3 \times 3 = 27 \text{ cm}^3$.

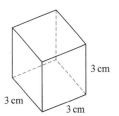

$$\text{density} = \frac{\text{mass}}{\text{volume}}$$

$$= \frac{308}{27}$$

$$= 11.4 \text{ grams per cm}^3$$

### Exercise 21H

1. An aeroplane travels a distance of 4800 km in 7.2 h. Calculate the average speed of the aeroplane.

2. A car travels at 45 mph for 1 h 20 min. Calculate the distance travelled by the car.

3. Roger runs a 1500 m race in 4 min 3.8 s. Calculate his average speed for the race in metres per second.

4. Jenny travelled from Perth to Liverpool by motorbike. the journey of 410 km took 5 h 45 min. Calculate her average speed, giving your answer (a) in kilometres per hour (b) in miles per hour.

5. Wesley runs 100 m in 9.95 s. Calculate his average speed in miles per hour.

6. A car travels 300 miles on 5 gallons of diesel. Calculate the fuel consumption of the car giving your answer
   (a) in miles per gallon
   (b) in kilometres per gallon
   (c) in kilometres per litre?

7. The mass of a gammon joint is 0.635 kg. The volume of the gammon joint is 485 cm³. Calculate the density of the gammon joint.

8. Estimate the density of your body.

9. A liquid has a density of 1.12 grams per cubic centimetre. Calculate the mass of 1 litre of this liquid.

## Worked exam question 5

In 1993, Noureddine Morcelli set a new world record for running the mile in 225 seconds.

Work out his average speed:

(i)   in miles per hour

(ii)  in metres per second.

(i)   $speed\ in\ mph = \dfrac{distance\ in\ miles}{time\ in\ hours}$ ●————— **Do:** Write this formula using miles and hours

$3600\ s = 1\ hour$

$225\ s = \dfrac{225}{3600} = 0.0625\ h$ ●————— Convert 225 secs to hours

$speed = \dfrac{1}{0.0625} = 16\ mph$

................ 16 mph ●——— Remember that distance = 1 mile

(ii)  $speed\ in\ metres\ per\ second = \dfrac{distance\ in\ metres}{time\ in\ seconds}$

$= \dfrac{1600}{225}$ ●—————— Remember that 1 mile ≈ 1600 metres

1 mile = 1760 yards
= 1760 × 3 feet
= 1760 × 3 × 12 inches
= 1760 × 3 × 12 × 2.54 cm
= 160 934.4 cm
= 1609.344 metres
but you do not need this level of accuracy

$= 7.11\ metres\ per\ second\ (to\ 2\ d.p.)$

................ $7.11\,ms^{-1}\ (to\ 2\ d.p.)$

## Exercise 211 (Mixed questions)

1. The signpost shows the distance from Lucea to Hightown as
   This distance is quoted correct to the nearest half mile.

   75 miles   HIGHTOWN

   (a) Write down:
       (i) the maximum distance from Lucea to Hightown.
       (ii) the minimum distance from Lucea to Hightown.
   (b) Convert 75 miles to kilometres.
   Mr Thomas travels the 75 miles from Lucea to Hightown in 1 hour 45 minutes.
   (c) Calculate Mr Thomas' average speed in:
       (i) miles per hour
       (ii) kilometres per hour
       (iii) metres per second.

2. The instructions for cooking a joint of gammon are:
   'Allow 50 minutes per kilogram and then an extra 30 minutes'.
   (a) Calculate the time required to cook a joint of gammon of weight 2.8 kg.
   (b) Calculate the maximum weight of a joint of gammon that can be cooked in 4 hours.

3. A brick is in the shape of a cuboid. The brick measures 22 cm by 10 cm by 7 cm. The brick weighs 4.1 kg. Calculate the density of the brick.

4. Mrs Wilson goes on a diet. She loses 7 kg in 6 weeks. Calculate her average weight loss per day.

5. The Jenkins family are on holiday in Germany. A signpost indicates that the distance to Munich is 200 kilometres.
   Convert 200 kilometres to miles.

**6.** A train travelled at a constant speed of 72 miles per hour for 2 hours and 10 minutes.
Calculate:
(a) the distance the train travelled in miles
(b) the distance the train travelled in kilometres.

**7.** Michael bought a wine pack which contained 3 litres of wine. Work out the volume of wine he bought:
(a) in gallons
(b) in pints.

## Test yourself

**1.** The distance between Preble and Lucea is recorded as 5.2 km, correct to one decimal place.

QUESTION    Write down (a) the shortest possible distance between Preble and Lucea, and (b) the longest possible distance between Preble and Lucea.

ANSWER    (a)   5.15 km
(b)   5.25 km

*If your answer is incorrect, review page 426, Section 21.3, Example 1 on approximating continuous measures.*

**2.** Christopher buys a fish tank. The dimensions of the tank are 91 cm × 32 cm × 35 cm.

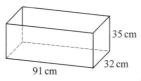

**PETS GALORE**
*TANKS NOW IN STOCK*
*2 feet, 3 feet, 4 feet or 5 feet*

*These sizes are the lengths of the tanks.*
length

Christopher bought the tank from a pet shop. He had a choice of four different sizes of tank.

QUESTION    (a)   Calculate the volume of the tank in cm³.
How many litres of water will the tank hold when full? (1000 cm³ = 1 litre)

ANSWER    Volume = 101 920 cm³    *If your answer is incorrect, review page 429, Section 21.5 on standard units of capacity.*
Water: 101.92 litres

QUESTION    (b)   Which size of tank did Christopher buy?

ANSWER    3 ft    *If your answer is incorrect, review page 434, Section 21.8 on imperial units.*

## Summary of key points to remember

**1.** Length, time and weight are **continuous** measures. (They can take *any* value on a continuous number line.)

Attendance at a football match, shoe size or runs scored in a cricket match are **discrete** measures. (They can only take distinct values.)

**2.** When the value of a continuous measure is given correct to the nearest unit, the actual value of that measure lies in the range from one half unit below to one half unit above the given value.

For example, if a length is given as 7 cm to the nearest centimetre, the actual length lies between 6.5 and 7.5 cm.

$6.5 \leqslant 7 < 7.5$

Here the **lower bound** 6.5 cm and the **upper bound** is 7.5 cm.

3.  The **metric units length, capacity** and **mass**.

- 1 km = 1000 m    • 1 litre = 1000 cm³    • 1 tonne = 1000 kg
  1 m  = 100 cm      1 litre = 1000 ml      1 kg   = 1000 g
  1 cm = 10 mm       1 litre = 100 cl       1 g    = 1000 mg

4.  You need to know the standard units of time:

60 s    = 1 minutes
60 min = 1 hour
24 h   = 1 day
1 year  = 365 days (366 in leap year)

and to know the non-standard units:

1 lunar month = 4 weeks

calendar months

> February 28 days (29 in leap year)
> April, June, September, November 30 days
> January, March, May, July, August, October, December 31 days

5.  The metric equivalents of some of the **imperial units** in current use in the UK.

| | | | |
|---|---|---|---|
| **1 mile** | **= 1.6 km** | **1 km** | **= $\frac{5}{8}$ mile** |
| **1 in** | **= 2.54 cm** | **1 m** | **= 39.37 in** |

| | | | |
|---|---|---|---|
| **1 gallon** | **= 4.55 litres** | | |
| **1 pint** | **= 0.57 litres** | **1 litre** | **= 1.75 pints** |
| **1 lb** | **= 0.454 kg** | **1 kg** | **= 2.2 lb** |
| **1 oz** | **= 28.35 g** | **100 g is approximately** | **$3\frac{1}{2}$ oz** |

6.  To estimate measures use sensible approximations.

7.  You get a **compound measure** when you multiply or divide two forms of measure. For example:

$$\text{average speed} = \frac{\text{total distance travelled}}{\text{total time taken}}$$

$$\text{density} = \frac{\text{mass}}{\text{volume}}$$

Check on the formulae sheet for your exam board to see whether you need to memorise these.

# 22 Accurate drawings

## 22.1 Introduction

In this unit you will be shown how to make full-size and scale drawings using lengths and angles. The unit covers the use of maps to find distances and three-figure bearings. It also involves calculating lengths in similar shapes and scale drawings.

## 22.2 Drawing accurately

In some shapes it is difficult to calculate the unknown lengths and angles. If you make an accurate drawing you can measure lengths and angles. For a large shape you can make a scale drawing and work out angles and lengths from it.

You could find the width CD of this river using a scale drawing. Start at A and look across at a fixed object such as a pole or tree at C. Find angle CAB (70°).

Then move 15 m along the river bank to B. Look across at C again and find angle CBA (80°).

Make a scale drawing of triangle ABC and draw CD at right angles to AB. Measure CD and convert it to a length in metres using the scale.

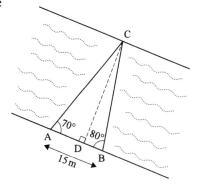

The answers obtained from drawings are accurate enough for many practical purposes, but they are not as accurate as calculated answers.

If a question states 'calculate' or 'work out' you must use a **calculation method**. You should not answer the question by drawing.

When you are given the three sides of a triangle you can construct the triangle accurately using compasses, a ruler and a sharp pencil.

When you are given angles you will also need a protractor.

When you are making an accurate drawing it is a good idea to make a rough sketch first.

A rough sketch helps you to plan your accurate drawing and gives you an idea of its shape. For a rough sketch you need not measure the lengths and the angles accurately, but make the biggest side look the longest and make the angles approximately the right size. Sometimes in exams the sketch is already drawn for you in the question.

When you make the accurate drawing it is usually best to
construct the longest side first.

### Example 1

Make an accurate drawing of triangle PQR with PQ = 6 cm, angle
P = 30° and angle Q = 70°.

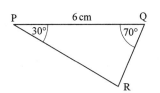

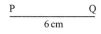  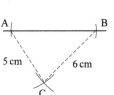 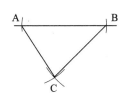

*Step 1:*

Draw a line
6 cm long and
label its ends
P and Q.

*Step 2:*

Place your
protractor over
the point P and
make a small mark
by the graduation
for 30°. Join the
mark to P.

*Step 3:*

In the same way,
draw the angle
of 70° at Q. The
point where the
lines from P and
Q cross is R.

*Step 4:*

Complete the
triangle PQR.

Leave in all the construction lines on your accurate drawing.
Do not rub them out.

### Example 2

Draw a triangle ABC with AB = 7 cm, BC = 6 cm and CA = 5 cm.

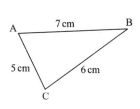

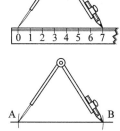 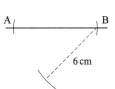

*Step 1:*

Draw the
longest side
first. Construct
a line 7 cm
long and label
its ends A and B.

*Step 2:*

Make the distance
between the point
and the pencil on
your compasses
(the radius) 6 cm.
Hold the compasses'
point at B and draw
an arc near where
you think C will be.

*Step 3:*

With centre A
and radius 5 cm
draw a second
arc. The point
C is where the
two arcs cross.

*Step 4:*

Join C to A
and B to
complete the
the triangle.

## Example 3

Construct triangle XYZ with XY = 5.3 cm, YZ = 8.5 cm and angle Y = 42°.

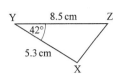

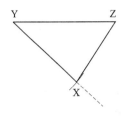

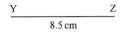

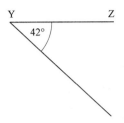

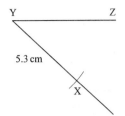

**Step 1:**

Draw the longest side, 8.5 cm, first and label it YZ.

**Step 2:**

At Y draw an angle of 42°.

**Step 3:**

With centre Y and radius 5.3 cm draw an arc across the line of the angle of 42°. Label this point X.

**Step 4:**

Join XZ to complete the triangle XYZ.

## Example 4

(a) Make an accurate drawing of quadrilateral ABCD with AB = 7.5 cm, AD = 4.3 cm, DC = 5.7 cm, BC = 6.2 cm and angle A = 108°.

(b) Measure angle BCD.

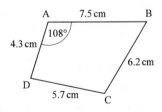

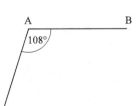

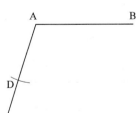

**Step 1:**

Make a rough sketch with the largest side, 7.5 cm, at the top. The vertices A, B, C and D should be in that order clockwise or anticlockwise around the quadrilateral.

**Step 2:**

Draw a line 7.5 cm long and label it AB.

**Step 3**

At A construct an angle of 108°.

**Step 4:**

With centre A and radius 4.3 cm draw an arc. Label the point D.

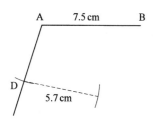
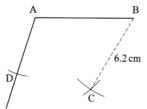
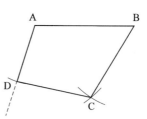
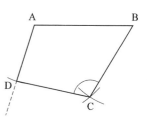

| *Step 5:* | *Step 6:* | *Step 7:* | *Step 8:* |
|---|---|---|---|
| Use centre D and radius 5.7 cm to draw an arc near where you expect C to be. | Use centre B and radius 6.2 cm to draw an arc near near where you expect C to be. | C is where the arcs in steps 5 and 6 meet. Join the points to form the quadrilateral ABCD. | Measure angle BCD. An answer of 109° is very accurate; but even 2° above or below this is good. |

---

### Exercise 22A

You will need compasses, a ruler and a protractor for this exercise.

**1.** Make accurate full size drawings of these triangles.

(a)

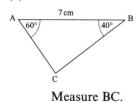

Measure BC.

(b)

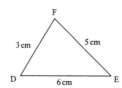

Measure angle E.

(c)

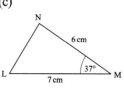

Measure NL.

(d)

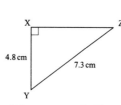

Measure angle Z.

**2.** (a) Make an accurate drawing of the quadrilateral ABCD:
(b) Measure angle BAD.

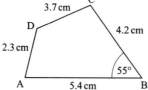

**3.** (a) Construct accurately the quadrilateral PQRS with PQ = 7.2 cm, QR = 4.5 cm, PS = 3.8 cm, angle P = 43° and angle Q = 64°.

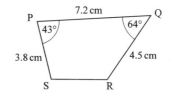

(b) Measure RS.

**4.**

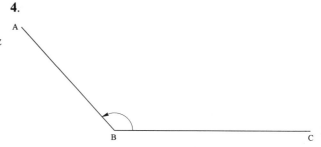

(a) Measure and write down the size of angle ABC. Copy the diagram accurately.
D is the point such that angle BCD is 102° and angle BAD is 68°.
(b) Mark the position of D on your diagram.    [London]

## 22.3 Three-figure bearings

To describe a **direction** you can use the compass bearings North, East, South and West.

Another method is to use three-figure bearings to give the angle measured clockwise from the north.

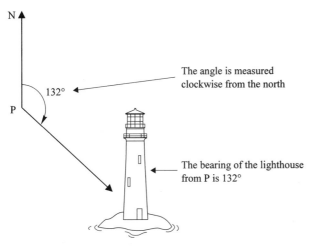

The angle is measured clockwise from the north

The bearing of the lighthouse from P is 132°

A **three-figure bearing** gives a direction in degrees. It is an angle measured clockwise from the North. As its name suggests, a three-figure bearing is always written with 3 figures (digits).

### *Example 5*

Write down the three-figure bearings of P from Q:

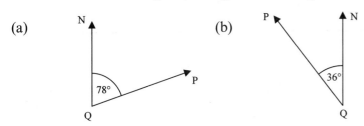

(a)   (b)

(a) The bearing of P from Q is 078°.

    (Note: the zero is included to make three digits.)

(b)

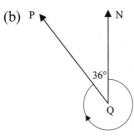

$360° - 36° = 324°$

The bearing of P from Q is 324°.

## Worked exam question 1

This diagram is not drawn to scale. It shows three airports $U$, $T$ and $V$. $V$ is due east of $U$. The angle $VUT$ is $30°$. The angle $UTV$ is $80°$.

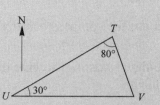

(a) What is the bearing of $T$ from $U$?

$90° - 30°$   *The bearing is 060°*

**Do:**
Calculate the angle between the North direction and UT

**Do:**
Put a nought in front of 60° because you are finding a three-figure bearing

(b) Calculate the angle $UVT$. You **must** show your working.

*Angle UVT + 30° + 80° = 180°*

*So angle UVT = 180° − 30° − 80° = 70°*

**Do:**
Use the fact that the angles of a triangle add up to 180° and show your working

(c) Calculate the bearing of $T$ from $V$.

*270° + 70° = 340°*

*The bearing of T from V is 340°*

**Remember:**
The angle for a bearing is measured from the North in a clockwise direction

(WJEC)

---

## Exercise 22B

You will need a protractor and squared paper for this exercise.

**1**. Write down the three-figure bearing of A from O:

(a)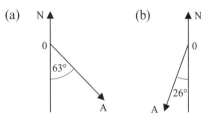

(b)

(c)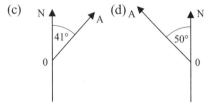

(d)

(e)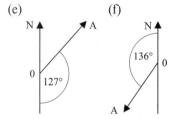

(f)

**2**. Draw diagrams like those in question **1** to illustrate these three-figure bearings:
(a) 065°   (b) 230°   (c) 150°   (d) 280°.

**3.** A map of an island is shown. Copy the map on to squared paper. At *H* there is a hotel and at *A* an airport.

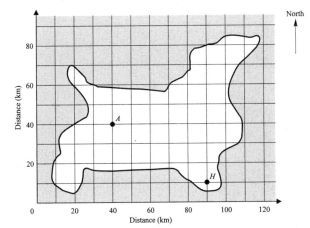

(a) A town, *T*, is due north of the hotel and on a bearing of 070° from the airport. Mark the position of *T* on the map.
(b) Measure and write down the 3-figure bearing of *A* from *H*.
(c) Use Pythagoras' theorem to calculate the distance from *A* to *H*. You must show your working. [SEG]

**4.** A map of part of the Mediterranean sea is shown.

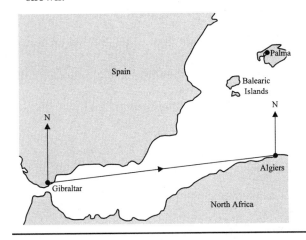

(a) A ship sails from Gibraltar to Algiers. The course is shown. On what bearing does the ship sail?
(b) Valencia is on the coast. The ship sails from Algiers on a bearing of 310° to Valencia. Mark the position of Valencia on the map. [SEG]

**5.** The diagram shows the positions of ancient monuments *P*, *Q* and *R*. *R* is due east of *P*. Angle PQR is 102° and angle RPQ is 47°.

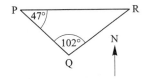

(a) What is the bearing of Q from P?
(b) Calculate angle PRQ.
(c) Calculate the three-figure bearing of Q from R.

**6.**

The diagram represents 2 points, *A* and *B* which are 60 m apart. *C* is the point such that the bearing of *C* from *A* is 040° and the bearing of *C* from *B* is 305°.
Copy the diagram. Make the line AB 7 cm long and at right angles to the north direction.
(a) Draw accurate lines to find the position of the point *C*. Mark the point with the letter *C*.
Fred is standing at *A*. He walks forward from *A* to *C*.
At *C* he turns to the right to face *B*.
(b) Calculate the angle through which Fred turns at *C*. [London]

# 22.4 Calculating with scales

When you use a map you are looking at a scale drawing.

If you want to work out how much carpet you need for a room you can draw a scale plan.

The *actual* distances between points are always the same multiple of the distances between the corresponding points on the scale drawing.

Corresponding angles remain the same.

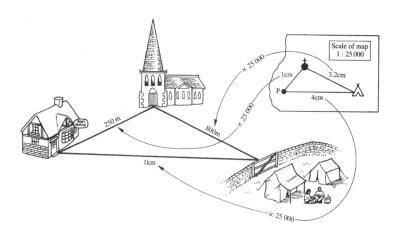

The scale 1 : 25 000 means that each distance on the map is multiplied by 25 000 to get the real distance.

The scale 4 cm represents 1 km means that a distance of 4 cm on the map represents a real distance of 1 km.

### Example 6

Lauren builds a scale model of a fire engine using a scale of 1 : 36

The length of the full size fire engine is 7.2 metres.

(a)  Calculate the length, in centimetres, of the model.

The top of the driver's cab on the model is 7.5 cm above the ground.

(b)  Work out the height, in metres, of the top of the full size cab above the ground.

(a) The real length is 7.2 metres = 7.2 × 100 cm = 720 cm

The length of the model is 720 ÷ 36 = 20 cm

(b) The real height of the cab is 7.5 cm × 36 = 270 cm = 2.7 m

### Example 7

The diagram represents the cross-section of the roof space of a house.

(a) Calculate the length AB, correct to 1 decimal place.

Badri makes a scale model of the house using a scale of 1 : 32. The height of the real house is 12.4 m.

(b) Calculate the height, in centimetres, of the scale model.

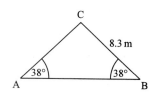

Draw in the height CD because triangle ABC is isosceles. Angle
BDC = 90°.

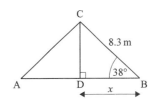

(a)  cosine $\theta = \dfrac{\text{adjacent}}{\text{hypotenuse}}$

$\cos 38° = \dfrac{x}{8.3}$

$8.3 \times \cos 38° = x$

$\qquad x = 6.5404$

So AB = $6.5404 \times 2 = 13.08\ldots$

$\qquad$ AB = 13.1 m (to 1 d.p.)

(b)  The height of the real house $\quad = 12.4$ m

$\qquad\qquad\qquad\qquad\qquad = 12.4 \times 100$ cm

$\qquad\qquad\qquad\qquad\qquad = 1240$ cm

Dividing by the scale factor:

Height of the scale model $\quad = 1240 \div 32$ cm

$\qquad\qquad\qquad\qquad\qquad = 38.75$ cm

---

## Worked exam question 2

A plan of a rectangular playing field is drawn using a scale of
1 : 2500. The width of the field on the plan is 5 cm.

(a)  (i)  Work out the real width of the field in centimetres.

$\qquad$ *Real width* = 5 *cm* × 2500

$\qquad\qquad\qquad$ =12 500 *cm*

$\qquad\qquad$ ...**12 500**... cm

**Do:**
Multiply by 2500 to convert the
plan measurement to the real
measurement

$\quad$ (ii)  Change your answer to metres.

$\qquad$ *Real width* = 12 500 ÷ 100 *m*

$\qquad\qquad\qquad$ =125 *m*

$\qquad\qquad$ ...**125**... m

**Do:**
Divide by 100 to change the
width in cm to metres

The area of the field on the plan is 31.5 cm².

(b)  (i)  Work out the length, in centimetres, of the playing
$\qquad$ field on the plan.

$\qquad$ *length* × *width* = *area of rectangle*

$\qquad\qquad$ *so* l ×5 = 31.5 *on the plan.*

$\qquad\qquad\qquad$ l = 31.5 ÷ 5 *cm*

$\qquad\qquad\qquad\qquad$ = 6.3 *cm*

$\qquad$ *The length of the playing field on the plan* = 6.3 cm

**Do:**
Use the area in cm² and the
width in cm

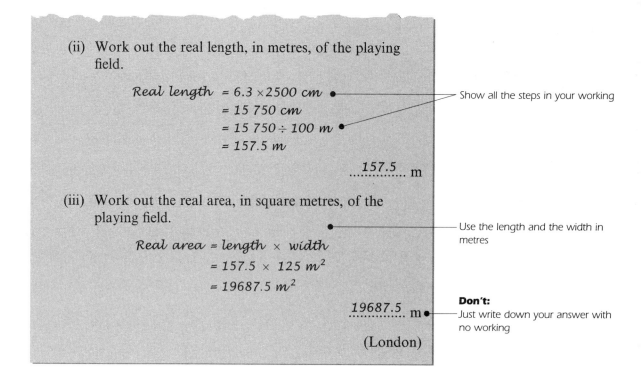

(ii) Work out the real length, in metres, of the playing field.

$$Real\ length = 6.3 \times 2500\ cm$$
$$= 15\ 750\ cm$$
$$= 15\ 750 \div 100\ m$$
$$= 157.5\ m$$

..........157.5...... m

*Show all the steps in your working*

(iii) Work out the real area, in square metres, of the playing field.

$$Real\ area = length \times width$$
$$= 157.5 \times 125\ m^2$$
$$= 19687.5\ m^2$$

..........19687.5...... m

*Use the length and the width in metres*

**Don't:**
*Just write down your answer with no working*

(London)

---

### Exercise 22C

You will need a ruler, a protractor and tracing paper for this exercise.

1. A model of a car is made to a scale of 1 : 20. The height of the model is 7 cm.
   Work out the height, in metres, of the full size car.

2. A map is drawn on a scale of 4 cm to 1 km.
   (a) Work out the real length of a lake which is 5.6 cm long on the map.
   (b) The distance between the youth hostel in Aleton and the post office in Barwick is 3.7 km.
   Work out the distance between them on the map.

3. The scale on a road map is 1 : 200 000.
   Lydney and Chepstow are 7 cm apart on the map.
   (a) Work out the real distance, in km, between Lydney and Chepstow.
   Frimley is 25 km in a straight line from Basingstoke.
   (b) Work out the distance of Frimley from Basingstoke on the map.

4. The diagram represents the tailfin of an aeroplane. $AB = 4.2$ metres and angle $ABC = 63°$.

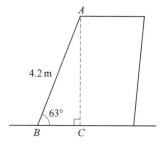

(a) Calculate the length $AC$.
Give your answer in metres correct to 2 decimal places.
Robin builds a scale model of the aeroplane using a scale of 1 : 72.
The length of the real aeroplane is 16.8 metres.
(b) Calculate the length, in centimetres, of the scale model.
Give your answer correct to one decimal place.                    [London]

# 22.5 Using maps

It can be helpful to use tracing paper to find angles and lengths on maps.

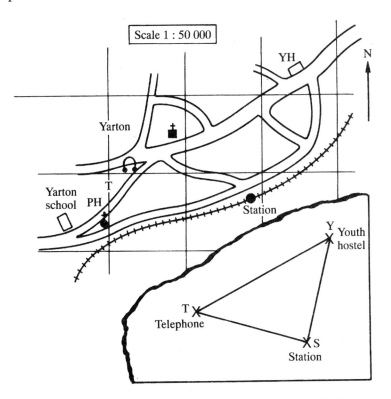

The simplified map shows some roads and landmarks in Yarton. You can use tracing paper to work out how far it is from the public telephone to the youth hostel.

*Step 1*: place tracing paper over the map. On the tracing paper mark the positions of the telephone, the youth hostel and the station with crosses.

Trace one of the grid lines in the North direction.

*Step 2*: remove the tracing paper from the map and join up T, Y and S.

*Step 3*: measure the distance TY. It should be 3.8 cm.

*Step 4*: using the scale, calculate the real distance:

$$3.8 \times 50\,000\,\text{cm} = 190\,000\,\text{cm} = 19\,000 \div 100\,\text{m}$$
$$= 1900\,\text{m}$$
$$= 1900 \div 1000\,\text{km} = 1.9\,\text{km}$$

So the youth hostel is 1.9 km from the public telephone.

You can find the three-figure bearing of the station from the telephone.

*Step 5*: On your tracing draw a line through T parallel to the North line. The three-figure bearing is the angle measured clockwise from the North, which is angle NTS.

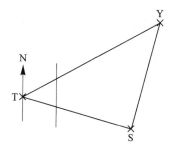

*Step 6*: use a protractor to measure NTS. It should be 107°.

So the three-figure bearing of the station from the telephone is 107°.

If you walked from the telephone for 1200 metres on a bearing of 230°, where would you end up?

*Step 7*: 230° − 180° = 50° so on your tracing draw a line at T making an angle of 50° with the South direction.

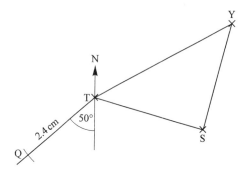

*Step 8*: 1200 metres = 12 000 cm

On the map this is represented by 120 000 ÷ 50 000 = 2.4 cm

Mark a point Q, 2.4 cm along the line from T.

*Step 9*: Place your tracing over the map again, so that the crosses coincide with the places on the map. You should find that Q is over Yarton School. (What if you had only walked 800 metres?)

### Example 8

(a) Use the map opposite to work out

   (i)   the distance, in kilometres, between the railway station at Foxton and the railway station at Shepreth

   (ii)  the three-figure bearing of Shepreth station from the station at Foxton.

(b) A balloon is blown 3 km from Foxton station on a bearing of 284°. The balloon then bursts. Where is the balloon when it bursts?

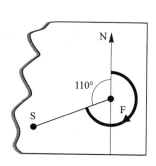

(a)   (i)   The distance on the map between the stations is 3.2 cm.

   So the real distance is 3.2 × 50 000 = 160 000 cm

   160 000 ÷ 100 m = 1600 m

   1600 ÷ 1000 km = 1.6 km.

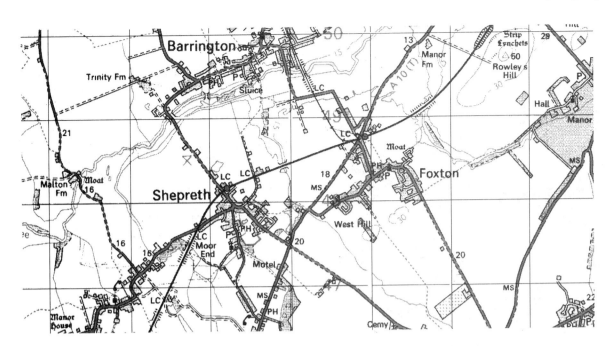

The scale on the map is 1 : 50 000.

(ii) On tracing paper mark the positions of the two stations and join them with a straight line. Draw a North line at Foxton station.

Using a protractor, angle NFS measures 110°.

So the bearing of Shepreth station from Foxton station is 360° − 110° = 250°

(b) A real distance of 3 km = 300 000 cm. This is represented by 300 000 ÷ 50 000 cm = 6 cm on the map.

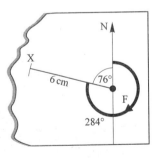

The bearing of 284° is measured clockwise from North, so it is in the same direction as a line making an angle of 360° − 284° = 76° anticlockwise from the North.

On tracing paper mark Foxton station F, and draw a North line. Draw a line making an angle of 76° with NF. Mark a point X on the line 6 cm from F.

Place the tracing paper on the map with F over Foxton station and FN parallel to the north-south grid lines. The point X is over Trinity Farm.

So the balloon bursts when it is over Trinity Farm.

## Exercise 22D

1.

The scale on the map is 1 : 50 000.
Ann walks along the Lanchester Valley Walk
from the point marked A on the map to the
point marked B.
Use the map to work out:
(a) the three-figure bearing of B from A
(b) the distance, in metres, from A to B.
Ron flies his helicopter from the point marked C
on the map.
He lands after he has flown 2.4 km on a bearing
of 043°.
(c) Where does Ron land his helicopter?

2.

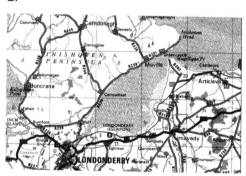

The scale on the map is 1 : 800 000

Maureen flies a jet plane in a straight line from
Londonderry (Eglinton) airport. After a short
time she is above the lighthouse at Inishowen
Head on the coast.
(a) Work out:
 (i) the distance in km
(ii) the three-figure bearing of the lighthouse at
     Inishowen Head from Londonderry
     (Eglinton) airport.
Saleem flies his light aircraft from the same
airport on a bearing of 307°.
(b) What is he above after he has travelled
    21 km?

3. The scale on the map is 2 cm to 1 km. Work out:
   (a) the distance in km
   (b) the three-figure bearing of
       New Farm from Thornberry Hill farm.
       The two farms are marked with crosses on
       the map.

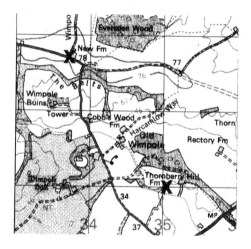

# 22.6 Accurate scale drawings

Before you can make a scale drawing of a real life situation you must convert all the lengths using the scale. Angles on the scale drawing remain the same as the corresponding angles on the real shape.

Remember to make a rough sketch before you make the accurate drawing.

### Example 9

Here is a sketch of a school field. The fence CB is in a North–south direction.

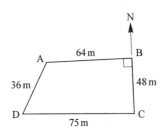

(a) Make a scale drawing of the field, using a scale of 1 cm to 20 metres.

(b) Measure angle BCD

(c) Work out the three-figure bearing of D from C.

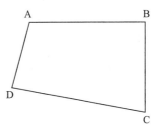

(a) A real distance of 64 m is represented by $64 \div 20 = 3.2$ cm in the scale drawing.

Using the same method, in the scale drawing BC = 2.4 cm, DC = 3.75 cm and AD = 1.8 cm.

The angle ABC is still 90° in the scale drawing.

(b) Angle BCD = 80°

(c) The three-figure bearing of D from C is $360° - 80° = 280°$.

---

### Exercise 22E

You will need compasses, a ruler and a protractor for this exercise.

1. The diagram represents the cross section of a small garden shed.

   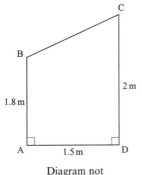

   Diagram not drawn to scale

   (a) Give the mathematical name for the shape ABCD.
   (b) Make an accurate scale drawing of the cross section ABCD. Use a scale of 10 cm to represent 1 metre.

   (c) From your scale drawing, measure and write down
       (i) the length of BC,
       (ii) the size of the angle ABC.
   (d) Calculate the area of the cross section of the shed.                    [London]

2. Witley is 2 km due south of Milford. The bearing of Hydestile from Milford is 125° and the distance from Milford to Hydestile is 2.8 km.
   (a) Make a scale drawing to show these three villages.
       Use a scale of 1 : 25 000.
   (b) Use your drawing to find:
       (i) the distance of Hydestile from Witley
       (ii) the bearing of Hydestile from Witley.

**3.** The diagram shows the positions of five villages *P*, *Q*, *R*, *S* and *T*.
The distance, in miles, between villages is shown. *P* is due north of *T*, *Q* is on a bearing of 080° from *P* and *S* is on a bearing 110° from *T*.

(a) Use a scale of 1 cm to 1 mile to show the positions of the five villages.

(b) A rubbish tip is to be sited on land between the villages.

It must be at least 5 miles from any village. Shade the region on the diagram where the tip could be sited.    [SEG]

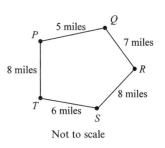

Not to scale

---

## 22.7 Similar shapes

In Unit 16 you met the idea of similar shapes.

Two shapes are mathematically **similar** when:

● one shape is an enlargement of the other shape.

● all the corresponding angles are equal.

● all the corresponding lengths are in the same ratio.

Similar shapes have the *same shape*.

Shape **P** is enlarged by the scale factor 3 to give the similar shape **Q**. A scale drawing of a shape is similar to the original shape.

A scale drawing is an enlargement of the original shape with a fractional scale factor (the scale factor is a fraction less than 1).

The scale drawing **B** is an enlargement of shape **A** with a scale factor of $\frac{2}{5}$.

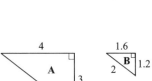

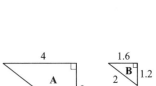

*Example 10*

PRT and QRS are straight lines. PQ is parallel to ST.

(a) Explain why triangle PQR and triangle TSR are similar.

(b) Calculate the lengths of (i) PR (ii) ST

(a) PQ is parallel to ST

So angle P = angle T (*alternate angles*)

and angle Q = angle S (*alternate angles*)

Also angle PRQ = angle TRS (*vertically opposite angles*)

The angles of triangle PQR are equal to the corresponding angles of triangle TSR so the triangles are the same shape and are similar.

(b) (i)  QR (= 4 cm) and RS (= 5 cm) are corresponding lengths as they are opposite the equal angles P and T. So triangle PQR is an enlargement of triangle TSR with scale factor $\frac{4}{5}$.

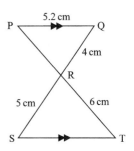

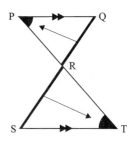

PR corresponds to TR (they are opposite equal angles)

So PR $= \frac{4}{5} \times 6\,\text{cm} = \frac{24}{5}\,\text{cm} = 4.8\,\text{cm}$

(ii) Triangle TSR is an enlargement of triangle PQR with a scale factor of $\frac{5}{4}$.

ST corresponds to QP (they are opposite equal angles)

So ST $= \frac{5}{4} \times 5.2\,\text{cm} = \frac{26}{4}\,\text{cm} = 6.5\,\text{cm}$

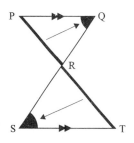

## Worked exam question 3

All of these triangles are similar.

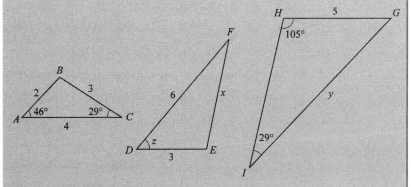

(a) Calculate the length $x$.

It is given that triangle ABC and triangle DEF are similar.

Ratio of shortest sides $= \dfrac{DE}{AB} = \dfrac{3}{2}$ •

Ratio of longest sides $= \dfrac{DF}{AC} = \dfrac{6}{4} = \dfrac{3}{2}$ •

**Do:**
Find which sides of the two similar triangles are corresponding

So triangle DEF is an enlargement of triangle ABC with a scale factor of $\dfrac{3}{2}$

EF and BC are corresponding lengths

So $x = \dfrac{3}{2} \times BC = \dfrac{3}{2} \times 3 = \dfrac{9}{2}$ •

Multiply the length of BC by the scale factor

$x = 4\dfrac{1}{2}$

$x = 4\dfrac{1}{2}$
..................

(b) Calculate the length $y$.

It is given that triangle ABC and triangle GHI are similar.

GH corresponds to AB because they are both opposite an angle of 29°. ●————————————

**Do:**
Find which sides of the two similar triangles are corresponding

So triangle GHI is an enlargement of triangle ABC with a scale factor of $\dfrac{GH}{AB} = \dfrac{5}{2}$

GI corresponds to AC (they are both opposite an angle of 105°)

So $y = \dfrac{5}{2} \times AC = \dfrac{5}{2} \times 4 = \dfrac{20}{2}$ ●————————

Multiply the length of AC by the scale factor

$y = 10$

...........$y = 10$...........

(c) What is the value of angle $z$?

Angle D in triangle DEF is opposite the side EF and angle A in triangle ABC is opposite the corresponding side BC.

So angle D corresponds to angle A

So angle D = angle A = 46° ●————————

**Remember:**
In similar shapes corresponding angles are equal

$z = 46°$

...........$z = 46°$...........

[SEG]

---

## Exercise 22F

1. Triangle PQR is similar to triangle ABC.
   PR = 6 cm, PQ = 12 cm, AC = 2 cm and angle QPR = 60°.

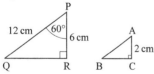

   (a) Write down the size of angle BAC.
   (b) Work out the length of AB.

2. Two similar steam engines, shown below and opposite, are cut out of a piece of card.

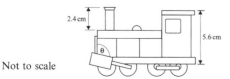

   Not to scale

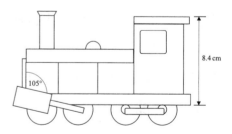

   Not to scale

   (a) Calculate the height of the funnel on the larger steam engine.
   (b) The circumference of a wheel on the larger steam engine is 5.7 cm. Calculate the circumference of the same wheel on the smaller steam engine.
   (c) What is the size of the angle marked $\theta$ on the smaller steam engine?          [SEG]

**3.** The width and depth of
a Small size packet of
pet food are 9 cm and
4.2 cm.
The Regular size is an
enlargement of the
Small size.
The width and height
of the Regular size are
15 cm and 10 cm.

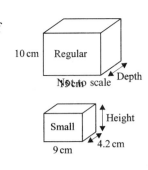

(a) Calculate the height
of the Small packet.
(b) Calculate the depth of the Regular
packet.                               [SEG]

**4.** In each pair of similar figures calculate the
marked lengths. *Remember*: angles marked in
the same way are equal

(a)

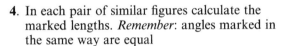

(b)

12 cm
9 cm
4 cm
*b*

(c)

7.5 cm
*c*
6 cm   4 cm
*d*   6 cm

(d)

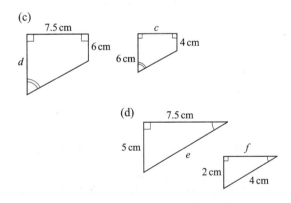

7.5 cm
5 cm
*e*
*f*
2 cm
4 cm

**5.** A school badge is made in two sizes.
The width of the small size is 3 cm.
The large size is an enlargement of the small size
in the ratio 2 : 3.

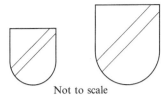

Not to scale

Calculate the width of the large size
badge.                                [SEG]

**6.** In the diagram TQ is parallel to SR.

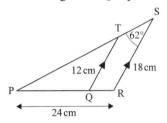

(a) Write down the size of angle PTQ.
(b) Work out the length of PQ.

**7.** The height of a cone is 32 cm and the diameter
of the base is 28.8 cm. The cone is cut parallel to
its base to make a smaller cone. The height of
the smaller cone is 24 cm.

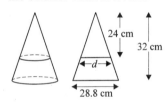

Calculate the diameter of the base of the smaller
cone.

---

### Exercise 22G (Mixed questions)

You will need a ruler and a protractor for this
exercise.

**1.** In the diagram, shown opposite, CD = 4 metres,
CE = 3 metres and BC = 5 metres.
AB is parallel to DE.
ACE and BCD are straight lines.

(a) Explain why
triangle ABC is
similar to
triangle EDC.
(b) Calculate the
length of AC.

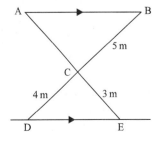

[London]

2. A roof has a symmetrical frame, with dimensions as shown.

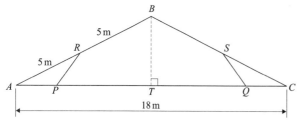

Not to scale

$AB = BC$, $PR = AP$, angle $ATB = 90°$.
(a) (i) Write down a triangle which is similar to triangle $ABC$.
   (ii) Calculate the length $PR$.
(b) Calculate the value of angle $BAT$.    [SEG]

3. The diagram below shows a bay in which yachts are moored.
The diagram has been drawn to a scale of 1 cm to 400 m.

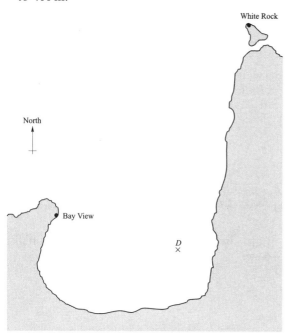

Make a tracing of the diagram.
(a) The yacht 'Daresa' is moored at $D$.
   Measure the bearing of this yacht from Bay View.
(b) The yacht 'Wet-n-Windy' is moored 1.2 km from White Rock on a bearing of 210°.
   Mark with a cross the position of this yacht on your diagram.

4. A child builds a tower from three similar cylindrical blocks.
The smallest block, $A$, has radius 2.5 cm and height 6 cm.
(a) Find the volume of the smallest block.

(b) Block $B$ is an enlargement of $A$ and block $C$ is an enlargement of $B$, each with a scale factor of $1\frac{3}{4}$. Find the total height of the tower.    [MEG]

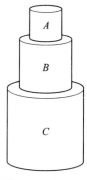

Not to scale

5. This diagram shows the badge of the Crossed-wires Society. $BE$ is perpendicular to $AD$. The length of $BE$ is 4 centimetres.

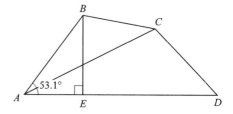

Angle $BAE$ is 53.1°.
(a) Calculate the length of side $AB$.
(b) Triangles $ABC$ and $ACD$ are similar.
   The length of $AC$ is 8 centimetres.
   Calculate the length of $AD$.    [WJEC]

6.

The diagram shows how an ironing board is supported by two legs $AOB$ and $COD$. The legs are hinged at $O$, and $C$ is hinged to the ironing board.
The distance between $A$ and $C$ can be varied.
(a) (i) When angle $BOD = 80°$, work out the size of angle $OBD$.
   (ii) What facts about angles did you use?
(b) The ironing board is placed on a horizontal floor and adjusted so that $BD = 92$ cm.
   (i) Use Pythagoras' theorem to calculate the height of $O$ above the floor.
   (ii) Use similar triangles to calculate the distance $AC$.
   (iii) Calculate the size of angle $OBD$.

**6.** (c) The ironing board is adjusted again so that
       *AC* is 90 cm above the floor.
       Calculate the height of *O* above the
       floor.                                    [MEG]

**7.** Cheese-wedge &
    Co. sells cheeses
    which are always
    shaped as right-
    angled triangular
    prisms with height,
    width and length in
    the ratio 3 : 4 : 7.
    The cheeses are
    named according to their heights.

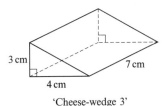

'Cheese-wedge 3'
Not to scale

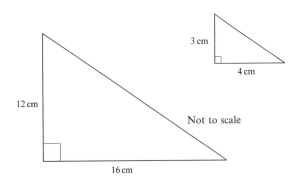

3 cm

4 cm

12 cm

16 cm

Not to scale

A 'Cheese-wedge 3' has height 3 cm, width 4 cm
and length 7 cm.
A 'Cheese-wedge 6' has height 6 cm, width 8 cm
and length 14 cm.
(a) Calculate the volume of a 'Cheese-wedge 3'.
(b) Calculate the total surface area of a 'Cheese-
    wedge 6'.

(c) The diagram above shows the triangular end
    faces of a 'Cheese-wedge 12' and a 'Cheese-
    wedge 3'.
    (i) How many small triangles can be cut
        from the large triangle?
    (ii) How many 'Cheese-wedge 3s' can be
        made from a 'Cheese-wedge 12'?   [MEG]

## Test yourself

**1.** The map shows part of the sea off the coast of South Australia
    and Kangaroo Island.

SOUTH
AUSTRALIA

N

Port
Adelaide

Kingscote

KANGAROO ISLAND

**QUESTION**   A ship sails from Port Adelaide to Kingscote. The course of the ship is shown.
            On what bearing does the ship sail?

**ANSWER**    222° (Between 221° and 223°)   *If your answer is not within 1° of 222° review page
                                            445, Section 22.3 on three-figure bearings.*

**2.** A scale drawing of a room has a scale of 1 : 40.

**QUESTION**   (a)   On the scale drawing, the distance between two chairs is 8 cm.
                  What is the actual distance between these chairs?          [WJEC]

**ANSWER**    (a)   3.2 metres            *If your answer is incorrect review page 447, Section
                                        22.4 on calculating with scales.*

QUESTION   (b)   The actual length of the room is 12 m.
                 Find, in cm, the length of the room on the scale drawing.        [WJEC]

ANSWER     (b)   30 cm                    *If your answer is incorrect review page 447, Section*
                                          *22.4 on calculating with scales.*

---

3.  In the diagram NO = 2 cm, LN = 7 cm and MN = 5 cm.
    LM is parallel to OP. LNP and MNO are straight lines.

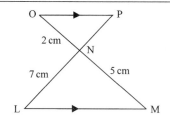

---

QUESTION   Calculate the length of NP.

ANSWER     2.8 cm                         *If your answer is incorrect review page 456, Section*
                                          *22.7 on similar shapes.*

## Summary of key points to remember

1.  If a question states 'calculate' or 'work out' you must use a **calculation method**. You should not answer the question by drawing.

2.  When you are making an accurate drawing it is a good idea to make a rough sketch first.

3.  Leave in all the construction lines on your accurate drawing. Do not rub them out.

4.  A three-figure bearing gives a direction in degrees. It is an angle measured clockwise from the north.

5.  You can use tracing paper to find bearings and lengths on maps.

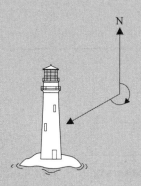

6.  Two shapes are mathematically **similar** when:

    • one shape is an enlargement of the other shape.

    • all the corresponding angles are equal.

    • all the corresponding lengths are in the same ratio.

    Similar shapes have the same shape.

7.  A scale drawing of a shape is similar to the original shape.

    Shape **P** is enlarged by the scale factor 3 to give the similar shape **Q**.

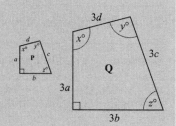

8. A scale drawing is an enlargement of the original shape with a fractional scale factor (the scale factor is a fraction less than 1).

The scale drawing **B** is an enlargement of shape **A** with a scale factor of $\frac{2}{5}$.

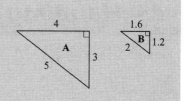

# 23 Handling data

## 23.1 What is handling data?

Handling data is a branch of statistics. Statistics is about collecting data, displaying the data and then looking at the data for patterns and trends. Many businesses use statistics to help predict things that may happen in the future. For example, insurance companies use statistics to calculate insurance premiums.

Statistics are also used in keeping records of sporting events, for example, statistical charts and records of the Olympic events over the years.

Statistics is a very important branch of mathematics and is always tested at GCSE.

This unit will show you how to design data capture sheets and questionnaires, and design and test hypotheses.

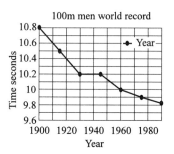

## 23.2 Data capture sheets for single items

A **data capture sheet** is any chart or form that you use to collect data. A simple data capture sheet is a **tally chart**.

This tally chart has been designed to collect data on how students get to college.

How students travel to college

| Method | Tally | Frequency |
|---|---|---|
| walk | \|\| | 2 |
| bus | ⌗ | 5 |
| train | ⌗ \|\|\|\| | 9 |
| bicycle | \|\|\|\| | 4 |
| motorbike | ⌗ \|\| | 7 |
| car | ⌗ ⌗ \|\|\| | 13 |

The frequency is the total number of students for each method of getting to college.

The tally column uses 'five bar gates' ⫴ to represent five. This makes it easy to collect the information and also easy to count the total for each method.

## Example 1

Design a simple data capture sheet for collecting information of the type of pets people have.

Type of pets survey

| Type of pet | Tally | Frequency |
|---|---|---|
| cat | | |
| dog | | |
| rabbit | | |
| fish | | |
| guinea pig | | |
| hamster | | |
| mouse | | |
| other | | |

## Example 2

30 students were asked their favourite colour. Their answers are listed below.

Draw up and complete a simple data capture sheet for this data.

blue, red, white, blue, green, blue, black, red,
blue, yellow, green, blue, blue, black, red, blue,
red, green, blue, blue, blue, black, red, blue,
yellow, red, blue, green, black, blue

Draw up a tally chart and use the five bar gates to add up the totals for each colour.

Favourite colour survey

| Colour | Tally | Frequency |
|---|---|---|
| blue | ⧼HHt HHt III⧽ | 13 |
| red | ⧼HHt I⧽ | 6 |
| green | IIII | 4 |
| yellow | II | 2 |
| black | IIII | 4 |
| white | I | 1 |
| | Total | 30 |

A total row is added here so that you can check that the frequencies add up to 30.

### Exercise 23A

1. Design a simple data capture sheet to find out the number of cars of different colours passing your home.

2. Design a simple data capture sheet to find out the favourite sport of people in your neighbourhood.

3. Design a simple data capture sheet to find out which newspapers your friends and neighbours read.

4. The scores in 15 football matches are listed opposite.
   Draw up and complete a simple data capture sheet for the number of goals scored in these matches.

| | | | | |
|---|---|---|---|---|
| 1–0 | 2–2 | 0–2 | 3–1 | 0–2 |
| 1–1 | 2–0 | 4–2 | 6–1 | 0–1 |
| 2–1 | 3–2 | 3–4 | 1–1 | 0–0 |

5. A survey was carried out to find the months in which people were born. The results were:

| | | | | | | | |
|---|---|---|---|---|---|---|---|
| July | Jan | Feb | Dec | Nov | Jan | June | April |
| May | Feb | April | Oct | Sept | June | Feb | Mar |
| Dec | July | Aug | Jan | April | Oct | Jan | May |
| Sept | Jan | Jan | Oct | Dec | Jan | Nov | Oct |
| Feb | Oct | Sept | Jan | May | Aug | Feb | Mar |

Draw and complete a tally chart for this information.

## 23.3 Data capture sheet for multiple items

Sometimes you may need to collect more than one piece of information. For example, you could collect information on height, weight and age at one time.

You can design a data capture sheet to collect data for more than one piece of information for each item.

*Example 3*

Design a data capture sheet to collect information on people in your family.

In questions like this you have to decide what information to collect.

| Name | David Irving |
|---|---|
| sex | male |
| shoe size | 9 |
| height | 1.86 m |
| age | 36 |
| colour of eyes | blue |

*Note*:

• You will need a data capture sheet for each person.

- You could collect the information in each category into a tally chart. For eye colour the tally chart would be:

| Colour of eyes | Tally | Frequency |
|---|---|---|
| blue | | |
| green | | |
| grey | | |
| other | | |

---

### Exercise 23B

1. Design a data capture sheet to collect information about people and their work. Include things like holidays, hours, name of employer, etc.

2. Design a data capture sheet for one of the following:
   (a) friends and colleagues: their names, likes, dislikes, job, telephone number, etc.
   (b) newspapers: cost, size, colour, number of sports pages, etc.
   (c) countries: their population, climate, agriculture, industry, etc.

---

## 23.4 Databases

A **database** is a collection of information.

Databases allow you to search and retrieve information that you need.

A telephone directory is an example of a database that you can search manually for information.

Computer databases allow you to search for and retrieve information very quickly.

### Worked exam question 1

Data about fruit trees has been entered into a computer database.

The computer database has been asked to print out details of fruit which is harvested from June to October.

| Crop | Form of tree | Space in metres between plants | Time in years before full grown | Harvest time |
|---|---|---|---|---|
| Apple | Bush | 3 | 3–4 | Aug–Oct |
| Apple | Cordon | 1 | 2–5 | Aug–Oct |
| Apple | Standard | 6 | 5–8 | Aug–Oct |
| Blackberry | Fan or rod | 3 | 2–3 | Aug–Sep |
| Cherry | Fan | 4.5 | 4–5 | Jun–Sep |
| Cherry | Standard | 7.5 | 5–7 | Jun–Sep |
| Gooseberry | Bush | 1.8 | 3–4 | Jun–Jul |
| Gooseberry | Cordon | 0.75 | 2–3 | Jun–Jul |
| Pear | Cordon | 1 | 3–4 | Aug–Oct |
| Pear | Espalier | 4.5 | 4–5 | Aug–Oct |
| Pear | Dwarf | 1 | 4–5 | Aug–Oct |
| Plum | Bush | 5 | 3–5 | Aug–Oct |
| Plum | Fan | 5 | 3–6 | Aug–Oct |

(a) Which crop has a space of 7.5 metres between plants?

*Cherry*

(b) Name the crop and form of tree which is planted with a space of 4.5 m between plants and can also be harvested in October.

*Pear Espalier* •

(London)

**Do:**
Find the trees that need a 4.5 m space. Then find which of these can be harvested in October

State both crop and tree

## Exercise 23C

Here is a computer database for cars for sale at a garage.

| Year | Registration | Make | Model | Colour | Mileage | Price |
|------|-------------|------|-------|--------|---------|-------|
| 1994 | M | Rover | 214Si | Red | 7500 | 7995 |
| 1992 | K | Austin | Maestro 1.3 | Blue | 21500 | 4750 |
| 1991 | J | Ford | Sapphire 1.6 | White | 41000 | 3995 |
| 1985 | B | Vauxhall | Astra 1.3 | Green | 78000 | 995 |
| 1994 | L | VM | Golf 1.8 | Red | 12000 | 8995 |
| 1992 | K | BMW | 320i | White | 46000 | 8750 |
| 1988 | E | Mazda | RX7 | Black | 67000 | 2950 |
| 1995 | N | Vauxhall | Corsa 1.2 | Blue | 5000 | 7295 |
| 1994 | M | Citroen | AX10 | White | 14000 | 5750 |
| 1995 | M | Ford | Escort 1.8 | Red | 11000 | 7999 |
| 1991 | J | Fiat | Panda 750L | Blue | 52000 | 2695 |
| 1992 | K | Nissan | Primera 1.6 | Red | 37000 | 5995 |
| 1995 | N | Ford | Fiesta 1100LX | Red | 9800 | 6495 |
| 1995 | N | Peugeot | 306XL | White | 6000 | 9795 |
| 1993 | L | Mazda | 626 | Black | 30000 | 7995 |
| 1989 | G | Austin | Montego | Red | 63000 | 3995 |

1. How many cars are:
   (a) black    (b) Ford    (c) year 1992
   (d) on sale for more than £7000?

2. (a) Which car is the most expensive?
   (b) Which car has the lowest mileage?
   (c) Which cars are the newest?
   (d) Which cars have recorded mileages of less than 2000?
   (e) What is the current stock of Vauxhalls?

3. Lucy wants to buy a blue car, with an L registration.
   List the cars available.

4. Joseph buys a 1995 red car with mileage less than 30 000.
   Which car is this?

5. Jessica wants to buy a black, red or blue car with mileage less than 40 000 and M registration.
   Which car could she buy?

## 23.5 Types of data

There are two types of data.

- Eye colour is an example of qualitative data. **Qualitative data** can only be described in words and falls into categories.

- Data that takes numerical values is called **quantitative data**. Quantitative data can be either discrete or continuous.

Shoe size is an example of discrete data.

**Discrete data** can only take certain values. These are usually whole numbers but may sometimes be fractions or decimals.

Height is an example of continuous data.

**Continuous data** has no exact value. It is measured within a certain range and can take any value in this range.

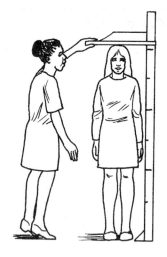

*Example 4*

State whether the following data are qualitative or quantitative. For quantitative data state whether they are discrete or continuous.

(a) Number of passengers in an aircraft

(b) Weight of people in a lift

(c) The way people travel to work

(d) Temperature in London at midday during July 1994

(e) The number of apples in a bag

(a) quantitative discrete      (b) quantitative continuous

(c) qualitative                (d) quantitative continuous

(e) quantitative discrete

---

### Exercise 23D

State whether the following data are qualitative or quantitative. For quantitative data state also whether they are discrete or continuous.
(a) Number of goals scored in netball match
(b) Time taken to get to work
(c) The population of Liverpool
(d) Types of car
(e) The width of an aeroplane's wings
(f) The number of spectators at a cricket match

---

## 23.6 Questionnaires

You can use a questionnaire when you want to find out people's opinions on an issue. You can also use a questionnaire to test a hypothesis.

A **hypothesis** is a general statement which needs data to justify it. For example, your hypothesis might be 'Adults think that everybody should learn to drive'.

Other examples of hypotheses are:

people prefer tea to coffee

people would rather travel by train than by car

To test a hypothesis you need to design a questionnaire and carry out a survey. A questionnaire should:

- ask short questions, that have either 'yes' or 'no' answers, or should give a choice of answers.

- be in a logical sequence.

- provide tick boxes so that questions can be answered easily.

- demonstrate that you have taken bias into account when constructing it by

  ■ not asking leading questions that invite certain responses.

  For example, 'You do think people should learn to drive, don't you?' is a leading question. It leads people to answer 'yes'.

  A better way of asking the question is

  Should all adults learn to drive?'

  Yes ☐                    No ☐

  ■ making sure you have a representative sample by choosing people from different age groups and of different genders.

  You should also consider other things. For example, for the hypothesis 'Adults think that everybody should learn to drive' you should not ask only driving instructors for their opinion, as this is not fair and does not represent everybody's views.

Here is a questionnaire to test the hypothesis 'People think that everybody should learn to drive'.

| | |
|---|---|
| Tick one box for each question. | |
| **1**  Gender | **2**  Age    16–21  ☐ |
|      Male    ☐ |        22–35  ☐ |
|      Female  ☐ |        36–50  ☐ |
| | over 50  ☐ |
| **3**  Should everybody learn to drive?    Yes  ☐ | |
| | No  ☐ |

The questionnaire should be given to a sample of at least 50 people over 16 years old. The first two questions prompt you to ask these questions of people of either sex and from different age groups. This helps to ensure that the sample is random and not biased to gender or age.

If you ask 50 people the question, then the hypothesis 'People think that everybody should learn to drive' should only be accepted if at least 30 people agreed with it.

You could use statistical charts and diagrams, such as pie charts or bar charts, to show the responses for the whole group or by gender or by age.

---

**Worked exam question 2**

Nadia wants to find out which computer games people play.

She has designed a questionnaire with only boxes to tick.

> ## QUESTIONNAIRE: COMPUTER GAMES
>
> 1.  Do you have a computer game at home?   | YES | NO |
>
> 2.  Tick the computer you have games for:
>
>     [ ]      [ ]      [ ]
>     *ZEGA*   *SAMURI*   *PC*
>
> 3.  Tick the type of computer game you like the best:
>
>     [ ]       [ ]        [ ]        [ ]        [ ]
>     *Arcade*  *Shoot'em*  *Fantasy*  *Factual*  *Educational*
>
> 4.  How many computer games have you bought in the last 12 months?
>
>     [ ]       [ ]      [ ]      [ ]
>     *None*     *1*      *2*      *3*

(a) How could you improve part 4 of the questionnaire

*Insert a box for 4 or more*

*Link the type of game with the number of games*

*bought in the last 12 months*

**Do:**
Look for how the question is ambiguous.

You cannot answer question 4 if you have bought 4 or more games.

Notice that question 4 does not mention the type of game

Nadia also wants to find out how much time people spend playing computer games each week.

(b) Design a question that she could use.

Include tick boxes for a response.

*How much time in hours do you spend playing computer games each week.*

☐    ☐    ☐    ☐

*1 to< 5    5 to <10    10 to <15    15 or more*

(London)

**Do:**
Add a question that has not already been asked, and that is relevant to the survey.

Give tick boxes to cover all the options.

Make sure that you answer both questions in (b)

---

### Exercise 23E

1. Design a questionnaire to test the hypothesis 'The local council should provide more leisure facilities.' Consider:
   (a) Do people's opinions vary with age?
   (b) Do people's opinions vary with gender?

2. Design a questionnaire to test the hypothesis that 'Salt and vinegar crisps are more popular with younger people'.

3. Design a questionnaire on an issue of your choice.
   Remember to state the hypothesis.

---

### Worked exam question 3

In an opinion poll, 200 men in Birmingham are asked how they intend to vote in a General Election.

(a) Give two reasons why this is an unreliable way of predicting the outcome of a General Election.

   (i)   *All the people asked are men.*

   (ii)  *All the people asked are in one part of the UK, Birmingham.*

(b) Give three ways in which the opinion poll could be improved.

   (i)   *Include both men and women.*

   (ii)  *Include people of various ages*

   (iii) *Sample from different parts of the country.*

(SEG)

**Do:**
Read the whole question first

**Do:**
Notice that the survey is biased with this sample.

**Do:**
Take out the men-only bias

Make the sample more representative of different ages

Take out the bias of just one part of the country being surveyed for a national election.

### Exercise 23F (Mixed questions)

1. Here is some information from a table in a gardening book.

| Plant | Use | Colours | Flowering period | Where to plant |
|-------|-----|---------|------------------|----------------|
| Alyssum | Edging | White, pink or purple | June–Sept | Full sun |
| Begonia | Small bedding | Pink, red or white | June–Sept | Any position |
| Convolvulus | Medium bedding | Red | July–Sept | Full sun or partial shade |
| Dahlia | Large bedding | Pink, red or white | July–Sept | Full sun or partial shade |

(a) Which plant **must** be planted in full sun?
(b) Write down the colour of a Convolvulus.
(c) Write down the name of a pink bedding plant. [London]

2. A sports shop keeps information about sports shoes on a database. Part of this database is shown below.

| Model | Manufacturer | Cost |
|-------|--------------|------|
| Flyer | Tiger | £39.99 |
| Racer | Cheetah | £37.29 |
| Runner | Cheetah | £35.99 |
| Strider | Tiger | £48.99 |
| Blinder | Lion | £33.49 |
| Sprinter | Leopard | £49.99 |

(a) Write down the name of the manufacturer of the cheapest shoe.
(b) How much dearer is the Strider than the Racer?

3. Some Year 11 pupils investigate the amount of time pupils in their school spend on homework. They conduct a survey and ask 30 pupils the following question:

> 'How many minutes homework did you do last night?'

Here are their results.

| | | | | |
|----|-----|----|-----|-----|
| 25 | 120 | 55 | 10 | 40 |
| 60 | 75 | 75 | 45 | 65 |
| 45 | 90 | 45 | 110 | 75 |
| 90 | 45 | 90 | 60 | 45 |
| 15 | 25 | 45 | 35 | 55 |
| 75 | 20 | 30 | 45 | 100 |

The pupils conducted this survey on a Thursday morning.

They asked each person in their Maths set how long they had spent on their homework the previous night.

(a) Suggest three reasons why their sample may not have been typical.
(b) Describe two ways in which they could improve their sample. [NEAB]

4. (a) A headline in a newspaper this year stated:

> # Students skip Breakfast
> *Our survey shows that few students are eating cereals, fruit, or bread for breakfast.*
> **In fact they eat nothing at all!**

You are asked to conduct a survey to find out what students eat for breakfast.
Design an observation sheet to collect the data you need.
Invent the first 20 entries on your data sheet.

(b) The newspaper made the following statement about the eating habits of teenagers.

> **Only one in a hundred teenagers eat fruit and vegetables each day. Over half eat no vegetables other than chips.**

You are asked to find out whether this statement is true in your area.
Give three questions you could ask teenagers to see if what the article says is true in your area. [NEAB]

**5.** A survey is done to find out which sports pupils take part in.
The results of the survey are shown below.

| | % Boys | % Girls |
|---|---|---|
| Athletics | 37.1 | 33.3 |
| Basketball | 12.7 | 4.5 |
| Cycling | 71.7 | 60.6 |
| Dancing | 4.9 | 31.5 |
| Football | 72.0 | 14.5 |
| Gymnastics | 5.0 | 16.3 |
| Hockey | 6.5 | 3.5 |
| Judo | 16.0 | 6.7 |
| Netball | 3.3 | 35.0 |
| Roller-skating | 7.3 | 26.0 |
| Rugby | 11.8 | 2.5 |
| Swimming | 53.1 | 55.0 |

(a) Which two sports are the most popular with **both** boys **and** girls.

(b) The question asked in the survey was:
*Which sports do you take part in?*
You want to find out more about pupils' involvement in sport.
Write down another question that you could ask.

**6.** The school governors are worried about road safety outside the school gates.
They think there ought to be a Pelican Crossing. To decide on this, they need to find out how much traffic comes along the road at different times of day and on different days of the school week.
Design an observation sheet to gather this information.

**7.** Mee Ling thinks that pupils who come to school by bus are more likely to be late than those who do not travel by bus.
In order to test whether or not this is true, she carries out a survey on 100 pupils, from years 7 and 8, for 5 consecutive Tuesdays.
The results are shown in the following table.

| Method of travel | Number of student-days | Number of lates |
|---|---|---|
| Bus | 150 | 40 |
| Cycle | 50 | 10 |
| Car | 100 | 22 |
| Walk | 200 | 25 |
| TOTAL | 500 | 97 |

(a) Do the results suggest that Mee Ling is correct?
Show the working on which you base your answer.

(b) Suggest 3 ways in which Mee Ling could have improved her survey.          [MEG]

## Test yourself

QUESTION   **1.** Design and complete a data capture sheet for peoples' favourite type of television programme. Include soap, sport, film, serial, documentary, etc.

*If you are unable to do this question review page 466, Section 23.3 on data capture sheets.*

QUESTION   **2.** Design and complete a data capture sheet for the holidays people take. Include place, data, duration, cost, how they travelled there, etc.

*If you are unable to do this question, review page 466, Section 23.3 Example 3 on data capture sheets.*

QUESTION

**3.** Here is a part of a computer database about the Wood family.

| Name | Eye colour | Sex | Shoe size | Height | Age |
|------|-----------|-----|-----------|--------|-----|
| William | brown | male | 8 | 1.68 m | 42 |
| Leonie | blue | female | 6 | 1.57 m | 39 |
| Jane | green | female | 5 | 1.54 m | 14 |
| Mary | blue | female | 7 | 1.61 m | 16 |

(a) What is Jane's shoe size?
(b) What is Mary's age?
(c) How tall is William?
(d) Who is older than 30?

ANSWER

(a)  5  (b)  16
(c)  1.68 m
(d)  William and Leonie

*If your answers are incorrect review page 467, Section 23.4 on databases.*

QUESTION

**4.** State whether the following data are discrete or continuous.
(a)  height of a tree  (b)  number of sweets in a packet
(c)  weight of a woman  (d)  time taken to run 400 m

ANSWER

(a), (c) and (d) continuous;
(b)  discrete

*If your answers are incorrect review page 469, Section 23.5, Example 4 on types of data*

QUESTION

Design a questionnaire to test the hypothesis 'people prefer plain crisps'.

*If you are unable to do this question refer to page 470, Section 23.6 on questionnaires*

## Summary of key points to remember

1. Data capture sheets are forms used to collect information.

2. A database is a collection of information. Computer databases allow you to search for and retrieve information very quickly.

3. There are two different types of data: **qualitative** and **quantitative**.

   Qualitative data can only be described in words, e.g. eye colour.

   Quantitative data takes numerical values.

   **Discrete quantitative data** can only take certain values. These are usually whole numbers but can be fractions or decimals, e.g. shoe size.

   **Continuous quantitative data** can take any value in a certain range, e.g. height.

4. A **hypothesis** is a general statement which needs data to justify it.

   Examples are:

   'Adults think that everybody should learn to drive'

   'People prefer tea to coffee'.

5. A questionnaire is used to test a hypothesis.

   A questionnaire should:

   - ask short questions, that have either yes or no answers, or should give a choice of answers.

   - not ask leading questions that invite certain responses.

   - be in a logical sequence.

   - provide tick boxes so that questions can be answered easily.

   - demonstrate that you have taken bias into account when constructing it.

# 24 Statistical diagrams

## 24.1 Statistical diagrams and tables

When you have collected data you can display it in a diagram or table.

A diagram or table has more visual impact than a list. It is easier to get an idea about the data from it.

This unit is about displaying data in tables or graphs.

**UK- how the country's wealth is produced**

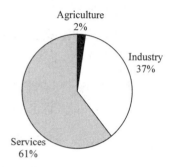

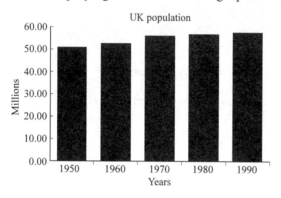

## 24.2 Pictograms

A **pictogram** is a statistical diagram used to display data that can be counted and represented using symbols or pictures. You can choose your symbol to best represent your data. This pictogram shows how people travel to work.

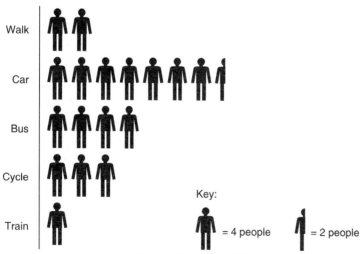

The pictogram shows that 8 people walk, 28 travel by car, 16 travel by bus, 12 cycle and 4 travel by train to work.

## Exercise 24A

1. This pictogram shows the number of banks in various towns.

Sharptown
| BANK | BANK | BANK | BANK | BANK |   | BANK | BANK | BANK | BANK | BANK |

Newtown
| BANK | BA: |

Bridgetown
| BANK | BANK | BANK | BANK | BANK |

Treetown
| BANK |

Key:

| BANK | = 2 banks

(a) How many banks are there in
  (i) Sharptown?
  (ii) Newtown?
(b) Which town has the most banks?
(c) Which town has the fewest banks?

## 24.3 Frequency tables

When data is arranged in a table it is called a frequency table. The frequency table shows how many of each type there are.

**Frequency** is the number of times each item occurs.

### Example 1

The numbers of people living in each house in a sample of 40 houses are:

8  2  4  5  3  3  6  1  3  4
3  6  5  3  3  7  4  5  4  1
4  3  4  4  2  4  5  3  3  2
7  4  3  4  6  2  3  5  3  4

Draw up a frequency table for this data.

| Number of people living in a house ($x$) | Frequency ($f$) |
|:---:|:---:|
| 1 | 2 |
| 2 | 4 |
| 3 | 12 |
| 4 | 11 |
| 5 | 5 |
| 6 | 3 |
| 7 | 2 |
| 8 | 1 |

In the table $x$ is used to represent the number of people and $f$ represents the frequency.

The frequency table shown in Example 1 can be represented in a bar chart.

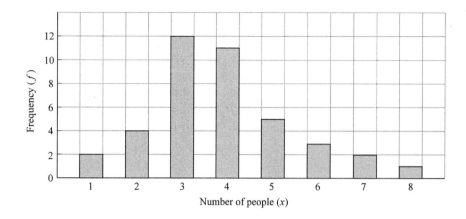

Bar charts are used to display data that can be counted. Notice that there are gaps between the bars. This is because data that can be counted is discrete and has no intermediate values.

---

### Exercise 24B

1. Draw up a frequency table for this data on the numbers of pets in 50 households.

```
1  0  1  2  1  1  5  0  3  1
4  1  1  1  2  1  2  0  2  1
0  0  1  2  1  2  3  1  0  1
1  2  1  1  2  4  1  2  3  1
1  1  1  2  0  2  2  1  1  1
```

Illustrate this data in a bar chart.

2. 50 people were asked which were their favourite crisps. The results are shown in the frequency table.

| Favourite crisps (x) | Frequency (f) |
|---|---|
| plain | 5 |
| cheese and onion | 11 |
| salt and vinegar | 15 |
| beef | 7 |
| tomato | 8 |
| other | 4 |

Illustrate this data in a bar chart.

---

## 24.4 Grouped frequency distributions

When there is a lot of data we often put it into groups. When data is put into groups it is called a **grouped frequency distribution**.

Grouped frequency distribution tables are used

● when the number of items is large

**or**

● when the data is continuous.

The groups that you put the data into are called **class intervals**. The class intervals must all have the same width. You must not have gaps between the class intervals. If there are no gaps then all the data can be included.

You should use at least 5 class intervals but no more than 12. This gives enough classes to reveal any pattern in the data, but not so many that the pattern disappears.

You can represent a grouped frequency distribution by a **histogram**. A histogram is like a bar chart but with no gaps.

### *Example 2*

In an examination the percentage marks of 80 students were:

```
91  31  48  59  52  61  85  67  76  84
57  62  95  44  71  68  79  63  67  59
70  79  70  51  56  33  43  62  62  76
59  45  53  61  70  72  65  69  87  97
77  61  49  82  81  63  51  58  74  63
79  53  35  44  54  70  63  67  66  82
76  41  77  51  73  69  66  70  77  56
73  52  72  46  74  62  81  39  51  47
```

(a) Draw up a grouped frequency distribution table for this data.

(b) Illustrate the data in a histogram.

(c) Comment on the distribution of marks.

The data ranges from 31 to 97 so choose class intervals with a width of 10, going up to 100. This makes sure that you have a sensible number of classes and all the data is included.

(a)

| Percentage mark (x) | Number of students (f) |
|:---:|:---:|
| 31–40 | 4 |
| 41–50 | 9 |
| 51–60 | 16 |
| 61–70 | 26 |
| 71–80 | 15 |
| 81–90 | 7 |
| 91–100 | 3 |

(b)

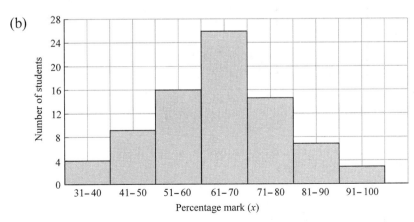

*Histogram showing percentage marks of 80 students.*

(c) Most students scored between 51 and 80 marks.

## Exercise 24C

**1.** The ages of 50 people are:

```
18  38  28  18  33  43  12  11  28  27
41  17  41  21  23  27  29  24  12   8
36  44  26  29  45  16   5  32  38  21
28  27  23  21  17  21  28  15  36  29
 8  35  25  28  21  32  15  22   7  31
```

(a) Copy and complete the grouped frequency distribution table.

| Age | Frequency |
|-----|-----------|
| 0–9 | |
| 10–19 | |
| 20–29 | |
| 30–39 | |
| 40–49 | |

(b) Illustrate the data in a histogram.

**2.** The heights of 50 sunflowers were measured to the nearest centimetre.

```
325  201  407  341  192
152  175  357  379  388
491  235  429  245  352
352  314  434  161  365
425  421  271  339  225
326  346  398  368  401
392  298  278  362  372
267  388  381  333  368
309  341  322  345  367
287  372  199  391  415
```

(a) Draw up a grouped frequency distribution table for the data.
(b) Illustrate the data in a histogram.

## 24.5 Other statistical diagrams

### Bar line graphs

This bar line graph shows the shoe sizes of 21 people.

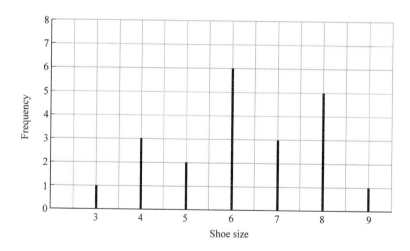

Bar line graphs are used in a similar way to bar charts, to show frequency distributions of items that are discrete data.

### Line graphs

This line graph shows the average monthly temperatures in Edinburgh for one year.

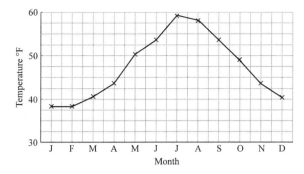

Line graphs are used to show trends over a period of time. The lines between the points show the trend, but have no meaning.

---

### Exercise 24D

1. The table below gives information about the numbers of people living in 35 houses.

| Number of people | 0 | 1 | 2 | 3 | 4 | 5 | 6 | 7 |
|---|---|---|---|---|---|---|---|---|
| Frequency | 2 | 5 | 8 | 7 | 6 | 4 | 2 | 1 |

   Draw a bar line graph for this frequency table.

2. Draw a line graph to show the monthly rainfall, in inches, for Edinburgh as shown in the table opposite.
   Comment on the seasonal variations.

| Rainfall (inches) | Month |
|---|---|
| 2.2 | J |
| 1.5 | F |
| 1.5 | M |
| 1.5 | A |
| 2.1 | M |
| 1.8 | J |
| 3.3 | J |
| 3.0 | A |
| 2.2 | S |
| 2.6 | O |
| 2.4 | N |
| 2.2 | D |

---

## 24.6 Pie charts

Pie charts are usually used to display information that can be counted or grouped. This pie chart shows how Mary spent her time during one 24-hour period.

The size of the angle of each sector represents the frequency (time spent) on each activity.

From the angle you can work out the number of hours. Remember that there are 360° in a circle.

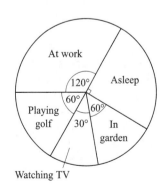

$$120° \text{ for at work} = \frac{120}{360} \text{ of 24 hours}$$
$$= \frac{1}{3} \text{ of 24 hours}$$
$$= 8 \text{ hours}$$

Work out for yourself the time spent on the other activities.

## Example 3

The table shows the type of weather recorded in November.

Work out the angles and illustrate this information in a pie chart.

| Type of weather | Snow | Sleet | Rain | Fog | Cloud | Sunny |
|-----------------|------|-------|------|-----|-------|-------|
| Number of days  | 1    | 2     | 13   | 3   | 10    | 1     |

First we work out the angle for each type of weather.

November has 30 days.

Snow: $\frac{1}{30}$ of $360° = 12°$

The angle of the snow sector is $12°$

Similarly, sleet: $\frac{2}{30}$ of $360° = 24°$

And in the same way

rain: $156°$   fog: $36°$   cloud: $120°$   sunny: $12°$

Now we can draw the pie chart.

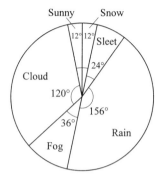

---

## Worked exam question 1

The incomplete pie chart represents the attendance at a concert by men, women and children. Altogether 1800 people attended the concert.

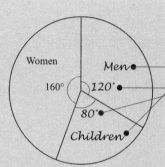

**Do:**
Label the pie chart

Label the angles in each sector

(a) Calculate the number of women at the concert.

$$Fraction\ of\ women = \frac{160}{360}$$

**Do:**
Write down the fraction of women

$$Number\ of\ women = \frac{160}{360} \times 1800 = 800$$

Write down your calculation to show your method

.......800....... women

600 men were at the concert.

(b) (i) Calculate the angle needed to represent them on the pie chart.

$$\frac{600}{1800}\ of\ 360°$$

**Do:**
Remember 'of' means multiply

$$= \frac{600}{1800} \times 360$$

......120°...... degrees

(ii) Use your answer to (b)(i) to complete the pie chart.

(London)

## 24.7 Frequency polygons

Frequency polygons can be used to display data as an alternative to histograms.

Frequency polygons are used to compare data for two or more distributions.

To draw a frequency polygon:

- imagine a histogram of the data
- plot the mid-points at the top of each bar of the histogram
- join the mid-points

*Example 4*

The weight of a farmer's flock of 80 sheep are

| Weight (kg) | 20–25 | 26–30 | 31–35 | 36–40 | 41–45 | 46–50 | 51–55 |
|---|---|---|---|---|---|---|---|
| No. of sheep | 4 | 9 | 18 | 29 | 12 | 6 | 2 |

Draw a frequency polygon of this data.

We plot the number of sheep for a class of weights against the middle of the class. So for the group 20–25 we plot the point (22.5, 4). For the group 25–30 we plot the point 27.5

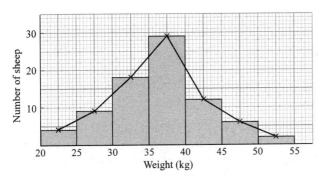

The frequency polygon can be closed by joining the first and last points to the horizontal axis.

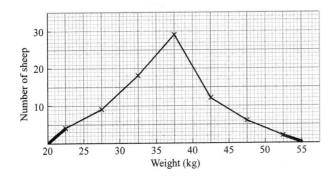

## Example 5

The table shows the age of workers at two different factories.

| Age | 25–29 | 30–34 | 35–39 | 40–44 | 45–49 | 50–54 | 55–59 | 60–64 | 65–69 |
|---|---|---|---|---|---|---|---|---|---|
| Numbers of workers in factory x | 1 | 3 | 6 | 11 | 15 | 8 | 6 | 4 | 1 |
| Number of workers in factory y | 2 | 8 | 12 | 15 | 8 | 5 | 4 | 1 | 0 |

(a) Draw a frequency polygon for factory x and factory y, both on the same grid.

(b) Compare the two sets of data.

(a)

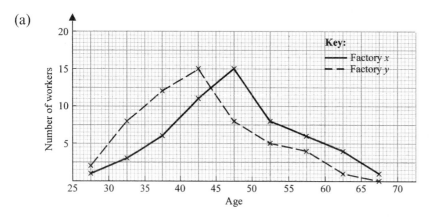

(b) You can see that factory x has older workers than factory y.

## Exercise 24E

**1.** Draw a pie chart to illustrate the information shown in the table below about the weather on the 30 days in April one year.

| Type of weather | Number of days |
|---|---|
| sunny | 5 |
| cloudy | 8 |
| rain | 11 |
| fog | 3 |
| snow | 2 |
| sleet | 1 |

**2.** The frequency table shows how 180 further education students travel to college.

| Method of travel | Frequency |
|---|---|
| car | 35 |
| motorbike | 26 |
| van | 4 |
| cycle | 7 |
| walk | 29 |
| bus | 61 |
| train | 18 |

Show this information in
(a) a bar chart
(b) a pie chart.

3. In a sports competition the marks obtained by 110 competitors were:

| Mark | Number of competitors |
|---|---|
| 1–10 | 2 |
| 11–20 | 7 |
| 21–30 | 10 |
| 31–40 | 15 |
| 41–50 | 28 |

| Mark | Number of competitors |
|---|---|
| 51–60 | 21 |
| 61–70 | 12 |
| 71–80 | 7 |
| 81–90 | 5 |
| 91–100 | 3 |

Illustrate this frequency distribution by drawing a frequency polygon.

4. The frequency distribution gives the weekly sales of shirts in *Feeling Shirty* for one year.

| Number of shirts sold | Number of weeks |
|---|---|
| 10–29 | 2 |
| 30–49 | 4 |
| 50–69 | 18 |
| 70–89 | 19 |

| Number of shirts sold | Number of weeks |
|---|---|
| 90–109 | 11 |
| 110–129 | 7 |
| 130–149 | 1 |

Draw a closed frequency polygon to display the distribution.

## Worked exam question 2

As part of his Geography fieldwork, Tony took measurements of the steepness of slopes. The steepness was measured as the angle the slope made with the horizontal.

Tony's results are shown below.

$$15°, 16°, \ 9°, 21°, 32°$$
$$37°, 25°, 36°, 40°, \ 8°$$
$$13°, 21°, 32°, 29°, 32°$$
$$7°, \ 4°, 18°, 17°, 32°$$

Tony decided to group the data into 4 equal class intervals on an observation sheet.

(a) Complete the observation sheet below, using 4 equal class intervals.

| Class interval (Steepness°) | Tally | Frequency |
|---|---|---|
| 1–10 | IIII | 4 |
| 11–20 | ++++ I | 6 |
| 21–30 | III | 3 |
| 31–40 | ++++ II | 7 |

**Do:**
Complete the tally

Make sure the tally equals the frequency

(b) Use the completed observation sheet to draw a frequency
diagram of the data on the grid below.

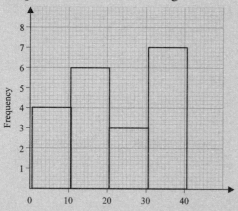

(London)

## Worked exam question 3

The table shows the frequency distribution of marks scored by
100 candidates in a Science examination.

| Marks | Mid-point | Frequency |
|-------|-----------|-----------|
| 0–9   | 4.5       | 3         |
| 10–19 | 14.5      | 5         |
| 20–29 | 24.5      | 12        |
| 30–39 | 34.5      | 20        |
| 40–49 | 44.5      | 24        |
| 50–59 | 54.5      | 18        |
| 60–69 | 64.5      | 12        |
| 70–79 | 74.5      | 6         |

$Mid\text{-}point = \dfrac{0+9}{2} = 4.5$

Draw a frequency polygon, on the grid below, to illustrate the
data. Use the mid-points.

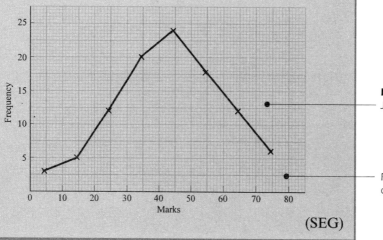

(SEG)

**Do:**
Choose the correct diagram. The
data is grouped and continuous,
so use a histogram or a frequency
polygon

**Don't:**
Shade the diagram, it wastes time
and does not gain marks

**Do:**
Notice that the class widths are all
10, so add 10 to the mid-point
each time

**Do:**
Join the points with straight lines

Read the scales on the axes
carefully

## Exercise 24F (Mixed questions)

**1.**

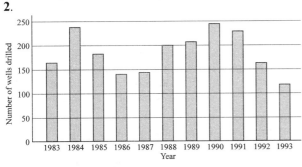

| 1992 | ⌐▲▬▬ ⌐▲▬▬ ⌐▲▬▬ ⌐▲▬▬ ⌐▲▬▬ |
|------|---------------------------|
| 1993 | ⌐▲▬▬ ⌐▲▬▬ ⌐▲▬▬ ⌐▬ |

⌐▲▬▬ = 10 ships

The diagram shows how many ships were in Mathsland's navy in 1992 and 1993. Use the diagram to answer these questions.
(a) How many ships were there in Mathsland's navy in 1992?
(b) How many ships were there in Mathsland's navy in 1993? [London]

**2.**

The bar chart shows the number of oil wells drilled in the North Sea between 1983 and 1993.
(a) In which year were the most wells drilled?
(b) How many wells were drilled in 1988?
(c) How many wells were drilled in 1991? [London]

**3.** A competition is held for the longest runner bean grown this year.
The lengths, recorded to the nearest millimetre, are shown in the table below.

| Length (mm) | 26–35 | 36–45 | 46–55 | 56–65 | 66–75 | 76–85 |
|-------------|-------|-------|-------|-------|-------|-------|
| Frequency | 4 | 20 | 15 | 7 | 3 | 1 |

(a) Draw a histogram to represent this information.
(b) Draw a frequency polygon to represent this information.
(c) In the previous year's competition to grow the longest runner bean the lengths, recorded to the nearest millimetre, were as shown in the table below

| Length (mm) | 26–35 | 36–45 | 46–55 | 56–65 | 66–75 | 76–85 |
|-------------|-------|-------|-------|-------|-------|-------|
| Frequency | 7 | 30 | 9 | 3 | 1 | 0 |

Superimpose the frequency polygon for the previous year on the frequency polygon for this year.
(d) Compare the two sets of data.

**4.** This question is about the way water is used in two Mozambique villages.

USE OF WATER IN VILLAGE A

(a) In village A, 324 litres of water are used each day.
The pie chart below shows how the water is used.
(i) How much water (in litres) is used each day for cooking?
(ii) What fraction of the water used is given to animals?
(b) In village B, the water is used as follows:

Cooking                  20%
Washing themselves       50%
Washing clothes          20%
Washing pots             10%

represent this information in a pie chart. [MEG]

**5.** (a) The pie chart compares the areas of four oceans.
The total area of these four oceans is 129.6 million square miles.
(i) Show that the area of the Pacific Ocean is twice the area of the Atlantic Ocean.
(ii) Calculate the area of the Arctic Ocean.
(b) The surface area of the Earth is approximately $1.971 \times 10^8$ square miles. The surface area of the Earth covered by water is approximately $1.395 \times 10^8$ square miles.
(i) Calculate the surface area of the Earth not covered by water.
Give your answer in standard form.
(ii) What percentage of the Earth's surface is not covered by water? [NEAB]

**6.** 300 young people were asked what they did after completing Year 11 at school. The pie chart shows the results of the survey.

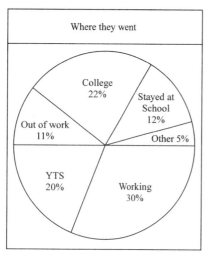

Diagram not accurately drawn

(a) How many of the young people were working?

Gwen made an accurate drawing of the pie chart.

She first drew the sector representing the young people out of work.

(b) Calculate the size of the angle of this sector. Give your answer correct to the nearest degree.

(c) Change to a decimal the percentage going to college.

(d) What fraction of the young people stayed at school?

Give your answer in its simplest form.

[London]

**7.** (a) A geography book contains the pie chart shown below.

COMPARISON OF DISTRIBUTION OF TROPICAL FORESTS BY AREA

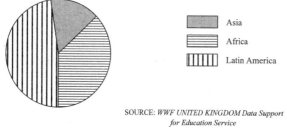

| | Asia |
| | Africa |
| | Latin America |

SOURCE: *WWF UNITED KINGDOM Data Support for Education Service*

This pie chart shows that about one third of the tropical forests lie in Africa.

Complete each of the following statements.
Answer (a) (i) About ............ of the tropical forests lie in Latin America.
(ii) The area of tropical forest in Latin America is about ............ times the area of the tropical forest in Asia.
(b) Another geography book contains the diagram shown below.

COMPARISON OF DISTRIBUTION OF TROPICAL FORESTS BY AREA

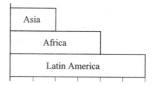

(i) Does the information in this bar chart agree exactly with the information in the pie chart?
Give a reason for your answer.
(ii) Using the bar chart, find the percentage of the total area of tropical forest which lies in Latin America. [MEG]

**8.** Sita spent £90.
The table shows what she spent it on.

| Items | Amount spent |
|---|---|
| Bus fares | £12 |
| Going out | £25 |
| Clothes | £30 |
| Records | £15 |
| Other | £8 |
| Total spending | £90 |

Sita is asked to construct a pie chart to show her spending.
(a) Work out the angle of each sector of the pie chart.

| Items | Angle of sector |
|---|---|
| Bus fares | |
| Going out | |
| Clothes | |
| Records | |
| Other | |
| Total of angles | 360° |

(b) Construct a pie chart.
(c) What fraction of Sita's spending was on clothes? [London]

**9.**

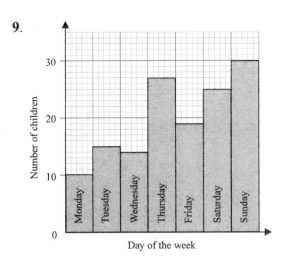

The diagram shows the number of children who played on the swings in a park during one week in June.

(a)  (i) How many children played on the swings on Wednesday?

(ii) What was the total number of children who played on the swings in the week?

(iii) Work out the mean number of children per day who played on the swings.

## Test yourself

**1.**  The examination marks in percentages of 39 students are shown below:

```
66  73  76  84  51  59  64  87  71  64  77  62  79
82  76  49  69  73  81  79  42  72  82  80  95  61
65  71  76  72  64  74  79  73  73  54  76  66  68
```

**QUESTION**   Draw up a grouped frequency distribution table using the class intervals 40–49, 50–59, 60–69, etc.

**ANSWER**

| Number of marks | 40–49 | 50–59 | 60–69 | 70–79 | 80–89 | 90–99 |
|---|---|---|---|---|---|---|
| Frequency | 2 | 3 | 10 | 17 | 6 | 1 |

*If your answer is incorrect review page 481, Section 24.4, Example 2 on grouped frequency distributions.*

**QUESTION**   Illustrate this data in a histogram.

*If you have difficulty answering this question review page 481, Section 24.4, Example 2 on grouped frequency distributions.*

**QUESTION**   Draw the frequency polygon on your histogram.

*If you have difficulty answering this question review page 485, Section 24.7 on frequency polygons*

**QUESTION**    Illustrate the data in your grouped frequency distribution table with a pie chart.

**ANSWER**

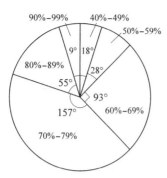

*If your answer is incorrect review page 483, Section 24.6 on pie charts.*

---

2. Here are the figures for sales of new cars in the UK over a 6-year period. (Figures to the nearest 100000)

| Year | 1987 | 1988 | 1989 | 1990 | 1991 | 1992 | 1993 | 1994 |
|------|------|------|------|------|------|------|------|------|
| Sales | 17 | 19 | 22 | 25 | 28 | 29 | 28 | 26 |

---

**QUESTION**    Draw a line graph to illustrate the data.
Comment on the trend shown.

**ANSWER**    The trend shows an increase in car sales to a peak in 1992 and then a gradual decline in sales from then on.

*If your answer is incorrect review page 482, Section 24.5 on line graphs.*

---

## Summary of key points to remember

1. Data can be displayed in tables. The data can be not grouped or grouped.

2. Diagrams can be used to illustrate data.

   - **Pictograms** are used when items can be counted and represented by symbolics or pictures.

   - **Bar charts** are used to display data that can be counted. There are gaps between the bars.

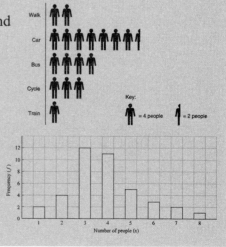

- **Histograms** are used to display grouped frequency distributions. There are no gaps between the bars.

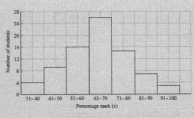

- **Bar line graphs** are used to display data that can be counted.

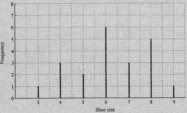

- **Line graphs** are used to show trends.

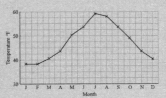

- **Pie charts** are usually used to display data that can be counted or grouped. The size of the angle of each sector represents the number of items (frequency) in that sector.

- **Frequency polygons** are used to display grouped frequency distributions. They can be used to compare data for two or more distributions.

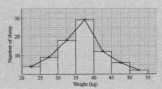

## 25.1 Introduction

You have already seen that unorganised lists of data are difficult to understand and interpret. In Unit 24 Statistical diagrams you learnt how to display data in tables and diagrams. In this unit you will learn other methods of describing and interpreting data using measures of average and spread.

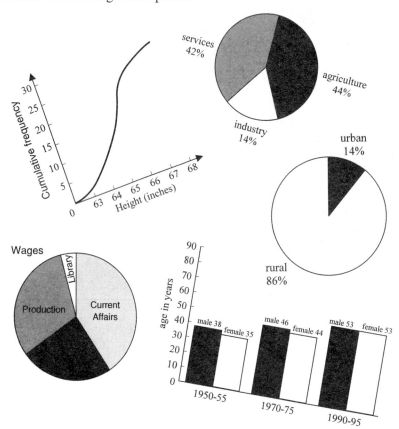

## 25.2 Measures of average and spread

There are three measures of average – the mean, the median and the mode.

- The **mean**

    The mean of a set of items is the sum of the items divided by the total number of items.

$$\text{Mean} = \frac{\text{sum of the items}}{\text{the total number of items}}$$

In symbols:    $\bar{x}$    is the mean

$\Sigma x$   means the sum of the items ($x$ values)

$n$    means the number of items

$\Sigma f$ means the sum of the frequencies

So    $\bar{x} = \dfrac{\Sigma x}{n}$  or  $\bar{x} = \dfrac{\Sigma x}{\Sigma f}$

The mean is sometimes called the 'arithmetic mean'.

- The **median**

  The median of a set of items is the middle item once the items are arranged in ascending (or descending) order.

  If there are an even number of items the median is the mean of the two middle items.

- The **mode**

  The mode of a set of items is the item which occurs most often. If all items occur only once then there is no mode. A set of items may more have more than one mode.

  For example, the set 2, 2, 3, 3, 3, 4, 4, 4, 5 has two modes, 3 and 4.

  3 and 4 both occur 3 times each. The other numbers do not occur as many times.

- The **range**

  The range is a measure of the spread of a set of data. The range of a set of items is the difference between the values of the smallest and largest items in the set.

  **Range = largest value − smallest value**

*Example 1*

The travelling expenses for nine people were £26, £28, £32, £32, £38, £45, £50, £63, £118.

(a) Find the mean, median and mode

(b) Which average best describes the data? Explain your answer.

(c) What is the range?

(a) Mean $\bar{x} = \dfrac{\Sigma x}{n} = \dfrac{26 + 28 + 32 + 32 + +38 + 45 + 50 + 63 + 118}{9}$

$= \frac{432}{9} = 48$

Mean = £48

The median is the middle item when the items are arranged in ascending order.

For 9 items the middle term is the $\dfrac{9+1}{2} = 5$th item.

$$26, 28, 32, 32, \;\boxed{38,}\; 45, 50, 63, 118$$
$$\uparrow$$
$$\text{middle item}$$

Median $= £38$

The mode is the item that occurs most often

$$26, 28, \;\boxed{32, 32,}\; 38, 45, 50, 63, 118$$
$$\uparrow$$
$$\text{occurs most often}$$

Mode $= £32$

(b) The mean can be distorted by extreme values (high or low). In this example one value much larger than the rest (£118) distorts the mean to give an average of £48.

In this case it is better to use the median because it describes the data more accurately and is not distorted by the extreme values.

The mode is easiest to calculate and eliminates the effect of extreme values. However it does not always give a good measure of average and is not often used because the mean or median are more representative of the measure of average.

The mode is used when the most common item is required. For example, a shoe manufacturer would want to know which shoe size is most common, that is the **modal** size.

However the mode is the only average that can be used for qualitative data.

(c) The range = largest value − smallest value $= 118 - 28 = 90$

This shows the biggest difference there could be between travelling expenses.

---

### Exercise 25A

**1.** (a) Find the mean, median, mode and range of these sets of data.
    (i) 2, 3, 4, 6, 8, 10, 14.
    (ii) 20, 24, 25, 27, 28, 29, 30, 35.
    (iii) 56, 57, 57, 58, 58, 60, 60, 62, 63.
    (iv) 4.6, 5.1, 5.4, 5.4, 5.4, 5.7, 5.8, 6.0, 6.3, 15.2.

(b) For each set, state which average best describes the data and why.

**2.** The weights of 7 adults are:
67 kg, 98 kg, 76 kg, 85 kg, 59 kg, 91 kg, 72 kg
Find the mean and median weights.

3. The temperature in degrees Celsius was measured at 13:00 each day for ten days. Here are the results:

22, 19, 27, 16, 21, 22, 18, 31, 23, 20

(a) Find the mean, the median and the modal temperature.

(b) Which average best describes the temperature? Explain your answer.

4. The heights of eleven students were measured.

157 cm, 182 cm, 162 cm, 159 cm, 173 cm, 169 cm 174 cm, 152 cm, 168 cm, 191 cm, 175 cm.

Calculate:

(a) the mean height    (b) the median height

---

## Worked exam question 1

The list below gives the ages, in years, of the Mathematics teachers in a school.

34, 25, 37, 33, 26.

(a) Work out:

(i) the mean age.

$$Mean = \frac{\Sigma x}{n} = \frac{34 + 25 + 37 + 33 + 26}{5}$$
$$= \frac{155}{5} = 31$$

........31........ years

**Do:**
Write down the rule you are using

Show your working

Check your answer is sensible

(ii) the range.

$$Range = largest\ value - smallest\ value$$
$$= 37 - 25 = 12$$

........12........ years

Show your working

In the same school, there are six English teachers. The range of their ages is 20 years.

(b) What do the ranges tell you about the ages of the Mathematics teachers and the English teachers?

*The mathematics teachers' ages have a smaller range than the English teachers' ages. The English teachers therefore have a wider range of ages than the maths teachers.*

**Do:**
Use the word 'range' in your answer

(SEG)

## 25.3 Calculating averages of frequency distributions

Remember that data can be arranged in a frequency table. You can calculate the mean, median and mode of a frequency distribution from a frequency table.

### Example 2

This data shows the number of people in each of 40 households.

Find the mean, median, mode and range.

```
4  4  3  2  5  4  3  3  4  6
3  7  6  2  8  4  2  5  3  3
3  5  2  3  4  2  5  4  6  7
2  3  3  6  5  3  7  2  3  4
```

First we draw up a frequency table for the data.

| Number of people (x) | Frequency (f) |
|:---:|:---:|
| 2 | 7 |
| 3 | 12 |
| 4 | 8 |
| 5 | 5 |
| 6 | 4 |
| 7 | 3 |
| 8 | 1 |

Now we add a third column to the table for frequency ($f$) × number of people in each family ($x$)

A shorter way of writing this is $fx$.

The frequency table then looks like this

| Number of people in each family (x) | Frequency (f) | fx |
|:---:|:---:|:---:|
| 2 | 7 | 14 |
| 3 | 12 | 36 |
| 4 | 8 | 32 |
| 5 | 5 | 25 |
| 6 | 4 | 24 |
| 7 | 3 | 21 |
| 8 | 1 | 8 |
| Totals | $\Sigma f = 40$ | $\Sigma fx = 160$ |

$\Sigma f$ means the sum of the frequencies.

$\Sigma fx$ means the sum of the frequencies $\times$ number of items.

Adding the values in the frequency column gives $\Sigma f$ (the sum of $f$), the number of households. Adding the values in the $fx$ columns gives the total number of people in all 40 households.

So the mean number of people in a household can be calculated by

$$\text{Mean } \bar{x} = \frac{\Sigma fx}{\Sigma f}$$
$$= \tfrac{160}{40} = 4$$

The mean is 4 people in a household.

The median is the middle item when the data are arranged in order. You find the middle item by:

$$\frac{\Sigma f + 1}{2} = \frac{40 + 1}{2} = 20.5$$

This tells you that there are two middle items – the 20th and the 21st – because the 20.5th item does not exist.

Counting down the frequency column you can see that these both occur in the 3rd row down. This row contains items 20 to 27 and has value 4. So the 20th and 21st items are both 4.

The median is the mean of these two middle values.

$$\text{Median} = \frac{4 + 4}{2} = 4$$

The mode is the most common item. Looking at the frequency column you can see that 3 is the most common item and it occurs 12 times.

So  mode  $= 3$

The range $=$ largest value $-$ smallest value
$= 8 - 2$
$= 6$

For a frequency distribution

$$\textbf{Mean } \bar{x} = \frac{\Sigma fx}{\Sigma f}$$

The most suitable diagram for displaying the frequency distribution in Example 2 is a bar chart because the data is discrete and there are only seven classes.

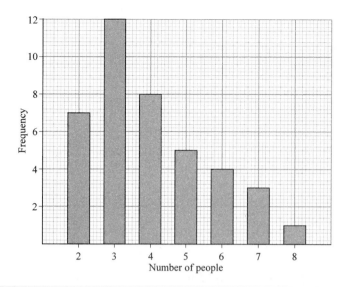

## Worked exam question 2

The temperatures at midnight in January 1995 in Shiverton were measured and recorded. The results were used to construct the frequency table.

| Temperatuure in ° C $x$ | 0 | 1 | 2 | 3 | 4 | 5 | 6 | 7 | 8 |
|---|---|---|---|---|---|---|---|---|---|
| Number of nights $f$ | 4 | 5 | 5 | 3 | 3 | 7 | 3 | 0 | 1 |

**Do:**
Label the x and f rows to help you

**Don't:**
Confuse range of temperature with number of nights

(a) Work out the range of temperatures.

Range = 8 − 0

............8............ °C

(b) Work out the mean temperature.

Give your answer correct to 1 decimal place.

$$\text{Mean} = \frac{\Sigma fx}{\Sigma f}$$

**Do:**
Write down the rule

$$= \frac{0 + 5 + 10 + 9 + 12 + 35 + 18 + 0 + 8}{4 + 5 + 5 + 3 + 3 + 7 + 3 + 0 + 1}$$

The working out in your head. It is quicker than using a calculator

$$= \frac{97}{31} = 3.129$$

............3.1............ °C

Give your answer to 1 decimal place

(MEG)

## Exercise 25B

1. Louise carried out a survey to find the number of different pets in 40 different families. The results are listed below:

```
1  0  2  1  1  0  3  2  1  0
0  2  1  1  2  0  1  4  1  0
2  1  2  3  1  1  1  0  0  2
0  1  1  2  2  1  0  1  3  1
```

(a) Draw up a frequency table for the data.
(b) Calculate the mean, median and mode.
(c) Illustrate the information with an appropriate statistical diagram.

2. Lee works in a clothing factory. He has cut 54 pieces of cloth to the nearest centimetre.

```
169  167  169  171  174  172  172  170  168
173  166  170  171  172  169  171  168  170
169  171  174  170  172  169  168  173  167
171  174  170  169  172  171  170  168  174
170  170  169  171  167  169  170  173  170
169  170  165  170  171  166  168  172  170
```

(a) Draw up a frequency table for this data.
(b) Calculate the mean, median and mode.
(c) Illustrate the data with a suitable statistical diagram.

3. (a) Find the mean, median and mode of this frequency distribution.

| $x$ | 10 | 11 | 12 | 13 | 14 | 15 | 16 | 17 | 18 | 19 |
|---|---|---|---|---|---|---|---|---|---|---|
| $f$ | 1 | 3 | 6 | 9 | 15 | 12 | 8 | 5 | 4 | 2 |

(b) Illustrate the frequency distribution with a suitable statistical diagram.

4. The examination marks of 100 students are given in the frequency distribution table.

| Mark ($x$) | Frequency ($f$) |
|---|---|
| 2 | 1 |
| 3 | 9 |
| 4 | 18 |
| 5 | 34 |
| 6 | 25 |
| 7 | 7 |
| 8 | 4 |
| 9 | 2 |

Calculate the mean and median examination mark.

# 25.4 Grouped frequency distributions

Data are often grouped into class intervals. This gives a **grouped frequency distribution**.

You can calculate an estimate of the mean of a grouped frequency distribution. You cannot find the true mean or median as you do not know the individual values of the data.

Since the data is grouped you cannot find the most common value – the mode. However, you can find the most common class interval – the modal class.

### Example 3

The examination results of 80 students were grouped in classes with width 10.

| Percentage mark | Number of candidates |
|---|---|
| 31–40 | 4 |
| 41–50 | 9 |
| 51–60 | 16 |
| 61–70 | 26 |
| 71–80 | 15 |
| 81–90 | 7 |
| 91–100 | 3 |

(a) Illustrate the data in a histogram.

(b) State the modal class.

(c) Calculate an estimate of the mean.

(a)

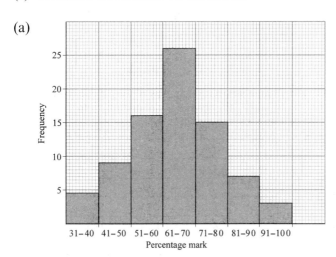

(b) From the histogram the most common class interval is 61–70.

The modal class is 61–70.

(c) We need to use the rule $\bar{x} = \dfrac{\Sigma fx}{\Sigma f}$ to find the mean. However, as we do not know the values of each item as data, we can only calculate an estimate of the mean.

To calculate an estimate of the mean first find the mid-point of each class interval.

The mid-point for the class 31–40 is

$$\frac{31 + 40}{2} = 35.5$$

As the class width is 10 the mid-points of the classes go up in 10s.

To calculate the estimate of the mean we add extra columns to the table.

| Percentage mark | Number of candidates ($f$) | Halfway Mark ($x$) | $fx$ |
|---|---|---|---|
| 31–40 | 4 | 35.5 | 142 |
| 41–50 | 9 | 45.5 | 409.5 |
| 51–60 | 16 | 55.5 | 888 |
| 61–70 | 26 | 65.5 | 1703 |
| 71–80 | 15 | 75.5 | 1132.5 |
| 81–90 | 7 | 85.5 | 598.5 |
| 91–100 | 3 | 95.5 | 286.5 |
| Totals | $\Sigma f = 80$ | | $\Sigma fx = 5160$ |

Use the rule $\bar{x} = \dfrac{\Sigma fx}{\Sigma f}$ to calculate an estimate of the mean.

The estimate of the mean $= \frac{5160}{80}$

$$\bar{x} = 64.5$$

## Exercise 25C

**1.** The frequency distribution shows the weights of 70 sheep.

| Weight in kg | 20 to under 30 | 30 to under 40 | 40 to under 50 |
|---|---|---|---|
| Number of sheep | 2 | 5 | 16 |

| Weight in kg | 50 to under 60 | 60 to under 70 | 70 to under 80 | 80 to under 90 |
|---|---|---|---|---|
| Number of sheep | 25 | 13 | 6 | 3 |

(a) Draw up a frequency distribution table. Include columns for the mid-point ($x$) and the frequency ($f$) multiplied by the mid-point, ($fx$).

(b) Calculate an estimate of the mean using the rule:

Estimate of mean $\bar{x} = \dfrac{\Sigma fx}{\Sigma f}$

(c) Illustrate the data in a histogram.

**2.** The distribution of the marks obtained by 100 students in a test is:

| Mark | 11–20 | 21–30 | 31–40 | 41–50 | 51–60 | 61–70 |
|---|---|---|---|---|---|---|
| Number of students | 3 | 5 | 6 | 14 | 23 | 30 |

| Mark | 71–80 | 81–90 | 91–100 |
|---|---|---|---|
| Number of students | 11 | 6 | 2 |

(a) Draw up a grouped frequency distribution table to include columns for $x$ and $fx$.

(b) Calculate an estimate of the mean using the rule:

Estimate of mean $\bar{x} = \dfrac{\Sigma fx}{\Sigma f}$

(c) Illustrate the data in a histogram.

**3.** The lifetimes in hours of 100 electric light bulbs are shown in the frequency distribution table.

| Time (hours) | Number of light bulbs |
|---|---|
| 0 to under 200 | 1 |
| 200 to under 400 | 4 |
| 400 to under 600 | 7 |
| 600 to under 800 | 10 |
| 800 to under 1000 | 14 |
| 1000 to under 1200 | 33 |
| 1200 to under 1400 | 20 |
| 1400 to under 1600 | 6 |
| 1600 to under 1800 | 5 |

(a) Draw up a grouped frequency distribution table that includes columns for $x$ and $fx$.

(b) Calculate an estimate of the mean.

(c) Illustrate the data in a histogram.

**4.** The weekly wages of 100 workers in the Midlands are given in the grouped frequency distribution table.

| Wage in £ | Number of workers ($f$) |
|---|---|
| 80 to under 90 | 1 |
| 90 to under 100 | 4 |
| 100 to under 110 | 9 |
| 110 to under 120 | 28 |
| 120 to under 130 | 37 |
| 130 to under 140 | 11 |
| 140 to under 150 | 7 |
| 150 to under 160 | 3 |

4. (a) Draw up a grouped frequency distribution table that includes columns for $x$ and $fx$.
   (b) Calculate an estimate of the mean.
   (c) Illustrate the data in a histogram.
   (d) State the modal class.

| Hours ($x$) | 0–9 | 10–19 | 20–29 | 30–39 | 40–49 |
|---|---|---|---|---|---|
| Frequency ($f$) | 13 | 19 | 41 | 15 | 12 |

   (a) Calculate an estimate of the mean
   (b) Illustrate the data with a suitable statistical diagram.

5. This grouped frequency distribution shows the marks scored by 50 students in a test.

| Mark ($x$) | 1–10 | 11–20 | 21–30 | 31–40 | 41–50 |
|---|---|---|---|---|---|
| Frequency ($f$) | 1 | 4 | 16 | 24 | 5 |

   (a) Calculate an estimate of the mean.
   (b) Illustrate the data with a suitable statistical diagram.

6. The number of hours of television watched in a week by 100 people is recorded in the grouped frequency distribution table.

7. The distance 50 people travel to work by car is recorded in the grouped frequency distribution table below.

| Distance miles ($x$) | 0–4 | 5–8 | 9–12 | 13–16 | 17–20 |
|---|---|---|---|---|---|
| Frequency ($f$) | 3 | 21 | 15 | 7 | 4 |

   (a) Calculate an estimate of the mean.
   (b) Illustrate your data with a suitable statistical diagram.

---

## Worked exam question 3

The lengths of telephone calls made by the Anchor Company were monitored over a week. The results are shown in the table.

| Length of call (minutes) | Mid-point ($x$) | Frequency ($f$) | $fx$ |
|---|---|---|---|
| 0 and less than 1 | 0.5 | 53 | 26.5 |
| 1 and less than 2 | 1.5 | 105 | 157.5 |
| 2 and less than 3 | 2.5 | 158 | 395 |
| 3 and less than 4 | 3.5 | 85 | 297.5 |
| 4 and less than 5 | 4.5 | 41 | 184.5 |
| 5 and less than 6 | 5.5 | 24 | 132 |
| 6 and less than 7 | 6.5 | 5 | 32.5 |

Totals $\Sigma f = 471$   $\Sigma fx = 1225.5$

**Do:**
Label the columns x and f
Use the third column for part (b)
Just add 1 each time for the mid-point as the class width is 1
Total the f and fx columns

**Don't:**
Round your answer off

(a) Complete the Mid-point column

(b) Calculate the mean length of their telephone calls.

   You may find it helpful to use the table above.

$$Mean = \frac{\Sigma fx}{\Sigma f} = \frac{1225.5}{471}$$

$$= 2.60$$

..........2.60.......... mins

**Do:**
Write down the rule you are using and show your working
Check your answer is sensible

**Don't:**
Write down all the digits on your calculator. Give your final answer to 3 significant figures

The lengths of telephone calls made by the Castle Company are represented by this frequency polygon.

(c) On the same axes draw the frequency polygon for the Anchor Company.

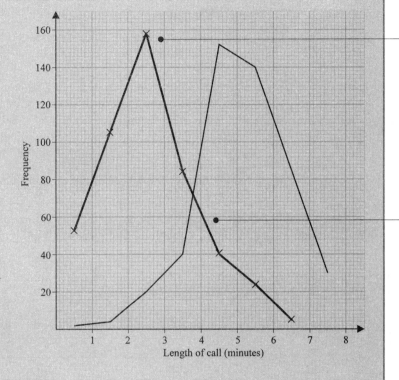

**Do:**
Plot the points at the mid-points of the class intervals

**Do:**
Join the points with straight lines

(d) Use the frequency polygons to compare the lengths of telephone calls made by the two companies

Answer  *The Anchor Company in general make* ●

*shorter calls than the Castle Company*

**Do:**
Mention both companies in your explanation

---

### Exercise 25D (mixed questions)

1. Here are the numbers of goals scored by a school football team in their matches this term.
   3, 2, 0, 1, 2, 0, 3, 4, 3, 2.
   (a) Work out the mean number of goals.
   (b) Work out the range of the number of goals scored.                    [London]

2. A fruit grower keeps a record of the weights (to the nearest kilogram) of plums he picks from each of 60 trees. The table opposite summarises his results.

| Weight per tree (kg) | Frequency (f) | Mid-point (m) | m × f |
|---|---|---|---|
| 1 to 5 | 1 | | |
| 6 to 10 | 13 | | |
| 11 to 15 | 28 | | |
| 16 to 20 | 15 | | |
| 21 to 25 | 3 | | |

2. (a) Which is the modal class?
   (b) Copy and complete the mid-point column.
   (c) Calculate an estimate of the mean weight of plums per tree.
   (d) This frequency polygon shows the distribution of the weights picked from a second set of 60 plum trees which, unlike the first, had been fertilised with GrowLots. Draw a frequency polygon to show the distribution of the weights picked from the first set on the same axes.

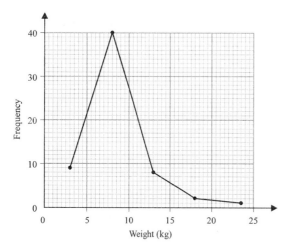

   (e) Would you advise the grower to keep using GrowLots? Give a reason for your answer.    [WJEC]

3. Vicki investigated the times taken to serve 120 customers at a supermarket called Pricewell. Her results are shown below.

| Time (seconds) | 20–30 | 30–40 | 40–50 | 50–60 | 60–70 |
|---|---|---|---|---|---|
| Number of customers | 4 | 17 | 48 | 16 | 35 |

   (a) (i) Calculate an estimate of the mean time to serve the customers.
      (ii) Write down the modal class for the serving times.
   Vicki decided to extend her investigation to another supermarket called Costsave. She obtained the times taken to serve 120 customers at Costsave. Her extended table is shown below.

| Time (seconds) | 20–30 | 30–40 | 40–50 | 50–60 | 60–70 |
|---|---|---|---|---|---|
| Number of customers at Pricewell | 4 | 17 | 48 | 16 | 35 |
| Number of customers at Costsave | 5 | 20 | 54 | 36 | 5 |

   (b) Vicki correctly worked out the mean and modal class for the times at Costsave. She also worked out correctly the median of the times for each supermarket.
   Use your answers to part (a) to complete the table below.

|  | Pricewell | Costsave |
|---|---|---|
| median | 48.1 | 46.5 |
| modal class |  | 40–50 |
| mean |  | 46.3 |

   Which average in this table represents the data most fairly? Give a reason for your answer.    [MEG]

4. Ian looked at a passage from a book. He recorded the number of words in each sentence in a frequency table using class intervals of 1–5, 6–10, 11–15, etc.

| Class interval | Frequency (f) | Mid-interval value (x) | f × x |
|---|---|---|---|
| 1–5 | 16 | 3 | 48 |
| 6–10 | 28 | ...... | ...... |
| 11–15 | 26 | 13 | 338 |
| 16–20 | 14 | ...... | ...... |
| 21–25 | 10 | 23 | 230 |
| 26–30 | 3 | ...... | ...... |
| 31–35 | 1 | 33 | 33 |
| 36–40 | 0 | ...... | ...... |
| 41–45 | 2 | 43 | 86 |
|  | TOTAL = .... |  | TOTAL = .... |

   (a) Copy and complete the table.
   (b) Write down
      (i) the modal class interval,
      (ii) the class interval in which the median lies.
   (c) Work out an estimate of the mean number of words in a sentence.

5. Cole's sells furniture and will deliver up to a distance of 20 miles. The diagram shows the delivery charges made by Cole's.

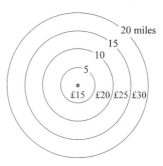

**5.** The table shows the information in the diagram and also the number of deliveries made in the first week of May 1994.

| Distance (d) from Cole's in miles | Delivery Charge in pounds | Number of deliveries |
|---|---|---|
| $0 < d \leq 5$ | 15 | 27 |
| $5 < d \leq 10$ | 20 | 11 |
| $10 < d \leq 15$ | 25 | 8 |
| $15 < d \leq 20$ | 30 | 4 |

(a) Calculate the mean charge per delivery for these deliveries.
(b) Calculate an estimate for the mean distance of the customers' homes from Cole's. [London]

**6.** Andrew is a checkout operator at the local supermarket.
At the end of a shift, he looked at the total amounts of money that people had spent.

| Amount spent (£x) | Number of people |
|---|---|
| $0 < x \leq 20$ | 25 |
| $20 < x \leq 40$ | 9 |
| $40 < x \leq 60$ | 10 |
| $60 < x \leq 80$ | 15 |
| $80 < x \leq 100$ | 8 |

(a) Calculate an estimate of the mean amount spent by his customers during that shift.
(b) The manager of the supermarket decides to give a bonus to the most efficient checkout operator. She decides that this will be the person who works at the fastest rate. Here is some information about the three checkout operators after their shift.

| Operator | Number of items sold | Time worked |
|---|---|---|
| Andrew | 10 500 | $7\frac{1}{2}$ hours |
| Barbara | 6 400 | 4 hours 15 min |
| Colin | 9 120 | 6 hours |

Who should get the bonus?
Give a reason for your answer and show all your working. [NEAB]

**7.** Thirty-five people took part in an ice-skating competition.
The points they scored are shown below.

```
18  24  19   3  24  11  25
10  25  14  25   9  16  26
21  27  13  23   5  26  22
12  27  20   7  28  21  20
22  16  12  25   7  25  19
```

(a) Work out the range of points scored.
(b) Copy and complete the frequency table. [London]

| Class interval | Frequency |
|---|---|
| 1–5 | 2 |
| 6–10 | 4 |
| 11–15 | |
| 16–20 | |
| 21–25 | |
| 26–30 | |

# Test yourself

**1.** These are the heights of eleven people, measured in centimetres.

171, 173, 181, 176, 179, 173, 175, 176, 178, 176, 180.

**QUESTION**  Calculate the mean, median, mode, range.

**ANSWER**  Mean = 176.2 cm
Median = 176 cm
Mode = 176 cm
Range = 10 cm

*If your answers are incorrect review page 494, Section 25.2, Example 1 on measures of average and spread.*

**2.** This frequency distribution shows the number of eggs laid by the chickens from one farm in one week.

| Number of eggs laid in one week (x) | 0 | 1 | 2 | 3 | 4 | 5 | 6 |
|---|---|---|---|---|---|---|---|
| Frequency (f) | 1 | 3 | 6 | 14 | 10 | 9 | 7 |

QUESTION    Calculate the mean number of eggs laid.

ANSWER    3.68    *If your answer is incorrect review page 498, Section 25.3, Example 2 on calculating averages of frequency distributions.*

QUESTION    Write down the mode.

ANSWER    3    *If your answer is incorrect review page 498, Section 25.3, Example 2 on calculating averages of frequency distributions.*

QUESTION    Work out the median.

ANSWER    4    *If your answer is incorrect review page 498, Section 25.3, Example 2 on calculating averages of frequency distributions.*

**3.** This frequency distribution shows the examination results for 25 students.

| Mark | Number of students |
|---|---|
| 1–5 | 1 |
| 6–10 | 3 |
| 11–15 | 4 |
| 16–20 | 8 |
| 21–25 | 12 |
| 26–30 | 2 |

QUESTION    Calculate an estimate of the mean.

ANSWER    18.5    *If your answer is incorrect review page 501, Section 25.4, Example 3 on grouped frequency distributions.*

QUESTION    Write down the modal class

ANSWER    21–25    *If your answer is incorrect review page 501, Section 25.4, Example 3 on grouped frequency distributions.*

# Summary of key points to remember

1. For a set of single items

   **Mean** $\bar{x} = \dfrac{\Sigma x}{\text{n}}$

2. The **median** is the middle item when the data is arranged in order. You find the middle item by:

   $\dfrac{\Sigma f + 1}{2}$

   For an even number of items the median is the mean of the two middle items.

3. The **mode** is the item which occuurs most often (the most common item). There is no mode if all items only occur once. There may be more than one mode.

4. The range is a measure of the spread of the data.

   **Range = largest value − smallest value**

5. The estimate of the mean of a frequency distribution is:

   **Estimate of mean** $\bar{x} = \dfrac{\Sigma fx}{\Sigma f}$

   For grouped frequency distribution the $x$-values are the mid-points of the class intervals.

6. For grouped frequency distributions we cannot find a mode, since we do not know what the individual items are. The **modal class** is the class that has the highest frequency.

# 26 Cumulative frequency

## 26.1 Cumulative frequency

Cumulative frequency is a branch of statistics used to estimate statistical measures such as median and interquartile range. You can plot a graph of cumulative frequency and use it to estimate values that are not given in the frequency table.

In this unit you will need to remember about frequency tables, class intervals and class widths.

The **class boundaries** are the upper and lower limits of the class. For example, for a class of 10–20

● the **lower class boundary (l.c.b.)** = **10**

● The **upper class boundary (u.c.b.)** = **20**

The **cumulative frequency** is the running total of the frequency up to a particular class boundary.

There is always a question on this topic in the GCSE exam.

*Example 1*

The frequency table shows the distribution of 140 students' marks in a test. Display this data in a cumulative frequency table.

| Marks ($x$) | 0 | 1 | 2 | 3 | 4 | 5 | 6 | 7 | 8 | 9 | 10 |
|---|---|---|---|---|---|---|---|---|---|---|---|
| Frequency ($f$) | 1 | 3 | 4 | 17 | 25 | 30 | 23 | 19 | 15 | 2 | 1 |

From the table you can see that $1 + 3 + 4 + 17 + 25 = 50$ students obtained a mark of 4 or less.

So the cumulative frequency up to 4 is 50.

| Marks ($x$) | Frequency ($f$) | Cumulative frequency |
|---|---|---|
| 0 | 1 | 1 |
| 1 | 3 | $1 + 3 = 4$ |
| 2 | 4 | $4 + 4 = 8$ |
| 3 | 17 | $8 + 17 = 25$ |
| 4 | 25 | 50 |
| 5 | 30 | 80 |
| 6 | 23 | 103 |
| 7 | 19 | 122 |
| 8 | 15 | 137 |
| 9 | 2 | 139 |
| 10 | 1 | 140 |

The cumulative frequency of a frequency distribution is the total frequency up to the upper class boundary.

You can check that your cumulative frequency total is correct by making sure it is the same as the total number of items in the distribution.

You can also calculate the cumulative frequencies for a grouped frequency table.

### Example 2

The grouped frequency table below gives the heights of 100 people.

| Height ($x$) | Frequency ($f$) | Cumulative frequency |
|---|---|---|
| 100 to < 110 | 2 | 2 |
| 110 to < 120 | 5 | 2 + 5 = 7 |
| 120 to < 130 | 9 | 7 + 9 = 16 |
| 130 to < 140 | 16 | 32 |
| 140 to < 150 | 27 | 59 |
| 150 to < 160 | 19 | 78 |
| 160 to < 170 | 12 | 90 |
| 170 to < 180 | 7 | 97 |
| 180 to < 190 | 3 | 100 |

### Exercise 26A

**1.** Draw up a cumulative frequency table for the following data about shoe sizes of 150 people.

| Shoe size | 4 | 5 | 6 | 7 | 8 | 9 | 10 | 11 | 12 |
|---|---|---|---|---|---|---|---|---|---|
| Frequency | 2 | 7 | 16 | 30 | 45 | 26 | 14 | 8 | 2 |

**2.** Copy and complete the cumulative frequency table for this grouped frequency distribution, whose sample size is 180.

| Examination mark ($x$) | Frequency ($f$) | Cumulative frequency |
|---|---|---|
| 0–5 | 3 | 3 |
| 6–10 | 8 | 11 |
| 11–15 | 15 | |
| 16–20 | 28 | |
| 21–25 | 37 | |
| 26–30 | 45 | |
| 31–35 | 23 | |
| 36–40 | 16 | |
| 41–45 | 4 | |
| 46–50 | 1 | |

**3.** Copy and complete the cumulative frequency table for this grouped frequency distribution.

| Weight in kg ($x$) | Frequency ($f$) | Cumulative frequency |
|---|---|---|
| 100 to < 110 | 4 | 4 |
| 110 to < 120 | 19 | 23 |
| 120 to < 130 | 39 | |
| 130 to < 140 | 60 | |
| 140 to < 150 | 53 | |
| 150 to < 160 | 34 | |
| 160 to < 170 | 16 | |
| 170 to < 180 | 3 | |
| 180 to < 190 | 2 | |

# 26.2 Cumulative frequency curves

You can plot the cumulative frequency data on a graph. Join the points on your graph with a smooth curve.

The graph of the cumulative frequencies is called a **cumulative frequency curve.**

The cumulative frequency is always on the *vertical* axis.

The item $(x)$ is on the *horixontal* axis.

### Example 3

Draw a cumulative frequency curve for this distribution.

| Mark $(x)$ | Frequency $(f)$ | Cumulative frequency |
|:---:|:---:|:---:|
| 0 | 1 | 1 |
| 1 | 3 | 4 |
| 2 | 4 | 8 |
| 3 | 17 | 25 |
| 4 | 25 | 50 |
| 5 | 30 | 80 |
| 6 | 23 | 103 |
| 7 | 19 | 122 |
| 8 | 15 | 137 |
| 9 | 2 | 139 |
| 10 | 1 | 140 |

First choose a scale for each axis and draw the axes with cumulative frequency on the vertical axis.

Then plot the points (Mark, Cumulative frequency) given in the table:

(0,1), (2,4), (2,8), (3,25), (4,50), (5,80)
(6,103), (7,122), (8,137), (9,139), (10,140)

Draw a smooth curve through the points.

The cumulative frequency curve is S-shaped. Another name for a cumulative frequency curve is **ogive**.

For grouped frequency distribution tables, the points plotted for a cumulative frequency curve are always at the upper limit of each group. For example in a group 10–20 kg the true upper limit is 20.5 but 20 is also acceptable. This is because the data is continuous.

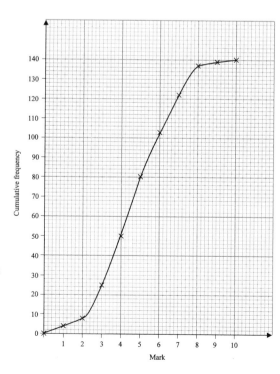

However, you must ensure that you use the same boundaries
consistently throughout the question.

### Example 4

The following table gives the heights of 100 people to the nearest
centimetre.

| Heights | 100–109 | 110–119 | 120–129 | 130–139 | 140–149 | 150–159 | 160–169 | 170–179 | 180–189 |
|---|---|---|---|---|---|---|---|---|---|
| **Frequency** | 2 | 5 | 9 | 16 | 27 | 19 | 12 | 7 | 3 |
| **Cumulative frequency** | 2 | 7 | 16 | 32 | 59 | 78 | 90 | 97 | 100 |

Draw a cumulative frequency curve for this data.

You will notice that the data is continuous and a gap exists
between one class interval and the next. You plot the points at the
upper bound of each class interval. The true upper class
boundaries are: 109.5, 119.5, 129.5, etc.

Therefore you plot the points at (109.5,2), (119.5,7), (129.5,16),
(139.5,32), (149.5,59), (159.5,78), (169.5,90), (179.5,97), (189.5,100)

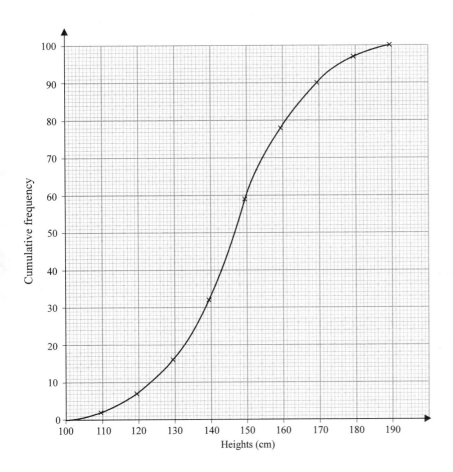

## Exercise 26B

You will need graph paper for this exercise.

1. (a) Copy and complete the cumulative frequency table.

| Mark (x) | Frequency (f) | Cumulative frequency |
|----------|---------------|----------------------|
| 10 | 2 | 2 |
| 11 | 9 | 11 |
| 12 | 21 | |
| 13 | 45 | |
| 14 | 81 | |
| 15 | 53 | |
| 16 | 34 | |
| 17 | 15 | |
| 18 | 7 | |
| 19 | 3 | |

(b) Plot the cumulative frequency data on a graph and draw the cumulative frequency curve. Label the axes and give your graph a title.

2. The weights of 100 students were recorded to the nearest kilogram and shown in a frequency table.

| Weight (kg) | Frequency |
|-------------|-----------|
| 20–29 | 8 |
| 30–39 | 13 |
| 40–49 | 41 |
| 50–59 | 20 |
| 60–69 | 14 |
| 70–79 | 3 |
| 80–89 | 1 |

(a) Draw up a cumulative frequency table for this data.
(b) Draw a cumulative frequency curve.

3. The heights of 288 people, measured to the nearest centimetre, are shown in the frequency table.

| Height (cm) | Frequency |
|-------------|-----------|
| 130–135 | 2 |
| 136–140 | 5 |
| 141–145 | 13 |
| 146–150 | 22 |
| 151–155 | 36 |
| 156–160 | 57 |
| 161–165 | 87 |
| 166–170 | 37 |
| 171–175 | 21 |
| 176–180 | 7 |
| 181–185 | 1 |

(a) Draw up a cumulative frequency table for this data.
(b) Draw a cumulative frequency curve.

## 26.3 Median, quartiles and interquartile range from cumulative frequency curves

You can use a cumulative graph to estimate the median, upper quartile, lower quartile and interquartile range.

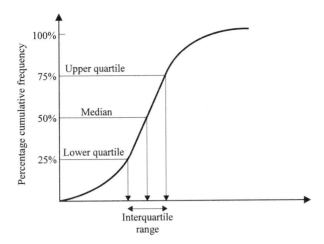

- **Median**

  The **median** is the middle value of a distribution.

  To find an estimate of the median from a cumulative frequency curve:

  - Find the value half way up the cumulative frequency axis.

  - Draw a horizontal line from this point to meet the cumulative frequency curve.

  - Where this horizontal line meets the curve draw a vertical line down to the horizontal axis.

  - Read off the value on the horizontal axis.

  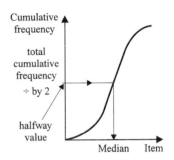

- **Lower quartile**

  The **lower quartile** is the value one quarter way into the distribution.

  To find an estimate of the lower quartile from a cumulative frequency curve:

  - Find one quarter way up the cumulative frequency axis.

  - Draw a horizontal line from this point to meet the cumulative frequency curve.

  - Where this horizontal line meets the curve draw a vertical line down to the horizontal axis.

  - Read off the value on the horizontal axis.

  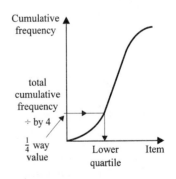

- **Upper quartile**

  The **upper quartile** is the value three quarters of the way into the distribution.

  You can find an estimate of the upper quartile from a cumulative frequency curve in a similar way to finding the lower quartile.

  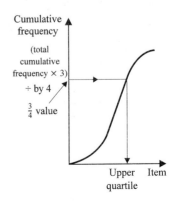

- **Interquartile range**

  The **interquartile range** is the difference between the upper quartile and the lower quartile.

  Interquartile range = Upper quartile − Lower quartile.

  The interquartile range gives the range of the middle half of the data. It is not distorted by extreme values at either end of the distribution, as the range can be. It shows how the distribution clusters around the median.

*Example 5*

Estimate the median, lower quartile, upper quartile and interquartile range from this cumulative frequency curve.

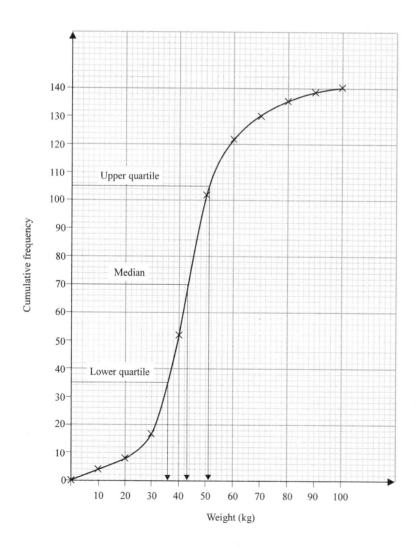

## Median

The value half way up the cumulative frequency axis is 70. Going across horizontally at 70 and then vertically down from the curve to the horizontal axis gives:

Median = 43 kg

## Lower quartile

The value one quarter up the cumulative frequency axis is 35. Going across horizontally at 35 and then vertically down from the curve to the horizontal axis gives:

Lower quartile = 36 kg

## Upper quartile

The value three quarters up the cumulative axis is 105. Going across horizontally at 105 and then vertically down from the curve to the horizontal axis gives:

Upper quartile = 51 kg

## The interquartile range

Interquartile range = Upper quartile − lower quartile

= 51 − 36

= 15 kg

## *Example 6*

The grouped frequency distribution table below shows the mark obtained by 200 people in a test.

| Mark % | Frequency |
|--------|-----------|
| 0–10 | 2 |
| 11–20 | 6 |
| 21–30 | 11 |
| 31–40 | 22 |
| 41–50 | 39 |
| 51–60 | 57 |
| 61–70 | 43 |
| 71–80 | 18 |
| 81–90 | 9 |
| 91–100 | 3 |

(a) Draw a cumulative frequency curve.

(b) Use your curve to estimate the median and interquartile range.

(c) What percentage of people scored more than 74 marks?

(d) What percentage of people scored between 25 and 74 marks?

(a) First we add a third column to the table for cumulative frequency.

| Mark % | Frequency | Cumulative frequency |
|--------|-----------|----------------------|
| 0–10 | 2 | 2 |
| 11–20 | 6 | 8 |
| 21–30 | 11 | 19 |
| 31–40 | 22 | 41 |
| 41–50 | 39 | 80 |
| 51–60 | 57 | 137 |
| 61–70 | 43 | 170 |
| 71–80 | 18 | 188 |
| 81–90 | 9 | 197 |
| 91–100 | 3 | 210 |

Then we draw the graph.

*Remember*: plot the points for (Mark, Cumulative frequency), using the upper boundary of each class interval for the marks data. That is, plot points (10,2) (20,8), etc.

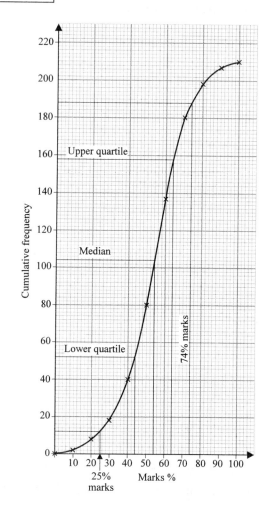

(b) The value half way up the cumulative frequency axis is $\frac{210}{2} = 105$

From the graph    median = 54

Interquartile range = upper quartile − lower quartile

$$= 64 - 44$$

$$= 20$$

(c) From the graph, 192 people scored 74 marks or less. So
210 − 192 = 18 people scored more than 74 marks.

As a percentage

$$\tfrac{18}{210} \times 100\% = 8.6\%$$

8.6% scored more than 74 marks.

(d) From the graph 12 people scored 25 marks or less. So
192 − 12 = 180 people scored between 25 and 74 marks.

As a percentage

$$\tfrac{180}{210} \times 100\% = 85.7\%$$

85.7% scored between 25 and 74 marks.

### Exercise 26C

You will need graph paper for this exercise.

**1.** Make a cumulative frequency table for this data about the distance that 240 people travel to work.

| Distance (km) | Frequency |
|---|---|
| 1–5 | 5 |
| 6–10 | 41 |
| 11–15 | 77 |
| 16–20 | 58 |
| 21–25 | 39 |
| 26–30 | 17 |
| 31–35 | 3 |

(a) Draw a cumulative frequency curve.
(b) Use the cumulative frequency curve to find an estimate for:
  (i) the median
  (ii) the lower quartile
  (iii) the upper quartile
  (iv) the interquartile range

**2.** The table below shows the ages, to the nearest year, of 200 people.

| Age (years) | Frequency |
|---|---|
| 0–10 | 5 |
| 11–20 | 19 |
| 21–30 | 47 |
| 31–40 | 79 |
| 41–50 | 32 |
| 51–60 | 15 |
| 61–70 | 2 |
| 71–80 | 1 |

(a) Draw up a cumulative frequency table.
(b) Construct a cumulative frequency curve.
(c) Find estimates for:
  (i) the median
  (ii) the lower quartile
  (iii) the upper quartile
  (iv) the interquartile range

3. The frequency table shows the weights of 300 students, measured to the nearest kilogram.

| Weight (kg) | Frequency |
|---|---|
| 30–39 | 3 |
| 40–49 | 11 |
| 50–59 | 24 |
| 60–69 | 56 |
| 70–79 | 123 |
| 80–89 | 70 |
| 90–99 | 13 |

(a) Draw up a cumulative frequency table for the data.
(b) Construct a cumulative frequency curve.
(c) Find estimates for:
   (i) the median
   (ii) the lower quartile
   (iii) the upper quartile
   (iv) the interquartile range.
(d) What percentage of students weigh 56 kg or less?
(e) What percentage of students weigh more than 72 kg?

4. The following frequency distribution shows the age distribution of a country's population.

| Age (years) | Frequency (millions) |
|---|---|
| 0–8 | 71 |
| 9–16 | 110 |
| 17–24 | 186 |
| 25–32 | 131 |
| 33–40 | 88 |
| 41–48 | 52 |
| 49–56 | 25 |
| 57–64 | 7 |

(a) Draw up a cumulative frequency table.
(b) Construct a cumulative frequency curve.
(c) Find estimates for:
   (i) the median
   (ii) the lower quartile
   (iii) the upper quartile
   (iv) the interquartile range.
(d) What percentage of the population is 49 years or older?
(e) What percentage of the population is less than 25 years old?
(f) What percentage of the population is aged between 9 and 32 inclusive?

## Worked exam question 1

The lengths of the middle finger of 105 female students are given in the table. The measurements are to the nearest millimetre.

**Do:**
Make sure the total is 105

| Finger length (mm) | Frequency | Cumulative frequency |
|---|---|---|
| 60–74 | 9 | 9 |
| 75–79 | 9 | 18 |
| 80–84 | 14 | 32 |
| 85–89 | 15 | 47 |
| 90–94 | 18 | 65 |
| 95–99 | 17 | 82 |
| 100–104 | 15 | 97 |
| 105–114 | 8 | 105 |

(a) Complete the cumulative frequency table.

**Do:**
Remember that cumulative frequency means running total

(b) (i) What is the upper class boundary of the class inteval that has a frequency of 14?

.....84.5..... mm •

**Do:**
Remember that the data is continuous and to give the upper bound of the class

(ii) Draw the cumulative frequency curve on the graph below.

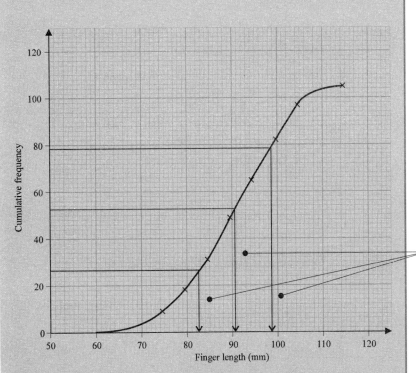

**Do:**
Remember to plot the upper bounds

Draw lines lines on the graph to find the median, lower quartile and upper quartile.

(c) Use your graph to find

(i) the median finger length,

$\frac{105}{2} = 52.5$

.....92..... mm

(ii) the interquartile range.

*interquartile range = upper quartile - lower*
*quartile*

**Do:**
Write down the rule

*= 99 – 82.5*

Read the values of your graph

*= 16.5*

.....16.5..... mm

(London)

## Worked exam question 2

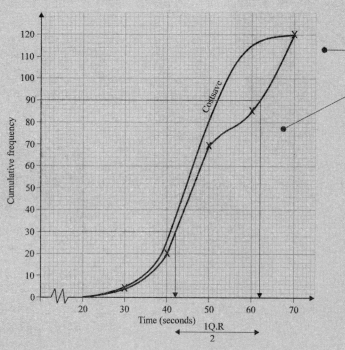

**Do:**
Label the points on the curve with crosses
Join the crosses with a smooth curve

The graph shows the cumulative frequency curve for the serving times at Costsave.

(i)   On the same axes, show the cumulative frequency curve for the serving times at Pricewell.

| Time (seconds) | 20–30 | 30–40 | 40–50 | 50–60 | 60–70 |
|---|---|---|---|---|---|
| **Number of customers at Pricewell** | 4 | 17 | 48 | 16 | 35 |
| **Number of customers at Costsave** | 5 | 20 | 54 | 36 | 5 |
| **Cumulative frequency (Pricewell)** | 4 | 21 | 69 | 85 | 126 |

**Do:**
Work out the cumulative frequency

(ii)   Complete the table below.

|  | Pricewell | Costsave |
|---|---|---|
| lower quartile | 42 | 41 |
| upper quartile | 62 | 53 |
| interquartile range | 20 | 12 |

Show on the graph how you worked out these values

(iii)   Use the information in the table to comment on the difference in the distributions of the serving times at Pricewell and Costsave.                    (SEG)

Comment on the statistics given and calculated

*Pricewell have a bigger interquartile range than Costsave. This indicates that the serving times are more widespread than Costsave. More customers have to wait longer to be served at Pricewell, shown by the higher upper quartile.*

### Exercise 26D (Mixed questions)

**1.** A forester records the ages, in complete years, of 200 trees in a wood. This table shows her results.

| Age (years) | Frequency |
|---|---|
| 0 to 19 | 6 |
| 20 to 39 | 12 |
| 40 to 59 | 18 |
| 60 to 79 | 38 |
| 80 to 99 | 45 |
| 100 to 119 | 35 |
| 120 to 139 | 32 |
| 140 to 159 | 14 |

(a) Copy and complete this cumulative frequency table.

| Age in years (Less than) | Cumulative frequency |
|---|---|
| 20 | |
| 40 | |
| 60 | |
| 80 | |
| 100 | |
| 120 | |
| 140 | |
| 160 | |

(b) Draw a cumulative frequency diagram to show this information on graph paper.
(c) Estimate how many of the 200 trees are at least 130 years old.
(d) (i) Estimate the median age of the trees in the sample.
(ii) Estimate the interquartile range of the ages of the trees in the sample.    [WJEC]

**2.** A wedding was attended by 120 guests. The distance, $d$ miles, that each guest travelled was recorded in the frequency table below.

| Distance ($d$ miles) | Number of guests |
|---|---|
| $0 < d \leqslant 10$ | 26 |
| $10 < d \leqslant 20$ | 38 |
| $20 < d \leqslant 30$ | 20 |
| $30 < d \leqslant 50$ | 20 |
| $50 < d \leqslant 100$ | 12 |
| $100 < d \leqslant 140$ | 4 |

(a) Using the mid-interval values, calculate an estimate of the mean distance travelled.
(b) (i) Complete the cumulative frequency table below.

| Distance ($d$ miles) | Number of guests |
|---|---|
| $d \leqslant 10$ | 26 |
| $d \leqslant 20$ | |
| $d \leqslant 30$ | |
| $d \leqslant 50$ | |
| $d \leqslant 100$ | |
| $d \leqslant 140$ | 120 |

(ii) Draw a cumulative frequency curve to represent the information in the table.
(c) (i) Use the cumulative frequency curve to estimate the median distance travelled by the guests.
(ii) Give a reason for the large difference between the mean distance and the median distance.    [MEG]

**3.** Laura and Joy played 40 games of golf together. The table below shows Laura's scores.

| Scores $x$ | Frequency |
|---|---|
| $70 < x \leqslant 80$ | 1 |
| $80 < x \leqslant 90$ | 4 |
| $90 < x \leqslant 100$ | 15 |
| $100 < x \leqslant 110$ | 17 |
| $110 < x \leqslant 120$ | 3 |

(a) On a copy of the grid below, draw a cumulative frequency diagram to show Laura's scores.

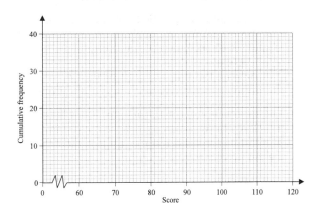

**3.** (b) Making your method clear, use your graph to find
(i) Laura's median score,
(ii) the interquartile range of her scores.
(c) Joy's median score was 103. The interquartile range of her scores was 6.
(i) Who was the more consistent player? Give a reason for your choice.
(ii) The winner of a game of golf is the one with the lowest score. Who won most of these 40 games? Give a reason for your choice.　　[NEAB]

**4.** A group of people took a fitness test. They exercised hard. Then they were timed to see how long their pulses took to return to normal.
The time taken for a pulse to return to normal is called the RECOVERY TIME.
The recovery times for the group are shown in the table below.

| Recovery time (seconds) | Frequency | Cumulative frequency |
|---|---|---|
| 0 up to but not including 20 | 0 | 0 |
| 20 up to but not including 40 | 7 | 7 |
| 40 up to but not including 60 | 9 | 16 |
| 60 up to but not including 80 | 18 | 34 |
| 80 up to but not including 90 | 13 | 47 |
| 90 up to but not including 100 | 12 | 59 |
| 100 up to but not including 120 | 9 | 68 |
| 120 up to but not including 140 | 6 | 74 |

(a) Use the figures in the table to draw a cumulative frequency curve.
(b) Use your cumulative frequency curve to estimate the value of
(i) the median,　(ii) the interquartile range.

A second group of people took the fitness test. The recovery times of people in this group had a median of 61 seconds and an interquartile range of 22 seconds.
(c) Compare the fitness results of the two groups.　　[London]

**5.** The speeds, in miles per hour (mph), of 200 cars travelling on the A320 road were measured.
The results are shown in the table at the top of the next column.

| Speed (mph) | Cumulative frequency |
|---|---|
| not exceeding 20 | 1 |
| not exceeding 25 | 5 |
| not exceeding 30 | 14 |
| not exceeding 35 | 28 |
| not exceeding 40 | 66 |
| not exceeding 45 | 113 |
| not exceeding 50 | 164 |
| not exceeding 55 | 196 |
| not exceeding 60 | 200 |
| TOTAL | 200 |

(a) On a grid draw a cumulative frequency graph to show these figures.
(b) Use your graph to find an estimate for
(i) the median speed (in mph),
(ii) the interquartile range (in mph).

**6.** The cumulative frequency graph below gives information on house prices in 1992. The cumulative frequency is given as a percentage of all houses in England.

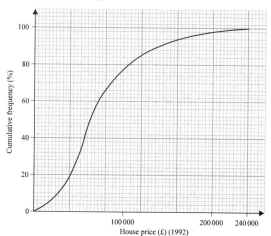

This group frequency table gives the percentage distribution of house prices ($p$) in England in 1993.

| House prices ($p$) in pounds 1993 | Percentage of houses in this class interval |
|---|---|
| $0 \leqslant p < 40\,000$ | 26 |
| $40\,000 \leqslant p < 52\,000$ | 19 |
| $52\,000 \leqslant p < 68\,000$ | 22 |
| $68\,000 \leqslant p < 88\,000$ | 15 |
| $88\,000 \leqslant p < 120\,000$ | 9 |
| $120\,000 \leqslant p < 160\,000$ | 5 |
| $160\,000 \leqslant p < 220\,000$ | 4 |

**6.** (a) Use the data above to complete the cumulative frequency table below.

| House prices (p) in pounds 1993 | Cumulative frequency (%) |
|---|---|
| $0 \leqslant p < \ 40\,000$ | |
| $0 \leqslant p < \ 52\,000$ | |
| $0 \leqslant p < \ 68\,000$ | |
| $0 \leqslant p < \ 88\,000$ | |
| $0 \leqslant p < 120\,000$ | |
| $0 \leqslant p < 160\,000$ | |
| $0 \leqslant p < 220\,000$ | |

(b) On a copy of the grid, construct a cumulative frequency graph for your table. In 1992 the price of a house was £100 000.

(c) Use both cumulative frequency graphs to estimate the price of this house in 1993. Make your method clear.                [London]

# Test yourself

The grouped frequency table shows the weights of 300 women measured to the nearest kilogram.

| Weight (kg) | 41–45 | 46–50 | 51–55 | 56–60 | 61–65 | 66–70 | 71–75 | 76–80 | 81–85 |
|---|---|---|---|---|---|---|---|---|---|
| Frequency | 8 | 18 | 34 | 76 | 100 | 46 | 12 | 5 | 1 |

**QUESTION**    Draw up a cumulative frequency table for the data.

**ANSWER**    Cumulative frequencies are: 8, 26, 60, 136, 236, 282, 294, 299, 300

*If your answers are incorrect review page 510, Section 26.1, Example 1*

**QUESTION**    Draw a cumulative frequency curve.

**ANSWER**

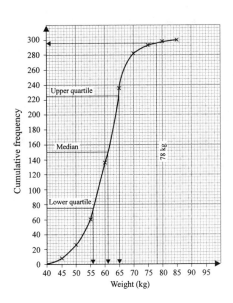

*If your answer is incorrect review page 512, Section 26.2 on drawing cumulative frequency curves.*

| QUESTION | Use your curve to estimate the median. |
|---|---|
| ANSWER | 62                           *If your answer is incorrect review page 514, Section 26.3 on estimating the median from a cumulative frequency curve* |

| QUESTION | Use your curve to estimate the interquartile range. |
|---|---|
| ANSWER | 8.5 kg                      *If your answer is incorrect review page 516, Section 26.3, Example 5* |

| QUESTION | Use your curve to estimate the percentage of women in the survey that weigh more than 78 kg |
|---|---|
| ANSWER | 1.3%                        *If your answer is incorrect review page 516, Section 26.3, Example 5* |

## Summary of key points to remember

1. **Cumulative frequency** is the running total of the frequency up to a particular class boundary. The final cumulative frequency is the same as the total number in the sample.

2. To draw a cumulative frequency curve, plot the points at the upper bound of each class interval against the cumulative frequency. Join the points with a smooth curve.

3. You can estimate values of the median and the upper and lower quartiles from a cumulative frequency curve.

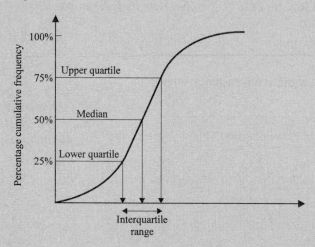

4. Interquartile range = upper quartile − lower quartile.

The interquartile range shows how the values are clustered around the median.

# 27 Scatter diagrams

## 27.1 Scatter diagrams

One way of seeing whether there is a relationship between two sets of data is to draw a **scatter diagram**.

- Draw an axis for each of the two sets of data.
- Plot the co-ordinates of the sets of data on a graph.
- Give the scatter diagram a title.

### Example 1

The heights and weights of eight students are given in the table.

| Height (cm) | 162 | 164 | 167 | 173 | 177 | 178 | 180 | 182 |
|---|---|---|---|---|---|---|---|---|
| Weight (kg) | 66 | 68 | 68 | 72 | 74 | 75 | 77 | 79 |

Draw a scatter diagram for this data.

We plot the points (162,66), (164,68), (167,68), (173,72) etc.

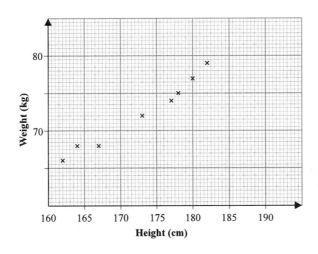

## 27.2 Correlation

Correlation is important in all aspects of research: education; medicine; industry; financial; road accidents; advertising and many more, because it helps people predict what might happen in the future.

You need to be able to recognise the different types of correlation from a scatter diagram.

● In this scatter diagram the points slope upwards. There is **good or strong correlation** because the pattern is clear. It is **positive correlation** because as the values of one set of data increase so do the values of the other set of data.

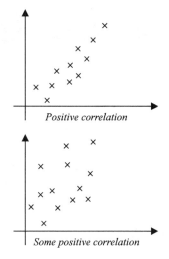

*Positive correlation*

● In this scatter diagram the points again slope upwards but there is greater spread amongst them. In this case there is evidence of **some positive correlation** but it is **not very good**.

*Some positive correlation*

● In this scatter diagram there is no correlation. The points are just randomly and widely spread about. There is **no evidence of correlation** or **zero correlation**.

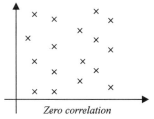

*Zero correlation*

● In this scatter diagram the points slope downwards and there is **good negative correlation** or **inverse correlation**. The values of one set of data increase while the values of the other set decrease.

*Negative correlation*

● In this scatter diagram there is **some negative correlation** as the points generally slope downwards, but it is not very good.

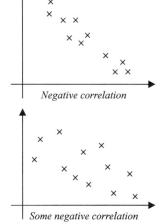

*Some negative correlation*

You should use these scatter diagrams to help you decide the type of correlation you get on the scatter diagrams you plot.

### Example 2

The table gives the weights in kilograms and the heights in centimetres of ten men.

Draw a scatter diagram for this data and comment on the correlation between height and weight.

| Height (cm) | 165 | 170 | 174 | 175 | 181 | 182 | 185 | 190 | 191 | 194 |
|---|---|---|---|---|---|---|---|---|---|---|
| Weight (kg) | 78 | 75 | 82 | 88 | 85 | 89 | 92 | 96 | 100 | 98 |

Here is the scatter diagram for the data.

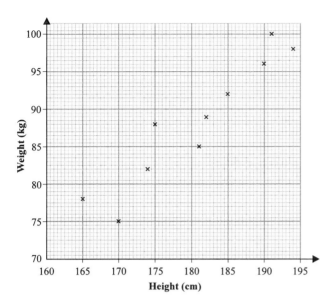

The points slope upwards and there is a good match between the height and weight. The values of weight increase with the values for height. In general the taller men are heavier than the shorter men.

There is good correlation and positive correlation.

## Exercise 27A

1. The heights and ages of ten people are shown below.

| Height (cm) | 159 | 173 | 159 | 165 | 151 |
|---|---|---|---|---|---|
| Age | 16 | 19 | 14 | 18 | 13 |

| Height (cm) | 162 | 156 | 161 | 167 | 176 |
|---|---|---|---|---|---|
| Age | 17 | 15 | 18 | 20 | 21 |

(a) Draw a scatter diagram for this information.
(b) Comment on the correlation.
(c) What conclusions do you draw from your graph?

2. The lengths and masses of twelve leaves from one tree were measured and recorded in the table below.

| Length (mm) | 66 | 89 | 63 | 68 | 87 | 80 | 89 |
|---|---|---|---|---|---|---|---|
| Mass (g) | 35 | 41 | 27 | 35 | 39 | 40 | 39 |

| Length (mm) | 61 | 73 | 77 | 85 | 91 |
|---|---|---|---|---|---|
| Mass (g) | 35 | 37 | 39 | 41 | 44 |

(a) Draw a scatter diagram for this data.
(b) Comment on the correlation.
(c) What conclusions do you draw from your graph?

3. The percentages gained by thirteen students in German and French examinations are shown in the table below.

| German | 61 | 79 | 34 | 68 | 45 | 56 | 83 |
|---|---|---|---|---|---|---|---|
| French | 65 | 74 | 29 | 75 | 39 | 51 | 85 |

| German | 72 | 93 | 88 | 51 | 39 | 77 |
|---|---|---|---|---|---|---|
| French | 72 | 88 | 91 | 56 | 36 | 78 |

(a) Draw a scatter diagram for this data.
(b) Comment on the correlation.

## 27.3 Line of best fit

The **line of best fit** drawn on a scatter diagram gives a clearer idea of the correlation between two sets of data.

The line of best fit is drawn to show the trend of the plotted points. The line should have an equal number of points on each side.

To draw a line of best fit, draw a line on the scatter diagram which shows the trend of the plotted points and has roughly an equal number of points on each side.

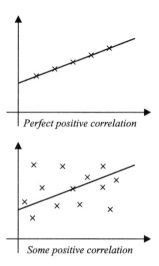

*Perfect positive correlation*

*Some positive correlation*

● This scatter diagram shows there is a **perfect positive correlation** as the line of best fit goes exactly through each point.

● This scatter diagram shows there is some positive correlation.

You can use a line of best fit to estimate values from one set of data when a value from the other set is known.

### *Example 3*

The marks achieved by twelve students in two science tests are given in the table below.

| Test 1 | 80 | 76 | 77 | 64 | 60 | 55 | 52 | 48 | 44 | 40 | 38 | 30 |
|--------|----|----|----|----|----|----|----|----|----|----|----|----|
| Test 2 | 84 | 80 | 79 | 62 | 65 | 60 | 52 | 54 | 50 | 48 | 44 | 42 |

(a) Draw a scatter diagram with a line of best fit.

(b) Comment on the correlation.

(c) Use your line of best fit to estimate a mark for Test 2 for a student who scores 50 in Test 1.

(a) First we draw and label the axes and plot the points on the scatter diagram.

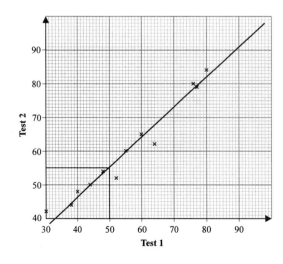

Then we can draw the line of best fit by eye, so that the trend of the plotted points is followed and there is roughly the same number of points above and below the line.

(b) The correlation is good positive correlation. The general trend is that students who scored the higher marks in Test 1 also scored higher marks in Test 2. Also, students who scored the lower marks in Test 1 scored lower marks in Test 2.

(c) To estimate a mark for Test 2 for a student who scores 50 in Test 1, using the best line of fit:
Draw a line from 50 on the Test 1 axis vertically up to the line of best fit. Draw a horizontal line from this point to meet the Test 2 axis. Read off the value 55. This is an estimate of the mark for Test 2 for a student who achieved a mark of 50 on Test 1.

---

### Exercise 27B

1. The heights and shoe sizes of eight people are shown below.

| Height (cm) | 162 | 176 | 179 | 165 | 159 | 185 | 150 | 168 |
|---|---|---|---|---|---|---|---|---|
| Shoe size | 5 | 8 | 10 | 6 | 5 | 11 | 3 | 6 |

   (a) Draw a scatter diagram for this data. Include the line of best fit.
   (b) Comment on the type of correlation.
   (c) Estimate the height of a person with shoe size 4.
   (d) Estimate the shoe size of a person of height 172 cm.

2. The sizes of engine and the number of kilometres travelled on 1 litre of petrol were recorded for ten cars.

| Engine size (cc) | Km per litre |
|---|---|
| 900 | 13 |
| 1100 | 16 |
| 1200 | 15.5 |
| 1400 | 14 |
| 1400 | 17 |
| 1500 | 13.5 |
| 1650 | 12 |
| 1750 | 10 |
| 2000 | 9.5 |
| 3500 | 8 |

   (a) Draw a scatter diagram for this data. Include a line of best fit.
   (b) Comment on the type of correlation.
   (c) Estimate the size of the engine of a car that travels 11 kilometres on one litre of petrol.

3. The table below shows the maximum temperature in June and the height above sea level for ten towns.

| Height above sea level (m) | June maximum temperature |
|---|---|
| 200 | 24 |
| 400 | 25 |
| 500 | 21 |
| 800 | 24 |
| 900 | 18 |
| 1200 | 21 |
| 1500 | 17 |
| 1800 | 14 |
| 2200 | 10 |
| 2500 | 11 |

   (a) Draw a scatter diagram for this data. Include the line of best fit.
   (b) Comment on the type of correlation.
   (c) Estimate the maximum June temperature of a town 1100 metres above sea level.

**4.** The lengths and weights of ten leeks were recorded in the table below.

| Length of leek (cm) | Weight of leek (g) |
|---|---|
| 30.2 | 100 |
| 32.1 | 130 |
| 32.8 | 90 |
| 34.9 | 140 |
| 38.0 | 180 |
| 41.2 | 180 |
| 43.7 | 150 |
| 44.8 | 200 |
| 45.1 | 200 |
| 46.9 | 230 |

(a) Draw a scatter diagram for this data. Include the line of best fit.
(b) Comment on the type of correlation.
(c) Estimate the length of a leek that weighs 155 grams.

## Worked exam question 1

The points on the scatter graph show the miles per gallon (mpg) and the size of engine (in cm$^3$) of thirteen cars.

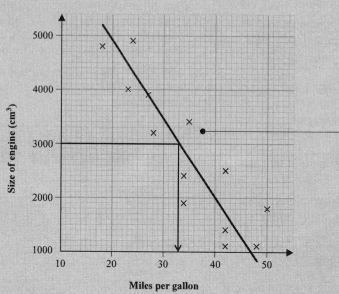

**Do:**
Show how you use the line of best fit to answer part (d)
Get an even spread of points above and below the line

(a) How does the miles per gallon change as the size of engine increases?

*The miles per gallon decrease as the size of engine*

*increases.*

(b) What type of correlation does the graph have?

*negative*

(c) Draw a line of best fit on the scatter graph.

A new car is made with an engine size of $3000\,\text{cm}^3$.

(d) Use your line of best fit to estimate the miles per gallon for this car.

..........*33*.......... miles per gallon

(London)

## Worked exam question 2

The gestation period and life expectancy for various mammals are given in the following table.

| Mammal | Gestation period (days) | Life expectancy (years) |
| --- | --- | --- |
| Mouse | 18 | 1.5 |
| Fox | 60 | 14 |
| Rat | 22 | 2 |
| Mole | 30 | 6 |
| Jack rabbit | 44 | 7 |
| Rabbit | 28 | 3 |
| Arctic wolf | 64 | 8 |
| Otter | 65 | 13 |

(a) Plot this information as a scatter graph.

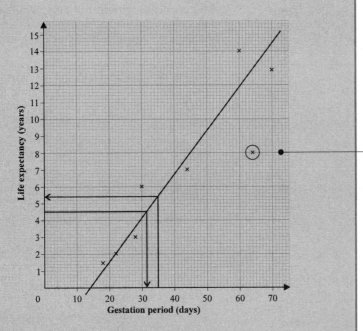

**Do:**
Plot your points with crosses
Notice that this point does not fit the general trend. Ignore this point when you draw the line of best fit

(b) One of the points does not fit very well.

(i) Circle this point.

(ii) Write down the name of the mammal represented by this point.

*Artic Wolf*

(c) Draw the line of best fit on the scatter graph.

(d) Use the line of best fit to estimate

(i) the life expectancy of a mammal that has a gestation period of 35 days,

*5.4* years

(ii) the gestation period of a mammal whose life expectancy is 4.5 years.

*31* days

(WJEC)

**Do:**
Show on the scatter graph where you have read off your answers

---

### Exercise 27C (Mixed questions)

1.

Sketches of six scatter diagrams A to F are shown above.
(a) Which scatter diagrams show
(i) direct (positive) correlation
(ii) inverse (negative) correlation
(iii) no correlation? [London]

2. Maria wants to buy a small car.
She collects the prices and ages of some cars of a particular type on sale in her town.
She displays the information in a table as shown below.

| Age of car in years | Price (£) |
|---|---|
| 6 | 2200 |
| 8 | 1400 |
| 7 | 2000 |
| 6 | 3300 |
| 2 | 7000 |
| 4 | 5500 |
| 4 | 4600 |
| 5 | 3600 |
| 3 | 5000 |
| 5 | 2300 |
| 3 | 6100 |
| 5 | 2600 |

(a) On a copy of the axes shown opposite, complete the scatter graph of price against age. The first four points have been plotted for you.

**2. (a)**

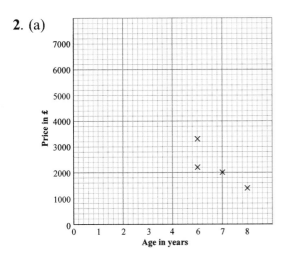

(b) What conclusion can you draw from your scatter graph? [MEG]

**3.** Ten people entered a craft competition. Their displays of work were awarded marks by two different judges.

| Competitor | A | B | C | D | E | F | G | H | I | J |
|---|---|---|---|---|---|---|---|---|---|---|
| First judge | 90 | 35 | 60 | 15 | 95 | 25 | 5 | 100 | 70 | 45 |
| Second judge | 75 | 30 | 55 | 20 | 75 | 30 | 10 | 85 | 65 | 40 |

The table shows the marks that the two judges gave to each of the competitors.
(a) (i) Draw a scatter diagram to show this information.
(ii) Draw a line of best fit.
(b) A late entry was given 75 marks by the first judge.
Use your scatter diagram to estimate the mark that might have been given by the second judge. (Show how you found your answer.) [NEAB]

**4.** This table shows the times (measured to the nearest minute) the contestants of various ages and sexes took to complete the first crossword in a competition.

| Sex | Age (years) | Time (minutes) |
|---|---|---|
| M | 56 | 11 |
| F | 60 | 8 |
| F | 20 | 12 |
| M | 23 | 9 |
| M | 43 | 16 |
| M | 42 | 23 |
| F | 26 | 19 |
| M | 24 | 14 |
| M | 55 | 15 |
| F | 70 | 9 |
| F | 30 | 21 |
| M | 35 | 7 |
| M | 19 | 6 |
| M | 54 | 19 |

Draw a scatter diagram to show the times taken by the contestants to complete the first crossword against their ages.

**5.** Ten pupils took two examination papers in Mathematics. Their marks out of 50 were as follows.

| Paper 1 | 44 | 24 | 40 | 48 | 30 | 25 | 10 | 37 | 38 | 34 |
|---|---|---|---|---|---|---|---|---|---|---|
| Paper 2 | 43 | 28 | 38 | 42 | 32 | 30 | 25 | 35 | 40 | 37 |

(a) Draw a scatter diagram of these marks.
(b) Draw a line of best fit for the points you have plotted.
(c) Omar was absent for Paper 2. He scored 32 marks on Paper 1.
(i) What mark do you think it fair to give him for Paper 2?
(ii) State how you got your answer.
(d) These pupils also took an examination paper in Art and one in Chemistry.
A scatter diagram of these marks is drawn. How might it be different from the one drawn for the two Mathematics papers? [NEAB]

**6.** A group of school children took a Mathematics test and a Physics test. The results for 12 children were plotted on a scatter diagram.

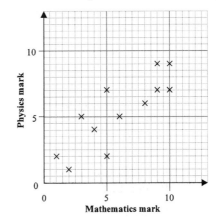

(a) Does the scatter diagram show the results you would expect? Explain your answer.
(b) Copy the graph.
(i) Add a line of best fit, by inspection, to the scatter diagram.
(ii) One pupil scored 7 marks for Mathematics but missed the Physics test.
Use the line of best fit to estimate the mark she might have scored for Physics.
(iii) One pupil was awarded the prize for the best overall performance in Mathematics and Physics.
Put a ring around the cross representing that pupil on the scatter diagram. [MEG]

# Test yourself

This table gives the marks scored by pupils in a French test and a German test.

| French | 15 | 35 | 34 | 23 | 35 | 27 | 36 | 34 | 23 | 24 | 30 | 40 | 25 | 35 | 20 |
|--------|----|----|----|----|----|----|----|----|----|----|----|----|----|----|----|
| German | 20 | 37 | 35 | 25 | 33 | 30 | 39 | 36 | 27 | 20 | 33 | 35 | 27 | 32 | 28 |

**QUESTION**  (a)  Draw a scatter diagram of the scores in the French and German tests.

**ANSWER**

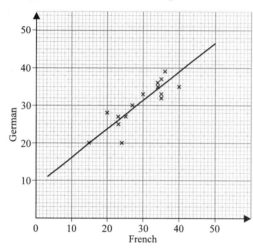

*If your answer is incorrect review page 527, Section 27.1 and Section 27.2 on scatter diagrams and correlation.*

**QUESTION**  (b)  Describe the correlation between the marks scored in the two tests.

**ANSWER**    There is positive correlation. The general trend is that the students who score higher in the German test also score higher in the French test.

*If your answer is incorrect review page 527, Section 27.2 on correlation.*

**QUESTION**  (c)  Estimate the mark for the German test for a student who scored 38 in the French test.

**ANSWER**    Between 38 and 39 is an acceptable answer

*If your answer is incorrect review page 530, Section 27.3, Example 3 on line of best fit.*

# Summary of key points to remember

1.  One way of seeing whether there is a relationship between two sets of data is to draw a **scatter diagram**:

   • draw an axis for each of the two sets of data.

   • plot the coordinates of the sets of data on a graph.

   • give the scatter diagram a title.

2. You need to be able to recognise the different types of **correlation** from a scatter diagram.

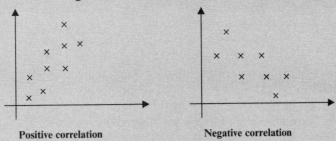

| Positive correlation | Negative correlation |

3. The **line of best fit** drawn on a scatter diagram gives a clearer idea of the correlation between two sets of data.

   To draw a line of best fit, draw a line on the scatter diagram which shows the trend of the plotted points and has roughly an equal number of points on each side.

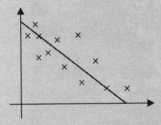

4. You can use a line of best fit to estimate values from one set of data when a value from the other set is known.

# 28 Simple Probability

## 28.1 Introduction

Many of the things that happen in life have some degree of uncertainty.

These might include fairly trivial things such as the outcome of the toss of a coin at the start of some sporting encounter.

They might also include more important matters such as whether or not there is a traffic hold up on the way to work.

Then they might also include very serious matters such as whether an accident occurs.

In all such cases there is always an element of **chance**.

**Probability** is the area of mathematics where we make a formal study of the laws of chance and uncertainty.

The subject originated in the seventeenth century as an attempt to work out the likelihoods of success or failure in games of chance, such as playing with dice or cards.

Today the theory of probability is still applied to gambling, such as on horse racing or in the National Lottery, but it also has serious applications in the Health Service, in insurance and industrial quality control.

In this unit you will learn about about the theory of probability – or the mathematical theory of chance. You should then be able to work out the probability (or chance) of you winning the National Lottery, or of a certain political party winning the next election, and similar problems.

## 28.2 The concept of fairness

You will have an intuitive concept of **fairness**. For example in games such as tennis, hockey and football the players or teams change ends at half-time so that no-one gains an unfair advantage due to the weather conditions.

Some political parties believe that there should be proportional representation in the House of Commons. They believe that it is fair that the number of MPs for each party should be in proportion to the number of votes cast for that party.

These are examples of interpretations of fairness.

### *Example 1*

Gulzar, Sinead and Tony play a game with an ordinary dice.

If the dice lands showing 1, 2, or 3 then Gulzar wins.

If it lands showing a 4 or 5 then Sinead winds.

If it lands showing a 6 then Tony wins.

Is this a fair game?

The dice has six faces. Gulzar will win if it lands showing a 1, 2, or 3. That is three out of the six faces. Sinead will win if it lands showing 4 or 5, that is two out of the six faces. Tony can only win if it lands showing a 6, that is one out of the six faces.

Clearly Gulzar has the best chance of winning, so the game is not fair.

A game such as the one above is said to be **biased**.

### Exercise 28A

1. Change the rules of the game in the example above so that it is fair. Explain why it is now fair.

2. Decide whether or not each of these is fair, and explain your answer.
   (a) A 10p coin is tossed to decide which player should serve first in a tennis match.
   (b) People at a sale are made to queue in alphabetical order.

(c) This spinner is spun to decide whether Georgie or Alex does the washing up. Alex does it if the spinner stops showing the letter A.

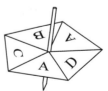

## 28.3 The likelihood scale

When you toss a coin, that is an **event**. This event has two possible **outcomes**: the coin showing heads and the coin showing tails.

When you roll a dice that is an event. This event has *six* possible outcomes: each of the six numbers that appear on the dice.

The **likelihood** of an **outcome** of an **event** can be described as:

- **impossible** – it has no chance of happening

- **unlikely** – it has a greater chance of not happening than of happening

- **evens** – it has as much chance of happening as of not happening

- **likely** – it has a greater chance of happening than of not happening

- **certain** – it is bound to happen.

You can create a **likelihood scale** like this.

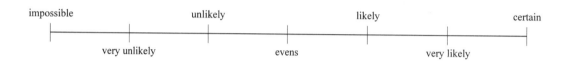

## *Example 2*

Mark each of these on a likelihood scale.

A   it will rain in England on at least one day in the year 1999.

B   the next baby to be born will be female.

C   your cat will live for ever.

D   it will be warm in England in August.

E   the next car to pass your home will be at least 7-years old.

F   your car or bicycle will have a puncture today.

G   the dice will land showing a number greater than or equal to 3.

Placing events on the scale is not an 'exact science'. It is the relative positions that you need to think about. Often, only outcomes that are impossible, certain or evens can be positioned exactly.

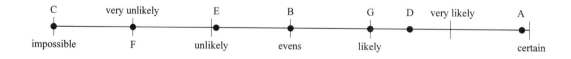

## Exercise 28B

**1.** Here is a list of outcomes of events. Mark them on a likelihood scale.

P    it will snow in London next July.

Q    someone will eat turkey on Christmas Day.

R    the car's battery will be flat tomorrow morning.

S    the song at the top of the charts this week will be in the top 10 next week.

T    a pig can fly by itself.

U    the coin will land Heads up.

V    the next train to arrive at Euston station will be at least a few minutes late.

W    someone will live for at least 70 years.

**2.** Use the words impossible, very unlikely, unlikely, evens, likely, very likely and certain to describe each of these events. Explain your reasoning in each case.

A    the car will break down today.

B    the next baby to be born will be male.

C    the dice will land showing a 6.

D    the sun will shine in Australia on Christmas Day.

E    the colour of a banana skin is blue.

F    the hockey player will score from a penalty flick.

G    it will rain next Thursday.

## 28.4 The probability scale

Any event which has no chance of happening is impossible.

We say that the **probability** of it happening is **zero**, or its probability = 0.

Any event which is bound to happen is certain.

We say that the **probability** of it happening is **one**, or its probability = 1.

Any event which has equal chances of happening and not happening is evens.

We say that the **probability** of it happening is **a half**, or its probability = $\frac{1}{2}$.

Now you can change the likelihood scale to a **probability scale**, using numbers from 0 to 1.

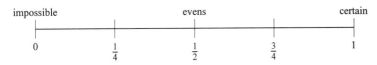

### Example 3

An ordinary pack of playing cards is shuffled. The top card is taken off the pack.

Mark the probabilities of these outcomes on a probability scale.

R    the top card is red

H    the top card is a Heart

N    the top card is *not* a Spade

A pack of playing cards contains four suits: Clubs (black), Diamonds (red), Hearts (red) and Spades (black). There is an equal number of cards in each suit. So half the pack is red and half is black. Each suit makes up a quarter of the pack.

The pack has been shuffled, so all the cards have an equal chance of being the top card.

The probability of R, the top card will be red is $\frac{1}{2}$.

The probability of H, that it will be a Heart is $\frac{1}{4}$.

The probability of N that it will not be a Spade is $\frac{3}{4}$ (since three-quarters of the pack are not Spades).

Your probability scale should look like this.

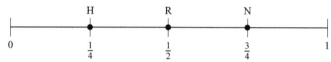

Of course you do not have to label the probability line only with 0, $\frac{1}{4}$, $\frac{1}{2}$, $\frac{3}{4}$ and 1. You can use other numbers between 0 and 1.

The numbers can be other fractions, like this.

They can be decimals, like this.

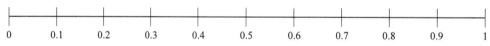

Or you can also label the probability scale using percentages.

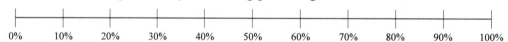

When you are asked to estimate or calculate a probability, your answer must be either a fraction, a decimal or a percentage.

## Example 4

The diagram shows a spinner in the shape of a regular pentagon. The spinner is spun once.

What is the probability that the spinner will land on

(a) 3        (b) 1        (c)      not 1?

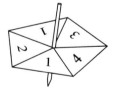

In each case give your answer as a fraction, a decimal and a percentage.

(d) Mark your answers on a probability scale marked in

(i) fractions

(ii) decimals

(iii) percentages

(a) The probability of the spinner landing on 3 is $\frac{1}{5} = 0.2 = 20\%$

(b) The probability of the spinner landing on 1 is $\frac{2}{5} = 0.4 = 40\%$

(c) For a score of 'not 1' the spinner can land on 2, 3 or 4. The probability of the spinner landing on not 1 is $\frac{3}{5} = 0.6 = 60\%$

(d) (i)

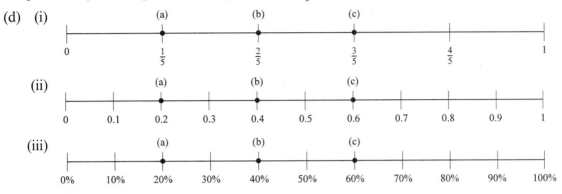

## Exercise 28C

1. Mark the probability of these events on a probability scale.
   (a) An ordinary dice lands with 3 uppermost (use fractions).
   (b) A fair coin shows heads when tossed (use decimals).
   (c) A playing card picked from a well-shuffled pack is a Spade (use percentages).

2. This spinner is spun. On a probability scale using fractions, decimals or percentages, mark:

   (a) the probability that it lands on A.
   (b) the probability that it lands on B.
   (c) the probability that it *does not* land on A.

3. Write down an event which has
   (a) a probability of $\frac{1}{4}$ of happening
   (b) a probability of 0.75 of not happening
   (c) a probability of 25% of happening
   (d) a probability of $\frac{1}{6}$ of happening
   (e) a probability of $\frac{2}{3}$ of not happening
   (f) a probability of 90% of happening
   (g) a probability of 0.3 of happening

# 28.5 Probability based on equally likely outcomes

When you toss a coin you do not know whether it will show heads or tails up. What you do know is that one or the other of these will occur. So for the event of tossing the coin there are two possible outcomes, which, for short, we call 'Heads' and 'Tails'.

When you look at a coin, you have no reason to believe that it is any more likely to show heads than tails. These two outcomes are the only possible outcomes of tossing a coin, and they are equally likely. (In saying this we have totally discounted the possibility of the coin landing on its edge.)

Because there are 2 outcomes and because you can see no reason why one should be more likely than the other, you can say that the probability of Heads is $\frac{1}{2}$

or      $P(H) = \frac{1}{2}$.

In a similar way the probability of Tails is $\frac{1}{2}$

or      $P(T) = \frac{1}{2}$.

When you roll a dice the outcome is the number on the top face when it comes to rest. There are 6 faces, numbered 1 to 6. You have no reason to believe that any face is more likely to be on top than any of the others.

So there are 6 equally likely outcomes: 1, 2, 3, 4, 5 and 6. You can say that the probability of a dice showing a 3 is $\frac{1}{6}$.

So      $P(3) = \frac{1}{6}$

and similarly   $P(1) = \frac{1}{6}$, $P(2) = \frac{1}{6}$, $P(4) = \frac{1}{6}$, $P(5) = \frac{1}{6}$, $P(6) = \frac{1}{6}$

Now look at this spinner. It is in the shape of a regular octagon: it has 8 sides of equal length.

The triangles making up the spinner are of different colours: 4 are white, 3 are black and 1 is grey.

When the spinner is spun, the outcome is the colour that ends up touching the table. The diagram above shows an outcome of white.

The 8 sides of the spinner are all equally likely to end up touching the table. Four sides are white and so the probability of spinner landing white is $\frac{4}{8} = \frac{1}{2}$.

You can write this as $P(W) = \frac{1}{2}$

and similarly      $P(B) = \frac{3}{8}$      $P(G) = \frac{1}{8}$

These are all examples of what is known as **inductive probability**, where we induce the probability of the outcome of some event using our knowledge, common sense and *degree of belief* about all the possible outcomes.

### Example 5

Ten balls of equal size are placed in a hat: 4 are red, 3 are blue, 2 are green and 1 is white. One of the balls is selected at random.

Write down the probability that the selected ball will be

(a) red      (b) green      (c) white      (d) not blue

(e) either red or green

(a) There are 10 balls in the bag, and 4 are red: the probability of selecting a red ball is $\frac{4}{10}$ or $\frac{2}{5}$ (or 0.4 or 40%).

(b) Because 2 of the 10 balls are green, the probability of selecting a green one is $\frac{2}{10}$ or $\frac{1}{5}$ (or 0.2 or 20%).

(c) Because only 1 of the 10 balls is white, the probability of it being selected is $\frac{1}{10}$ (or 0.1 or 10%).

(d) Of the 10 balls, 3 are are blue, so the number of balls that are not blue is 7. The probability of selecting a ball that is not blue is $\frac{7}{10}$ (or 0.7 or 70%).

(e) For the ball to be either red or green there are 6 different possibilities: this is the number of red balls plus the number of green balls.

The probability of the selected ball being either red or green is therefore $\frac{6}{10}$ or $\frac{3}{5}$ (or 0.6 or 60%).

---

### Exercise 28D

1. A bag contains 20 coloured balls of equal size: 8 of the balls are red, 7 are blue, 1 is green and 4 are white.
A ball is selected at random. Work out the probability that the selected ball will be:
(a) red      (b) blue      (c) either red or blue
(d) not green    (e) neither red nor green.

2. Here is a spinner in the shape of a regular octagon. Work out the probability that the spinner will stop on
(a) white      (b) black

(c) striped           (d) not grey
(e) black or white    (f) grey or white
(g) neither black nor white
(h) neither black nor grey.

3. An ordinary pack of 52 playing cards has 4 suits: Clubs, Diamonds, Hearts and Spades. There are 13 cards in each suit. One card is selected at random.
Work out the probability that the selected card will be:
(a) a Heart         (b) not a Spade
(c) either a Diamond or a Heart.

---

### Worked examination question 1

A bag contains a red bead, a black bead, a yellow bead and a white bead. One single bead is to be picked out at random. What is the probability that the bead picked will be

(a) red,     *Prob (red)* = $\frac{1}{4}$            $\frac{1}{4}$ ............

**Do:**
Write your answer as a fraction, decimal or percentage

(b) pink,     *Prob (pink)* = 0          0 ............
          *none are pink*

**Don't:**
Write your answer as 1 chance in 4, 1 out of 4, a ratio 1 : 4 or anything similar

(c) not white? *1 white 3 not white*       $\frac{3}{4}$ ............
       *so Prob (not white)* = $\frac{3}{4}$

**Do:**
Show your working

(London)

## 28.6 Estimating probability from statistical evidence

In a game such as football or netball there are three possible outcomes for a team: win, draw or lose.

If all three outcomes were equally likely, the probability of winning a match would always be $\frac{1}{3}$. You know, of course, that this is not the case. For instance, if a football team from the Premier Division were to play a team from division two, the Premier Division side would be more likely to win.

In a case like this, to estimate the probability of the Premier Division team winning, you would need to take some statistical evidence into account. Estimates could be based on the results of previous encounters between the two teams, or on the results of the last 2 years' encounters between Premier Division and 2nd Division sides.

When insurance companies work out the insurance premiums for car drivers they take statistical evidence into account. The evidence suggests that drivers under the age of 25 years are more likely to be involved in accidents than older drivers, so insurance companies charge younger drivers higher insurance premiums.

When you use statistical evidence to estimate probability you can either research the evidence collected by other people, or perform experiments to find your own statistical evidence.

## 28.7 Relative frequency

You have already seen that when a coin is tossed the probability of Heads is $\frac{1}{2}$. You have accepted it because there seems to be no reason to think that a coin may be biased.

Suppose that you were not confident about this. You could use a statistical method to find a very good estimate of the probability of Heads.

You could toss the coin a large number of times and record the number of times it landed heads up. Then you could work out the fraction

$$\frac{\text{Number of Heads}}{\text{Total number of tosses}}$$

The long term trend of this fraction would be your estimate of the probability of heads.

The fraction is called the **relative frequency** of Heads. For an ordinary fair coin this relative frequency will get closer and closer to $\frac{1}{2}$ the more times you toss it.

Probabilities obtained by using relative frequencies are called **statistical probabilities**.

During World War One a man named Kerrich was held prisoner in Denmark. He spent some of his time tossing a coin 10 000 times and recording the numbers of Heads and Tails.

He obtained these results:

Number of Heads: 5 067        Number of Tails: 4 933.

So the relative frequencies he obtained were

Heads: $\dfrac{5\,067}{10\,000} = 0.5067$

Tails: $\dfrac{4\,933}{10\,000} = 0.4933$

These two relative frequencies are both very close to $\frac{1}{2}$, which is the theoretical result, or the result we would expect using inductive probability.

Kerrich also plotted a graph for the relative frequency of Heads. It looked like this:

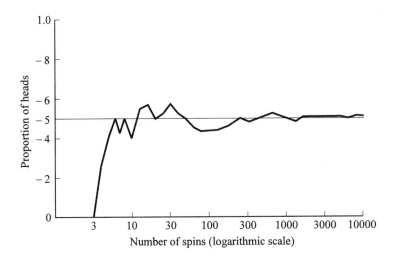

You can see that the relative frequency of Heads fluctuated quite widely at the start but the more he tossed the coin the more it settled down to be somewhere near to 0.5. It seems reasonable to assume that if he had been able to continue tossing the coin, these fluctuations would have settled down more and more and the relative frequency would have been nearer and nearer to the predicted value of 0.5. But the war came to an end and Kerrich was released.

### Exercise 28E

Try an experiment similar to Kerrich's. Use a coin, a dice or a pack of cards. For a coin, record the number of Heads; for a dice, record the number of times the outcome is 3; for a pack of cards, record the number of times that the top card (after a thorough shuffle) is a Heart.

Draw a graph of the relative frequency and see how it fluctuates.

Compare your results with those you expect through inductive probability.

---

### Example 6

A survey was conducted on 10 000 people taking their driving test for the first time.

Of these it was found that 6500 passed the test at the first attempt.

Use this evidence to estimate the probability that a randomly selected person would pass the driving test at the first attempt.

Relative frequency =

$$\frac{\text{number of people who passed the test at the first attempt}}{\text{total number of people in the sample}}$$

$$= \frac{6500}{10\,000} = \frac{65}{100} = 0.65 \text{ (or 65\%)}$$

The best estimate we can make of the probability that someone passes the test at the first attempt is 0.65, or 65%.

If anything is known about their driving skill, a more informed estimate might be made.

### Example 7

It is estimated that the probability of a randomly selected student at Preble College being over the age of 23 years is 0.24. There are 6000 students at the college. Give a best estimate for the total number of students at the college who are over 23 years old.

This is really the reverse of the last problem.

We know that the relative frequency is 0.24, so

$$\frac{\text{number of students aged over 23}}{\text{total number of students}} = 0.24$$

So:    number of students aged over 23 = 0.24 × total number
of students

$$= 0.24 \times 6000$$

$$= 1440.$$

Our best estimate of the number of students aged over 23 years is 1440.

## Example 8

A dice was rolled 1200 times and the outcome recorded. The results are shown in the table below.

| Outcome | 1 | 2 | 3 | 4 | 5 | 6 |
|---------|-----|-----|-----|-----|-----|-----|
| Frequency | 186 | 203 | 207 | 193 | 205 | 206 |

Is there any evidence to suggest that the dice is biased. Explain your answer.

If the dice has no bias, the probability of any particular outcome is $\frac{1}{6}$. So:

$P(1) = \frac{1}{6}$, $P(2) = \frac{1}{6}$, $P(3) = \frac{1}{6}$, $P(4) = \frac{1}{6}$, $P(5) = \frac{1}{6}$ and $P(6) = \frac{1}{6}$.

where $P(1)$ means the probability of a 1, and so on.

But $P(1) = \dfrac{\text{total number of 1s}}{\text{total number of rolls}}$

so for an unbiased dice you would expect

$$\frac{\text{total number of 1s}}{\text{total number of rolls}} = \frac{1}{6}.$$

You can rearrange this:

$$\text{total number of 1s} = \tfrac{1}{6} \times \text{total number of rolls.}$$

In this case there were 1200 rolls, so for an unbiased dice you would expect

$$\text{total number of 1s} = \tfrac{1}{6} \times 1200 = 200.$$

The same argument holds for the number of 2s, the numbers of 3s and so on: we would expect each outcome to occur 200 times.

The table shows that the different outcomes did all occur approximately 200 times. You would not expect them to occur *exactly* 200 times each, and the variations are small enough to convince us that they are due to chance rather than to bias.

---

### Exercise 28F

1. One summer 600 000 students took the GCSE mathematics examination. Of these, 240 000 obtained a pass at Grade C or above.
   Use these figures to determine the probability of a randomly selected student obtaining a GCSE pass in mathematics at Grade C or above.

2. A survey was conducted of voting intentions in a local by-election. In the survey 1800 people were asked which political party they intended to vote for. Their responses are shown in the table opposite.

| Conservative | Labour | Liberal Democrats | Others |
|--------------|--------|-------------------|--------|
| 576 | 756 | 324 | 144 |

Use these results to work out the probability of a randomly selected person
(a) voting Conservative
(b) voting Labour
(c) voting for neither Conservative or Labour.

3. It is estimated that the probability of someone being left-handed is 0.21.
Give an estimate for the number of left-handed people in a randomly selected sample of 20 000 people.

4. It is known that, on average, 35% of all students in a college take a vocational course. There are 12 000 students at Sametide College. Give a best estimate for the number of students at Sametide College who are taking a vocational course.

5. The probability of a new battery being faulty is known to be 0.002. A company manufactures 3 000 000 batteries in a year. Give a best estimate for the number of these batteries likely to be faulty.

6. A pack of playing cards was shuffled and after each shuffle the suit of the top card was recorded. This was done 600 times: the results are summarised below

| Top Card | Club | Diamond | Heart | Spade |
|---|---|---|---|---|
| Frequency | 144 | 158 | 155 | 143 |

Do these results indicate that there is a bias in favour of one suit?

7. A coin was tossed 2000 times to find out whether it was biased. The results are summarised below.

| Outcome | Heads | Tails |
|---|---|---|
| Frequency | 982 | 1018 |

It was decided that the coin would be regarded as biased if the actual number of Heads or Tails differed from the expected number by more than 20%. What would the conclusion be in this case? Explain your answer.

8. A survey of 1600 people was conducted to find out their voting intentions at a General Election. In the survey, 640 people indicated that they would vote Labour.
(a) Work out the best estimate of the probability of a randomly selected person voting Labour at the next General Election.
(b) It is forecast that 24 000 000 people will vote at the General Election. Work out a best estimate of the total number of people likely to vote Labour.

9. The diagram shows an 8-sided spinner. The faces are marked with letters A to H.
(a) Assuming that the spinner is unbiased, work out the probability that, when it is spun once, it will land on the letter B.
(b) If the spinner is spun 1000 times, how many times would you expect it to land on the letter A?
(c) The spinner was spun 200 times and the results are shown in the table.

| Letter | A | B | C | D | E | F | G | H |
|---|---|---|---|---|---|---|---|---|
| Frequency | 27 | 26 | 24 | 25 | 28 | 22 | 25 | 23 |

---

## Worked examination question 2

In a school fete contestants throw two dice and add the two numbers showing. Contestants who score 10 or more win a prize.

(a) Complete the following table to show all the possible outcomes for the game.

| | 1 | 2 | 3 | 4 | 5 | 6 |
|---|---|---|---|---|---|---|
| 6 | 7 | 8 | 9 | 10 | 11 | 12 |
| 5 | 6 | 7 | 8 | 9 | 10 | 11 |
| 4 | 5 | 6 | 7 | 8 | 9 | 10 |
| 3 | 4 | 5 | 6 | 7 | 8 | 9 |
| 2 | 3 | 4 | 5 | 6 | 7 | 8 |
| 1 | 2 | 3 | 4 | 5 | 6 | 7 |

**Do:**
Be careful with the arithmetic

**Do:**
Fill in all the spaces

**Do:**
Check that there are 36 outcomes

(b) Jeremy has one turn at the game.

What is the probability that he will win a prize?

$$\frac{6}{36} = \frac{1}{6}$$

**Do:**
Give your answer as a fraction
**Don't:**
Write your answer as 6 out of 36 etc

(c) At the fete, 270 people each play the game once.

Approximately how many are likely to win a prize?

$$270 \times \frac{1}{6}$$

$$= 45$$

**Do:**
Show your working

(NEAB)

## 28.8 Mutually exclusive outcomes

This spinner is in the shape of a regular pentagon: it has 5 sides and is made up of 5 equal triangles. The triangles are coloured as follows: 2 are black, 1 is white, 1 is grey and 1 is striped.

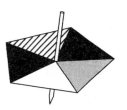

We shall assume that the spinner has an equal chance of landing on any of its 5 sides. So as far as the sides are concerned it is unbiased.

If we spin the spinner once and record the colour of the side it lands on, this event has a total of 4 outcomes: there are 4 colours and it cannot land on two or more colours at once. We say that the outcomes are mutually exclusive.

You can see that the probability of the spinner landing on black is $\frac{2}{5}$ (or 0.4 or 40%), so you can write

$$P(B) = \tfrac{2}{5} \text{ (or 0.4 or 40\%).}$$

Similarly you can see that the probability of the spinner landing on white is $\frac{1}{5}$ (or 0.2 or 20%) so

$$P(W) = \tfrac{1}{5} \text{ (or 0.2 or 20\%).}$$

Similarly

$$P(G) = \tfrac{1}{5} \text{ (or 0.2 or 20\%)}$$

and

$$P(S) = \tfrac{1}{5} \text{ (or 0.2 or 20\%).}$$

When you add these probabilities together you obtain the answer 1:

$$P(B) + P(W) + P(G) + P(S) = \tfrac{2}{5} + \tfrac{1}{5} + \tfrac{1}{5} + \tfrac{1}{5}$$
$$= 1.$$

It is in fact always the case that for mutually exclusive outcomes the sum of the probabilities is 1.

When you toss a coin there are two mutually exclusive outcomes, Heads and Tails. You know that for an unbiased coin the probabilities of heads (H) and tails (T) are

$$P(H) = \tfrac{1}{2} \quad \text{and} \quad P(T) = \tfrac{1}{2}$$

So:

$$P(H) + P(T) = \tfrac{1}{2} + \tfrac{1}{2} = 1.$$

When you roll an ordinary dice there are six mutually exclusive outcomes. These are 1, 2, 3, 4, 5, and 6. Again assuming that the dice is unbiased,

$$P(1) = \tfrac{1}{6} \quad P(2) = \tfrac{1}{6} \quad P(3) = \tfrac{1}{6} \quad P(4) = \tfrac{1}{6} \quad P(5) = \tfrac{1}{6} \quad P(6) = \tfrac{1}{6}.$$

Therefore the sum of the probabilities is:

$$P(1) + P(2) + P(3) + P(4) + P(5) + P(6) = \tfrac{1}{6} + \tfrac{1}{6} + \tfrac{1}{6} + \tfrac{1}{6} + \tfrac{1}{6} + \tfrac{1}{6} = 1.$$

This again confirms the result.

## 28.9 The probability of something not happening

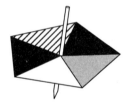

Here is the 5-sided spinner again.

You have already seen that the probabilities of the spinner landing on each colour are

$$P(B) = \tfrac{2}{5} \quad P(W) = \tfrac{1}{5} \quad P(G) = \tfrac{1}{5} \quad P(S) = \tfrac{1}{5}$$

What is the probability of the spinner *not* landing on black?

To not land on Black, the spinner must land on either white, grey or striped. In other words there are 3 ways in which it can land on not black, out of a total of 5 ways of landing.

Probability of spinner landing on white, grey or striped $= \tfrac{3}{5}$ so probability of spinner not landing on black $= \tfrac{3}{5}$.

You can write this as

$$P(\text{not } B) = \tfrac{3}{5}$$

Notice that

$$P(\text{not } B) = 1 - \tfrac{2}{5} = 1 - P(B)$$

This result can be generalised. Its general form is usually written:

If the probability of something happening = p, then
the probability of it not happening = 1 − p.

### Example 9

The spinner in the picture is known to be biased.

The probabilities of it landing on each letters A to E are shown in the table but the probability of it landing on F is unknown.

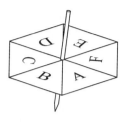

| Letter | A | B | C | D | E |
|--------|-----|------|------|------|------|
| Frequency | 0.2 | 0.15 | 0.18 | 0.14 | 0.21 |

Calculate the probability of the spinner landing on F.

Since the six outcomes are mutually exclusive we know that

$$P(A) + P(B) + P(C) + P(D) + P(E) + P(F) = 1$$

So: $$0.2 + 0.15 + 0.18 + 0.14 + 0.21 + P(F) = 1$$

Adding the decimals we have

$$0.88 + P(F) = 1$$
$$P(F) = 1 - 0.88$$
$$P(F) = 0.12.$$

The probability of the spinner landing on F is 0.12.

### Example 10

The probability of a new electrical component being faulty is 0.03.

Calculate the probability of it not being faulty.

We use the rule above:

Probability of it not being faulty = 1 − probability of it being faulty

so     Probability of it not being faulty = 1 − 0.03
$$= 0.97$$

### Example 11

Each time a tennis player serves, the probability of her winning the point is estimated to be 76%. Calculate the probability of the tennis player losing the point.

The tennis player can either win a point or lose a point on her serve: the point cannot be drawn. So the outcomes Win and Lose are mutually exclusive.

So you can write

$$P(\text{Win}) + P(\text{Lose}) = 1$$

But in this case the probabilities are expressed in percentages, so we must change the formula to

$$P(\text{Win}) + P(\text{Lose}) = 100\%$$

or                     $P(W) + P(L) = 100\%$.

Substituting 76% for P(W), the probability of a Win, gives

$$76\% + P(L) = 100\%$$

So:                     $P(L) = 100\% - 76\% = 24\%$

The probability of the tennis player losing the point when she serves is 24%.

## Exercise 28G

1. The probability of a car passing its MOT test is estimated as 0.85. Calculate the probability of the car failing its MOT test.

2. A bag contains 20 equal sized beads. 4 of these beads are red. One bead will be drawn from the bag at random.
   (a) Write down the probability that this bead will be red.

   (b) Work out the probability that this bead will not be red.

3. At a sporting event it is estimated that the probability that George will win the race is 20%. Work out the probability that George will not win the race.

---

## Worked examination question 3

The spinner shown is weighted (biased).

The probability of getting a 3 is 0.2, and the probability of getting a 1 is 0.3.

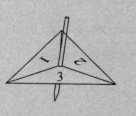

The spinner is going to be spun 100 times.

Approximately how many times will it show 1 or 3?

*Probability of (1 or 3) = 0.2 + 0.3*

                  *= 0.5*

**Do:**
Show your working

Remember that 'showing 1' and 'showing 3' are mutually exclusive events

*So number of times it will show 1 or 3 out of 100 times is*
*100 × 0.5 = 50*

...........50........... times

(MEG)

## Worked exam question 4

A letter is sent by first class post.

The probability that it will arrive the next day is 0.87.

(a) Calculate the probability that the letter will not arrive the next day.

$$Prob\ (not\ arriving) = 1 - Prob\ (arriving)$$
$$= 1 - 0.87$$
$$= 0.13$$

**Do:**
Show your working

On Tuesday 14 July a Post Office receives 2000 letters all with a first class stamp.

(b) Calculate the best estimate for the number of these letters likely to be delivered on Wednesday 15 July.

$$Probability\ of\ letter\ arriving\ next\ day$$
$$= \frac{No.\ of\ letters\ arriving\ next\ day}{Total\ no.\ of\ letters}$$

$$0.87 = \frac{No.\ of\ letters\ arriving\ next\ day}{2000}$$

Show your working

$$No.\ of\ letters\ arriving\ next\ day = 2000 \times 0.87$$
$$= 1740$$

Multiply both sides by 2000

(London)

## Worked exam question 5

A company manufactures small electrical components. The probability of such a component being faulty is 0.06.

One year the company manufactures 2 500 000 such components.

How many of these are likely to be perfect?

$$prob\ (perfect) = 1 - prob\ (faulty)$$
$$prob\ (perfect) = 1 - 0.06$$
$$= 0.94$$

**Do:**
Show your working

So number perfect is likely to be

$$2\ 500\ 000 \times 0.94 = 2\ 350\ 000$$

**Don't:**
Round your answer up or down

### Exercise 28H (Mixed questions)

1. A bag contains a red bead, a black bead, a yellow bead and a white bead. One bead is to be picked out at random.
   Calculate the probability that the bead will be
   (a) red   (b) pink   (c) not white.

2. A bag contains 10 snooker balls: 5 are red, 2 are blue, and 3 are white. One ball is pulled out at random.
   Calculate the probability that this ball will be
   (a) red   (b) white   (c) either blue or white
   (d) not blue

3. A 4-sided spinner, with its edges labelled A, B, C and D, is biased. If it is spun once, the probability of it landing on A is 0.3, the probability of it landing on B is 0.2 and the probability of it landing on C is 0.17.
   (a) Calculate the probability of the spinner landing on D after 1 spin.
   (b) Calculate the probability of the spinner landing on either B or C after 1 spin.
   (c) The spinner is to be spun 500 times. Calculate the number of times that it is likely to land on A.

4. A newspaper article states that the probability of winning the National Lottery jackpot prize with one £1 ticket is $\frac{1}{14\,000\,000}$.
   Using this figure, what is the probability, with one £1 ticket, of *not* winning the National Lottery jackpot?

5. In the summer of 1995, approximately 600 000 students sat the GCSE exam in English Language. Approximately 250 000 of these students gained a pass at Grade C or above. The name of one of the students who sat the exam was selected, at random, by a computer. Estimate the probability that this student will have gained a pass at Grade C or above in the exam.

6. Surjit has a bag containing 10 beads: 5 are blue, 3 are red and the rest are black. A bead is chosen at random from the bag.
   What is the probability that the bead will be
   (a) red   (b) black?

7. John has a spinner in the shape of a regular pentagon. Scores of 1, 2, 3, 4 and 5 are equally likely when the spinner is spun once. John spins the spinner 200 times and records the scores each time.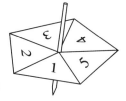

Approximately how many times will the score be an even number?

8. A charity sells 500 raffle tickets numbered 1 to 500. One prize is to be awarded. David buys tickets numbered 5, 6, 7 and 8. Liz buys tickets numbered 53, 54 and 55.
   What is the probability that either David or Liz will win the prize?

9. On each weekday George goes to work. The probability that he will leave home before 0700 is 0.25 The probability that he will leave home later than 0715 is 0.30
   (a) Calculate the probability that George will leave home between 0700 and 0715 on a weekday.
   (b) During any year, George goes to work on 220 days. Work out a best estimate for the number of times he will leave home before 0700 in any year.

10. A computer is programmed to print a random number between 1 and 50 (inclusive). Calculate the probability that the number printed will be
    (a) 30   (b) even
    (c) between 10 and 20 (inclusive)   (d) prime
    (e) a multiple of 3   (f) not a square number

11. On General Election day, 1800 people, randomly selected across the country, were asked to indicate which party they had voted for. Of these, 684 said that they had voted for the Conservative Party.
    (a) Give a best estimate for the probability that a voter randomly selected from the survey group voted for the Conservative Party.
    (b) In the General Election, a total of 23 500 000 votes were cast. Give a best estimate for the number of votes for the Conservative Party.

12. An ordinary dice has its six faces numbered 1 to 6.
    The dice is known to be biased. The probabilities of it showing each of the numbers from 1 to 5 are given in the table.

| Number | 1 | 2 | 3 | 4 | 5 |
|---|---|---|---|---|---|
| Probability | 0.13 | 0.18 | 0.17 | 0.21 | 0.12 |

(a) Calculate the probability of the dice showing 6.
(b) The dice is rolled 1000 times. Calculate the number of times it is likely to show 6.
(c) The dice is rolled once. Which number is it most likely to show? Explain your answer.

**13.** The table shows the frequencies of the age ranges of the students at Wheatridge College.

| Age range | Frequency |
|-----------|-----------|
| 16–18 | 2485 |
| 19–21 | 3983 |
| 22–24 | 1601 |
| 25–27 | 956 |
| over 27 | 775 |

The Principal picks the name of one student at random from the college register.
(a) Calculate the probability of that student having an age in the range 19–21 years.
(b) Calculate the probability of that student having an age in the range 16–21 years.
(c) Calculate the probability of that student having an age outside the range 16–21 years.

**14.** Nirmal rides to work along a cycle track. He has to cross a road where there are traffic lights. He has estimated these probabilities:
Probability lights are Red    = 0.75,
Probability lights are Amber   = 0.1.
(a) Suggest how Nirmal estimated these probabilities.
(b) What is the probability that the lights are Green?
Nirmal always stops unless the lights are Green.
(c) What is the probability that he has to stop?

---

## Test yourself

**1.** A spinner is in the shape of a regular pentagon, and is labelled with the letters A, B, C and D as shown.
The spinner is spun once.

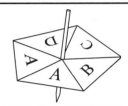

**QUESTION**    Calculate the probability that the spinner will land on
(a)   B    (b)   either A or B    (c)   a letter other than B.

**ANSWER**    (a) $\frac{1}{5}$ (b) $\frac{3}{5}$ (c) $\frac{4}{5}$     *If your answer is incorrect review page 543, Section 28.5 on probability based on equally likely outcomes*

---

**2.** A company produces electric light bulbs, and it is known that the probability of a newly produced light bulb being faulty is 0.015.

**QUESTION**    Calculate the probability of a newly produced light bulb not being faulty.

**ANSWER**    0.985     *If your answer is incorrect review page 552, Section 28.9 on the probability of something not happening*

**QUESTION**    In one week the company produces 200 000 light bulbs. Give a best estimate for the number of these light bulbs that are likely to be faulty.

**ANSWER**    3000     *If your answer is incorrect review page 546, Section 28.7 on relative frequency*

---

**3.** An ordinary dice has six faces labelled 1, 2, 3, 4, 5, 6. The dice is biased. When it is rolled once the probabilities of it showing the faces are:

P(1) = 0.15    P(2) = 0.13    P(3) = 0.18
P(4) = 0.17    P(5) = 0.21

| QUESTION | Calculate the probability of it showing a 6 when you roll it once. |
| --- | --- |
| ANSWER | $P(6) = 0.16$         *If your answer is incorrect review page 551, Section 28.8 on mutually exclusive outcomes* |

## Summary of key points to remember

1. Tossing a coin is an **event**. It has two possible **outcomes**: showing a head or a tail.

   When outcomes occur at **random** each outcome is equally likely to occur.

2. The **likelihood** of an event can be described as:

   - impossible – it has no chance of happening.
   - evens – it has as much chance of happening as of not happening.
   - unlikely – it has a greater chance of not happening than of happening.
   - evens – it has as much chance of happening as of not happening.
   - likely – it has a greater chance of happening than of not happening.
   - certain – it is bound to happen.

   Evens means a probability of $\frac{1}{2}$.

3. **Probability** is the mathematical theory of chance.

   It is measured on a scale of 0 to 1.

   Probability must always be expressed as a fraction, a decimal or a percentage.

4. The **probability scale** can be labelled with fractions, decimals or percentages.

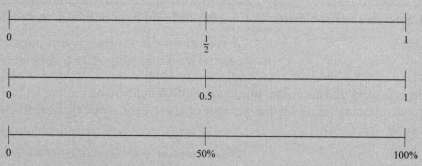

5. In situations where all possible outcomes are equally likely, the probability of any outcome is given by

   $$p = \frac{\text{number of ways of this outcome occurring}}{\text{total number of possible outcomes}}$$

   This is called **inductive probability**.

6. Where probabilities are based on statistical evidence the probability of an outcome is calculated using the **relative frequency** of its occurrence.

$$p = \frac{\text{number of times this outcome has occurred}}{\text{number of times event has occurred}}$$

This is called **statistical probability**.

7. If an event has exactly three possible outcomes and no more than one of them can occur for each event, then the three outcomes are **mutually exclusive**. Their probabilities will add up to 1.

8. The probability of something not happening is one minus the probability of it happening.

If the probability of something happening is $p$, then the probability of it not happening is $1 - p$.

# 29 Combining Probabilities

## 29.1 Introduction

Suppose that you are driving along a road on which there are two sets of traffic lights. What is the probability that both sets of lights will be red as you approach them?

Suppose that you buy a £1 ticket in the National lottery and a ticket in the local raffle. What is the probability that you will win at least one prize?

These are examples of **multiple outcome** problems. You will learn how to tackle them in this chapter.

## 29.2 Listing multiple outcomes

This spinner is to be spun once.    This coin is to be tossed once.

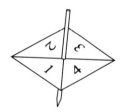

The outcomes of spinning the spinner are the four numbers 1, 2, 3 and 4.

The outcomes of tossing the coin are either Heads (H) and Tails (T).

The **joint outcomes** are all the possible combinations of outcomes from these two events.

You can represent joint outcomes in three different ways.

- **List**

| | |
|------|------|
| 1, H | 1, T |
| 2, H | 2, T |
| 3, H | 3, T |
| 4, H | 4, T |

When listing all of these joint outcomes it is important to work in an ordered, systematic way. Here we have put the outcomes involving Heads in the left hand column, and the corresponding ones for Tails in the right hand column.

- **Two-way table**

| Spinner/coin | H | T |
|:---:|:---:|:---:|
| 1 | 1, H | 1, T |
| 2 | 2, H | 2, T |
| 3 | 3, H | 3, T |
| 4 | 4, H | 4, T |

This ensures that the outcomes are listed systematically and is useful in complex problems.

- **Tree diagram**

  Many GCSE exam questions on multiple outcomes ask you to draw a tree diagram.

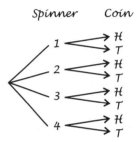

### Worked examination question 1

A six-faced dice and a coin are thrown at the same time. One possible outcome is a Head and a 1 (H, 1).

List all the other possible outcomes.

(H,1),  (H, 2),  (H, 3),  (H, 4),  (H, 5),  (H, 6)

(T,1),  (T, 2),  (T, 3),  (T, 4),  (T, 5),  (T, 6)

(London)

**Do:**
List the outcomes systematically

## 29.3 Independent events

When you spin a spinner and toss a coin, the outcome of the event 'spin the spinner' does not affect the outcome of the event 'toss a coin'. The outcome of one event does not affect the outcome of the other.

We say that the events are **independent**.

For the 4-sided spinner and the coin in Section 29.2,

the event 'spin the spinner' has 4 outcomes.

the event 'toss the coin' has 2 outcomes.

From the tree diagram above, the event 'spin the spinner' *and* toss the coin' has 8 outcomes and $8 = 4 \times 2$

In general for two independent events, Event 1 and Event 2, if

Event 1 has $n$ outcomes and

Event 2 has $m$ outcomes.

Then the number of joint outcomes of Event 1 *and* Event 2 is

$n \times m$

*Example 1*

The Parkinson family have decided to go on holiday.

They could go to either France, Italy, Greece or Spain.

They could go by Car, Rail or Air.

One choice of holiday is Greece by Rail which can be written as G, R.

(a) Draw a tree diagram to show all of the possible holidays they can choose.

(b) How many different choices of holiday do they have?

(a) The tree diagram is:

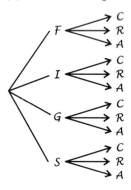

(b) The Parkinson family have a choice of 4 different places to go and a choice of three different forms of transport.

The places to go and forms of transport are independent, so the total number of different choices for the type of holiday is $4 \times 3 = 12$

---

### Exercise 29A

1. A hotel offers its customers a choice at breakfast time. They can choose one type of food and one type of drink.
   There are 5 types of food to choose from:
   Full English, Continental, Boiled Eggs, Scrambled Eggs or Kippers.
   There are 2 types of drink to choose from:
   Tea or Coffee.
   A choice of breakfast is the combination of food and drink.
   (a) Draw a tree diagram to show all the possible choices of breakfast.

   (b) Calculate the total number of different choices of breakfast that are possible.

2. David has a spinner and a dice as shown. He spins the spinner once, and rolls the dice once.
   (a) List or tabulate all of the joint outcomes of these two events.
   (b) Calculate the total number of joint outcomes.

3. Asha has a red dice and a blue dice. She rolls each dice once only. She adds together the scores shown on the upper faces of the dice to give a total score.
   (a) List all the ways in which she can obtain a total score of 5.
   (b) In how many different ways can she obtain a total score of 8?

4. Wesley plays cricket for his college. His team can either win, lose or draw a match.
   His sister, Grace, plays tennis for her school. She can either win or lose a match.
   One day Wesley plays in a cricket match and Grace plays in a tennis match.
   (a) Make a list, a two-way table or a tree diagram to show all of the possible joint outcomes of their matches.

   (b) Calculate the total number of possible joint outcomes.

5. A coin is tossed 3 times and the results recorded. One joint outcome of the three tosses is that it lands Heads, then Heads, then Tails. This is recorded as H, H, T.
   (a) Show that there are eight different joint outcomes.
   (b) Now the coin is tossed 4 times. Calculate the number of different joint outcomes.
   (c) Now the coin is tossed $n$ times. Write down a general expression for the number of different outcomes when the coin is tossed $n$ times.

## 29.4 Probability of mutually exclusive outcomes

An unbiased 4-sided spinner is spun once.

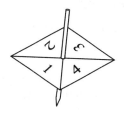

There are four equally likely mutually exclusive outcomes: it will land on 1, 2, 3 or 4.

So    $P(1) = \frac{1}{4}$    $p(2) = \frac{1}{4}$,    $P(3) = \frac{1}{4}$    $P(4) = \frac{1}{4}$

The probability of the spinner landing on either 1 *or* 2 is $\frac{2}{4} = \frac{1}{2}$ since there are 2 chances of this happening, and 4 possible outcomes.

In general, if an event has two mutually exclusive outcomes A and B then $P(A \text{ or } B) = P(A) + P(B)$

### *Example 2*

A spinner is in the shape of a regular hexagon:

3 of its 6 sections are black,

2 of its 6 sections are white,

1 of its 6 sections is grey.

The spinner is spun once.

Calculate:

(a) the probability that the spinner will land on either black or grey;

(b) the probability that the spinner will land on either white or grey.

(a) Writing P(B) for the probability of the spinner landing on black, P(W) for white and P(G) for grey, we have

$$P(B) = \tfrac{3}{6} \qquad P(W) = \tfrac{2}{6} \qquad P(G) = \tfrac{1}{3}$$

Since the outcomes are all mutually exclusive

$$P(B \text{ or } W) = P(B) + P(W)$$
$$= \tfrac{3}{6} + \tfrac{2}{6}$$
$$= \tfrac{5}{6}$$

(b)
$$P(W \text{ or } G) = P(W) + P(G)$$
$$= \tfrac{2}{6} + \tfrac{1}{6}$$
$$= \tfrac{3}{6} = \tfrac{1}{2}$$

---

### Exercise 29B

**1.** An ordinary dice is rolled once. Calculate the probability that it shows
(a) 2 or 3  (b) 1 or 3 or 5

**2.** Jenny has an unbiased spinner in the shape of a regular octagon as shown opposite. Jenny spins the spinner once.

Calculate the probability that the spinner will land on:
(a) either black or white
(b) either black or striped
(c) either grey or white or striped

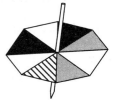

---

## 29.5 Probability of joint outcomes

Jason has an unbiased 4-sided spinner and an unbiased coin.

He spins the spinner once and tosses the coin once.

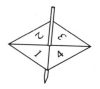

The outcomes for the spinner are: 1, 2, 3, 4
and   $P(1) = \tfrac{1}{4}$   $P(2) = \tfrac{1}{4}$   $P(3) = \tfrac{1}{4}$   $P(4) = \tfrac{1}{4}$

The outcomes for the dice are: heads (H) and tails (T) and
$P(H) = \tfrac{1}{2}$   $P(T) = \tfrac{1}{2}$

The joint outcomes are

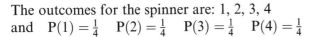

|      |      |
|------|------|
| 1,H  | 1,T  |
| 2,H  | 2,T  |
| 3,H  | 3,T  |
| 4,H  | 4,T  |

There are 8 joint outcomes.

The two events 'spin the spinner' and 'toss the coin' are independent, since the outcome of one does not affect the outcome of the other. Also, the coin and the spinner are both unbiased and so the 8 joint outcomes are all equally likely.

You can now think of the two events as a single event: 'spin the spinner and toss the coin'. This event has 8 mutually exclusive outcomes. Each outcome is equally likely and so occurs with probability $\frac{1}{8}$.

For example, the probability of the outcome 2,H is $P(2, H) = \frac{1}{8}$

But $P(H) = \frac{1}{2}$ and $P(2) = \frac{1}{4}$ and so you can see that $P(2 \text{ and } H)$ $= P(2) \times P(H) = \frac{1}{8}$

This result can be generalised: when two outcomes A and B are *independent* the probability of the joint outcome (A *and* B) is given by multiplying together the probabilities of the single outcomes A and B:

$$P \text{ (A and B)} = P(A) \times P(B)$$

We can extend this result to 3 independent outcomes A, B and C:

$$P(A \text{ and } B \text{ and } C) = P(A) \times P(B) \times P(C)$$

### *Example 3*

An ordinary dice is rolled once and a 4-sided spinner with sides A, B, C, D is spun once.

Calculate the probability of the joint outcome that the dice will show a 3 and the spinner will land on A.

For the dice $\qquad P(3) = \frac{1}{6}$

For the spinner, $\qquad P(A) = \frac{1}{4}$

Because these outcomes are independent,

$$P(3 \text{ and } A) = P(3) \times P(A)$$

So:

$$P(3, A) = \frac{1}{6} \times \frac{1}{4}$$
$$= \frac{1}{24}$$

We could have done this by listing all the outcomes as

| | | | |
|---|---|---|---|
| 1,A | 1,B | 1,C | 1,D |
| 2,A | 2,B | 2,C | 2,D |
| 3,A | 3,B | 3,C | 3,D |
| 4,A | 4,B | 4,C | 4,D |
| 5,A | 5,B | 5,C | 5,D |
| 6,A | 6,B | 6,C | 6,D |

The result we are looking for is (3,A) with a probability of $\frac{1}{24}$.

## 29.6 Tree diagrams

Let us look again at the problem of Jason's spinner and coin.

He spins the spinner once and tosses the coin once.

Again we want the probability of the joint outcome (2,H) – a 2 on the spinner and a Head.

You can draw a tree diagram to show all the joint outcomes.

You can write the probability of each event on the 'branch' of the tree diagram.

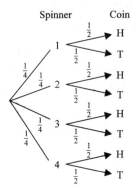

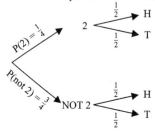

probability of the spinner landing on 2 $= \frac{1}{4}$
probability of the spinner landing on not 2 $= \frac{3}{4}$
probability of the coin landing heads up $= \frac{1}{2}$
probability of the coin landing tails up $= \frac{1}{2}$

To find the probability of the outcome (2,H) follow the 2 and H arrows. Multiply the two probabilities on these arrows.

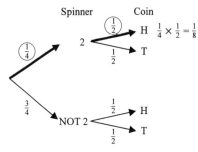

This gives:      $P(2, H) = \frac{1}{4} \times \frac{1}{2} = \frac{1}{8}$

You can read off the probabilities of the other outcomes in the same way.

For example:

$$P(2, T) = \frac{1}{4} \times \frac{1}{2} = \frac{1}{8}$$
$$P(\text{not } 2, H) = \frac{3}{4} \times \frac{1}{2} = \frac{3}{8}$$

*Example 4*

When Asif and Jill play a game of table tennis, the probability that Asif will win is $\frac{5}{8}$.

When Asif and Jill play a game of darts, the probability that Jill will win is $\frac{2}{3}$.

(a) Copy and complete the tree diagram below.

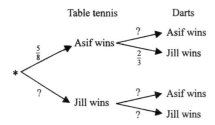

(b) Calculate the probability that Jill will win both games.

(a) The completed tree diagram is

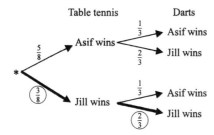

(b) For Jill to win both games we must follow the 'Jill wins' and 'Jill wins' arrows.

The probabilities along this route are $\frac{3}{8}$ and $\frac{2}{3}$.

So the probability that Jill will win both games is

$$\frac{3}{8} \times \frac{2}{3} = \frac{1}{4}$$

### *Example 5*

This unbiased spinner is spun 3 times. Calculate the probability that it will land on black on all 3 occasions.

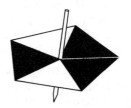

**Method 1**

The probability of the spinner landing on black when spun once is $\frac{3}{5}$.

So we can write        $P(B) = \frac{3}{5}$

and similarly        $P(W) = \frac{2}{5}$

We want the spinner to land black, black, black when spun 3 times. So we are looking for $P(B \text{ and } B \text{ and } B)$. Since the three spins are independent events, we can write

$$P(B \text{ and } B \text{ and } B) = P(B) \times P(B) \times P(B)$$
$$= \frac{3}{5} \times \frac{3}{5} \times \frac{3}{5}$$
$$= \frac{27}{125}$$

## Method 2
The tree diagram for this situation is like this.

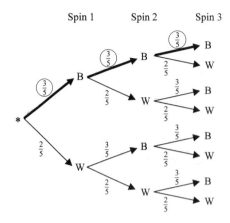

To obtain black and black and black, we need to follow the arrows shown.

From the diagram you can see that

$$P(B \text{ and } B \text{ and } B) = \tfrac{3}{5} \times \tfrac{3}{5} \times \tfrac{3}{5}$$
$$= \tfrac{27}{125}$$

## Exercise 29C

1. An ordinary dice is rolled twice. Calculate the probability that it will land on 6 on both occasions.

2. Jeremy shuffles a pack of cards, then looks at the top card and records the suit. He puts the card back. He shuffles the pack again, then looks again at the top card and records its suit. Calculate the probability that the two suits recorded will both be Spades.

3. Bag 1 contains 10 equal-sized balls: 5 are red, 3 are blue and 2 are white.
   Bag 2 contains 10 equal-sized balls: 4 are red, 4 are green and 2 are yellow.
   A ball is selected at random from each bag.
   Calculate the probability that
   (a) both balls will be red
   (b) the ball from bag 1 will be blue and the ball from bag 2 will be yellow
   (c) neither ball will be red.

4. A coin is biased in favour of Heads: it is known that the probability of the coin landing heads up is 0.58. The coin is tossed once.
   (a) Calculate the probability that the coin will land tails up.
   The coin is now tossed 3 times.

   (b) Calculate the probability that it will land heads up on all 3 occasions.
   (c) Calculate the probability that it will land tails up on all 3 occasions.

5. Gwen and her brother William are both taking an examination in Music. She estimates that the probability that she will pass the examination is 75%. She estimates that the probability that William will pass the examination is 60%. Estimate the probability that
   (a) they will both pass the examination;
   (b) Gwen will pass the examination and William will fail the examination;
   (c) Gwen will fail the examination and William will pass the examination;
   (d) they will both fail the examination.

6. It is estimated that the probability that a person selected at random will vote Labour at a General Election is 0.4.
   A market research company selects two people at random immediately after they have voted. These people are asked to say for which party they have cast their vote. Both people answer truthfully.
   Calculate the probability that they will both say that they voted Labour.

## 29.7 Combinations of joint outcomes

An ordinary dice is rolled twice. The scores shown each time are added together. What is the probability that the total score will be 5?

This is a more complicated problem than you have met so far, because there are several ways of the total score being 5. For example the outcome of the first roll could be 4 and the outcome of the second roll 1, or vice versa. There are other ways, too. You are looking for the probability of one of several joint outcomes occurring.

The complete set of joint outcomes is listed below.

1 and 1,   1 and 2,   1 and 3,   1 and 4,   1 and 5,   1 and 6
2 and 1,   2 and 2,   2 and 3,   2 and 4,   2 and 5,   2 and 6
3 and 1,   3 and 2,   3 and 3,   3 and 4,   3 and 5,   3 and 6
4 and 1,   4 and 2,   4 and 3,   4 and 4,   4 and 5,   4 and 6
5 and 1,   5 and 2,   5 and 3,   5 and 4,   5 and 5,   5 and 6
6 and 1,   6 and 2,   6 and 3,   6 and 4,   6 and 5,   6 and 6

There are 36 of these joint outcomes, all of which are equally likely. So the probability of obtaining each of these joint outcomes is $\frac{1}{36}$.

The outcomes which give a total score of 5 are (1 and 4), (2 and 3), (3 and 2), (4 and 1). There are 4 of these.

The probability of obtaining a score of 5 is therefore

$$4 \times \tfrac{1}{36} = \tfrac{4}{36}$$

which will cancel to give $\frac{1}{9}$.

### Example 6

Winston has a spinner in the shape of a square, and Alison has a spinner in the shape of a regular pentagon, as shown.

They each spin their spinner once and record the outcome.

Calculate the probability that

(a) the total score on the two spinners will be 6;

(b) the difference between the two scores on the spinners will be 1.

The total number of joint outcomes for the two spins is:

$$4 \times 5 = 20$$

The outcomes can be listed like this.

1,1   1,2   1,3   1,4   1,5
2,1   2,2   2,3   2,4   2,5
3,1   3,2   3,3   3,4   3,5
4,1   4,2   4,3   4,4   4,5

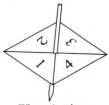

Winston's spinner

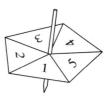

Alison's spinner

(a) The outcomes giving a total of 6 are shown in the table, along with their probabilities.

| Winston | Alison | Probability for Winston | Probability for Alison |
|:---:|:---:|:---:|:---:|
| 1 | 5 | $\frac{1}{4}$ | $\frac{1}{5}$ |
| 2 | 4 | $\frac{1}{4}$ | $\frac{1}{5}$ |
| 3 | 3 | $\frac{1}{4}$ | $\frac{1}{5}$ |
| 4 | 2 | $\frac{1}{4}$ | $\frac{1}{5}$ |

The probability of each of these joint outcomes is

$$\tfrac{1}{4} \times \tfrac{1}{5} = \tfrac{1}{20}$$

Since there are 4 joint outcomes that give the required total of 6, the probability of a total score of 6 is

$$4 \times \tfrac{1}{20} = \tfrac{4}{20} = \tfrac{1}{5}$$

(b) The joint outcomes giving a difference of 1 are listed below. Notice that the difference can be either Winston's score minus Alison's score, or Alison's score minus Winston's score.

| Winston | Alison |
|:---:|:---:|
| 1 | 2 |
| 2 | 1 |
| 2 | 3 |
| 3 | 2 |
| 3 | 4 |
| 4 | 3 |
| 4 | 5 |

Each of these joint outcomes has a probability of $\frac{1}{4} \times \frac{1}{5} = \frac{1}{20}$ as before. There are 7 of them.

So the probability of the difference between the scores being 1 is $7 \times \frac{1}{20} = \frac{7}{20}$

### Example 7

An ordinary coin is tossed 3 times.

Calculate the probability that it will land showing

(a) exactly 2 Heads

(b) at least 2 Heads.

(a) We could do this problem using tabulation, but instead we will use a tree diagram.

From the tree diagram, the outcomes that give two heads are:

H  H  T    with probability $\frac{1}{2} \times \frac{1}{2} \times \frac{1}{2} = \frac{1}{8}$

H  T  H    with probability $\frac{1}{2} \times \frac{1}{2} \times \frac{1}{2} = \frac{1}{8}$

T  H  H    with probability $\frac{1}{2} \times \frac{1}{2} \times \frac{1}{2} = \frac{1}{8}$

Since there are 3 joint outcomes, each with a probability of $\frac{1}{8}$, the probability of obtaining exactly 2 Heads is

$$3 \times \tfrac{1}{8} = \tfrac{3}{8}$$

(b) To obtain at least 2 Heads, we can have either exactly 2 Heads or 3 Heads.

The probability of getting exactly 2 Heads is $\frac{3}{8}$, from part (a).

From the tree diagram the route which gives 3 Heads is H H H and the probability of this outcome is

$$\tfrac{1}{2} \times \tfrac{1}{2} \times \tfrac{1}{2} = \tfrac{1}{8}$$

Since exactly 2 Heads and 3 Heads are mutually exclusive outcomes

$$P(\text{at least 2 Heads}) = P(\text{exactly 2 Heads}) + P(3 \text{ Heads})$$
$$= \tfrac{3}{8} + \tfrac{1}{8}$$
$$= \tfrac{4}{8}$$
$$= \tfrac{1}{2}$$

## Exercise 29D

**1.** Jim has a spinner in the shape of a regular pentagon. He spins it twice and adds together the numbers on which it lands. Calculate the probability that the total score will be
(a) 3    (b) 5
(c) at least 6.

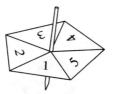

**2.** Jane and Saleem each have an ordinary dice. They both roll their dice once only and record the score. Calculate the probability that
(a) the sum of their scores will be 9

(b) the difference between their scores will be 2
(c) their two scores will be equal.

**3.** Laura plays netball. The probability of Laura scoring when she takes a penalty shot is estimated at 0.6.
During one match she is required to take 3 penalty shots.
Calculate the probability that Laura will score from
(a) exactly 2 of these penalty shots
(b) at least 2 of these penalty shots.

## Worked exam question 2

When you drop a matchbox on to a table, there are three ways it can land.

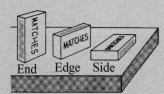

June has found that the probability of its landing on one end is approximately 0.1 and the probability of it landing on one side is approximately 0.6.

(a) Estimate the probability that the matchbox will land on one edge. Show your method clearly.

*Sum of Probabilities = 1*

*0.1 + 0.6 + Prob (edge) = 1* ●————

**Do:**
Show your working

*So Prob (edge) = 1 – 0.7 = 0.3*

(b) Jane drops two identical matchboxes.

What is the probability that both boxes will land on one end?

*0.1 × 0.1 = 0.01* ●————

**Do:**
Show your working

(c) Jane and Sarah are playing a game.

Sarah

I will drop two boxes.
If they land the same way up, I win.
If they don't land the same way up, you win.

Jane

Who is more likely to win the game?

Show all your working.

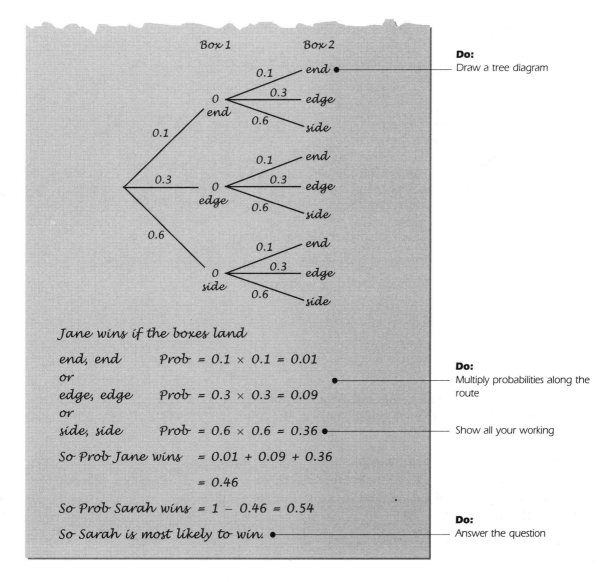

Jane wins if the boxes land

| | |
|---|---|
| end, end | Prob = 0.1 × 0.1 = 0.01 |
| or | |
| edge, edge | Prob = 0.3 × 0.3 = 0.09 |
| or | |
| side, side | Prob = 0.6 × 0.6 = 0.36 |

So Prob Jane wins  = 0.01 + 0.09 + 0.36

        = 0.46

So Prob Sarah wins = 1 − 0.46 = 0.54

So Sarah is most likely to win.

**Do:**
Draw a tree diagram

**Do:**
Multiply probabilities along the route

Show all your working

**Do:**
Answer the question

## 29.8 When two events are not mutually exclusive

Pritesh has a spinner in the shape of a regular pentagon. Its five sections are labelled with one of the numbers from 1 to 5. He spins the spinner once.

Katya has an ordinary coin. She spins the coin once.

What is the probability that **either** the spinner will land on 1 **or** the coin will land on Heads?

The outcomes of spinning the spinner and tossing the coin are independent.

They are **not mutually exclusive** because it is possible for the spinner to land on 1 **and** the coin to land Heads – that is, both outcomes could occur.

You can start the problem by listing all of the possible outcomes like this.

$$
\begin{array}{ll}
1,\text{H} & 1,\text{T} \\
2,\text{H} & 2,\text{T} \\
3,\text{H} & 3,\text{T} \\
4,\text{H} & 4,\text{T} \\
5,\text{H} & 5,\text{T}
\end{array}
$$

There are 10 of these joint outcomes, and they are all equally likely. So the probability of any one of the joint outcomes occurring is $\frac{1}{10}$.

The outcomes which involve **either** the spinner on 1 **or** the coin landing heads up are listed here.

1,H      (This is the joint outcome where they **both** occur.)
1,T
2,H
3,H
4,H
5,H

You can see that 6 of the 10 outcomes satisfy our requirements. So the probability of either the spinner landing on 1 or the coin landing heads up is $\frac{6}{10}$.

You might have thought of solving this problem by adding the probability of an outcome of 1 from the spinner and the probability of an outcome of Heads from the coin. But you would have got a different answer.

The probability of getting a 1 on the spinner is $\frac{2}{10}$ (2 out of the 10 joint outcomes).

The probability of getting Heads on the coin is $\frac{5}{10}$ (5 out of the 10 joint outcomes).

Adding these, you would get $\frac{5}{10} + \frac{2}{10} = \frac{7}{10}$.

The answer you want is $\frac{6}{10}$. Why have you got an extra $\frac{1}{10}$?

If you think about it, the joint outcomes you counted to get the probability $\frac{2}{10}$ for a 1 on the spinner were (1,H) and (1,T). The joint outcomes you counted to get the probability $\frac{5}{10}$ or a Head on the coin were (1,H), (2,H), (3,H), (4,H) and (5,H). Both of these lists include the outcome (1,H).

So if you add $\frac{2}{10}$ to $\frac{5}{10}$ you are counting the outcome (1,H) twice.

If you want to calculate the probability of either a Head or a 1 by adding the probabilities, you have to deduct P(1,H) from the answer so that you don't count it twice.

$$P(1 \text{ or } H) = P(1) + P(H) - P(1, H)$$
$$= \tfrac{2}{10} + \tfrac{5}{10} - \tfrac{1}{10} = \tfrac{6}{10}$$

This can be generalised to:

When A and B are two outcomes of independent events and A and B are not mutually exclusive then

$$P(A \text{ or } B) = P(A) + P(B) - P(A \text{ and } B)$$

This type of problem is the most advanced that can be set in an Intermediate level GCSE exam. A question on this is rare.

### *Example 8*

Fatima rolls an ordinary dice once. Alex tosses a coin once.

Calculate the probability of *either* the dice showing a 3 *or* the coin showing tails.

Because the two events and their outcomes are independent and not mutually exclusive we use

$$P(3 \text{ or } T) = P(3) + P(T) - P(3 \text{ and } T)$$

But:

$$P(3) = \tfrac{1}{6}, \qquad P(T) = \tfrac{1}{2}, \quad \text{and} \quad P(3 \text{ and } T) = \tfrac{1}{6} \times \tfrac{1}{2} = \tfrac{1}{12}$$

So:

$$P(3 \text{ or } T) = \tfrac{1}{6} + \tfrac{1}{2} - \tfrac{1}{12}$$
$$= \tfrac{2}{12} + \tfrac{6}{12} - \tfrac{1}{12}$$
$$= \tfrac{7}{12}$$

The probability of either a 3 on the dice or tails on the coin is $\tfrac{7}{12}$.

### Exercise 29E

1. Megan has a spinner in the shape of a regular pentagon like this. She also has an ordinary dice.
   Megan spins the spinner once and rolls the dice once.
   Calculate the probability of either the spinner landing on B or the dice landing on 4.

2. Ashley plays hockey for his college. It is estimated that the probability of his team winning a match is 0.4.
   Wendy plays tennis for her college. It is estimated that the probability of her winning a match is 0.7.

On Saturday Ashley plays hockey and Wendy plays tennis.
Calculate the probability that either one (but not both) of them will win on Saturday.

3. The probability of Dennis being given a tie for his 18th birthday is 0.2.
   The probability of him being given a shirt for his 18th birthday is 0.4.
   Calculate the probability that Dennis will be given either a shirt or a tie for his 18th birthday.

4. You are playing a game of chance. Each letter of the alphabet is written on a piece of paper. The pieces of paper are placed in a hat. One piece of paper is drawn at random from the hat.

4. You win if the piece of paper contains either a vowel, or a letter from the second half of the alphabet.
Calculate the probability of you winning this game of chance.

5. A computer prints a random number between 1 and 100, inclusive. Calculate the probability of the computer printing either an even number or a multiple of 3.

6. Linda and her sister are playing a board game. In order to decide who should start they each roll two ordinary dice. The person who first rolls a six on either dice starts the game. Linda has the first roll of the two dice.
Calculate the probability that Linda will be able to start the board game immediately after her first roll of the two dice.

7. Rangers are to play a soccer fixture with a home match and an away match.
The probability that they will win the home match is estimated at 0.7
The probability that they will win the away match is estimated at 0.4.
Estimate the probability that they will win at least one of these matches.

---

**Worked exam question 3**

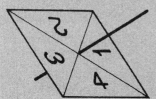

A spinner, with its edges numbered one to four, is biased.

For one spin the probability of scoring 1 is 0.2,

the probability of scoring 3 is 0.3

and the probability of scoring 4 is 0.15.

(a) Calculate the probability of scoring 2 with one spin.

$P(2) = 1 - (0.2 + 0.3 + 0.15) = 1 - 0.65$ •——————

**Do:**
Show your work

(a) ........0.35........

Check that
$0.2 + 0.3 + 0.15 + 0.35 = 1$

(b) The spinner is used in a board game called 'Steeplechase'. In the game, a player's counter is moved forwards at each turn by the score shown on the spinner.

If the player's counter lands on one of the two squares numbered 27 and 28 (labelled 'WATER JUMP'), the player is out of the game.

| | 23 | 24 | 25 | 26 | WATER JUMP 27 | 28 | 29 | 30 | 31 | |
|---|---|---|---|---|---|---|---|---|---|---|

(i) Ann's counter is on square 26.

Find the probability that she will not be out of the game after one more turn.

Prob (scoring 1) = 0.2   Prob (scoring 2) = 0.35 •——————

**Do:**
Show your working

Prob (scoring 1 or 2) = 0.55

Add 0.2 and 0.35!

(b)(i) ......0.55......

(ii)   Peter's counter is on square 25.

Find the probability that, after two more turns, his counter will be on square 29.

*To go from 25 to 29 Peter must score 4*

*His outcomes are (1 and 3) or (2 and 2) or*

*(3 and 1)*

*P (1 and 3 or 2 and 2 or 3 and 1)*

*= (0.2 × 0.3) + (0.35 × 0.35) + (0.3 × 0.2)*

*= 0.06 + 0.1225 + 0.06 = 0.0245*

(b)(ii)  *0.0245*

**Don't:**
Round your answer

## Worked exam question 4

Ahmed and Kate play a game of tennis.

The probability that Ahmed will win is $\frac{5}{8}$.

Ahmed and Kate play a game of snooker.

The probability that Kate will win is $\frac{4}{7}$.

(a)   Complete the probability tree diagram below.

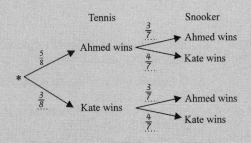

**Do:**
Complete the tree diagram

Remember that prob (Kate wins) = 1 − prob (Ahmed wins)

**Don't:**
Cancel the fractions

Convert $\frac{5}{8}$, $\frac{3}{7}$ etc. to decimals or percentages

(b) Calculate the probability that Kate will win both games.

*(b) Prob (Kate wins both games)*

$$= \frac{3}{8} \times \frac{4}{7} = \frac{12}{56} \left( or\ \frac{3}{14} \right)$$

(c) Calculate the probability that Ahmed will win at least one of the two games.

**(c)** Prob (Ahmed wins Tennis or Snooker, or both)

**Do:**
Remember Ahmed can win both

= P (T or S)

= P(T) + P(S) − P(T and S)

$$= \frac{5}{8} + \frac{3}{7} - \frac{5}{8} \times \frac{3}{7}$$

**Do:**
Work in fractions
Remember the formula

$$= \frac{35}{56} + \frac{24}{56} - \frac{15}{56}$$

$$= \frac{35 + 24 - 15}{56}$$

$$= \frac{44}{56} \left( or \; \frac{11}{14} \right)$$

(NEAB)

## Exercise 29F (Mixed questions)

1. Winston and Lesley are taking their driving tests.
   The probability that Winston will pass at the first attempt is estimated to be 0.75.
   The probability that Lesley will pass at the first attempt is estimated to be 0.6.
   Using these two estimates, calculate estimates for
   (a) the probability that Winston will fail the driving test at the first attempt;
   (b) the probability that Winston and Lesley will both pass the driving test at the first attempt;
   (c) the probability that at least one of them will pass the driving test at the first attempt.

2. Nick has a spinner in the shape of a regular pentagon, which he spins once. Vicky has an ordinary dice, which she rolls once. Calculate the probability that
   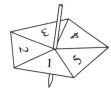
   (a) the total score on the spinner and the dice will be 7;
   (b) the score on the spinner will be greater than the score on the dice;
   (c) at least one of them will land showing the number 5.

3. The probability of a new electric light bulb being perfect is 0.97. The light bulbs are sold in packets of three.
   Calculate the probability that a single packet will contain
   (a) 3 light bulbs all of which are faulty;
   (b) at least one faulty light bulb.

4. Della and Ron play a game of chess. The probability that Della will win is $\frac{2}{3}$.
   Della and Ron play a game of darts. The probability that Ron will win is $\frac{5}{8}$.
   (a) Complete this tree diagram.
   (b) Calculate the probability that Della will win both games.

   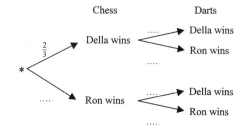

   (c) Calculate the probability that Ron will win at least one of the games.

5. The probability of a new born baby being a girl is 0.5.
   Mrs Jones, Mrs Khan and Mrs Hook are all expecting babies.
   Calculate the probability that
   (a) all three babies will be girls
   (b) at least two of the babies will be boys.

6. A computer prints a random integer between 1 and 100 inclusive.
   Calculate the probability that the printed number will be a multiple of 3 or a multiple of 5.

7. Bag 1 contains 10 coloured balls, 3 of which are red.
   Bag 2 contains 10 coloured balls, 6 of which are red.
   One ball is chosen at random from each bag.
   Calculate the probability that
   (a) both balls will be red
   (b) at least one ball will be red.

8. Bag 1 contains 12 sweets; 5 are chocolates and 7 are toffees.
   (a) What is the probability that a sweet chosen from the bag at random will be a toffee?
   (b) Bag 2 contains 10 sweets, of which 4 are mints and 6 are chocolates.

   Alex takes one sweet at random from each bag.
   (b) Complete the tree diagram showing the possible outcomes and their probabilities.

   (c) Calculate the probability that Alex selects
   (i) two chocolates
   (ii) exactly one chocolate
   (iii) at least one chocolate

9. A dice is biased. The probability of it landing showing 6 when rolled once is 0.2.
   The dice is rolled three times. Calculate the probability of it landing showing
   (a) 6 on all 3 rolls;
   (b) 6 on the first roll, 6 on the second roll but not 6 on the third roll;
   (c) 6 on exactly two of the three rolls;
   (d) 6 at least once in the three rolls.

10. In a game two dice are thrown and their scores are added together. The first dice has the numbers 1, 2, 2, 4, 6, 8 on it. The second dice has the numbers 1, 3, 5, 7, 7, 8 on it.
    (a) Complete this table to show the possible total scores.

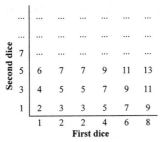

(b) Julian needs exactly 7 to win the game. What is the probability that he wins the game on his next throw?    [WJEC]

11. In a survey about children, Valerie asks 40 women how many boys and girls they each have. Her findings are shown in the table.

| Number of girls | | | | | | |
|---|---|---|---|---|---|---|
| 5 | | | | | | |
| 4 | 1 | 1 | | | | |
| 3 | 3 | 4 | | | | |
| 2 | 3 | | 1 | | | 1 |
| 1 | 4 | 7 | 1 | | 1 | |
| 0 | 8 | 3 | 1 | | 1 | |
| | 0 | 1 | 2 | 3 | 4 | 5 |

**Numbers of boys**

(a) What is the modal number of boys for these women?
(b) How many boys did these women have altogether?
(c) One of these women is chosen at random.
   (i) What is the probability that she has no children?
   (ii) What is the probability that she has at least one child?
   (iii) What is the probability that she has two children?

12. The probability of different numbers of births per week in a village are as follows.

| Number of births | 0 | 1 | 2 | 3 |
|---|---|---|---|---|
| Probability | 0.4 | 0.3 | 0.2 | 0.1 |

The probability of different numbers of deaths per week in the village are shown in the following table.

| Number of deaths | 0 | 1 | 2 | 3 |
|---|---|---|---|---|
| Probability | 0.1 | 0.3 | 0.4 | 0.2 |

Assume that the number of births per week and the number of deaths per week are independent.
(a) Find the probability that during any particular week, there are exactly two births and two deaths.
(b) Find the probability that during any particular week, the number of births and deaths are the same.

# Test yourself

1. An ordinary dice has its faces numbered from 1 to 6. The dice is known to be biased. In one roll of the dice the probability of scoring 1 is 0.2, of scoring 2 is 0.15, of scoring 3 is 0.18, of scoring 4 is 0.17 and of scoring 5 is 0.16.

| | |
|---|---|
| QUESTION | Calculate the probability of scoring 6 with one roll of the dice |
| ANSWER | 0.14 *If your answer is incorrect review page 551, Section 28.8 and page 563, Section 29.4 on mutually exclusive outcomes* |

The dice is used to play a game of Snakes and Ladders.
A player's counter is moved forward at each turn by the score shown on the dice.
If the counter lands at the foot of a ladder the counter is then moved up the ladder.
If the counter lands at the mouth of a snake the counter is then moved down the snake.
Jamie's counter is on square 20. The next two snakes start at squares 21 and 26.

| | |
|---|---|
| QUESTION | Calculate the probability that Jamie's counter will not land on a snake after one more turn. |
| ANSWER | 0.66 *If your answer is incorrect review page 551, Section 28.8 and page 563, Section 29.4 on mutually exclusive outcomes* |

Kate's counter is on square 10. There are no snakes between square 10 and square 21, but there is a ladder starting on square 19.

| | |
|---|---|
| QUESTION | Calculate the probability that Kate's counter will land on this ladder after she has had exactly two more turns. |
| ANSWER | 0.1048 *If your answer is incorrect review page 564, Section 29.5 onwards* |

2. Amy and Chris are taking an English examination.
The probability that Amy will pass the examination is $\frac{4}{5}$.
The probability that Chris will pass the examination is $\frac{3}{5}$.

| | |
|---|---|
| QUESTION | Calculate the probability that at least one of them will pass the examination. |
| ANSWER | $\frac{23}{25}$ *If your answer is incorrect review page 564, Section 29.5 and page 569, Section 29.7 on combinations of joint outcomes* |

3. In the game of 'Pass the Pigs', two identical toy pigs are thrown. Each pig can land in one of five positions. The five positions and the probabilities that the pig will land in each of these positions are shown in the table.

| Position | Sider | Trotter | Razorback | Snouter | Leaning Jowler |
|---|---|---|---|---|---|
| Probability | 0.57 | 0.2 | 0.2 | 0.02 | 0.01 |

Both pigs are thrown.

| QUESTION | (a) | Work out the probability that they will both land in the Trotter position. |
|---|---|---|
| ANSWER | (a) | 0.04 | *If your answer is incorrect review page 564, Section 29.5 on probability of joint outcomes* |

| QUESTION | (b) | Work out the probability that at least one pig will land in the Sider position. |
|---|---|---|
| ANSWER | (b) | 0.8151 | *If your answer is incorrect review page 569, Section 29.7 on combination of joint outcomes* |

A 'Double Trotter' (when both pigs land in the Trotter position) scores 10 points. The only other way of scoring 10 points in one throw is when one of the pigs lands in the Snouter position and the other lands in the Sider position.

| QUESTION | (c) | Work out the probability that 10 points will be scored on one throw of the pigs. |
|---|---|---|
| ANSWER | (c) | 0.0628 | *If your answer is incorrect, review page 569, Section 29.7 on combination of joint outcomes. Check also that you have used all 3 ways of obtaining 10 points in your calculations. These are Double Trotter, Sider and Snouter and Snouter and Sider* [London] |

## Summary of key points to remember

1. When solving a problem involving more than one event it is useful to list or tabulate all the possible outcomes, or to represent them in a tree diagram.

2. If Event 1 has $n$ outcomes and Event 2 has $m$ outcomes then the combination of these two events has $n \times m$ outcomes.

3. You should be able to use a tree diagram.

4. When A and B are *mutually exclusive* and occur with probabilities P(A) and P(B) then

   P(A *or* B) = P(A) + P(B)

   and this idea of adding extends to more than 2 outcomes, so that

   P(A *or* B *or* C) = P(A) + P(B) + P(C) and so on.

5. When two outcomes, A and B, are *independent* and occur with probabilities P(A) and P(B) then

   P(A *and* B) = P(A) × P(B) and similarly for 3 outcomes

   P(A and B and C) = P(A) × P(B) × P(C) and so on.

6. When A and B are **not mutually exclusive**, that is in cases where they can both occur simultaneously

   P(A *or* B) = P(A) + P(B) − P(A and B)

# Revision routemaster

This routemaster is designed to help you prepare for your examination.

## Practising for your examination

One of the best ways of revising for a mathematics examination is to work through past exam papers or questions similar to those set in the papers.

We recommend that you obtain copies of past examination papers for the exam board and syllabus you are following and try the questions as a key part of your revision.

## Which questions will appear in the exam?

No one can ever be certain which questions will appear in any paper. However, certain **key questions** and **topics** are highly likely to appear in GCSE exam papers in mathematics.

To be absolutely sure that you have covered **all** of the topics which might appear in the examination paper you need to cover all the work in the syllabus – and that means full coverage of the content of this book. Depending on the amount of time you have left for your revision this may or may not be possible.

## How to use this routemaster

This revision routemaster uses a similar method to the Test Yourself sections in each chapter to help you prepare for your exam.

It provides you with a list of **key topics**. Each topic has an associated **key question**.

Try each key question:

- if you can do it and get the correct answer then consolidate your knowledge and understanding by working through some of the exercises set on the same topic in this book and in past exam papers.

- if you cannot do the question or get an incorrect answer or part answer then review again the appropriate chapter or section in this book as shown in the answer section for each question.

# Key topics

| Number | |
|---|---|
| N1 | Estimation, approximation at significant figures |
| N2 | Solving numerical problems with and without a calculator |
| N3 | Fractions, decimals and percentages |
| N4 | Ratio, proportion and proportional change |
| N5 | Money management |
| N6 | Standard form |

| Algebra | |
|---|---|
| A1 | Find the next and $n$th term in a sequence |
| A2 | Trial and improvement |
| A3 | Inequalities |
| A4 | Linear equations |
| A5 | Manipulation |
| A6 | Linear graphs |
| A7 | Simultaneous equations |

| Shape, space and measures | |
|---|---|
| S1 | Angle properties and symmetry |
| S2 | Pythagoras' Theorem |
| S3 | Circumference and area of a circle |
| S4 | Lengths, areas and volumes |
| S5 | Enlargements |
| S6 | Compound measures |
| S7 | Trigonometry |

| Handling data | |
|---|---|
| D1 | Frequency diagrams and pie charts |
| D2 | Mean, mode, median and range |
| D3 | Testing a hypothesis |
| D4 | Frequency polygons |
| D5 | Scatter diagrams and line of best fit |
| D6 | Cumulative frequency curves |
| D7 | The probability of an event not happening |
| D8 | Relative frequency and probability |
| D9 | Probability of combined events |

## Key questions

**N1** Sally needs to work out the value of $\dfrac{3.96 \times 9.83}{1.007}$

using her calculator.

(a) Write down an approximation for each number in the sum which would give Sally an appropriate answer.

(b) Work out the value of the sum using your calculator. Record all the figures in the answers on your calculator display.

(c) Write down the answer correct to three significant figures.

| **Answer** | **If your answer is incorrect, review** |
|---|---|
| (a)  4, 10, 1 | Unit 3, Sections 3.1–3.6, pages 47–60 |
| (b)  38.65620655 | Unit 3, Sections 3.1–3.6, pages 47–60 |
| (c)  38.7 | Unit 3, Sections 3.1–3.6, pages 47–60 |

---

**N2** (a)  Megan is 5 feet 3 inches tall.

$1\text{cm} = 0.394$ inches

$12$ inches $= 1$ foot

Calculate Megan's height in centimetres

Give your answers to an appropriate degree of accuracy.

(b) An electronic weighing scale gives Megan's weight as 63.4792 kg.

Give her weight correct to an appropriate degree of accuracy.

[SEG]

| **Answer** | **If your answer is incorrect, review** |
|---|---|
| (a)  159.9 cm | Units 3, 4, 5 and 6, pages 47–129 |
| (b)  63.5 kg | Unit 3, Sections 3.3 and 3.4, pages 48–51 |

---

**N3** Calculate 16% of £420.00.

| **Answer** | **If your answer is incorrect, review** |
|---|---|
| £67.20 | Unit 1, Sections 1.10 and 1.11, pages 14–19 and Unit 5, Sections 5.4–5.9, pages 84–96 |

---

**N4** In a sale a shop reduces all original prices by 15%.

Calculate:

(a) The sale price of a coat which had an original price of £64.00.

(b) The original price of a dress which has a sale price of £30.00.

| **Answer** | **If your answer is incorrect, review** |
|---|---|
| (a)  £54.40 | Unit 5, Sections 5.4–5.9, pages 84–96 |
| (b)  £35.29 | Unit 5, Sections 5.4–5.9, pages 84–96 |

---

**N5** Joan marks examination papers.

She is paid £1.75 for each paper she marks.

She marks 600 papers.

She has to pay income tax at a rate of 25% on her earnings.

Calculate her net earnings for marking the papers after income tax is deducted.

| **Answer** | **If your answer is incorrect, review** |
|---|---|
| £787.50 | Unit 6, Sections 6.10–6.12, pages 117–127 |

---

**N6** (a)  The dinosaurs roamed the Earth about 150 000 000 years ago.

Write 150 000 000 in standard form.

(b)  The probability of a single ticket winning the National Lottery is approximately $\dfrac{1}{14\,000\,000}$

Write this probability in standard form.

(c)  Calculate $3.2 \times 10^3 + 1.5 \times 10^2$, giving your answer in standard form.

| **Answer** | **If your answer is incorrect, review** |
|---|---|
| (a)  $1.5 \times 10^8$ | Unit 6, Section 6.9, pages 114–116 |
| (b)  $7.1 \times 10^{-8}$ | Unit 6, Section 6.9, pages 114–116 |
| (c)  $3.35 \times 10^3$ | Unit 6, Section 6.9, pages 114–116 |

---

**A1** Here are the first four terms of a number sequence:

   5, 9, 13, 17

Write down an expression for the $n^{\text{th}}$ term of this sequence.

| **Answer** | **If your answer is incorrect, review** |
|---|---|
| 4n + 1 | Unit 7, Sections 7.5–7.6, pages 136–140 |

---

**A2** (a)  Show that a solution of the equation

   $x^3 - 2x = 15$
   lies between $x = 2$ and $x = 3$

(b)  Use a method of trial and improvement to find this solution correct to two decimal places.

| **Answer** | **If your answer is incorrect, review** |
|---|---|
| (a) $2^3 - 2(2) = 8 - 4 = 4 < 15$ | Unit 13, Sections 13.1–13.7, pages 261–268 |
| (b) $x = 2.74$ | Unit 13, Sections 13.1–13.7, pages 261–268 |

---

**A3** (a) List all the possible integer values of $n$ such that

$$-2 \leq n < 3$$

(b) Solve the inequality

$$3x + 1 \leq 13$$

| **Answer** | **If your answer is incorrect, review** |
|---|---|
| (a) $-2, -1, 0, 1, 2$ | Unit 11, Section 11.6, pages 229–232 |
| (b) $x \leq 4$ | Unit 11, Section 11.6, pages 229–232 |

---

**A4** Solve each of the equations

(a) $3x - 2 = 11$      (b) $2 - 5y = 8$

(c) $4z - 3 = 2z + 7$      (d) $3(4p + 2) = 15$

| **Answer** | **If your answer is incorrect, review** |
|---|---|
| (a) $x = 4\frac{1}{3}$ | Unit 11, Sections 11.2–11.4, pages 216–223 |
| (b) $y = -1\frac{1}{5}$ | Unit 11, Sections 11.2–11.4, pages 216–223 |
| (c) $z = 5$ | Unit 11, Sections 11.2–11.4, pages 216–223 |
| (d) $p = \frac{3}{4}$ | Unit 11, Sections 11.2–11.4, pages 216–223 |

---

**A5** (a) Factorise completely

$$4pq^2 - 12p^2q$$

(b) Make $t$ the subject of the formula

$$s = at + b$$

| **Answer** | **If your answer is incorrect, review** |
|---|---|
| (a) $4pq(q - 3p)$ | Unit 10, Sections 10.3–10.5, pages 196–202 |
| (b) $t = \dfrac{s - b}{a}$ | Unit 10, Section 10.8, pages 207–210 |

---

**A6** (a) Complete the table of values for

$$y = 9 - 3x$$

| $x$ | $-3$ | $-2$ | $-1$ | 0 | 1 | 2 | 3 |
|---|---|---|---|---|---|---|---|
| $y$ | 18 | | | | 6 | | |

(b) Draw the graph of

$$y = 9 - 3x$$

for values of $x$ from $-3$ to $3$

**Answer**

(a)

| x | −3 | −2 | −1 | 0 | 1 | 2 | 3 |
|---|---|---|---|---|---|---|---|
| y | 18 | 15 | 12 | 9 | 6 | 3 | 0 |

(b)

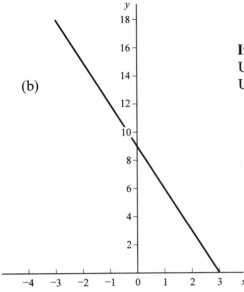

**If your answer is incorrect, review**
Unit 9, Sections 9.1–9.5, pages 165–173
Unit 9, Sections 9.1–9.5, pages 165–173

---

**A7** Solve the simultaneous equations:

$3x - y = 5$

$x + 2y = -3$

**Answer**                          **If your answer is incorrect, review**
$x = 1$                             Unit 11, Section 11.5, pages 223–229
$y = -2$

---

**S1** ABCDE is a regular pentagon, centre O

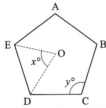

(a)  Write down the number of lines of symmetry for ABCDE.

(b)  Calculate the angle marked

   (i) $x°$
   (ii) $y°$

**Answer**                          **If your answer is incorrect, review**
(a)  5                              Unit 16, Section 16.2, pages 312–314
(b)  (i) $x = 72°$                  Unit 16, Section 16.8, pages 326–328
     (ii) $y = 108°$

---

**S2** PQR is a right-angled triangle.

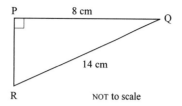

PQ = 8 cm        QR = 14 cm

Calculate the length of PR

**Answer**                          **If your answer is incorrect, review**
  PR = 11.49 cm                     Unit 19, Section 19.6, pages 406–408

---

**S3** A circle has diameter 8 cm.

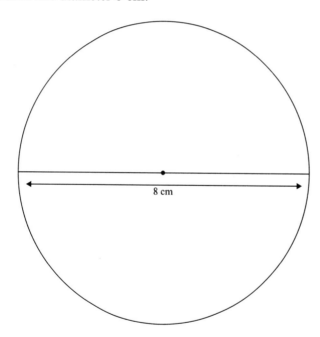

Calculate:

(a)   the circumference of the circle

(b)   the area of the circle.

**Answer**                          **If your answer is incorrect, review**
  (a)   25.13 cm                    Unit 18, Section 18.7, pages 383–386
  (b)   50.27 cm$^2$                Unit 18, Section 18.7, pages 383–386

**S4** The diagram shows a paint trough in the shape of a prism.

Each shaded end of the trough is a vertical trapezium.

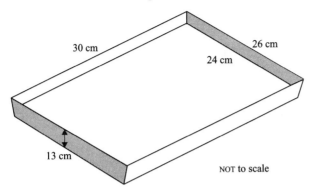

30 cm    26 cm

24 cm

13 cm

NOT to scale

Calculate the **volume** of paint which the trough can hold when it is full.

**Answer**
9750 cm³

**If your answer is incorrect, review**
Unit 18, Section 18.10, pages 389–392

[SEG]

---

**S5** The diagram shows a quadrilateral OABC.

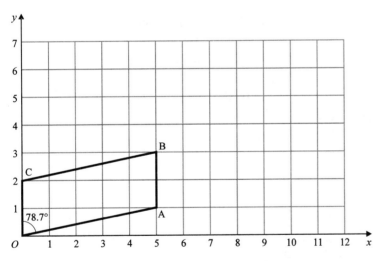

(a)   What type of quadrilateral is OABC?

(b)   The quadrilateral OABC is enlarged, with centre O and scale factor 2, to give O′A′B′C′. Draw the quadrilateral O′A′B′C′.

**Answer**
  (a)   Parallelogram
  (b)   O′ → (0, 0)
        A′ → (10, 2)
        B′ → (10, 6)
        C′ → (0, 4)

**If your answer is incorrect, review**
Unit 14, Sections 14.3 and 14.5, pages 283–285
Unit 17, Section 17.6, pages 352–354

[SEG]

**S5** The temperature is recorded as 19°C to the nearest degree.

Write down the lowest possible value of that temperature.

**Answer**                                   **If your answer is incorrect, review**
   18.5° C                                      Unit 21, Sections 21.1–21.3, pages 424–426

**S6** Darren drives 38 km at an average speed of 63 km per hour.

Calculate how long his journey takes. Give your answer in minutes.

**Answer**                                   **If your answer is incorrect, review**
   36.2 mins                                    Unit 21, Section 21.9, pages 436–438

[SEG]

---

**S7** In the triangle ABC below, AC = 12 cm and the angle BAC = 41°

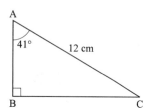

Calculate the length of AB.

**Answer**                                   **If your answer is incorrect, review**
   9.06 cm                                      Unit 19, Section 19.6, pages 406–408

---

**D1** In a town 1800 cars were stolen in a year. The table shows information about the times of day when they were stolen.

| Time | Number of cars |
|---|---|
| Midnight to 6 am | 700 |
| 6 am to midday | 80 |
| Midday to 6 pm | 280 |
| 6pm to midnight | 470 |
| Time unknown | 270 |

This information can be shown in a pie chart.

(a)  Work out the angle of each sector of the pie chart.

| Time | Number of cars |
|---|---|
| Midnight to 6 am | |
| 6 am to midday | |
| Midday to 6 pm | |
| 6pm to midnight | |
| Time unknown | |
| Total of angles | 360° |

[London]

(b)  Construct the pie chart in the circle below.

(c)  What fraction of the number of cars was stolen between midday and 6 pm?

| Answer | If your answer is incorrect, review |
|---|---|
| (a)  angles 140°, 16°, 56°, 94° 54° | Unit 24, Section 24.6, pages 483–484 |
| (b)  pie chart, with above angles | Unit 24, Section 24.6, pages 483–484 |
| (c)  $\dfrac{7}{45}$ | Unit 24, Section 24.6, pages 483–484 |

**D2** Bronwen owns a pet shop.

The table gives information about the weights of hamsters in Bronwen's shop.

| Weight, $w$, of hamsters in g | Number of hamsters | | |
|---|---|---|---|
| $28 \le w < 30$ | 9 | | |
| $30 \le w < 32$ | 5 | | |
| $32 \le w < 34$ | 4 | | |
| $34 \le w < 36$ | 2 | | |
| | | | |

Calculate an estimate for the mean weight of the hamsters in Bronwen's shop.

| Answer | If your answer is incorrect, review |
|---|---|
| 30.9 | Unit 25, Section 25.4, pages 501–505[London] |

**D3** A newspaper reports that 'People in Germany earn higher wages than people in the UK.'

Give two statistical measures which could be used to test this statement.

| Answer | If your answer is incorrect, review |
|---|---|
| Mean wage in each country, range of wages in each country. (Or median and interquartile range or mode and any measure of spread.) | Unit 25, Sections 25.1 and 25.2, pages 494–497 |

**D4** The table gives information about the weights of a group of twenty-five young children.

| Weight, w, of children in kg | Number of children |
|:---:|:---:|
| $28 \leq w < 30$ | 4 |
| $30 \leq w < 32$ | 6 |
| $32 \leq w < 34$ | 10 |
| $34 \leq w < 36$ | 3 |
| $36 \leq w < 38$ | 2 |

Draw the frequency polygon for this data.

**Answer**                    **If your answer is incorrect, review**
Unit 24, Section 24.7, pages 485–488

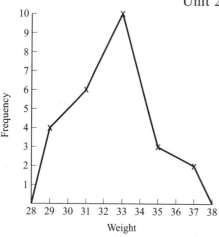

**D5** The table lists the weight of twelve books and the number of pages in each one.

| Number of pages | 80 | 155 | 100 | 125 | 145 | 90 | 140 | 160 | 135 | 100 | 115 | 165 |
|:---:|:---:|:---:|:---:|:---:|:---:|:---:|:---:|:---:|:---:|:---:|:---:|:---:|
| Weight (g) | 160 | 330 | 200 | 260 | 320 | 180 | 290 | 330 | 260 | 180 | 230 | 350 |

(a)   Draw a scatter graph to show the information in the table.

(b)   Describe the correlation between the number of pages in these books and their weights.

(c)   Draw a line of best fit on your scatter graph.

(d)   Use your line of best fit to estimate
    (i)    the number of pages in a book of weight 280 g,
    (ii)   the weight, in grams, of a book with 110 pages.

[London]

**Answer**

(a)

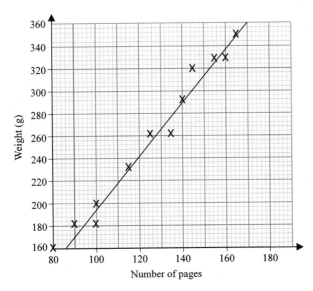

**If your answer is incorrect, review**
Unit 27, Sections 27.1–27.3, pages 527–534

(b)   Positive.

Unit 27, Sections 27.1–27.3, pages 527–534

(c)   See graph above.

Unit 27, Sections 27.1–27.3, pages 527–534

(d)   (i)    136

Unit 27, Sections 27.1–27.3, pages 527–534

     (ii)    217

Unit 27, Sections 27.1–27.3, pages 527–534

**D6** A survey was conducted to find the speeds ($s$) in miles per hour (m.p.h.) of 100 vehicles travelling on a main road at midday.

The speeds are recorded in the frequency table below.

| Speed ($s$, m.p.h.) | Frequency | Cumulative Frequency |
|---|---|---|
| $0 < s \leq 10$ | 3 | |
| $10 < s \leq 20$ | 8 | |
| $20 < s \leq 30$ | 14 | |
| $30 < s \leq 40$ | 17 | |
| $40 < s \leq 50$ | 28 | |
| $50 < s \leq 60$ | 18 | |
| $60 < s \leq 70$ | 8 | |
| $70 < s \leq 80$ | 4 | |

(a)   Complete the cumulative frequency column for the table above.

(b)   Draw a cumulative frequency curve.

(c)   Use your cumulative frequency curve to work out estimates of
    (i)    the median speed of the 100 vehicles travelling on the main road at midday
    (ii)    the interquartile range of these speeds.

A second survey was conducted on the speeds of 100 vehicles travelling on the same main road at 6 pm. The results of this survey show that the median speed at 6 pm was 52 m.p.h. with an interquartile rage of 40 m.p.h.

(d)    Compare the speeds of the vehicles using the main road at mid-day with that of the vehicles using the main road at 6 p.m.

**Answer**

**If your answer is incorrect, review**
Unit 26, Sections 26.1–26.3, pages 510–522

(a)

| cf |
|---|
| 3 |
| 11 |
| 25 |
| 42 |
| 70 |
| 88 |
| 96 |
| 100 |

(b)                                           Unit 26, Sections 26.1–26.3, pages 510–522

(c)    (i)    About 47 m.p.h.          Unit 26, Sections 26.1–26.3, pages 510–522
       (ii)   About 23 m.p.h.

(d)    Median 2nd group             Unit 26, Sections 26.1–26.3, pages 510–522
       > median 1st group
       1 qr of 2nd group much
       > 1 qr 1st group hence
       speeds of 2nd group more
       spread out.

---

**D7** A spinner is made in the shape of a pentagon.

Each of the sections of the spinner is labelled with one of the letters A, B, C, D and E.

The spinner is not quite regular, so that when it is spun once, the probabilities that it will land on each of the letters is given by the table below.

| Letter | A | B | C | D | E |
|---|---|---|---|---|---|
| Probability | 0.21 | 0.23 | 0.16 | 0.22 | |

**D7** Calculate the probability that the spinner will land on the letter E, when it is spun once.

The spinner is spun 10 000 times.

It lands on a particular letter 2 308 times.

**D8** Give, with a reason, which letter this is most likely to be.

The spinner is spun twice.

**D9** Work out the probabilities that it will land
   (i)   on the letter A on both of these occasions
   (ii)  that it will land firstly on the letter C and then on the letter D.

| **Answer** | | **If your answer is incorrect, review** |
|---|---|---|

**Answer**

**D7** (a)  0.18

**D8** (b)  B, because
prob(B) = 0.23 and
0.23 × 1000 = 2300
– the likely total and
2308 in close 2300

**D9** (c)  (i)  0.0441
        (ii)  0.0352

**If your answer is incorrect, review**

Unit 28, Sections 28.8 and 28.9, pages 551–555
Unit 28, Section 28.7, pages 546–551

Unit 29, Sections 29.5, pages 564–565

# Answers

## Exercise 1A

1. (a) 3, 9, 13, 16, 24, 25, 31, 42, 48 ; 24
   (b) 12, 29, 31, 44, 56, 63, 66, 84, 89 ; 56
   (c) 112, 245, 339, 342, 465, 532, 671, 865, 999 ; 465
   (d) 52, 67, 76, 98, 189, 223, 432, 521, 777 ; 189
   (e) 7, 8, 10, 45, 67, 100, 132, 221, 1221 ; 67
2. (a) 23 543, 19 675, 12 332, 884, 453, 285, 34, 0
   (b) Old Conservative    (c) 57 206    (d) 3868
   (e) 5th

## Exercise 1B

1. (a) 3    (b) 4
2. (a) 460    (b) 290    (c) 3420    (d) 2800
   (e) 34 100    (f) 87 100    (g) 21 000    (h) 52 000
   (i) 10 000

## Exercise 1C

1. 1520
2. (a) 520    (b) 1560    (c) 4160    (d) 5200
   (e) 10 400    (f) 20 800
3. (a) 3120    (b) 6760    (c) 8320    (d) 10 920
   (e) 12 480    (f) 23 400
4. $100 \times 52 = 5200$, $10 \times 52 = 520$, $90 \times 52 = 5200 - 520 = 4680$
   $10 \times 52 = 520$, $520 \times 9 = 4680$
   $5 \times 10 \times 90 = 4500$, $2 \times 90 = 180$, $4500 + 180 = 4680$
5. 3000

## Exercise 1D

1. (a) 14    (b) 56    (c) 328    (d) 37    (e) 563
   (f) 80    (g) 56    (h) 56    (i) 340
2. (a) 150    (b) 15

## Exercise 1E

1. 160
2. £1120
3. 70
4. (a) $4400 \div 10 = 440$; $440 \div 5 = 88$; $88 \times 2 = 176$
   (b) $4400 \div 100 = 44$; $44 \times 4 = 176$

## Exercise 1F

1. (a) $-9°C$, $-6°C$, $-2°C$, $3°C$, $5°C$, $8°C$
   (b) $-16°C$, $-10°C$, $-7°C$, $-5°C$, $-4°C$, $0°C$
   (c) $-45°C$, $-15°C$, $-7°C$, $-1°C$, $0°C$, $1°C$, $19°C$
   (d) $-13°C$, $-12°C$, $-11°C$, $-10°C$, $-9°C$, $-8°C$
2. (a) 670 m    (b) 670 m
3. (a) £3    (b) £12    (c) £6    (d) £4    (e) £2
   (f) £6
4. (a) $£12 - £9 = £3$    (b) $-£4 - £8 = -£12$
   (c) $£15 - £21 = -£6$    (d) $£10 - £14 = -£4$
   (e) $-£9 - (-£7) = -£2$    (f) $£13 - £7 = £6$
5. (a) 11    (b) 2    (c) 6    (d) $-6$    (e) 3
   (f) $-2$
6. (a) $-1$    (b) 2    (c) 2    (d) 1    (e) 3
   (f) 1
7. £184
8. (a) 16, 19    (b) $-1$, $-3$    (c) $-8$, $-12$    (d) 0, 2
   (e) $-14$, $-21$

## Exercise 1G

1. (a) $\frac{6}{30}$ or $\frac{1}{5}$    (b) $\frac{2}{30}$ or $\frac{1}{15}$    (c) $\frac{3}{30}$ or $\frac{1}{10}$
2. (a) 32    (b) 4    (c) 9    (d) $\frac{9}{32}$    (e) $\frac{14}{19}$
3. (a) $\frac{1}{2}$ of 33 is not a whole number    (b) 36
   (c) 6    (d) $\frac{6}{36}$ or $\frac{1}{6}$
4. (a) $\frac{1}{2}$    (b) $\frac{1}{3}$    (c) $\frac{1}{6}$
5. (a) $\frac{1}{4}$; $\frac{1}{5}$    (b) $\frac{3}{4}$    (c) $2\frac{1}{2}$ hours
6. (a) $\frac{1}{5}$    (b) $\frac{3}{10}$    (c) $\frac{7}{20}$
7. (a) $\frac{1}{6}$
   (b) the hexagon has not been divided into equal parts.

## Exercise 1H

1. (a) $\frac{1}{2}$ of the square shapes do not have holes in.
   (b) $\frac{1}{2}$ of the triangular shapes have holes in.
   (c) $\frac{1}{4}$ of the shapes are square shapes with holes in
2. (a) a third of the original amount has been added at no extra cost
   (b) the buyer could think that a third of the new amount is free

## Exercise 1I

1. (a) £436    (b) £18    (c) £206    (d) £1230
2. 744 coffees; 372 teas; 992 chocolate; 868 orange
3. (a) Gail 30 km; Roy 48 km; Sally 50 km; Mark 35 km
   (b) Sally
4. foundations £114; base £608; building £532; labour £1520; profit £266
5. (a) £4000    (b) £2400    (c) £5600    (d) $\frac{7}{15}$
6. (a) 25 506    (b) 654    (c) $\frac{1}{40}$
7. (a) £720    (b) £180    (c) £120    (d) $\frac{1}{4}$

## Exercise 1J

1. (a) 2.15, 2.9, 3.1, 3.4, 4.2, 4.25
   (b) 2.01, 2.55, 2.66, 2.87, 2.98, 2.99
   (c) 1.6, 2.0, 3.2, 4.4, 5.1, 6.8, 6.9
   (d) 4.64, 4.975, 5.79, 5.81, 9.01, 9.76
   (e) 2.543, 2.555, 3.87, 5.43, 8.0, 8.01, 9
2. (a) (i) 9.36 (ii) 13.02 (iii) 11.5 (iv) 10.22 (v) 16.12 (vi) 9.76
   (b) 9.36, 9.76, 10.22, 11.5, 13.02, 16.12
3. (a) (i) 1.510204 (ii) 1.5 (iii) 1.3333333 (iv) 1.5288018 (v) 1.5897435
   (b) 1.3333333, 1.5, 1.510204, 1.5288018, 1.5897435

## Exercise 1K

1. (a) 0.75    (b) 0.4    (c) 0.45    (d) 0.28
   (e) 0.125    (f) 0.375    (g) 0.6666666
   (h) 0.4444444    (i) 0.5833333
2. (a) English 0.8; French 0.76; German 0.84; Science 0.85; Maths 0.82
   (b) 0.85, 0.84, 0.82, 0.8, 0.76
3. 2340 mm, 2410 mm, 2449 mm, 2450 mm, 2457 mm, 2480 mm, 2570mm, 2620 mm
4. (a) 18.6 g; 23.1 g

(b)

| Interval | Tally | Frequency |
|---|---|---|
| 18.0 to 18.9 | || | 2 |
| 19.0 to 19.9 | ||| | 3 |
| 20.0 to 20.9 | |||| | 4 |
| 21.0 to 21.9 | |||| | 4 |
| 22.0 to 22.9 | | | 1 |
| 23.0 to 23.9 | | | 1 |
| | Total | 15 |

5. (a) Sally (b) Jessie (c) Sally, Jenny, Jessie

## Exercise 1L

1. (a) £42 (b) £25.60 (c) £44.50 (d) £1.40
   (e) £6.50 (f) £9.20 (g) £2.25 (h) £6.49
   (i) £13.58
2. (a) £600 (b) £855 (c) £345 (d) £85
   (e) £150 (f) £56.25 (g) £22 (h) £11.25
   (i) £3
3. (a) 936 (b) 2664
4. (a) 9800 (b) 18 200 (c) 65%
5. (a) 420 (b) 840 (c) 1260 (d) 2205
   (e) 3045
6. (a) 384 (b) 448 (c) 848 (d) 80

## Exercise 1M

1. (a) 11%
   (b) Norman £970.32; Wesley £696.64; Shaz £547.36;
   Charity £273.68
2. (a) £70 (b) £84 (c) £14 (d) £112
   (e) £26.25
3. (a) £32 (b) £224

## Exercise 1N

1.

| Subject | Mark | Decimal equivalent | Percentage |
|---|---|---|---|
| English | $\frac{28}{50}$ | $28 \div 50 = 0.56$ | $0.56 \times 100 = 56\%$ |
| Science | $\frac{33}{60}$ | $33 \div 60 = 0.55$ | $0.55 \times 100 = 55\%$ |
| Maths | $\frac{23}{40}$ | $23 \div 40 = 0.575$ | $0.575 \times 100 = 57.5\%$ |

2. (a) 50% (b) 60% (c) 55% (d) 70%
   (e) 74% (f) 57.5% (g) 70% (h) 40%
   (i) 42%
3. (a) 30% (b) 25% (c) 7.5%
4.

| Colour | Number of times | Percentage of total number of spins |
|---|---|---|
| red | 12 | 15% |
| yellow | 22 | 27.5% |
| green | 28 | 35% |
| blue | 18 | 22.5% |

## Exercise 1O

1. (a) 62.5% (b) 26.5625% (c) 550%
   (d) 27.777777% (e) 68.055555%
   (f) 18.02091%
2. (a) 84% (b) 16%
3. (a) 0.375, 37.5% (b) 770
4. (a) 0.07 (b) $\frac{7}{100}$
5. (a) 40 (b) $\frac{1}{10}; \frac{1}{5}; \frac{3}{20}; \frac{1}{4}; \frac{1}{8}; \frac{7}{40}$
   (c) 10%; 20%; 15%; 25%; 12.5%; 17.5%
6. (a) $\frac{13}{100}; \frac{19}{100}; \frac{23}{100}; \frac{1}{5}; \frac{1}{4}$ (b) 52; 76; 92; 80; 100

## Exercise 1P

1. (a) 4, 8, 13, 34, 50, 65, 87, 88, 101 ; 50

(b) 0, 7, 56, 65, 81, 123, 143, 432, 3400 ; 81
2. (a) (i) 92 (ii) 80 (iii) 90 (iv) 50 (v) 71
   (b) 50; 71; 80; 90; 92
3. (a) £57 × 10 = £570
   (b) 30 = 3 × 10; £57 × 10 = £570; £570 × 3 = £1710
   (c) 230 = (2 × 100) + (3 × 10); £64 × 100 = £6400;
   £64 × 10 = £640,
   Total cost = (2 × £6400) + (3 × £640)
   = £12 800 + £1920 = £14 720
4. 6000
5. (a) 160 (b) (i) 400 (ii) 800 (iii) 1200
6. £3800 ÷ 25 = £152
7. (a) −7, −5, −3, 2, 5, 6, 8
   (b) −15, −7, −3, −2, 1, 7, 12
   (c) −16, −14, −10, −9, −8, −7, −6, −4
8. 13°C
9. (a) 9°C (b) −2°C
10. (a) $\frac{1}{2}$ (b) $\frac{2}{9}$ (c) $\frac{1}{2}$
11. (a) 32 (b) 25%
12. (a) $\frac{1}{4}$ of the round shapes are shaded;
   $\frac{3}{4}$ of the round shapes are not shaded
   (b) $\frac{2}{3}$ of the square shapes are shaded;
   $\frac{1}{3}$ of the square shapes are not shaded
   (c) $\frac{2}{3}$ of the shaded shapes are square;
   $\frac{1}{3}$ of the shaded shapes are round
13. coffee 448; tea 336; orange 168; hot chocolate 392
14. (a) £175
   (b) Planet supplies since £575 − £175 = £350
15. (a) 1.01, 1.099, 1.1, 1.15, 1.2, 1.9
   (b) 2.4, 4.32, 7.56, 7.65, 8.85, 8.9
   (c) 0.01, 5.543, 7.85, 9.99, 12, 14.6, 34
16. 0.5625, 0.6, 0.625, 0.6666666, 0.75, 0.7777777
17. (a) £65 (b) £44 (c) £12.50
18. 240 aged 45 or over; 360 aged 25–45; 492 aged 15–25;
   108 aged 15 and under
19. (a) 0.8 (b) 0.75 (c) 0.3125 (d) 0.2222222
20. (a) 12% (b) 65% (c) 66% (d) 89.5%
21. (a) 40% (b) 87.5% (c) 90%
   (d) 77.777777%
22. (a) 0.8 (b) 80%
23. (a) £267 (b) 25%
24. (a) £60 (b) $\frac{1}{6}$ (c) 0.1666666 (d) 16.66666%
25. (a) 160 (b) $\frac{2}{5}$ (c) 0.4 (d) 40%
26. (a) $\frac{1}{2}$ (b) Brenda 50%; Carol 40%; Maureen 10%
   (c) Brenda £1000; Carol £800; Maureen £200
27. (a) $\frac{7}{10}$ (b) 0.07
28. (a) 0.175 (b) $\frac{7}{40}$

## Exercise 2A

1. (a) 1, 2, 5, 10 (b) 1, 3, 5, 15 (c) 1, 3, 7, 21
   (d) 1, 7, 49
2. (a) 1, 2, 4, 5, 8, 10, 20, 40 (b) 1, 2, 3, 4, 6, 8, 9, 12,
   18, 24, 36, 72
   (c) 1, 2, 4, 5, 10, 20, 25, 50, 100
   (d) 1, 2, 3, 4, 6, 8, 9, 12, 16, 18, 24, 36, 48, 72, 144
3. (a) (i) 1, 3, 11, 33 (ii) 1, 67
   (iii) 1, 2, 4, 5, 10, 20, 25, 50, 100 (iv) 1, 151
   (b) 100 (c) 67, 151
4. 21; It has 4 factors, the others only have 2.

## Exercise 2B

1. (a) 5 (b) 32 (c) 36 (d) 25 (e) 1 (f) 28
2. (a) 96 (b) 160 (c) 32
3. 2 m
4. (a) 40 cm squares (b) 63

## Exercise 2C

1. (a) $\frac{2}{5}$ (b) $\frac{12}{25}$ (c) $\frac{3}{4}$ (d) $\frac{1}{25}$ (e) $\frac{1}{3}$ (f) $\frac{2}{5}$

## Exercise 2D

1. 5, 13, 31, 41
2. 9 has factors 1, 3, 9; 15 has factors 1, 3, 5, 15; 25 has factors 1, 5, 25; 33 has factors 1, 3, 11, 33; 49 has factors 1, 7, 49; 65 has factors 1, 5, 13, 65; 100 has factors 1, 2, 4, 5, 10, 20, 25, 50, 100
3. (a) 2 has only two factors, 1 and 2 so it is a prime number
   (b) 1 has only one factor
   (c) all even numbers must have at least 3 factors, 1, 2 and the number itself.
4. 2, 3, 5, 7, 11, 13, 17, 19, 23, 29, 31, 37, 41, 43, 47
5. (a) $2 \times 5$ (b) $3 \times 2 \times 2$ (c) $3 \times 2 \times 2 \times 2$ (d) $3 \times 5 \times 2$
6. (a) $2 \times 3 + 1 = 7$; $2 \times 3 \times 5 + 1 = 31$; $2 \times 3 \times 5 \times 7 + 1 = 211$
   (b) $2 \times 3 \times 5 \times 7 \times 11 + 1 = 2311$
   (c) They are prime numbers
7. (a) 1, 2, 3, 6, 9, 18 (b) 6 (c) 2, 3
8. 2, 3, 7

## Exercise 2E

1.
2.
3. (a) 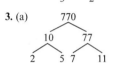 (b)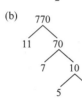
4. (a) e.g. 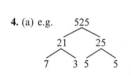 4. (b) e.g.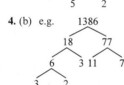
4. (c) e.g.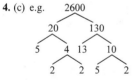
5. No. $1007 = 53 \times 19$

## Exercise 2F

1. (a) 28 (b) 32 (c) 48
2. (a) 48, 54, 60 (b) 72
3. (a) 3, 6, 9, 12, 15, 18, 21, 24, 27, 30, 33, 36, 39, 42, 45
   (b) 5, 10, 15, 20, 25, 30, 35, 40, 45 (c) 15, 30, 45
4. (a) 10, 20, 30, 40, 50 (b) 12, 24, 36, 48
   (c) 28, 56, 84 (d) 132, 264

## Exercise 2G

1. (a) after 12 seconds (b) after 20 seconds
   (c) after 15 seconds (d) after 60 seconds
2. 72 g
3. (a) 5 boxes of 7 eggs or 7 boxes of 3 eggs and 2 boxes of 7 eggs
   (b) (i) 2 sevens and 2 threes (ii) 4 sevens and 2 threes
   (iii) 5 sevens and 5 threes or 2 sevens and 12 threes
4. She will have 1 egg left over.
5. (a) 8 boxes of 8 or 8 boxes of 3 and 5 boxes of 8
   (b) 4 boxes of 8 and 1 box of 5

## Exercise 2H

1. 9 units
2. (b) and (d)
3. (a) 25 (b) 225 (c) 625 (d) 1156 (e) 2025
4. (a) true (b) false (c) false (d) true (e) true (f) true (g) false (h) true

## Exercise 2I

1. (a) 7 cm (b) 7
2. (a) 10 cm (b) 10
3. (a) 4 (b) 8 (c) 11 (d) 14 (e) 21 (f) 24 (g) 32 (h) 43
4. 10; 17.20465; 31.304951

## Exercise 2J

1. (a) 64 (b) 343 (c) 1331 (d) 9261
2. (a) (i) 9 (ii) 36 (iii) 100 (b) squared numbers
3. (a) true (b) true

## Exercise 2K

1. 32
2. (a) 8 (b) 7 (c) 10 (d) 12 (e) 15
3. (a) 3 cm (b) 9 cm$^2$
4. (a) 21 cm (b) 441 cm$^2$
5. (a) 19 cm (b) 6859 cm$^3$
6. 60 000

## Exercise 2L

1. (a) 100 (b) 10 000 (c) 1 (d) 0.01
2. (a) $10^4$ (b) $10^9$ (c) $10^{-6}$
3. (a) 1 500 000 (b) 700 (c) 12 000 000 (d) 30
4. (a) $10^3$ (b) $10^4$ (c) $10^1$ (d) $10^6$ (e) $10^5$ (f) $10^3$
5. (a) $10^{-4}$ (b) $10^{-6}$ (c) $10^{-1}$
6. (a) $10^{-3}$ (b) $10^{-4}$ (c) $10^{-5}$
7. (a) 0.0001 (b) 0.000 000 1 (c) 0.000 01
8.

| Power of 10 | $10^3$ | $10^2$ | $10^1$ | $10^0$ | $10^{-1}$ | $10^{-2}$ | $10^{-3}$ |
|---|---|---|---|---|---|---|---|
| Number | 1000 | 100 | 10 | 1 | 0.1 | 0.01 | 0.001 |

## Exercise 2M

1. (a) 6 million (b) 3.4 million (c) 7.8 million
   (d) 5.5 million (e) 2.65 million (f) 7.642 million
2. (a) $3.1 \times 10^6$ (b) $4.3 \times 10^6$ (c) $0.5 \times 10^6$
   (d) $2.4 \times 10^6$ (e) $7.8 \times 10^6$ (f) $8.6 \times 10^6$
   (g) $4 \times 10^6$ (h) $9 \times 10^6$ (i) $0.4 \times 10^6$

## Exercise 2N

1. (b) $2.6 \times 10^2$ (c) $6.8 \times 10^5$ (d) $9.9 \times 10^6$
   (e) $6.2 \times 10^1$ (f) $8 \times 10^0$
2. (a) $1.6 \times 10^1$ (b) $4.3 \times 10^3$ (c) $6.5 \times 10^5$
   (d) $8.7 \times 10^7$ (e) $6.7 \times 10^2$ (f) $8.65 \times 10^2$
   (g) $9.87 \times 10^6$ (h) $9.85 \times 10^4$ (i) $8.05 \times 10^{11}$
3. (a) 420 (b) 67 000 (c) 5500 (d) 7 500 000
   (e) 620 000 (f) 73 000 (g) 24 000 000
   (h) 11 (i) 7.25
4. (a) $6.5 \times 10^2$ (b) $9.6 \times 10^3$ (c) $4.05 \times 10^4$
   (d) $3.90625 \times 10^5$

## Exercise 2O

1. (a) $2.4 \times 10^{-3}$ (b) $2 \times 10^{-1}$ (c) $6 \times 10^{-5}$
   (d) $1.5 \times 10^{-1}$ (e) $7 \times 10^{-3}$ (f) $4.5 \times 10^{-4}$
   (g) $3.46 \times 10^{-2}$ (h) $1.25 \times 10^{-3}$
2. (a) $2 \times 10^{-3}$ (b) $1.5 \times 10^{-1}$ (c) $4 \times 10^{-4}$
   (d) $5.4 \times 10^{-2}$ (e) $8 \times 10^{-6}$ (f) $6.8 \times 10^{-11}$
   (g) $3.46 \times 10^{-1}$ (h) $9 \times 10^{-2}$ (i) $5.6 \times 10^{-3}$

3. (a) 0.35    (b) 0.06    (c) 0.000 72    (d) 0.002 2
   (e) 0.000 013 5    (f) 0.000 005 33
   (g) 0.000 000 000 88    (h) 0.000 000 44    (i) 0.4999

## Exercise 2P

1. (a) 40, 45    (b) 5    (c) 2, 5
2. (a) 64    (b) 72    (c) 41    (d) 56
3. (a) 43 or 53    (b) 26 or 52 or 65    (c) 62 and 23
   (d) 26
4. (a) 60 days    (b) Tuesday
5. (a) 15    (b) 1.5 m
6. (a) 26    (b) 6 and 4 to make 36 or 5 and 5 to make 36
7. (a)

   (b) $560 = 7 \times 5 \times 2^4$    (c) $210\,600 = 7 \times 5^2 \times 2^7 \times 3^2$
8. (a) $1.27 \times 10^4$ km    (b) $5.91 \times 10^3$ km
9. (a) 295 000 mm    (b) 295 m
10. (a) 38 880    (b) 14 191 200    (c) $1.41912 \times 10^7$
11. (a) (i) 1, 4, 9, 16, 25, 36, or 49 (ii) 2, 5, 10, 20 or 25
     (iii) 5, 10, 15, 20, 25, 30, 35, 40 or 45
   (b) (i) 49 (ii) 2 (iii) 42
12. (a) (i) 8, 16, 24, 32, 40 (ii) 36 (iii) $2 \times 5 \times 7$
     (iv) 27 ; 5
   (b) 16, 19
13. (a) $5 \times 10^{101}$    (b) 0.000 000 05 m; $5 \times 10^{-8}$
   (c) $1 \times 10^{10}$
14. (a) 57024    (b) $2^9 \times 3^4 \times 11$    (c) $4.56192 \times 10^5$
15. $2 \times 10^{11}$ tonnes

## Exercise 3A

1. (a) 1548 km per hour    (b) 3.1 million    (c) 38°C
   (d) 1 A    (e) 15 000 people

## Exercise 3B

1. (a) 280    (b) 150    (c) 30    (d) 5440
   (e) 9300    (f) 3340    (g) 10    (h) 0    (i) 10
2. (a) 4    (b) 7    (c) 58    (d) 1    (e) 0
   (f) 80    (g) 4    (h) 6    (i) 2
3. (a) $3 \times 6$    (b) $4 \times 4$    (c) $7 \times 4$    (d) $12 \times 3$
   (e) $5 \times 5$    (f) $1 \times 6$
4. (a) (i) 37 440 (ii) 37 400 (iii) 37 000 (iv) 40 000
   (b) 40 000 has most impact

## Exercise 3C

1. (a)

        (b) 46.383

2. (a) 308.64197 metres per minute    (b) (i) 309 (ii) 308.6
(iii) 308.64 (iv) 308.642
3. (a) 45.48    (b) Ronson, King, White
4. (a) 134.3    (b) 0.6738    (c) 2.0    (d) 2.00
   (e) 17.993    (f) 2.0067
5. (a) 95.047    (b) 9.760    (c) 10.91    (d) 176.0
6. (a) 3.14    (b) 3.1416

## Exercise 3D

1. (a) 3250    (b) 8420    (c) 1.3    (d) 0.039
   (e) 84.3
2. £140.00
3. 9.86

4. 4.6
5. 3.9 + 1.2 = 5.1 to 2 s. f.;
   3.87 + 1.16 = 5.03 = 5.0 to 2 s.f.

## Exercise 3E

1. (a) 6; 12; 8.5    (b) 35; 48; 40.488    (c) 2; 6; 4.6706
   (d) 120; 143; 134.3632    (e) 60, 120; 76.704
   (f) 0, 27; 8.0736
2. (a) 7    (b) 6    (c) 10    (d) 3    (e) 8
   (f) 10    (g) 7    (h) 8    (i) 6    (j) 3
   (k) 10    (l) 4
3. (a) 3.020 408 1    (b) 5.615 384 6    (c) 5.180 232 5
   (d) 8.557 692 3    (e) 7.977 249 2    (f) 9.611 538 4
   (g) 383.147 41
4. (a) £16    (b) £12    (c) £15
   (d) £160    (e) £45
5. (a) 5.06 cm    (b) 24 cm
6. (a) 12.25 cm    (b) 122.5 cm    (c) 38.7 cm

## Exercise 3F

1. (a) 13    (b) 4.5    (c) 30    (d) 20    (e) 24
   (f) 0.25    (g) 4    (h) 7.5    (i) 4    (j) 8
   (k) 15    (l) 60
2. (a) 36 cm$^2$
   (b) Actual area = 34.751 cm$^2$. Difference 1.249 cm$^2$
3. (a) (i) $\frac{5 \times 20}{10}$ (ii) $\frac{6 \times 200}{4}$ (iii) $\frac{3 \times 15}{4}$ (iv) $\frac{7 \times 34}{8}$ (v) $\frac{1 \times 29}{3}$ (vi) $\frac{1 \times 69}{9}$
     (vii) $\frac{93 \times 45}{15 \times 10}$ (viii) $\frac{5 \times 14}{7 \times 2}$
   (b) (i) 10 (ii) 300 (iii) 11 (iv) 30 (v) 10 (vi) 8 (vii) 28
     (viii) 5
   (c) (i) 10.4 to 3 s.f. (ii) 314.1 to 4 s.f. (iii) 10.5 to 3 s. f.
     (iv) 29.5 to 3 s.f. (v) 5.4 to 2 s.f. (vi) 2.2 to 2 s. f.
     (vii) 26.9 to 3 s.f. (viii) 4.1 to 2 s.f.
   (d) (i) 0.4; close (ii) 14.1; relatively close
     (iii) 0.5; fairly close (iv) 0.5; fairly close
     (v) 4.6; poor estimate because of the approximation 1
     (vi) 5.8; poor estimate because of the approximation 1
     (vii) 1.1; close (viii) 0.9; close
4. (a) 25 or 36    (b) 30.25    (c) 5.25 or 5.75
5. (a) (i) 9 or 16 (ii) 16 or 25 (iii) 36 or 49 (iv) 49 or 64
   (b) (i) 12.25 (ii) 20.25 (iii) 42.25 (iv) 56.25
   (c) (i) 12.25 − 9 = 3.25 or 16 − 12.25 = 3.75
     (ii) 20.25 − 16 = 4.25 or 25 − 20.25 = 4.75
     (iii) 42.25 − 36 = 6.25 or 49 − 42.25 = 6.75
     (iv) 56.25 − 49 = 7.25 or 64 − 56.25 = 7.75
   (e) 110.25
6. 8
7. (a) 300 metres per minute    (b) 18 km per hour
8. (a) $6 \times 6 = 36$    (b) 35.9424    (c) (i) 35.9 (ii) 36
9. (a) $\frac{40}{(3 \times 4)}$    (b) 4    (c) 4.10

## Exercise 3G

1.

| College | Attendance | Smallest possible number | Largest possible number |
|---|---|---|---|
| Folks | 2800 | 2750 | 2849 |
| Westown | 2400 | 2350 | 2449 |
| Eastgrove | 800 | 750 | 849 |
| Northbury | 1600 | 1550 | 1649 |
| Southfold | 1000 | 950 | 1049 |

2. (a) 8350    (b) 8587
3. (a) (i) 9 cm; 11 cm (ii) 22.5 cm; 27.5 cm
     (iii) 27 cm; 33 cm
   (b) 0; 1cm
4. (a) 26 km; 28 km    (b) 2km; 4km
5. (a) 5995    (b) 5995 to 6004 = 9

**6.** (a) 5950 to 6049 = 99　(b) qu.5; more accurate
**7.** (a) 355 500 to 356 499 = 999 and 541 500 to 542 499 = 999
(b) 897 000 to 898 998 = 1998　(c) 186999; 185001
**8.**

| Unit | Equivalent unit | Approximation interval |
|---|---|---|
| 1 inch | 2.54 centimetres | 2.535 cm to 2.545 |
| 1 yard | 91.4 centimetres | 91.35 to 91.45 cm |
| 1 litre | 1.76 pints | 1.755 to 1.765 pints |
| 1 ton | 1.016 tonnes | 1.0155 to 1.0165 tonnes |
| 1 kilometre | 0.621 mile | 0.6205 to 0.6215 mile |
| 1 mile | 1.609 kilometres | 1.6085 to 1.6095 km |

**9.** (a) 5.55 to 5.65; 4.75 to 4.85　(b) 20.6 cm; 21 cm
(c) 26.3625 cm; 27.4025 cm
**10.** (a) 7.7 m s$^{-1}$　(b) 7.6 ms$^{-1}$ to 7.7 ms$^{-1}$
**11.** (a) 20.5 cm　(b) 20.05 cm; 19.95 cm
**12.** (a) 2.85 cm　(b) 11cm ; 11.4 cm

## Exercise 3H

**1.** (a) $v = 1.0$　(b) $v = \frac{15}{3 \times 5} = 1$
**2.** (a) 99.5 m　(b) (i) 14.75 seconds (ii) 14.85 seconds
**3.** $y = 59.4$
**4.** (a) $f = 2.691\,964\,2$ cm (b) (i) $f = 2.7$ cm
(ii) consistent with given values
**5.** (a) 250; 40; 6　(b) Incorrect by a factor of 2
**6.** (a) 11.5 pounds　(b) (i) 5.6136363 (ii) 6 kg
**7.** (a) Greatest = 3560.5 feet, Least = 3559.5 feet
(b) 1084.856 m
**8.** (a) 5800 × 20　(b) (i) 116 000 (ii) No
**9.** (a) 3.14　(b) 3.142
**10.** 10.5 cm$^2$ correct to 3 s.f.
**11.** (a) 0.0945　(b) 0.095
**12.** 91.4 cm

## Exercise 4A

**1.** (a) 170　(b) 260　(c) 1410　(d) 340
(e) 2700　(f) 540　(g) 2100　(h) 3400
(i) 2800　(j) 24 400　(k) 63 300　(l) 93 600
**2.** 1536
**3.** (a) 492　(b) 455　(c) 1148　(d) 540
(e) 1072　(f) 1860
**4.** 10 × 62 = 620; 620 × 2 = 1240; 1240 − 62 = 1178
**5.** 624
**6.** (a) 338　(b) 546　(c) 660　(d) 1344
(e) 432　(f) 2226　(g) 2592　(h) 1239
(i) 7938

## Exercise 4B

**1.** 3024 hours
**2.** (a) 5130　(b) 7788　(c) 4495　(d) 17 466
(e) 19 968　(f) 17376　(g) 25 220　(h) 47 550
(i) 75 938　(j) 104 598

## Exercise 4C

**1.** 26
**2.** (a) 14　(b) 17　(c) 24　(d) 13　(e) 12
(f) 19

## Exercise 4D

**1.** 19
**2.** (a) 1　(b) 12　(c) 26　(d) 15　(e) 18
(f) 22　(g) 15　(h) 35　(i) 4　(j) 20
(k) 47　(l) 9

## Exercise 4E

**1.** (a) 5　(b) 3.4　(c) 20　(d) 6.6　(e) 17.5
(f) 44.8　(g) 240　(h) 180　(i) 72　(j) 44
(k) 6　(l) 32
**2.** (a) 200　(b) 1500　(c) 400　(d) 3000
(e) 400　(f) 300　(g) 200　(h) 4000
(i) 40　(j) 12　(k) 40　(l) 400　(m) 80
(n) 4
**3.** (a) 12　(b) 5　(c) 1.6　(d) 100　(e) 120
(f) 300　(g) 4　(h) 120　(i) 100　(j) 100
(k) 300　(l) 300　(m) 48　(n) 12
**4.**

| Area (cm$^2$) | Length (cm) | Width (cm) |
|---|---|---|
| 24 | 12 | 2 |
| 24 | 8 | 3 |
| 24 | 6 | 4 |
| 24 | 1 | 24 |
| 24 | 0.5 | 48 |
| 24 | 0.4 | 60 |
| 24 | 0.2 | 120 |
| 24 | 0.02 | 1200 |

**5.**

| Perimeter (cm) | Length (cm) | Width (cm) | Area (cm$^2$) |
|---|---|---|---|
| 24 | 8 | 4 | 32 |
| 24 | 6 | 6 | 36 |
| 24 | 2 | 10 | 20 |
| 24 | 1 | 11 | 11 |
| 24 | 0.2 | 11.8 | 2.36 |
| 24 | 0.1 | 11.9 | 1.19 |

**6.** (a) 40 × 80　= 3200　(b) 40 ÷ 80　= 0.5
40 × 8　= 320　　　40 ÷ 8　= 5
40 × 0.8　= 32　　　40 ÷ 0.8　= 50
40 × 0.08　= 3.2　　40 ÷ 0.08　= 500
40 × 0.008 = 0.32　40 ÷ 0.008 = 5000
**7.** Jamie. Multiplying by a number less than 1, e.g. 10 × 0.5 = 5
**8.** No. e.g. 50 ÷ 0.02 = 2500

## Exercise 4F

**1.** (a) 3.9 cm　(b) 15.21 cm$^2$　(c) 3.873 cm
**2.** 51.43°
**3.** 5.857 cm
**4.** 2.154

## Exercise 4G

**1.** (a) 27 km　(b) 108 km　(c) 67.5 km
**2.** (a) 18 g　(b) 180 g　(c) 450 g
**3.** (a) 40 p　(b) £6.00
**4.** (a) £9 per hour　(b) £216
**5.** (a) (i) $2 (ii) $16 (iii) $32　(b) £6.25
**6.** Generally the price per unit decreases as the quantity increases
**7.** (a) 0.048 p per ml　(b) 10.87 ml per penny
(c) Larger bottle. Cost is less per unit
**8.** (a) (i) 0.0625 mm (ii) 3.152 mm　(b) 336 pages
(c) 80 mm or 8 cm

## Exercise 4H

**1.** 2 days
**2.** (a) 6 days　(b) 3 days　(c) 2 days　(d) 0.4 days
**3.** (a) 6 days　(b) 3 days
**4.** (a) 4 days　(b) Yes
**5.** (a) 45 hours　(b) 2.5 hours

## Exercise 4I

1.  42 km
2.  (a) 62 mm       (b) 372 mm
3.
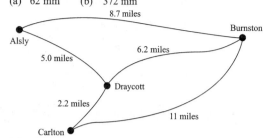

4.  1.3 gallons
5.  (a) 12.5 m       (b) 3.05 m
    (c) 6 times (the 7th bounce is < 1 m)
6.  (a) 1.24 mm       (b) 4216 mm       (c) 600 sheets
7.  (a) 3668 pints       (b) 191 260 pints       (c) 108 670 litres
8.  (a) 464 tonnes       (b) 680 tonnes       (c) $4.032 \times 10^6$ kg
9.  (a) 28.575 miles per hour       (b) 46.014 km per hour
10. $18°$
11. 17.7 km per litre
12. (a) 13 714.285 paces       (b) 214.3 minutes
13. (a) £2219.70       (b) £67.95       (c) 120 tonnes
    (d £360.80
14. (a) £53.40       (b) £57.50       (c) £44.40; £45.00
    (d 171.5 miles
15. (a) £59.73       (b) £1493.25       (c) 16
16. (a) 4500 Deutschmarks       (b) £100
    (c) £1200

## Exercise 4J

1.  (a) (i) 615 pesetas (ii) 385 pesetas       (b) (i) 96 people
    (ii) 22 times
2.  (b) $142 \times 40 = £56.80$       (c) $5680p - 142p = £55.38$
3.  (a) 14 discs       (b) 10 p
4.  (a) 8 cm       (b) 7.937 cm
5.  (a) (i) 24 cm$^2$ (ii) 35 cm$^2$       (b) 4.7 cm
6.  (a) 15 inches       (b) 4.6875 inches       (c) 5 seconds
    (d) 281 feet 3 inches
7.  (a) £3422       (b) $30 \times £120 = £3600$       (c) 14.75
8.  (a) $\frac{1}{8}$       (b) 12.5%
9.  250 ml
10. 1261.208 Guilders
11. (a) 0.0138 cm       (b) 4.692 cm
12. (a) 23       (b) 15 cm

## Exercise 5A

1.  (a) Tony 6; Gaynor 9       (b) $\frac{2}{5}; \frac{3}{5}$       (c) same proportions
2.  (a) $\frac{2}{5}$       (b) £1.20       (c) £1.80

## Exercise 5B

1.  (a) $\frac{1}{6}; \frac{1}{3}; \frac{1}{2}$       (b) 4; 8; 12
2.  (a) $\frac{4}{15}; \frac{1}{3}; \frac{2}{5}$       (b) £12; £15; £18
3.  (a) Jean $\frac{3}{5}$; Derek $\frac{2}{5}$       (b) Jean £2400 ; Derek £1600
    (c) £2400 + £1600 = £4000
4.  (a) 8       (b) $\frac{3}{8}$       (c) £120       (d) $\frac{5}{8}$       (e) £200
5.  (a) 7; 3       (b) $\frac{7}{10}$       (c) £27       (d) £50.40
6.  (a) 4; 1       (b) 18
7.  (a) $\frac{1}{2}$       (b) 144       (c) £57.60
8.  (a) 540       (b) 180       (c) 324       (d) 216

## Exercise 5C

1.  9.37 km per litre
2.  (a) No       (b) 112 km per hour
3.  (a) 50       (b) 37.5
4.  (a) 1265

## Exercise 5D

1.  $0.34 \times 6.36$
2.  (a) 0.58       (b) 6.67 kg
3.  (a) £20.48       (b) £20.48
4.  (a) 0.25       (b) 0.56       (c) 0.62       (d) 0.11
    (e) 0.7       (f) 0.07       (g) 0.125       (h) 0.675
    (i) 1.1       (j) 1.5       (k) 2.43       (l) 4.5
5.  (a) 2688 g       (b) 1.12 m       (c) 180 ml
    (d) £0.12       (e) 192 cm       (f) 0.8 minutes
    (g) 960 kg       (h) 1.4 m       (i) 9.4 m
6.  (a) 19.68 g       (b) 161.04 g

## Exercise 5E

1.  (a) 115%       (b) 112.5%       (c) 102.5%
    (d) 109%       (e) 117.5%
2.  (a) 88%       (b) 89%       (c) 95%       (d) 78%
3.  (a) old value $\times 0.66$ = new value       (b) £3.465
4.  779 kg
5.  (a) £96       (b) 42 kg       (c) 2.016 m
    (d) £1109.80       (e) 123.48 cm
6.  (a) $£100 \times 1.065$       (b) £106.50
    (c)

| Date | Amount |
|---|---|
| 1 January 94 | £100 |
| 1 January 95 | £107 |
| 1 January 96 | £114 |
| 1 January 97 | £121 |
| 1 January 98 | £129 |

7.  (a) £19 200
    (b)

| new value | £24 000 |
|---|---|
| value after 1 year | £19 200 |
| value after 2 years | £16 320 |
| value after 3 years | £14 688 |
| value after 4 years | £13 219 |
| value after 5 years | £11 897 |

8.  (a) initial investment $\times 1.12$
    (b) value after 1 year $\times 1.08 = 1.2096 \times$ initial investment
    (c) increased by 9.3%
9.  99% of original value

## Exercise 5F

1.  (a) $\frac{1}{4}$       (b) $\frac{5}{8}$       (c) 25%       (d) 30%
2.  (a) 33.3%       (b) 60%       (c) 16.7%       (d) 20%
3.  (a) 8 km per litre       (b) 10.6 km per litre       (c) 32.5%
4.  (a) 20% decrease       (b) 25% decrease
    (c) 33.3% decrease       (d) 25% decrease
5.  (a) 5.5 km per hour       (b) 8.1% to 1 d.p.

## Exercise 5G

1.  (a) £459       (b) 37%
2.  (a) 4.5 litres       (b) 18.75%
3.  (a) £520       (b) 32.5%       (c) 20.6%
4.  (a) 33%       (b) 27%       (c) 12%
    (d) 8%       (e) 55%
5.  (a) 20%       (b) 12.8%
6.  (a) 32.8%       (b) 29.4%       (c) 6.25% decrease

## Exercise 5H

1.  (a) 90%       (b) [ Price ] → [ × 0.9 ] → [ £540 ]
    (c) £600
2.  (a) 112%       (b) £250
    (c) 12% of £250 = £30; £250 + £30 = £280

**3.** (a) 85.1% to 1 d.p.

(b) £320 ⟶ × 0.851 ⟶ original price

(c) £272.32

**4.** (a) 175    (b) 14

**5.** (a) £17 647.06    (b) £20 761.25    (c) 27.75%

## Exercise 5I

**1.** (a) $\frac{3}{4}$    (b) $\frac{4}{5}$    (c) $\frac{5}{8}$    (d) $\frac{1}{2}$    (e) $\frac{7}{10}$

**2.** (a) $\frac{4}{5}$    (b) (i) £403.20 (ii) £998.40 (iii) £284.80

**3.** (a) $\frac{4}{3}$    (b) $\frac{8}{5}$    (c) $\frac{3}{8}$

**4.** (a) £780 × $\frac{9}{8}$ = £877.50    (b) £780 ×1.10 = £858

**5.** Lux

**6.** (a) $\frac{11}{8}$    (b) 1.375    (c) 137.5%    (d) 2266

**7.** (a) Paul    (b) Paljit

**8.** Reduce weight. Receive more money per unit weight.

**9.** (a) 17.5% decrease    (b) $\frac{33}{40}$

**10.** Jackie. After 4 yrs she will have £316.41 remaining

## Exercise 5J

**1.** 2400; 2000; 1600

**2.** £6348

**3.** 15%

**4.** (a) £86    (b) £328    (c) £414    (d) £16

**5.** (a) £3.20    (b) £15.60

**6.** (a) £9    (b) £189

**7.** (a) £100    (b) £900    (c) £135    (d) 1035

**8.** (a) £26.39    (b) £2.99    (c) £145.12

**9.** (a) 92 p    (b) £126.18    (c) £51.18    (d) 68.24%

## Exercise 6A

**1.** (a) 8    (b) 3

**2.** (a) 24    (b) 3

**3.** (a) 10    (b) 30

**4.** (a) No    (b) No    (c) No    (d) Yes

**5.** (a) Yes    (b) No    (c) Yes    (d) Yes

(e) Yes    (f) No

**6.** (a) Horizontal axis $s$, vertical axis $h$, line passing through (0,0) and (12,18)    (b) $s = \frac{2}{3}h$ or $3s = 2h$

(c) 21.75 m    (d) 10.67 m

**7.** (a) Horizontal axis $l$, vertical axis $a$, line passing through (0,0) and (14,42)    (b) $a = 3l$    (c) 73.2 cm$^2$

(d) 4.87 cm

## Exercise 6B

**1.** (a) 14.7    (b) 14.7    (c) 43.1    (d) 11.9

**2.** (a) $w = 1.1h$    (b) $h = 1.1s$    (c) $p = 1.1l$

(d) $a = 0.9s$

**3.** (a) $d = 12.5h$    (b) 3.2 m

**4.** (a) 9.72 V; 5.4 A    (b) $v = 1.8I$    (c) I = 6.4 amps

(d) $v = 4.428$ V

**5.** (a) $r = 1.67$    (b) $t = 16.53$

## Exercise 6C

**1.** 88.4 km h$^{-1}$

**2.** 33.9 miles per hour

**3.** (a) 0.25 hr    (b) 0.6 hr    (c) 0.8 hr    (d) 0.33 hr

(e) 0.75 hr    (f) 0.07 hr

**4.** (a) 72 minutes    (b) 1.2 hrs

## Exercise 6D

**1.** (a) 18 minutes    (b) 5 hours 24 minutes

(c) 3 hours 45 minutes    (d) 6 hours 17 minutes

(e) 3 hours 58 minutes    (f) 9 hours 29 minutes

**2.** (a) Shane by 9 minutes

**3.** (a) 5 hours 6 minutes    (b) 5 km per hour

**4.** (a) 315 km    (b) 5 hours 48 minutes

(c) 54.3 kmh$^{-1}$

## Exercise 6E

**1.** (a) 4800 cm$^3$    (b) 3.2 m

**2.** (a) 9065 kg    (b) 46 cm$^3$

**3.** 10 g per cm$^3$

## Exercise 6F

**1.** 14.5 km per litre

**2.** (a) 12.5 km per litre    (b) 150 km

**3.** (a) 1260 km    (b) 4 litres    (c) 42 km

**4.** (a) 0.86 p per hour; 0.78 p per hour

(b) 117 hours; 128 hours

(c) super platinum ; lasts more hours per £ spent

**5.** (a) 0.13 litres per km    (b) (i) 20 km (ii) 2.67 litres

## Exercise 6G

**1.**

| End of the | Value at beginning of year | Calculation | Value at end of year |
|---|---|---|---|
| 7$^{th}$ year | £793.44 | £793.44 × 1.08 | £856.92 |
| 8$^{th}$ year | £856.92 | £856.92 × 1.08 | £925.47 |
| 9$^{th}$ year | £925.47 | £925.47 × 1.08 | £999.51 |
| 10$^{th}$ year | £999.51 | £999.51 × 1.08 | £1079.47 |

**2.** £279.47 more after 10 years with compound interest

**3.** (a) 15 years    (b) 25 years

**4.** (a) £1102    (b) £1474.78    (c) £2174.97

**5.** (a) £3840    (b) £11.20    (c) £3974.40

(d) £393.36

## Exercise 6H

**1.** 1 hour 19 minutes

**2.** (a) $9.4 \times 10^{12}$ km    (b) $12.4 \times 10^{23}$

**3.** (a) $3.78 \times 10^7$    (b) $3.48 \times 10^9$

**4.** (a) $4.096 \times 10^3$    (b) 7 hours

**5.** $2.9 \times 10^{-2}$

**6.** (a) $7 \times 10^{-12}$    (b) $3.64 \times 10^{-6}$

**7.** (a) $4.5 \times 10^{19}$ Joules    (b) $2.8 \times 10^{-10}$ kg

**8.** $9.46 \times 10^9$

## Exercise 6I

**1.** (a) $1.5 \times 10^5$    (b) 360 kg

**2.** $3.818 \times 10^3$

**3.** (a)

| End of year | Value plus annual payment | Interest earned | Current total |
|---|---|---|---|
| 1 | 100 | 100 × 1.08 | £108 |
| 2 | 108 + 100 | 208 × 1.08 | £224.64 |
| 3 | 224.64 + 100 | 324.64 × 1.08 | £350.61 |
| 4 | 350.61 + 100 | 450.61 × 1.08 | £486.66 |
| 5 | 486.66 + 100 | 586.66 × 1.08 | £633.59 |
| 6 | 633.59 + 100 | 733.59 × 1.08 | £792.28 |

(b) £1564.55

**4.** (a) $2.3 \times 10^8$    (b) 1 : 389    (c) $7.03 \times 10^{13}$ miles

**5.** (a) 1.57 marks per dollar    (b) $0.64 per mark

## Exercise 6J

**1.** (a) £355.58    (b) £9.88 per hour

**2.** The £11 500 per annum job (the other pays £11 273.60 per annum)

3.  £307.20
4.  £225

## Exercise 6K
1.  (a) £229.50    (b) £5.10
2.  (a) £214.80    (b) £4.13

## Exercise 6L
1.  (a) £263.30    (b) £5.06
2.  (a) £14 660    (b) £281.15    (c) £9.05

## Exercise 6M
1.  (a) £380.00    (b) £30.56
2.  (a) £420.00    (b) £31.46
3.  £31.46

## Exercise 6N
1.  £242.10
2.  (a) 11 149.04    (b) £1692.96

## Exercise 6O
1.  (a) £1750
    (b) Yes. She needs £33 250 and can borrow £33 600
2.  (a) £42 800    (b) £49 800

## Exercise 6P
1.  (a) £4140    (b) £1140
2.  (a) £10 941    (b) £182.35

## Exercise 6Q
1.  (a) £24.60    (b) £61.50
2.  2%

## Exercise 6R
1.  (a) £1223.40    (b) £61.17
2.  (a) £764.62    (b) £38.23    (c) £774.43
    (d) £38.72

## Exercise 7A
1.  20
2.  40
3.  14
4.  10
5.  2.5
6.  1.75
7.  16
8.  64
9.  8
10. 25
11. 16
12. 9

## Exercise 7B
1.  (a) 9    (b) $(3 + 4) \times 2 - 5$
2.  (a) 7.5    (b) 4    (c) 4    (d) 12    (e) 9
    (f) 15    (g) 3    (h) 1.5    (i) 1
3.  (a) 0.67    (b) 1.67

## Exercise 7C
1.  (a) $10.5 \text{ m}^2$    (b) $11.55 \text{ m}^2$    (c) $8.04 \text{ m}^2$
    (d) $9.6 \text{ m}^2$
2.  (a) 2.5    (b) 16.8    (c) 151.2
3.  (a) 292    (b) 180    (c) 430.4
4.  (a) $51.1 \text{ cm}^3$    (b) $676.3 \text{ cm}^3$    (c) $639.9 \text{ cm}^3$
5.  (a) 1059.4 mm    (b) 883.6 mm    (c) 560 mm
    (d) 200 mm
6.  438 kg

7.  5391 kg
8.  (a) $30.77 \text{ cm}^2$    (c) $134.39 \text{ cm}^2$

## Exercise 7D
1.  (a) 8    (b) $-1$
2.  (a) 26, 31; $5n - 4$; 126    (b) 28, 32; $4n + 4$; 108
    (c) 23, 27; $4n - 1$; 103    (d) 37, 43; $6n + 1$; 157
    (e) 41, 48; $7n - 1$; 181

## Exercise 7E
1.  (a) 3    (b) 1
2.  (a) 8    (b) 9
3.  (a) $-2, -6; -4n + 22; -62$
    (b) $-3, -7; -4n + 17; -67$
    (c) $-9, -15; 27 - 6n; -99$
    (d) $-12, -14; -2n - 2; -44$
    (e) $-5.5, -8; 7 - 2.5n; -45.5$

## Exercise 7F
1.  (a)

(b)

| pattern | 1st | 2nd | 3rd | 4th | 5th |
|---|---|---|---|---|---|
| number of matchsticks | 6 | 11 | 16 | 21 | 26 |

(c) $5n + 1$    (d) 106
2.  (a)

(b)

| pattern | 1st | 2nd | 3rd | 4th | 5th | 6th |
|---|---|---|---|---|---|---|
| number of matchsticks | 4 | 7 | 10 | 13 | 16 | 19 |

(c) $3n + 1$    (d) 166
3.  $4n - 3$

## Exercise 7G
1.  (a)

| Term | 1st | 2nd | 3rd | 4th | 5th | 6th |
|---|---|---|---|---|---|---|
| value | 6 | 11 | 18 | 27 | 38 | 51 |
| 1st difference | 5 | 7 | 9 | 11 | 13 | |
| 2nd difference | 2 | 2 | 2 | 2 | 2 | |
| squared pattern | $1^2 + 5$ | $2^2 + 7$ | $3^2 + 9$ | $4^2 + 11$ | $5^2 + 13$ | $6^2 + 15$ |

(b) $2n + 3$    (c) $n^2 + 2n + 3$    (d) 627
2.  (a)

| Pattern | 1st | 2nd | 3rd | 4th | 5th | 6th |
|---|---|---|---|---|---|---|
| no. of matchsticks | 5 | 8 | 13 | 20 | 29 | 40 |
| 1st difference | 3 | 5 | 7 | 9 | 11 | |
| 2nd difference | 2 | 2 | 2 | 2 | 2 | |
| squared pattern | $1^2 + 4$ | $2^2 + 4$ | $3^2 + 4$ | $4^2 + 4$ | $5^2 + 4$ | $6^2 + 4$ |

(b) $n^2 + 4$    (c) 629
3.  (a) (i) 20, 30 (ii) $n^2 - n$ (iii) 600    (b) (i) 35, 48
    (ii) $n^2 + 2n$ (iii) 675    (c) (i) 16, 25 (ii) $n^2 - 2n + 1$ (iii) 576    (d) (i) 32, 45 (ii) $n^2 + 2n - 3$ (iii) 672
    (e) (i) 44, 58 (ii) $n^2 + 3n + 4$ (iii) 704    (f) (i) 27.5, 39
    (ii) $n^2 + \frac{n}{2}$ (iii) 637.5
4.  (a) 2, 6, 12, 20, 30, 42    (b) $\frac{n^2 + n}{2}$    (c) 5050

**5.** (a) 1; the 2$^{nd}$ difference should be 2 (b) and (c)

| Term | 1st | 2nd | 3rd | 4th | 5th |
|---|---|---|---|---|---|
| value 1st difference 2nd difference | 2  1  2 | 3  3  2 | 6  5  2 | 11  7  2 | 18  9 |

(d) $n^2 - 2n + 3$

**6.** (a) 48, 63; 63, 80    (b) $n^2 - 1$; $n^2 + 2n$
(c) $n^2 + 6n + 8$    (d) $n = 3$; $3^2 + (6 \times 3) + 8 = 35$

## Exercise 7H

**1.** (a) 13   (b) 25   (c) 34
**2.** (a) → ×6 → +3   (b) → ×3 → −7
(c) → +4 → ×5   (d) → ÷2 → +8
**3.** (a) 51   (b) 17   (c) 60   (d) 12

## Exercise 7I

**1.** (a) 10   (b)

| input | output |
|---|---|
| 1 | 1 |
| 2 | 4 |
| 3 | 7 |
| 4 | 10 |
| 5 | 13 |

**2.**

| input | output |
|---|---|
| 1 | −6 |
| 5 | 6 |
| 6 | 9 |
| 8 | 15 |
| 13 | 30 |

**3.** (a)

| input | output |
|---|---|
| 2 | 9 |
| 3 | 15 |
| 4 | 21 |
| 5 | 27 |
| 6 | 33 |

(b)

| input | output |
|---|---|
| 3 | 20 |
| 4 | 24 |
| 5 | 28 |
| 6 | 32 |

(c)

| input | output |
|---|---|
| 2 | −1 |
| 4 | 1 |
| 6 | 3 |
| 8 | 5 |

(d)

| input | output |
|---|---|
| 0 | 2 |
| 2 | 4 |
| 4 | 6 |
| 6 | 8 |

**4.** (a)

| input | output |
|---|---|
| −2 | −1 |
| −1 | 1 |
| 0 | 3 |
| 1 | 5 |
| 2 | 7 |

(b)

| input | output |
|---|---|
| −3 | 3 |
| −2 | 6 |
| −1 | 9 |
| 0 | 12 |
| 1 | 15 |

(c)

| input | output |
|---|---|
| −4 | 10 |
| −3 | 9 |
| −2 | 8 |
| −1 | 7 |
| 0 | 6 |

## Exercise 7J

**1.** (a)

| input | output |
|---|---|
| 3 | 1 |
| 4 | 2 |
| 5 | 3 |
| 6 | 4 |
| 7 | 5 |

(b)

| input | output |
|---|---|
| 2 | 3 |
| 3 | 2 |
| 4 | 1 |
| 5 | 0 |
| 6 | −1 |

(c)

| input | output |
|---|---|
| −1 | 2 |
| 0 | 6 |
| 1 | 10 |
| 2 | 14 |
| 3 | 18 |

(d)

| input | output |
|---|---|
| 1 | 1 |
| 2 | 4 |
| 3 | 9 |
| 4 | 16 |

(e)

| input | output |
|-------|--------|
| 0 | 2 |
| 2 | 6 |
| 4 | 18 |
| 6 | 38 |

**2.** (a)

| input | output |
|-------|--------|
| −3 | 9 |
| −2 | 4 |
| −1 | 1 |
| 0 | 0 |
| 1 | 1 |

(b)

| input | output |
|-------|--------|
| −2 | 1 |
| −1 | −2 |
| 0 | −3 |
| 1 | −2 |
| 2 | 1 |

(c)

| input | output |
|-------|--------|
| −2 | 2 |
| −1 | 0 |
| 0 | 0 |
| 1 | 2 |
| 2 | 6 |

(d)

| input | output |
|-------|--------|
| −4 | 28 |
| −3 | 18 |
| −2 | 10 |
| −1 | 4 |
| 0 | 0 |

## Exercise 7K

**1.** (a) $n \to n + 2$  (b) $n \to 2n$  (c) $n \to 3n + 1$
    (d) $n \to n - 2$

## Exercise 7L

**1.** 826.87 cm$^3$ (correct to 2 d.p.)
**2.** (a) 200  (b) −236.645
**3.** (a) 48, 63  (b) 120  (c) $n^2 + 2n$
**4.** (a) ::::
        :::::
    (c) (i) $n^2$ (ii) $(n+1)^2 = n^2 + 2n + 1$  (d) $2n + 1$
**5.** f = −4.615
**6.** 607.7531
**7.** (a) 13  (b) −17  (c) −2  (d) −5
    (e) −0.5  (f) −3
**8.** (a) 4  (b) −3  (c) 5.5  (d) −5.6

## Exercise 8A

**1.** (a) $r - s$  (b) $rs$  (c) $2r$
**2.** $2m + 3$
**3.** (a) $x - 5$  (b) $2x - 5$  (c) 5  (d) $x^2 - 5x$
    (e) $x - 2.5$

**4.** (a) £42  (b) £$\frac{A}{10}$  (c) $\frac{A}{n}$
**5.** (a) £0.20  (b) £ $0.2n$  (c) $mp$ pence
**6.** (a) $a, b, c, d; a + b + c + d$  (b) $2a + c + d$
    (c) $4a$
**7.** (a) $2x - 4; 2x + 4$  (b) $x^2 - 4x; x^2 + 4x$
**8.** (a) the total number of cups of tea and coffee served in a
        day
    (b) the difference between the number of cups of tea and
        the number of cups of coffee served in a day
    (c) the difference between the number of cups of coffee
        and the number of cups of tea served in a day
    (d) the number of cups of coffee served over $d$ days
    (e) the total number of cups of tea and coffee served in $d$
        days
**9.** (a) the length of one metal bar
    (b) the weight of one metal bar
    (c) adding the length to the weight is meaningless − the
        units are different

## Exercise 8B

**1.** $P = 26.5$ cm
**2.** $A = lw$ or $A = l \times w$
**3.** (a) 312 kg  (b) $52n$ kg  (c) $np$ kg  (d) $\frac{3x}{n}$ kg
**4.** (a) $m = \frac{(r+s+t+u+v)}{5}$  (b) $m = 9.6$
**5.** (a) $\frac{1}{2}(a+b)$  (b) $\frac{1}{2}h(a+b)$  (c) 52.7 cm ; 70.8 cm
**6.** (a) $3n$  (b) $m = nh$  (c) £235.60  (d) $150 = nh$
**7.** (a) $P = c + rt$  (b) $P = £85$
**8.** (a) $g = \frac{1}{2}(l - 4u)$  (b) 600 mm
**9.** (a) $\frac{m}{(s+d)}$  (b) $A = \frac{m}{(s+d)}$  (c) £17 500
**10.** (a) (i) 20 m (ii) 125 m (iii) 281.25 m  (b) 35 m
    (c) 10 seconds
**11.** (a) $h$ = height of cliff, $d$ = distance to horizon ;
        $d = \sqrt{(12.5h)}$  (b) $d = 15.8$ m (to 1 d.p.)

## Exercise 8C

**1.** (a) $5n + 3 = 18$  (b) $5n - 3 = 42$  (c) $4n + 15 = 47$
    (d) $7n + 5 = 50$  (e) $n - 4 = 12$  (f) $4 - n = 12$
**2.** (a) $A = xy$  (b) $24 = xy$  (c) 24 has many factors
**3.** (a) $A = x^2$  (b) $x = \sqrt{25}$ cm  (c) 5 cm

## Exercise 8D

**1.** (a) $3x + 2 = x + 3$  (b) $4x - 5 = 7x + 3$
    (c) $2x + 1 = x - 4$  (d) $10 - x = x^2 + 6$
    (e) $3(4 + x) = 3x - 2$
**2.** (a) Multiplying a number by 4 and adding 5 gives the
        same result as multiplying the number by 3 and
        subtracting 2.
    (b) Multiplying a number by 2 and subtracting 3 gives
        the same result as multiplying the number by 4 and
        subtracting 5.
    (c) Multiplying a number by 6 and adding 2 gives the
        same result as multiplying the number by 3 and
        subtracting 12.
**3.** (a) $A = x^2$  (b) $P = 4x$  (c) $x^2 = 4x$
    (d) $x = 4$

## Exercise 8E

**1.** $S = 20 + 4n$
**2.** (a) $2x - 3$  (b) $2x - 3 = 41$  (c) $x = 22$
**3.** $C = 40 + 0.25x$
**4.** (a) $x + 3$  (b) $P = 4x + 9$  (c) $20 = 4x + 9$
**5.** $2x^2 + 6x + \frac{\pi x^2}{2}$

## Exercise 9A

**1.** (a) (3,11), (2,8), (1,5), (0,2), (−1, −1) ; (4, 2), (2,4), (0,6),
        (−2, 8), (−4,10)  (b) $x \to 3x + 2; x \to 6 - x$

(c)

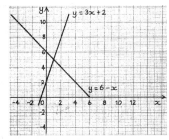

(d)  $y = 3x + 2$ ; $y = 6 - x$
(d)  $y$ is the function of $x$

**2.**  (a)(i)

| input | output |
|-------|--------|
| −1 | −5 |
| 0 | −2 |
| 1 | 1 |
| 2 | 4 |
| 3 | 7 |

(ii)  (−1,−5) (0,2) (1,1) (2,4) (3,7)
(iii) plot of points in part (ii)  (iv) label graph $y = 3x - 2$

(b)(i)

| input | output |
|-------|--------|
| −2 | 0 |
| −1 | 1 |
| 0 | 2 |
| 1 | 3 |
| 2 | 4 |
| 3 | 5 |

(ii)  (−2,0) (−1,1) (0,2) (1,3) (2,4) (3,5)
(iii) plot of points in part (ii)  (iv) label graph $y = x + 2$

(c)(i)

| input | output |
|-------|--------|
| −1 | 1 |
| 0 | 3 |
| 1 | 5 |
| 2 | 7 |
| 3 | 9 |
| 4 | 11 |

(ii)  (−1,1) (0,3) (1,5) (2,7) (3,9) (4,11)
(iii) plot of points in part (ii)  (iv) label graph $y = 3 + 2x$

(d)(i)

| input | output |
|-------|--------|
| −3 | 9 |
| −2 | 8 |
| −1 | 7 |
| 0 | 6 |
| 1 | 5 |
| 2 | 4 |

(ii)  (−3,9) (−2,8) (−1,7) (0,6) (1,5) (2,4)
(iii) plot points in part (ii)  (iv) label graph $y = 6 - x$

(e)(i)

| input | output |
|-------|--------|
| −2 | 1 |
| −1 | −1 |
| 0 | −3 |
| 1 | −5 |
| 2 | −7 |
| 3 | −9 |

(ii)  (−2, 1) (−1, −1) (0, 3) (1, −5) (2, −7) (3, −9)
(iii) plot of points in part (ii)  (iv) label graph
$y = -2x - 3$

**3.**  (a)  A(0,4), B(1,7), C(2,10), D(3,13)
(b)

| input | output |
|-------|--------|
| 0 | 4 |
| 1 | 7 |
| 2 | 10 |
| 3 | 13 |

(c)  $y = 3x + 4$

**4.**  (a)(i) (−3,−2) (−2,−1) (−1,0) (0,1) (1,2) (2,3) (3,4)
(ii) (0,−2) (1,0) (2,2) (3,4) (b)

| input | output |
|-------|--------|
| −3 | −2 |
| −2 | −1 |
| −1 | 0 |
| 0 | 1 |
| 1 | 2 |
| 2 | 3 |
| 3 | 4 |

;

| input | output |
|-------|--------|
| 0 | −2 |
| 1 | 0 |
| 2 | 2 |
| 3 | 4 |

(c)  $x \to x + 1 ; x \to 2x - 2$
(d)  $y = x + 1$ ; $y = 2x - 2$

**5.**  (a)  $x \to -3x - 3 ; y = -3x - 3$
(b)  $x \to -\frac{2}{3}x + 1 ; y = -\frac{2}{3}x + 1$

## Exercise 9B

**1.**  (a)(i) 4 (ii) steeper      (b) (i) 1.5 (ii) steeper
(c)(i) 0.5 (ii) less steep    (d) (i) 0.6 (ii) less steep
(e)(i) 4 (ii) steeper      (f) (i) 0.75 (ii) less steep
**2.**  (a) 1     (b) 0.25     (c) $\frac{4}{3}$     (d) 0.5     (e) 4
**3.**  (a) A(1,1), B(4,3)     (b) $\frac{2}{3}$

## Exercise 9C

**1.**  0.25
**2.**  (a) $\frac{3}{7}$     (b) $\frac{1}{2}$     (c) $\frac{1}{2}$     (d) $\frac{4}{3}$     (e) $\frac{2}{5}$     (f) 3
**3.**  (a) 0     (b) $y = 0$

## Exercise 9D

**1.**  (a) $\frac{-3}{2}$     (b) −4     (c) 1     (d) $\frac{1}{4}$     (e) −3
**2.**  (a) −0.5     (b) −3     (c) 2.5     (d) 1     (e) $\frac{-1}{7}$
(f) $\frac{2}{3}$     (g) $\frac{7}{3}$     (h) $\frac{6}{7}$
(i) $-\frac{3}{2}$     (j) $\frac{4}{5}$
**3.**  (a) $-3 ; \frac{1}{3}$     (b) $\frac{-1}{2}$
**4.**  (a) 4     (b) 5     (c) b and g ; d and e
(d) a and c ; g and h ; b and h

## Exercise 9E

**1.**  (a) $y = 2x + 2$     (b) $y = 2x - 3$
**2.**  (a) $\frac{-2}{3}$     (b) $y = -\frac{2}{3}x + 2$     (c) $y = -\frac{2}{3}x - \frac{2}{3}$

**3.**

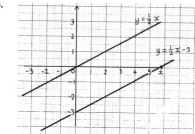

**4.** (a) 5; 6 (b) −5; −4 (c) 0.75; −0.5 (d) 0.6; 1.8

**5.**

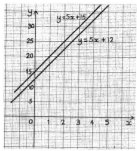

**6.** (a) $y = x + 4$ (b) $y = -\frac{3}{4}x + 6$
(c) $y = -4x - 6$ (d) $y = \frac{7}{12}x - \frac{23}{6}$

## Exercise 9F

**1.** (a)

| $x$ | 1 | 2 | 3 | 4 | 5 | 6 |
|---|---|---|---|---|---|---|
| $y$ | 0 | 2 | 4 | 6 | 8 | 10 |

(b) line through points in (1,0) (2,2) (3,4) etc
(c) 2; −2 (d) $y = 2x - 2$

**2.** (a)

| $x$ | −2 | −1 | 0 | 1 | 2 | 3 | 4 |
|---|---|---|---|---|---|---|---|
| $y$ | 2 | 0 | −2 | −4 | −6 | −8 | −10 |

(b) line through points in (a) (c) $y = -2x - 2$

**3.** (a)

| input | output |
|---|---|
| 3 | 13 |
| 5 | 19 |
| 8 | 28 |

(b) line through (3,13) (5,19) (8,28) (c) $y = 3x + 4$
(d) $\frac{10}{3}$

## Exercise 9G

**1.** (a)

| weight (kg) | 1 | 2 | 3 | 4 | 5 | 6 |
|---|---|---|---|---|---|---|
| cooking time (mins) | 65 | 110 | 155 | 200 | 245 | 290 |

(b) time = $45n + 20$
(c) gradient is 45 ; $y$-intercept or $c = 20$

**2.** (a)

| height of tower (h metres) | 0 | 4 | 8 | 12 | 16 | 20 | 24 |
|---|---|---|---|---|---|---|---|
| height ball bounced (b metres) | 0 | 1 | 2 | 3 | 4 | 5 | 6 |

(b) Line through (0,0) (4,1) (8,2) (12,3) (16,4) (20,5) (24,6)
(c) $b = \frac{h}{4}$ (d) 3.75 (e) 9.6

**3.** (a)

| number of days (d) | 0 | 1 | 2 | 3 | 4 | 5 | 6 |
|---|---|---|---|---|---|---|---|
| number of boxes left (n) | 24 | 20 | 16 | 12 | 8 | 4 | 0 |

(b) $n = -4d + 24$
(c) line through (0,24) (1,20) (2,16) (3,12) (4,8) etc

(d) gradient is −4, $c = 24$

**4.** (a) and (b)

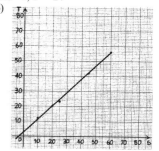

(c) $T = \frac{9}{10} S + 2$ (d) 29 mph
(e) 76 mph

**5.** (a)

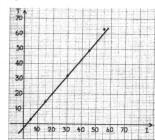

(b) $T = \frac{23}{20} I - 3$ (c) 11.3 kg

**6.** (a) Line through (2,28) (3,40) (4,52) (5,64) (6,76)
(b) $T = \frac{D}{12} - \frac{1}{3}$

## Exercise 9H

**1.** (a) graph of $3x - 4y = 12$ passes through (0,−3) (4,0)
(b) graph of $2x + 6y = 12$ passes through (0,2) (6,0)
(c) graph of $5x + 2y = 10$ passes through (0,5) (2,0)
(d) graph of $3x - 2y = 6$ passes through (0,−3) (2,0)
(e) graph of $4y - 2x = 8$ passes through (0,2) (−4,0)
(f) graph of $3x + 5y = 15$ passes through (0,3) (5,0)
(g) graph of $3x + 4y = -12$ passes through (0,−3) (−4,0)
(h) graph of $4x - 2y = -10$ passes through (0,5) (−2.5,0)
(i) graph of $2x + 2y = 7$ passes through (0,3.5) (3.5,0)

**2.** (a) $x + y = 3$ passes through (0,3) (3,0);
$2x - y = -6$ passes through (0,6) (−3,0)
(b) (−1,4)

## Exercise 9I

**1.** (a) $3x + y = 2$ passes through (0,2) (1,−1)
(b) $3x + 2y = 7$ passes through (1,2) (3,−1)
(c) $5x - 4y = 1$ passes through (5,6) (1,1)
(d) $4x - 3y = 11$ passes through (2,−1) (5,3)
(e) $2x + 5y = 12$ passes through (1,2) (6,0)

**2.** (a) $4x - 3y = 1$ passes through (1,1) (2.5,3)
(b) $2x + 3y = 19$ passes through (0.5,6) (8,1)
(c) $2x - 5y = 8$ passes through (4,0) (−1,−2)
(d) $3x + 4y = 0$ passes through (0,0) (4,−3)
(e) $2x + 3y = 2.5$ passes through (2,−0.5) (0.5,0.5)
(f) $6x + 3y = 51$ passes through (8,1) (1,15)

## Exercise 9J

**1.** (a) $x - y = 1$ passes through (1,0) (0,−1) ; $x + 2y = 7$
passes through (7,0) (1,3)
(b) Lines meet at point (3,2) which gives the solution.

**2.** (a) $x = 3, y = -1$ (b) $x = 1, y = 0$
(c) $x = -1, y = -1$ (d) $x = 2.5, y = 1.5$
(e) $x = 0, y = 3$ (f) $x = 2, y = -3$
(g) $x = -2, y = 11$ (h) $x = -1, y = -2$

**3.** (b) Lines are parallel so there is no solution.

**4.** (b) Lines are the same so there are an infinite number of solutions.

## Exercise 9K

1. c
2. c
3. a
4. b

## Exercise 9L

1. (a) 32°F    (b) 113°F    (c) 37.4°C
2. (a) 27 litres    (b) 9.8 gallons    (c) 12 gallons

## Exercise 9M

1.

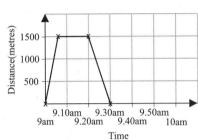

2. (a) 800m    (b) 15 minutes
   (c) 3200 metres per hour    (d) 1230pm
3. (a) 0725
   (b)

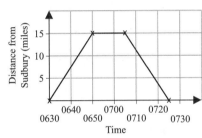

4. OA – It takes Ravi $\frac{3}{4}$ hour to walk $1\frac{1}{2}$ km to school. This
   is 2 km/h
   AB – Ravi stays at school for $7\frac{3}{4}$ hours
   BC – He walks home in $\frac{1}{2}$ an hour, a speed of 3 km/h

## Exercise 9N

1. (a) $b = 0.4h$    (b) Line through (0,0) (2,5) (4,10) (8,20)
2. (a) 3; 1    (b) 2 ; −5    (c) −1; 3    (d) 1 ; 1
   (e) −2 ; 1    (f) −1 ; 3    (g) −3 ; 2    (h) 2.5; 3
   (i) $\frac{-2}{3};\frac{5}{3}$    (j) $\frac{1}{3};\frac{-4}{3}$
3. (a) $y = -x + 3$ passes through (−5, 8) (0,3) (3,0) ;
      $2y - 3x = 2$ passes through (−5,−4) (0,1)(2,8)
   (b) (0.8,2.2)
4. $2y + x = 3$ passes through (1,1) (−1,2) ( 3,0);
   $y - 3x = 5$ passes through (0,5) (−1,2); solution is (−1,2)
5. 90 miles

## Exercise 10A

1. (a) $3x - 5y$    (b) $5a - 2b$    (c) $8s - 7t$
   (d) $2x - 3y + 3z$    (e) $-x - 5y + 3z$    (f) $r - 4s$
   (g) $2x - 2z$    (h) $p - 7q + r$    (i) $2x + 2y + z$

## Exercise 10B

1. (a) $3x + 6y$    (b) $2p + 6q$    (c) $15a + 10b$
   (d) $14r + 21s$    (e) $4b + 6w + 8r$    (f) $3p + 6q + 3s$
   (g) $6a + 4b + 10c$    (h) $12x + 9y$    (i) $12x + 20y$
   (j) $10x + 2y$    (k) $10a + 4b$    (l) $2x + 6y + 2z$
   (m) $6u + 15v + 3w$    (n) $15x + 5y + 20z$
   (o) $3w + 6x + 9y + 15z$
2. (a) $8x - 6y$    (b) $3x - 6y$    (c) $5x - 15y$
   (d) $8x - 4y$    (e) $12x - 24y$    (f) $15a - 6b$

(g) $7a - 14b$    (h) $10r - 4s$    (i) $2x - 2y$
(j) $3x - 3y$    (k) $3r - 6$    (l) $5x - 15$
(m) $10 - 2x$    (n) $2x + 6y - 2z$
(o) $12x - 4y + 4z - 8w$    (p) $5x - 10y - 15z - 25$
3. (a) $x^2 - 3xy$    (b) $2x^2 + 4x$    (c) $3x^2 - 4x$
   (d) $x^2 - 3xy$    (e) $2x^2 + 3xy$    (f) $5x^2 - 2xy$
   (g) $2a^2 - ab$    (h) $4p^2 + 3p$    (i) $c^2 - 3c$
   (j) $a^3 + a^2b$    (k) $3a^2 - a^3$    (l) $x^2 + 2xy$
   (m) $x^2 - x$    (n) $p^2 - 2p$
   (o) $3t^2 - 5t$    (p) $6t^2 + 10t$    (q) $\pi r^2 - \pi r$
   (r) $3r + \pi r^2$    (s) $x^2 + x$    (t) $y^3 - xy + y$

## Exercise 10C

1. (a) $8x + 4y$    (b) $6x + 14y$    (c) $5x + 5y$
   (d) $8x + 2y$    (e) $12x + 8y$    (d) $7x + 34$
   (g) $7a + 5b$    (h) $10a$    (i) $9x + 19y$
   (j) $5x - y$    (k) $5p + 7q$    (l) $8x - 11$
   (m) $8x - 28$    (n) $10a - 4b$    (o) $11b - 2a$
   (p) $-4x - 3y$    (q) $5y$    (r) 0
2. (a) $-2x + 4y$    (b) $4x + 3y$    (c) $2a - 10b$
   (d) $6s$    (e) $15q$    (f) $20q$    (g) $-x + 12y$
   (h) $14x$    (i) $2t$    (j) $10t$    (k) $4a + 9b$
   (l) $-8x + 3y$    (m) $a + b$    (n) $-3s - 8t$
   (o) $-2x - 6y$    (p) $10s$    (q) $3x + y$
   (r) $2x - 9y$
3. (a) $5x^2 + x$    (b) $2x^2 + x$    (c) $5y^2 - 7y$
   (d) $x^2 + y^2$    (e) $2r^2 - 2rs + 2s^2$    (f) $7x^2 - x$
   (g) $2p^3 - p^2 - 2p$    (h) $4x^3 - x^2 - 3x$    (i) $x - y$
   (j) $3x^2 - x - 2$    (k) $2p^2 + q^2$    (l) $4p - 2p^2$
   (m) $3t + t^2 - 8$    (n) $x^2 - 2x$    (o) $y^2 + x^2$

## Exercise 10D

1. (a) $3(x + 2y)$    (b) $2(x + 2y)$    (c) $2(b + 4w)$
   (d) $3(x - 2)$    (e) $2(x - 2)$    (f) $5(x - 1)$
   (g) $5(2 - a)$    (h) $3(x + 5)$    (i) $5(x - 6y)$
   (j) $7(2 - x)$
2. (a) $3(2x + 5)$    (b) $3(3x + 4y)$    (c) $6(5a - 2b)$
   (d) $8(a - 2b)$    (e) $6(2x - 7y)$    (f) $3(5 - 3x)$
   (g) $8(2t + 5s)$    (h) $6(5y + 3x)$    (i) $3(3x - 8y)$
   (j) $12(3x + 2y)$
3. (a) $3ab(4a + 5b)$    (b) $3xy(2x - 5y)$
   (c) $3p^2q^2(2p + 5q)$    (d) $pq(p - q^2)$
   (e) $3a(b - 2a)$    (f) $a(a + b)$    (g) $2xy(x + 3y)$
   (h) $\pi r(4r - 1)$    (i) $3xy(y^2 - 3x^2)$    (j) $2xy(2x + 3y)$

## Exercise 10E

1. (a) $x^2 + 7x + 10$    (b) $x^2 + 10x + 21$
   (c) $y^2 - 8y + 15$    (d) $p^2 - 9p + 14$
   (e) $x^2 - 5x - 6$    (f) $x^2 + 3x - 10$
   (g) $2a^2 + 7a + 3$    (h) $3x^2 + 16x + 5$
   (i) $2y^2 + 9y + 7$    (j) $8t^2 + 14t + 3$
   (k) $x^2 - 1$    (l) $x^2 - 3x - 28$    (m) $3y^2 - 11y + 6$
   (n) $4x^2 - 13x + 3$    (o) $2x^2 + 7x - 15$
   (p) $3p^2 + 10p - 8$    (q) $2s^2 - s - 15$
   (r) $10y^2 - y - 3$    (s) $8t^2 + 22t - 21$
   (t) $3x^2 - 13x - 10$
2. (a) $9x^2 + 12x + 4$    (b) $4x^2 + 20x + 25$
   (c) $4x^2 - 12x + 9$    (d) $25y^2 - 20y + 4$
   (e) $16p^2 - 24p + 9$    (f) $4t^2 - 4t + 1$
   (g) $9x^2 + 6x + 1$    (h) $16x^2 - 8x + 1$
   (i) $25t^2 + 30t + 9$    (j) $36x^2 - 60x + 25$

## Exercise 10F

1. (a) $12r^3$    (b) $15p^5$    (c) $3x^2$    (d) $2x$    (e) $4t^6$
   (f) $27x^6$    (g) $\frac{2}{x^2}$    (h) $648x^{11}$    (i) $x^6y^2$
   (j) $125x^3y^6$    (k) $50y^5$    (l) $32r^3$    (m) $4x^2$

(n) $x^5$  (o) $x^2$  (p) $x^6$  (q) $x^3$
(r) $48x^4$  (s) $t^5$  (t) $64x^5$

## Exercise 10G

1. (a) $x = \frac{(y-2)}{3}$  (b) $x = \frac{(y+3)}{5}$  (c) $x = \frac{(y-b)}{a}$
   (d) $x = \frac{(k-y)}{3}$  (e) $x = \left[\frac{(y-b)}{a}\right]^2$  (f) $x = \frac{(t-y)}{k}$
   (g) $x = \sqrt{\left[\frac{(y-1)}{3}\right]}$  (h) $x = \sqrt{\left[\frac{(4-y)}{3}\right]}$
   (i) $x = \left[\frac{(y+c)}{m}\right]^2$  (j) $x = \left[\frac{(2k-y)}{2a}\right]^2$
   (k) $x = \sqrt{\left[\frac{(21-y)}{3k}\right]}$  (l) $x = \frac{(y+ab)}{am}$

## Exercise 10H

1. (a) $3(x+3)$  (b) $5(1-2x)$  (c) $4(2t+3)$
   (d) $5(x+3y)$  (e) $x(x-6)$  (f) $xy(x+y)$
   (g) $2pq(pq-2)$  (h) $ab(a^2-2b)$  (i) $2st(2s+3t)$
   (j) $\pi r^2(h+2r)$
2. (a) $x^2+11x+28$  (b) $y^2+5y+6$
   (c) $x^2+10x+25$  (d) $2x^2+7x+3$
   (e) $3x^2-5x+2$  (f) $4y^2+y-3$
   (g) $x^2-9$  (h) $4t^2-1$  (i) $3s^2-7s-6$
   (j) $2x^2+x-15$
3. (a) $a^5$  (b) $6b^7$  (c) $10b$  (d) $3a^5$  (e) $ab$
   (f) $a^2b$  (g) $\frac{2}{x^2}$  (h) $p^2q^2$  (i) $4t$
   (j) $\frac{12x^3}{5y}$
4. (a) $x = \frac{(y+5)}{3}$  (b) $x = \frac{(y-c)}{m}$  (c) $x = \frac{(a-y)}{b}$
   (d) $x = \sqrt{\frac{(y+b)}{a}}$  (e) $t = \frac{x}{(u+v)}$  (f) $h = \frac{V}{\pi r^2}$
   (g) $r = \sqrt{\frac{V}{\pi h}}$  (h) $x = \frac{(V-ah)}{a}$  (i) $t = \sqrt{\frac{(s+r)}{g}}$
   (j) $z = \frac{t^2 g}{4\pi^2}$  (k) $g = \frac{4\pi^2 z}{t^2}$  (l) $r = 0.5\sqrt{\frac{S}{\pi}}$
   (m) $x = \frac{(c-y)}{(a-b)}$  (n) $t = \frac{(b+d)}{(a-c)}$

## Exercise 11A

1. (a) $x=2$  (b) $x=11$  (c) $x=12$  (d) $y=9$
   (e) $p=9$  (f) $z=2\frac{1}{2}$  (g) $x=-2$
   (h) $x=-6$  (i) $y=-4$

## Exercise 11B

1. (a) $x=-5$  (b) $x=-8$  (c) $y=-4$
   (d) $x=-3$  (e) $z=-15$  (f) $p=-13$
   (g) $x=-2$  (h) $p=-9$  (i) $y=-7$

## Exercise 11C

1. (a) $x=5$  (b) $x=6$  (c) $x=4\frac{1}{2}$  (d) $x=5$
   (e) $x=6$  (f) $x=2\frac{1}{2}$  (g) $x=6$  (h) $x=12$
   (i) $x=16$  (j) $x=8$  (k) $x=9$  (l) $x=-5\frac{1}{3}$

## Exercise 11D

1. (a) $x=-1$  (b) $y=-2$  (c) $x=-1\frac{1}{2}$
   (d) $x=-6$  (e) $x=-16$  (f) $x=8$
   (g) $x=-4$  (h) $y=36$  (i) $x=-16$
   (j) $x=-28$  (k) $x=-1\frac{1}{2}$  (l) $x=-6$

## Exercise 11E

1. (a) $x=8$  (b) $x=2$  (c) $x=-2$  (d) $x=3$
   (e) $x=2$  (f) $x=-3\frac{1}{2}$  (g) $x=1$  (h) $x=6$
   (i) $x=-\frac{5}{7}$  (j) $x=-1\frac{4}{7}$

## Exercise 11F

1. (a) $x=4$  (b) $x=6$  (c) $x=2$  (d) $x=-6$
   (e) $x=2$  (f) $x=4$  (g) $x=1$  (h) $x=-1$
   (i) $x=-3$  (j) $x=7\frac{1}{5}$

## Exercise 11G

1. (a) $x=3, y=1$  (b) Lines intersect at $x=3, y=1$

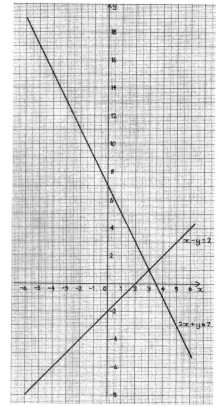

2. $x=6\frac{1}{2}, y=5\frac{1}{2}$
3. $x=1, y=-2$
4. $p=2, q=-1$
5. (a) $x=1, y=3$  (b) $x=1, y=-1$
   (c) $x=2, y=3$  (d) $x=2, y=1$
   (e) $x=1, y=-1$  (f) $x=2, y=5$
   (g) $x=2, y=-\frac{1}{2}$

## Exercise 11H

1. $-5, -4, -3, -2, -1, 0, 1, 2$
2. $-2, -1, 0, 1, 2, 3, 4, 5, 6, 7, 8, 9, 10$
3. (a) $x \geq 10$  (b) $x > -2\frac{1}{2}$  (c) $x \leq -4$
   (d) $1, 2, 3, 4, 5, 6, 7$  (e) $x > -4$  (f) $x \leq 11$

## Exercise 11I

1. (a) $x=9$  (b) $x=5$  (c) $x=5\frac{1}{4}$  (d) $x=-3$
   (e) $x=-2$  (f) $x=-1\frac{2}{5}$  (g) $x=6$
   (h) $x=-4$  (i) $x=17$  (j) $x=-1$
2. (a) $x=10$  (b) $x=2$
3. $x=4\frac{1}{2}$
4. (a) $x=1, y=-4$
5. (a) $x=3$  (b) $p=3, q=-3$
6. $-2, -1, 0, 1, 2, 3$
7. $x > -3\frac{3}{5}$
8. $1, 2, 3, 4$

## Exercise 12A

1. (a)

| $x$ | $-4$ | $-3$ | $-2$ | $-1$ | $0$ | $1$ | $2$ | $3$ | $4$ |
|---|---|---|---|---|---|---|---|---|---|
| $y$ | $19$ | $12$ | $7$ | $4$ | $3$ | $4$ | $7$ | $12$ | $19$ |

(b)

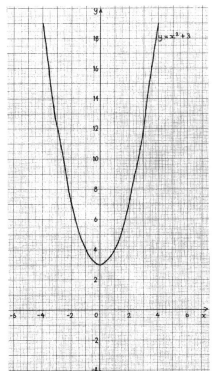

$y = x^2 + 3$

**2.** (a)

| x | −4 | −3 | −2 | −1 | 0 | 1 | 2 | 3 | 4 |
|---|---|---|---|---|---|---|---|---|---|
| y | 13 | 6 | 1 | −2 | −3 | −2 | 1 | 6 | 13 |

(b)

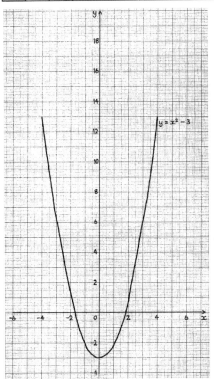

$y = x^2 - 3$

**3.** (a) to (j)

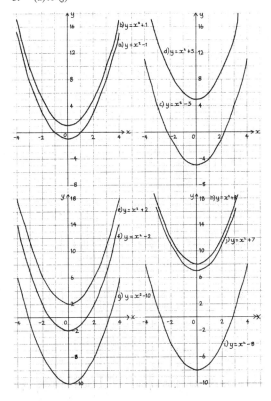

b) $y = x^2 + 1$
a) $y = x^2 - 1$
d) $y = x^2 + 5$
c) $y = x^2 - 5$
e) $y = x^2 + 2$
f) $y = x^2 - 2$
g) $y = x^2 - 10$
h) $y = x^2 + 8$
j) $y = x^2 + 7$
i) $y = x^2 - 8$

**Exercise 12B**

**1.** (a)

| x | −4 | −3 | −2 | −1 | 0 | 1 | 2 | 3 | 4 |
|---|---|---|---|---|---|---|---|---|---|
| y | −62 | −25 | −6 | 1 | 2 | 3 | 10 | 29 | 66 |

(b)

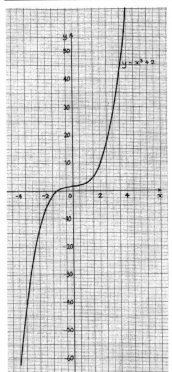

$y = x^3 + 2$

**2.**

|  | $x$ | $-4$ | $-3$ | $-2$ | $-1$ | 0 | 1 | 2 | 3 | 4 |
|---|---|---|---|---|---|---|---|---|---|---|
| (a) | $y$ | $-66$ | $-29$ | $-10$ | $-3$ | $-2$ | $-1$ | 6 | 25 | 62 |
| (b) | $y$ | $-61$ | $-24$ | $-5$ | 2 | 3 | 4 | 11 | 30 | 67 |
| (c) | $y$ | $-68$ | $-31$ | $-12$ | $-5$ | $-4$ | $-3$ | 4 | 23 | 60 |
| (d) | $y$ | $-59$ | $-22$ | $-3$ | 4 | 5 | 6 | 13 | 32 | 69 |
| (e) | $y$ | $-63$ | $-26$ | $-7$ | 0 | 1 | 2 | 9 | 28 | 65 |
| (f) | $y$ | $-65$ | $-28$ | $-9$ | $-2$ | $-1$ | 0 | 7 | 26 | 63 |

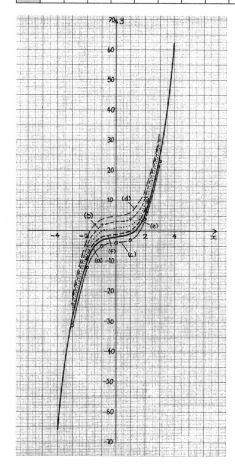

**3.**

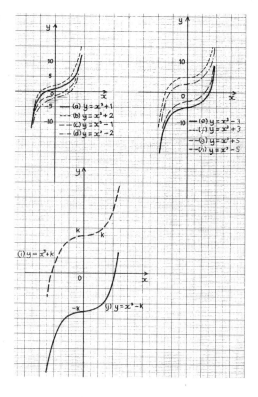

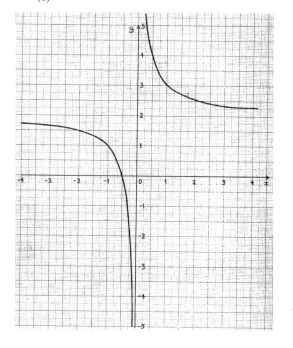

**Exercise 12C**

**1.** (a)

| $x$ | $-4$ | $-3$ | $-2$ | $-1$ | 1 | 2 | 3 | 4 |
|---|---|---|---|---|---|---|---|---|
| $y$ | 1.75 | 1.67 | 1.5 | 1 | 3 | 2.5 | 2.33 | 2.25 |

(b)

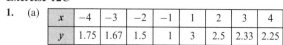

**2.**

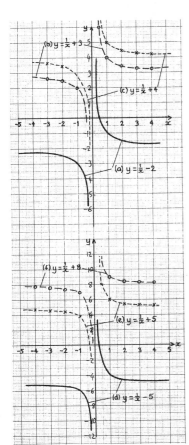

**3.**

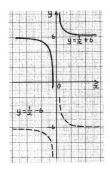

**Exercise 12D**

**1.**

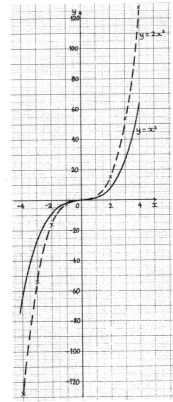

**2.** (a)

| $x$ | $-4$ | $-3$ | $-2$ | $-1$ | 0 | 1 | 2 | 3 | 4 |
|---|---|---|---|---|---|---|---|---|---|
| $y$ | $-32$ | $-13.5$ | $-4$ | $-0.5$ | 0 | 0.5 | 4 | 13.5 | 32 |

(b)

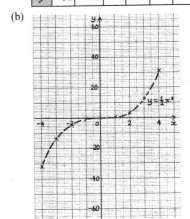

(c) $y = \frac{1}{2}x^3$ is half as steep as $y = x^3$

**3.** (a)

| $x$ | 1 | 2 | 3 | 4 | 5 | 6 | 7 | 8 | 9 | 10 | 11 | 12 |
|---|---|---|---|---|---|---|---|---|---|---|---|---|
| $y$ | 6 | 3 | 2 | 1.5 | 1.2 | 1 | 0.86 | 0.75 | 0.67 | 0.6 | 0.55 | 0.5 |

(b)

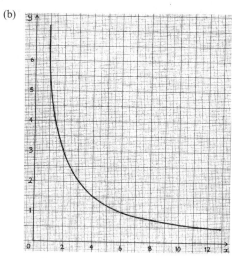

(c) $y = \frac{6}{x}$ is six times as steep as $y = \frac{1}{x}$

## Exercise 12E

**1.**

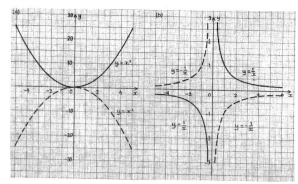

**2.** (a)

| x | −4 | −3 | −2 | −1 | 0 | 1 | 2 | 3 | 4 |
|---|----|----|----|----|---|---|---|---|---|
| y | −15 | −8 | −3 | 0 | 1 | 0 | −3 | −8 | −15 |

(b)

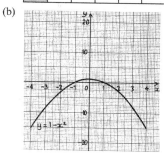

**3.** (a)

| x | −4 | −3 | −2 | −1 | 0 | 1 | 2 | 3 | 4 |
|---|----|----|----|----|---|---|---|---|---|
| y | 68 | 31 | 12 | 5 | 4 | 3 | −4 | −23 | −60 |

(b)

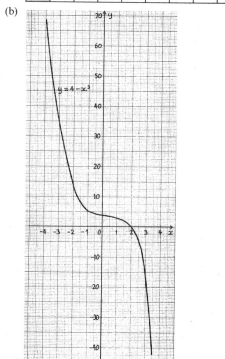

**4.**

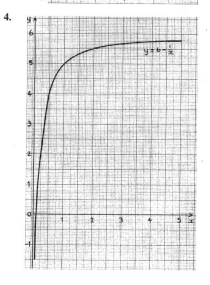

## Exercise 12F

**1.** (a)

| x | −1 | 0 | 1 | 2 | 3 | 4 | 5 | 6 | 7 |
|---|----|---|---|---|---|---|---|---|---|
| y | 24 | 15 | 8 | 3 | 0 | −1 | 0 | 3 | 8 |

(b)

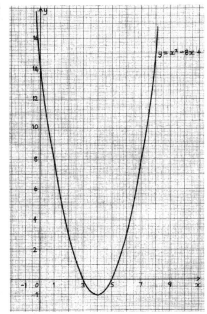

(c) (i) $x = 3, x = 5$ (ii) $x = 1.6, x = 6.4$

2. (a)

| $x$ | −3 | −2 | −1 | 0 | 1 | 2 | 3 | 4 | 5 | 6 | 7 |
|---|---|---|---|---|---|---|---|---|---|---|---|
| $y$ | 40 | 21 | 6 | −5 | −12 | −15 | −14 | −9 | 0 | 13 | 30 |

(b)

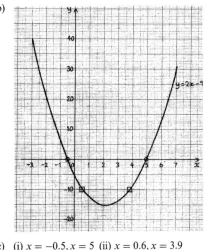

(c) (i) $x = -0.5, x = 5$ (ii) $x = 0.6, x = 3.9$

## Exercise 12G

1. (a)

| $x$ | −4 | −3 | −2 | −1 | 0 | 1 | 2 | 3 | 4 |
|---|---|---|---|---|---|---|---|---|---|
| $y$ | −3 | 22 | 29 | 24 | 13 | 2 | −3 | 4 | 29 |

(b)

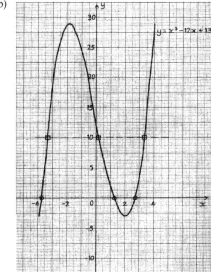

(c) (i) $x = -3.9, x = 1.2, x = 2.7$
    (ii) $x = -3.6, x = 0.3, x = 3.3$

2.  $x = -3.5, x = 1.2, x = 4.7$

## Exercise 12H

1.

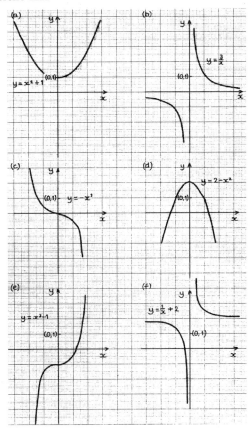

**2.** (a)

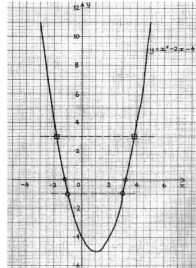

(b) (i) $x = -1.2, x = 3.2$ (ii) $x = -1.8, x = 3.8$
(iii) $x = -1.0, x = 3.0$

**3.** (a)

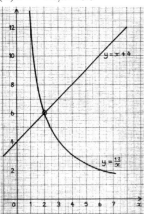

(b) $x = 2$

**4.** (a)

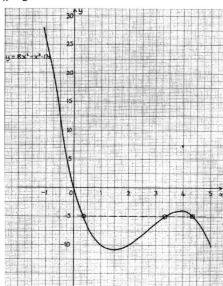

(b) $x = -0.3$

**5.** (a)

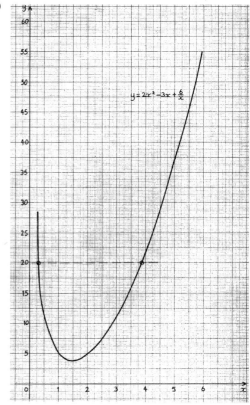

(b) $x = 0.3, x = 3.9$

**6.** (a)

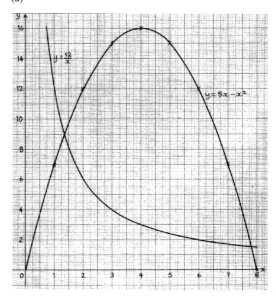

(b) $x = 1.3, x = 7.8$

**Exercise 13A**

**1.** $x = 3.52$ to 2 decimal places
**2.** $x = 2.83$ to 2 decimal places

## Exercise 13B

1.  (a)

| $x$ | $x^3 + 2x$ | |
|---|---|---|
| 1 | $1^3 + 2 \times 1 = 3$ | $< 5$ |
| 2 | $2^3 + 2 \times 2 = 12$ | $> 5$ |

Root lies between 1 and 2.

(b) $x = 1.33$ to 2 decimal places

## Exercise 13C

1.  (a) $x = 1 : 2x^3 + 3x \qquad = 5 \qquad (< 15)$
    $x = 2 : (2 \times 2^3) + (3 \times 2) = 22 \qquad (> 15)$
    Solution lies between $x = 1$ and $x = 2$

    (b) $x = 1.70$ to 2 decimal places

## Exercise 13D

1.  $x = 4 : 4^3 + 2 \times 4 = 72 \qquad (< 100)$
    $x = 5 : 5^3 + 2 \times 5 = 135 \qquad (> 100)$
    Solution lies between $x = 4$ and $x = 5$; $x = 4.50$ to 2 decimal places

2.  $x = 3 : x^2 - 2x = 3 \qquad (< 6)$
    $x = 4 : x^2 - 2x = 8 \qquad (> 6)$
    Solution lies between $x = 3$ and $x = 4$; $x = 3.65$ to 2 decimal places or
    $x = -1 : x^2 - 2x = 3 \qquad (< 6)$
    $x = -2 : x^2 - 2x = 8 \qquad (> 6)$
    Solution lies between $x = -1$ and $x = -2$;
    $x = -1.65$ to 2 decimal places

3.  (a)

| x | 1 | 2 | 3 | 4 |
|---|---|---|---|---|
| y | $-10$ | $-15$ | $-8$ | 17 |

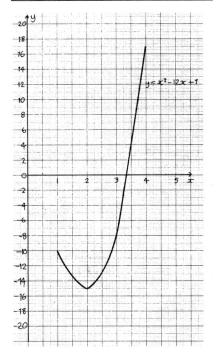

(b) First approximation: $x = 3.4$
(c) $x = 3.42$ to 2 decimal places

## Exercise 13E

1.  (a) $x = 4$ and $x = -5$    (b) $x = 12$ and $x = -10$
    (c) $x = 5$ and $x = -10$

## Exercise 13F

1.  (a) $x = 4 : x^2 - 6x + 8 = 16 - 24 + 8 = 0$, so $x = 4$ is a solution
    $x = 2 : x^2 - 6x + 8 = 4 - 12 + 8 + 0$, so $x = 2$ is a solution
    (b) $x = 5 : x^2 - 11x + 30 = 25 - 55 + 30 = 0$, so $x = 5$ is a solution
    $x = 6 : x^2 - 11x + 30 = 36 - 66 + 30 = 0$, so $x = 6$ is a solution
    (c) $x = +3 : x^2 + 2x - 15 = 9 + 6 - 15 = 0$, so $x = 3$ is a solution
    $x = -5 : x^2 + 2x - 15 = 25 - 10 - 15 = 0$, so $x = -5$ is a solution
    (d) $x = 7 : x^2 - 4x - 21 = 49 - 28 - 21 = 0$, so $x = 7$ is a solution
    $x = -3 : x^2 - 4x - 21 = 9 + 12 - 21 = 0$, so $x = -3$ is a solution

2.  $x = 2, x = 4$

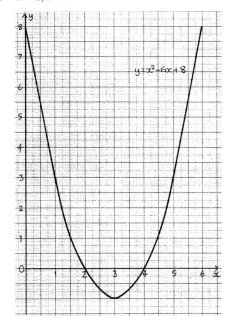

## Exercise 13G

1.  (a) $x = 4, 8$   (b) $x = 3, 4$   (c) $x = 4, 5$
    (d) $x = 3, 6$   (e) $x = -5, -3$   (f) $x = -8, -7$
    (g) $x = -4, -3$   (h) $x = -5, 3$   (i) $x = -6, 3$
    (j) $x = -1, 7$   (k) $x = -8, 3$   (l) $x = 8, -3$
    (m) $x = -7, 2$   (n) $x = 7, -2$   (o) $x = 3, 3$
    (p) $x = 4, 4$   (q) $x = 7, -3$   (r) $x = -4, 7$
    (s) $x = 9, -2$   (t) $x = 2, -1$

## Exercise 13H

1.  (a) $(x + 4)(x + 3) = 0; x = -3, -4$
    (b) $(x - 4)(x - 3) = 0; x = 4, 3$
    (c) $(x - 6)(x - 5) = 0; x = 5, 6$
    (d) $(x - 6)(x - 2) = 0; x = 2, 6$
    (e) $(x - 7)(x + 4) = 0; x = -4, 7$
    (f) $(x + 8)(x - 3) = 0; x = 3, -8$
    (g) $(x - 2)(x - 3) = 0; x = 2, 3$
    (h) $(x - 3)(x - 10) = 0; x = 3, 10$
    (i) $(x + 6)(x - 1) = 0; x = 1, -6$
    (j) $(x - 5)(x - 1) = 0; x = 1, 5$
    (k) $(x + 2)(x - 1) = 0; x = 1, -2$
    (l) $(x - 3)(x + 2) = 0; x = 3, -2$

2.  (a) $(x - 8)(x - 4) = 0; x = 4, 8$
    (b) $(x - 4)(x - 3) = 0; x = 3, 4$

(c)   $(x-5)(x-4) = 0; x = 4, 5$
(d)   $(x-3)(x-6) = 0; x = 3, 6$
(e)   $(x+5)(x+3) = 0; x = -5, -3$
(f)   $(x+8)(x+7) = 0; x = -7, -8$
(g)   $(x+4)(x+3) = 0; x = -3, -4$
(h)   $(x+5)(x-3) = 0; x = -5, 3$
(i)   $(x+6)(x-3) = 0; x = -6, 3$
(j)   $(x-7)(x+1) = 0; x = -7, 1$
(k)   $(x+8)(x-3) = 0; x = 3, -8$
(l)   $(x-8)(x+3) = 0; x = 8, -3$
(m)   $(x+7)(x-2) = 0; x = -7, 2$
(n)   $(x-7)(x+2) = 0; x = 7, -2$
(o)   $(x-3)(x-3) = 0; x = 3, 3$
(p)   $(x-4)(x-4) = 0; x = 4, 4$
(q)   $(x-7)(x+3) = 0; x = 7, -3$
(r)   $(x+4)(x-7) = 0; x = -4, 7$
(s)   $(x-9)(x+2) = 0; x = 9, -2$
(t)   $(x-2)(x+1) = 0; x = 2, -1$

## Exercise 13I

1.   12.7 or −13.7 to 1 decimal place
2.   $x = 3.58$ to 3 significant figures
3.   $x = 1.86$ or $-1.70$ to 2 decimal places
4.   $x = 2 : x^3 + 2x = 12$        $(< 20)$
     $x = 3 : x^3 + 2x = 33$        $(> 20)$
     Solution lies between $x = 2$ and $x = 3; x = 2.47$ to 2 decimal places
5.   (a)
     (b)   First approximation = 1.4; Solution is 1.52 to 2 decimal places

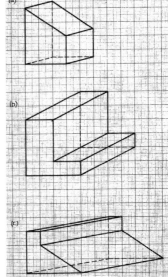

6.   (a)  $x = 3, 4$    (b)  $x = -6, -7$    (c)  $x = -7, 3$
     (d)  $x = 7, -3$   (e)  $x = -2, 3$     (f)  $x = -6, 1$
     (g)  $x = 6, -1$   (h)  $x = -8, 3$     (i)  $x = 8, -3$
     (j)  $x = -6, 2$

## Exercise 14A

1.   (a)  Rectangle     (b)  Equilateral triangle     (c)  Kite
     (d)  Isosceles triangle     (e)  Rhombus
     (f)  Trapezium     (g)  Pentagon     (h)  Parallelogram
     (i)  Hexagon
2.   (a)  Isosceles triangle     (b)  Pentagon
     (c)  Equilateral triangle     (d)  Hexagon
     (e)  Regular octagon
3.   (a)  Square     (b)  Trapezium
4.   (a)  Parallelogram, square, rectangle, rhombus
     (b)  Square, rectangle     (c)  Square, rhombus
     (d)  Kite, rectangle, parallelogram

## Exercise 14B

1.   A and D; B and H; E and G
2.

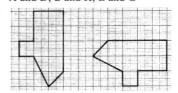

## Exercise 14C

1.   e.g.

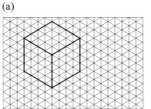
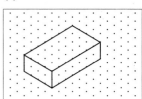
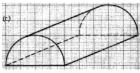
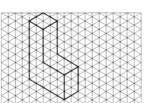

2.
(a)                                    (b)

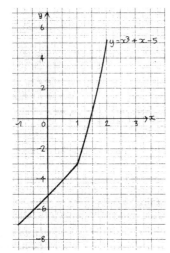
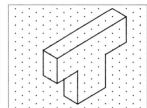

(c)                                    (d)

3.

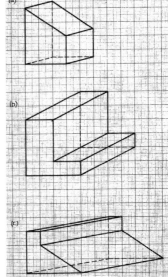

## Exercise 14D

1. (a) Cuboid

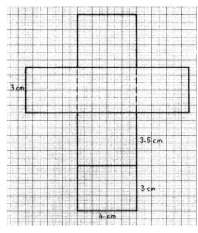

(b) Right pyramid with rectangular base

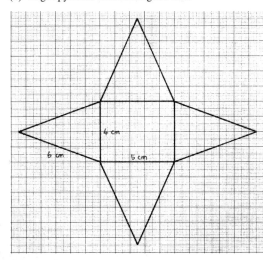

(c) Prism with triangular cross-section

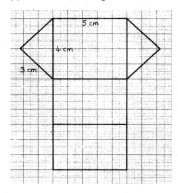

(d) Pyramid with triangle base and all edges 6 cm

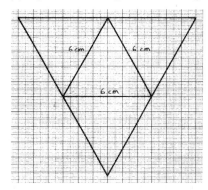

2. Tabs are shaded

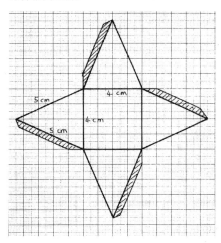

## Exercise 14E

1. A and M; E and H; K and N
2. (a) Rectangle (b) Isosceles triangle (c) Decagon
   (d) Scalene triangle (e) Trapezium
   (f) Square, rhombus
3.

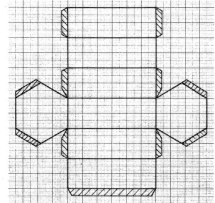

**4.**

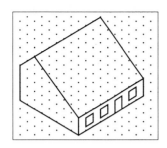

## Exercise 15A

**1.** (a)  A is $(2, 5)$, B is $(6, 1)$
**2.** Rectangle

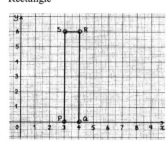

**3.** $(-2, -2)$
**4.** $(5, 0)$
**5.** (b) $(\frac{1}{2}, 6)$ (c) $(-2\frac{3}{4}, 4)$
**6.** $(0, 5), (-1, 0), (4, -1)$

## Exercise 15B

**1.** (a)

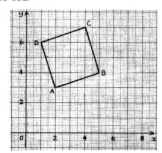

(b)  square    (c)  10 square units
**2.** $2\frac{1}{2}$ square units
**3.** (a)

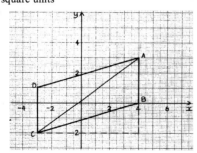

(b)  Parallelogram    (c)  $10\frac{1}{2}$ square units

## Exercise 15C

**1.** Locus is the angle bisector

**2.** (a)

(b)  The locus is a circle, centre P
**3.** (a)

(b)  87 km
**4.** (a)

(b)  24.57 cm
**5.**

## Exercise 15D

**1.**

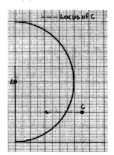

**2.** (a) and (b)

(c)  1.73 metres

## Exercise 15E

1. (a)

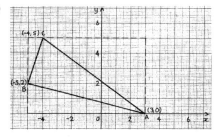

(b) 13 square units

2. (a)

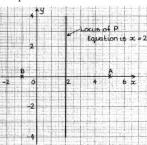

(b) $x = 2$

3.

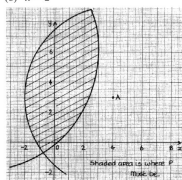

4.

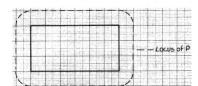

5.

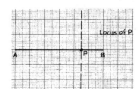

6. (a)

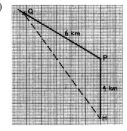

(b) 8.7 km

## Exercise 16A

1.

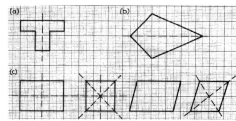

2.

3. e.g T shape as in question **1**(a)
4. e.g. A square as in question **1**(c)

## Exercise 16B

1. (a) order 2     (b) order 3     (c) none
   (d) order 4     (e) order 2     (f) order 6
   (g) order 4     (h) order 6
2. (a) e.g. a 'Z' shape
   (b) e.g. a plus sign
   (c) e.g. an equilateral triangle
   (d) e.g. a regular octagon

## Exercise 16C

1. e.g.

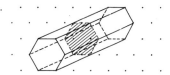

2. (a)

(b)

(c)

(d)

## Exercise 16D

1. (a) $a = 133°$; Angles on a straight line
   (b) $b = 77°$; Sum of angles at a point
   (c) $p = 103°$; Sum of angles of triangle

$q = 52°$; Vertically opposite angles
(d) $x = 116°$; Angles on a straight line
$y = 31°$ : Sum of angles of triangle
(e) $c = 124°$; Vertically oppoite angles
$d = 56°$; Angles on straight line
(f) $w = 124°$ Sum of angles of quadrilateral
(g) $e = 32°$; Base angles of isosceles triangle
$f = 116°$; Sum of angles of triangle
(h) $l = m = 23°$; Base angles of isosceles triangle
(i) $r = u = 75°$; Base angles of isosceles triangle
$w = 51°$; Angles on a straight line
$s = 51°$; Base angles of isosceles triangle
$t = 78°$; Sum of angles of triangle
**2.** $x = 79°$
**3.** (a) $BAC = 50°$; Base angles of isosceles triangle
(b) $AEC = 80°$; Sum of angles of triangle
**4.** (a) $BCD = 134°$; Sum of angles on straight line
(b) $ABC = 73°$; Sum of angles of triangle

## Exercise 16E

**1.** (a) Square, rectangle
(b) Square, rhombus, rectangle, parallelogram
(c) Square, rhombus
(d) Square, rectangle, rhombus, parallelogram
(e) Square, rectangle
(f) Square, rhombus, rectangle, parallelogram
(g) Square, rhombus, kite    (h) Square, rhombus
(i) Square, rhombus, rectangle, parallelogram, trapezium
**2.** (a) $a = 72°$    (b) (i) $b = 108°$ (ii) $c = 108°$
**3.** (a) $27°$    (b) $54°$
**4.** (a) $56°$    (b) $112°$
**5.** $54°$
**6.** $43°$
**7.** $90°$
**8.** (a) $90°$    (b) $32°$    (c) $58°$

## Exercise 16F

**1.** (a) $p = 66°$; Sum of exterior angles of polygon
$q = 114°$; Angles on a straight line $= 180°$)
(b) $x = 88°$; Sum of angles of a pentagon
**2.** $140°$
**3.** (a) $10$    (b) $900°$
**4.** (a) $6$    (b) (i) $60°$ (ii) Equilateral
**5.** (a) Hexagon    (b) $p = 120°$    (c) $q = 60°$
(d) $1 : 2$

## Exercise 16G

**2.** P, Q
**4.** (a) Trapezium
**5.** (a) (i) $72°$ (ii) $54°$
(c) Angle at each vertex $= 108°$. Vertices cannot meet and form exactly $360°$.
**7.** Regular hexagon, equilateral triangle, square

## Exercise 16H

**1.** (a) $x = 67°$; Corresponding angles, $y = 113°$; Angles on a straight line
(b) $v = 132°$; Corresponding angles, $w = 48°$; Angles on a straight line
(c) $a = 52°$; Alternate angles, $b = 128°$; Angles on a straight line
(d) $c = 143°$; Alternate angles, $d = 37°$; Angles on a straight line
(e) $m = 55°$; Sum angles of triangle $l = 68°$; Alternate angles
(f) $p = 74°$; Corresponding angles, $q = 74°$; Vertically opposite angles, $r = 53°$; Sum of angles of triangle
**2.** (a) Corresponding angles    (b) $r = 80°$
(c) $x = 80°$; Altnerate angles

**3.** (a) $64°$    (b) $52°$
**4.** (a) $70°$    (b) $40°$

## Exercise 16I

**1.** (a) Angle $BAC = 65°$; Base angles of isosceles triangle, angle $ABC = 50°$; Sum of angles of triangle
(b) Angle $CED = 110°$. Extend $CD$ beyond $D$. The exterior angle $= 70°$ as it is a corresponding angle and angle $CDE$ is then $110°$
**2.** (a) $x = 126°$    (b) Isosceles    (c) $y = 63°$
**3.** (a) $5\,m$    (b) Kite    (c) $x = 28°$
**4.** (a) (i) $4$ (ii) $2$    (b) $36°$. Alternate angles
(c) Angle $PQS = 54°$. Sum of angles of triangles $= 180°$ and angle POQ $= 90°$ – a property of a rhombus
**5.**

**6.** (a) $p = 45°$    (b) $q = 135°$

## Exercise 17A

**2.** (a)

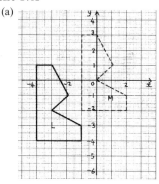

(b) $(0, 0), (1, 1), (0, 3), (-1, 3), (-1, -2), (2, -2), (2, -1)$
**3.** (a)

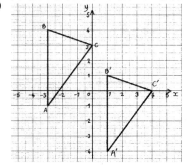

(b) A$'$ is $(1, -4)$; B$'$ is $(1, 1)$; C$'$ is $(4, 0)$
**4.** Translation vector $\binom{-5}{-2}$

## Exercise 17B

**1.**

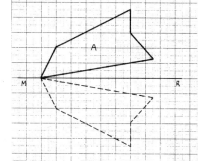

**2.**

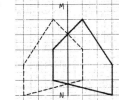

**3.**

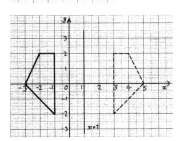

**4.**

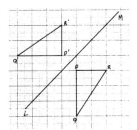

**5.**

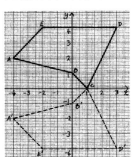

**6.**   (a)

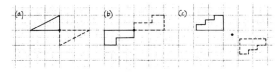

(b)  $(8,1)$     (c)   $x = 3$

**7.**   Reflection in the line $y = -4$

**Exercise 17C**

**1.**

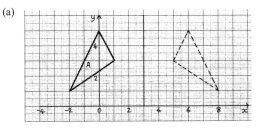

**2.**

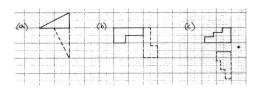

**3.**

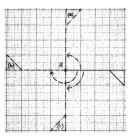

**4.**

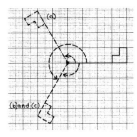

**Exercise 17D**

**1.**

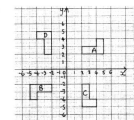

**2.**

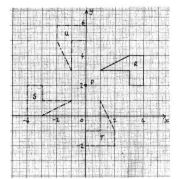

**3.**

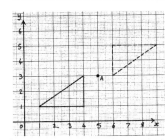

**4.**   Rotation of 180° clockwise about $(0,0)$

## Exercise 17E

**1.**

**2.**

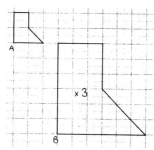

**3.**

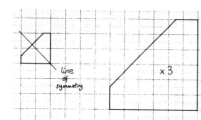

## Exercise 17F

**1.**

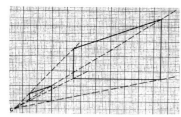

**2.** (a) A′ is (9, 3), B′ is (6, −12), C′ is (−9, 3)
(b)

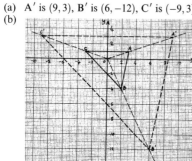

**3.** (a) 3   (b) Centre of enlargement is (6.5, 1)
**4.** (a) Enlargement. Scale factor = 2, centre (7, 1)
(b) Enlargement. Scale factor = ½, centre (7, 1)
**5.**

## Exercise 17G

**1.** 63 cm
**2.** (a) 60°   (b) 8 cm
**3.** (a) $a = 12$ cm   (b) $b = 5$ cm
(c) $c = 4$ cm, $d = 9$ cm   (d) $e = 4$ cm, $f = 7.5$ cm
**4.** 7.2 cm

## Exercise 17H

**1.** C and I; A and H
**2.** (a) (i) 6 cm (ii) 4 cm (iii) 5 cm   (b) Angle CED
(c) Parallel
**3.** PSO and PQO; PSR and PSR; OSR and OQR
**4.** ABC and PQR; ACD and PRS

## Exercise 17I

**1.** (a)

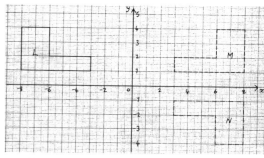

(c) Rotation of 180° centre (0, 0)
**2.** (a)

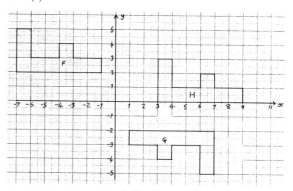

(c) Translation by $\begin{pmatrix} 10 \\ -2 \end{pmatrix}$
**3.** (a)

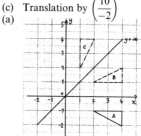

(c) Rotation of 90° anticlockwise, centre (0, 0)
**4.** (a)

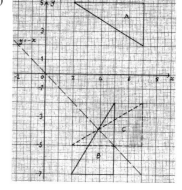

(c) Reflection in *x*-axis

5. (a)

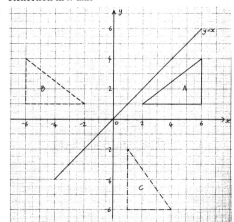

(c) Rotation of 90° centre $(0, 0)$

6. (a)

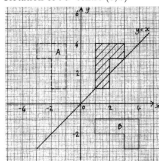

(c) Reflection in line $y = x$

## Exercise 17J

1. (a) Reflection in line $y = x$
   (b) Enlargement; Scale factor 2, centre $(-7, 1)$
2. (a) 2 cm$^2$
   (b) $A'' B'' = 1.2$ cm
3. (b) (i) Parallelogram (ii) 133.8° (iii) 5300

## Exercise 18A

1. (a) Perimeter $= 10 + 2a$ cm; Area $= 5a$ cm$^2$
   (b) Perimeter $= 36$ cm; Area $= 71$ cm$^2$
   (c) Perimeter $= 22$ m; Area $= 28$ m$^2$
2. (a) 4 cm    (b) 40 cm$^2$
3. 250,000 m$^2$
4. £72
5. 6 cm
6. (a) 32 cm
   (b) Possible answers: 12 cm × 4 cm, 11 cm × 5 cm, 13 cm × 3 cm, 14 cm × 2 cm, 15 cm × 1 cm, 10 cm × 6 cm, 9 cm × 7 cm; Area of square $= 64$ cm$^2$. All areas of three rectangles are less than 64 cm$^2$

## Exercise 18B

1. (a) 25 cm$^2$    (b) 24 cm$^2$    (c) 30 cm$^2$
2. 360 m$^2$
3. 6 cm
4. (a) Perimeter $= 4x + 2$    (b) $x = 7$ cm
5. (a) 46 cm    (b) 90 cm$^2$

## Exercise 18C

1. (a) 80 cm$^2$    (b) 60 cm$^2$    (c) 54 cm$^2$

2. 4 cm
3. (a) 36 cm$^2$    (b) $7\frac{1}{5}$ cm
4. 25.3 cm

## Exercise 18D

1. 90 cm$^2$
2. 196 m$^2$
3. 1.2 m$^2$

## Exercise 18E

1. (a) Circumference $= 31.42$ cm, Area $= 78.54$ cm$^2$
   (b) Circumference $= 45.24$ cm, Area $= 162.86$ cm$^2$
   (c) Circumference $= 25.13$ cm, Area $= 50.27$ cm$^2$
   (d) Circumference $= 59.06$ cm, Area $= 277.59$ cm$^2$
2. 49.74 cm$^2$
3. 35.45 cm
4. (a) 11.31 m    (b) 10.18 m$^2$
5. 51.73 cm$^2$
6. (a) 8.08 m    (b) 3.57 m$^2$

## Exercise 18F

1. (a) 648 cm$^2$    (b) 468 cm$^2$
2. 2.304 m$^3$ (to 3 decimal places)
3. (a) 336 cm$^3$    (b) 244 cm$^2$
4. 9.65 cm
5. 6 cm

## Exercise 18G

1. (a) 600 cm$^3$    (b) 450 cm$^3$    (c) 720 cm$^3$
2. (a) 280 cm$^3$    (b) 6.54 cm
3. (a) 1680 cm$^3$    (b) 847.9 cm$^2$

## Exercise 18H

1. (a) 1021.02 cm$^3$    (b) 1696.46 cm$^3$
2. (a) 2120.58 cm$^3$    (b) 12.85 cm
3. 8.92 cm

## Exercise 18I

1. $4\pi r^2$ is of dimension 2 – formula for area of surface
   $\frac{4}{3}\pi r^3$ is of dimension 3 – formula for volume
2. $3\mu x^3$         – dimension 3 – volume
   $2\lambda(a + b)$   – dimension 1 – length
   $a^2 b$             – dimension 3 – volume
   $\alpha b^2 + 2c^2$ – dimension 2 – area
   $\sqrt{\pi r^2}$    – dimension 1 – length
   $\dfrac{abc}{h}$    – dimension 2 – area
3. $2\pi r^2 + 2\pi rh$; Both terms of dimension 2 – area
4. $\pi ab$ is of dimension 2 – area

## Exercise 18J

1. (i) 56.55 cm (ii) 254.47 cm$^2$
2. 800 cm$^3$
3. (a) 1809.56 cm$^3$    (b) 12.19 cm
4. Expressions which could represent a volume (i.e. of dimension 3) are: $\lambda a^2 b, \pi r^2 h, \mu \dfrac{a^2 b^2}{h}, \pi(a^2 b + ab^2)$
5. (a) 25.13 m$^2$    (b) 6031.86 m$^3$
6. 51.73 cm$^2$

## Exercise 19A

1. (a) 16    (b) 12.25    (c) 400    (d) 94.09
   (e) 384.16    (f) 1324.96
2. (a) 7    (b) 15    (c) 1.3    (d) 5.8    (e) 0.9
   (g) 17.23

3. (a) 15.9    (b) 48.4    (c) 4.28    (d) 5.43
    (e) 92.1    (f) 1350

### Exercise 19B

1. (a) (i) 16 (ii) 9 (iii) 25    (b) 25
    (c) Part (b) answer = Part (a) (iii) answer
2. (a) (i) 144 (ii) $12\frac{1}{4}$ (iii) $156\frac{1}{4}$    (b) $156\frac{1}{4}$
    (c) Sum of (a) (i) and (a) (ii) = (a) (iii)

### Exercise 19C

1. (a) 15 cm    (b) 13 cm    (c) 37.5 cm    (d) 7.5 m
2. (a) 9.4 cm    (b) 36.2 cm    (c) 9.0 m    (d) 18.1 m
3. 17 cm
4. 2140 km

### Exercise 19D

1. (a) 12 cm    (b) 36 cm    (c) $c = 2.5$ cm
    (d) 1.4 cm
2. (a) 6.2 m    (b) 33.4 cm    (b) 5.9 cm
    (d) 20.5 cm
3. 61.6 cm

### Exercise 19E

1. 13.9 cm
2. 17.0 km
3. 1.72 m
4. 12 cm
5. 36.6 cm
6. 12.4 m
7. 36.1 m
8. 8.6 km
9. 10 cm
10. 24.7 km

### Exercise 20A

1.

| triangle | hypotenuse | opposite | adjacent |
| --- | --- | --- | --- |
| (a) | 5 cm | 3 cm | 4 cm |
| (b) | 13 cm | 5 cm | 12 cm |
| (c) | 10 cm | 6 cm | 8 cm |
| (d) | 20 cm | 16 cm | 12 cm |
| (e) | 26 cm | 10 cm | 24 cm |
| (f) | z | y | x |
| (g) | p | r | q |
| (h) | 25 cm | 24 cm | 7 cm |
| (i) | 41 cm | 40 cm | 9 cm |

### Exercise 20B

1.

| angle in degrees | sine | cosine | tangent |
| --- | --- | --- | --- |
| 0 | 0.0 | 1.0 | 0.0 |
| 10 | 0.1736 | 0.9848 | 0.1763 |
| 15 | 0.2588 | 0.9659 | 0.2679 |
| 20 | 0.3420 | 0.9397 | 0.3640 |
| 33 | 0.5446 | 0.8387 | 0.6494 |
| 45 | 0.7071 | 0.7071 | 1.0 |
| 52 | 0.7880 | 0.6157 | 1.2799 |
| 60 | 0.8860 | 0.5000 | 1.73205 |
| 75 | 0.9659 | 0.2588 | 3.73205 |
| 80 | 0.9848 | 0.1736 | 5.6713 |
| 88 | 0.9994 | 0.0349 | 28.63625 |

2. (a) 25.72°   (b) 55.92°   (c) 27.10°   (d) 39.00°
    (e) 66.50°   (f) 88.92°   (g) 82.91°   (h) 2.61°
    (i) 6.01°

### Exercise 20C

1. (a) $x = 36.87°$   (b) $y = 41.41$   (c) $p = 32.01°$
    (d) $x = 33.56°$   (e) $x = 30.96°$   (f) $y = 32.23°$
    (g) $x = 30.96°$   (h) $x = 73.61°$   (i) $y = 41.81°$

### Exercise 20D

1. (a) $x = 5.0$ cm   (b) $x = 9.19$ cm   (c) $x = 8.34$ cm
    (d) $p = 5.63$ cm   (e) $x = 9.37$ cm   (f) $y = 4.64$ cm
2. 248.53 metres
3. 10.29 km

### Exercise 20E

1. (a) 6.5 m    (b) 22.62°
2. (a) 1.75 m    (b) 2.41 m    (c) 43.3°
3. (a) 44.22°    (b) 4.39 cm    (c) 12.76 cm
4. (a) 25.32 m    (b) 9.09°
5. Ratio $\dfrac{O}{H} = \dfrac{7}{10}$ *but* $\sin 35° = .5736$ *not* 0.7. It is not possible to draw the triangle
6. Height $= 40.63$ m
7. (a) 3.595 m    (b) 68.08°
8. (a) $x = 5.88$ cm   (b) $y = 10.29$ cm
    (c) $z = 8.66$ cm   (d) $p = 17.33$ cm
    (e) $q = 9.33$ cm   (f) $r = 11.13$ cm
    (g) $z = 30.78$ cm   (h) $t = 34.29$ cm
9. 22.55 km
10. 3.13 m
11. 64.94 m

### Exercise 21A

1. (a) Continuous   (b) Continuous   (c) Discrete
    (d) Discrete   (e) Discrete   (f) Continuous
    (g) Continuous   (h) Discrete   (i) Continuous
    (j) Discrete

### Exercise 21B

1. (a) 5.965 cm    (b) 5.955 mm
2. (a) 2 mins 32.315 s
    (b) 2 mins 32.305 s

### Exercise 21C

1. (a) 1.5 km    (b) 250 mm    (c) 3000 m
    (d) 1000 m
2. (e) 8.3 cm, 83 mm (estimate)
    (g) 36.5 cm (estimate)
3. (c) is a sensible estimate. (a), (d), (e), (f) are all small and (b) is large

### Exercise 21D

1. (a) 3000 ml    (b) 5 litres    (c) 15 litres
    (d) 10 000 ml
2. (a) (i) 12 000 cm$^3$ (ii) 12 litres (iii) 1200 cl (iv) 12 000 ml
    (b) 16 bottles

### Exercise 21E

1. (a) 3000 g    (b) 4000 kg    (c) 4 000 000 g
    (d) 5.4 kg    (e) 0.3 g    (f) 3200 mg
    (g) 1 000 000 g or $1.0 \times 10^6$ g
    (h) 2 000 000 000 mg or $2.0 \times 10^9$ mg
2. (a) (i) 10 176 g (ii) 10.176 kg    (b) 2359 tins
3. $3 \times 10^9$ mg

## Exercise 21F

1. 8897 seconds
2. 44 640 minutes
3. 3 minutes   20 seconds
4. (a)  18 years      (b)   6725 days
5. 145 minutes
6. (a)  (i) 318 minutes (ii) 5 h   18 min      (b)   07 : 42

## Exercise 21G

1. (a)  14.08 lb      (b)   14 lb 1 oz
2. 60 ft 1 inch
3. £2.58
4. 148 880 000 km or $1.4888 \times 10^8$ km

## Exercise 21H

1. $666\frac{2}{3}$ km hr$^{-1}$
2. 60 miles
3. 6.15 m sec$^{-1}$
4. (a)  71.3 km h$^{-1}$      (b)   44.6 mph
5. 22.6 mph
6. (a)  60 mpg      (b)   96 km per gallon
   (c)  21.1 km per litre
7. 1.31 g per cm$^3$
9. 1120 g or 1.12 kg

## Exercise 21I

1. (a)  (i) 75.5 miles (ii)74.5 miles      (b)   120 km
   (c)  (i) 42.86 mph (ii) 68.57 km h$^{-1}$ (iii) 19.05 m sec$^{-1}$
2. (a)  2h   50 min      (b)   4. 2kg
3. 2.66 g per cm$^3$
4. 0.167 kg per day or 167 g per day
5. 125 miles
6. (a)  156 miles      (b)   249.6 km
7. (a)  0.66 gallon      (b)   5.28 pints

## Exercise 22A

1. (a)  6.2 cm      (b)   30°      (c)   4.2 cm      (d)   41°
2. (b)  103°
3. (b)  2.85 cm
4. (a)  134°      (b)   D is 12.4 cm from A and 8.1 cm from C

## Exercise 22B

1. (a)  117°      (b)   206°      (c)   041°      (c)   310°
   (e)  053°      (f)   224°
2.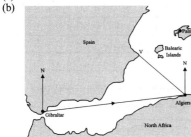
3. (b)  301°
   (c)  58.3 km
4. (a)  083°
   (b)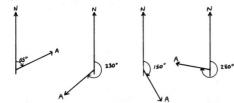
5. (a)  137°      (b)   31°      (c)   239°

6. 85°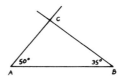

## Exercise 22C

1. 1.4 metres
2. (a)  1400 m or 1.4 km      (b)   14.8 cm
3. (a)  14 km      (b)   12. 5 cm
4. (a)  3.74 m      (b)   23.3 cm

## Exercise 22D

1. (a)  329°      (b)   1200 m      (c)   Lodge Farm
2. (a)  (i) 26 km (ii) 036°
   (b)  Road R238 at Ballymagan
3. (a)  2.2 km      (b)   322°

## Exercise 22E

1. (a)  Trapezium      (c)  (i) 1.51 m
   (c)  (ii) 98°      (d)   2.85 m$^2$
2. (a)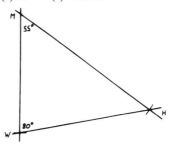

   (b)  (i) 2.325 km      (b)  (ii) 080°
3.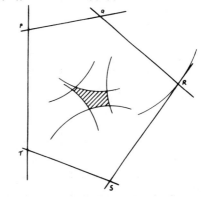

## Exercise 22F

1. (a)  60°      (b)   4 cm
2. (a)  3.6 cm      (b)   3.8 cm      (c)   105°
3. (a)  6 cm      (b)   7 cm
4. (a)  10 cm      (b)   3 cm      (c)  (i) $c = 5$cm, $d = 9$ cm
   (d)  (i) $e = 10$ cm, $f = 3$ cm
5. 4.5 cm
6. (a)  62°      (b)   16 cm
7. 21.6 cm

## Exercise 22G

1. (a)  ∠ACB = ∠DCE (vertically opposite); ∠ABC = ∠CDE
   (alternate); ∠CAB = ∠CED (alternate) –
   Corresponding angles are equal so triangles are
   similar
   (b)  3.75 cm

2.  (a) (i) APR or SQC (ii) 2.78 m (b) 25.8°
3.  (a) 103°
4.  (a) 117.8 cm$^3$ (b) 34.875 cm
5.  (a) 5 cm (b) 12. 8 cm
6.  (a) (i) 50°
       (ii) Base angles of isosceles triangle are equal. Sum of angles of triangle = 180°
    (b) (i) 59.24 cm (ii) 44.16 cm (iii) 52.2°
    (c) 60.8 cm
7.  (a) 42 cm$^3$ (b) 384 cm$^2$ (c) (i) 16 (ii) 64

## Exercise 23A

1.

| Colours | Tally | Total |
|---|---|---|
| green | | |
| blue etc. . . | | |

2.

| Sports | Tally | Total |
|---|---|---|
| tennis etc. . . | | |

3.

| Newspapers | Tally | Total |
|---|---|---|
| Daily Mail etc. . . | | |

4.

| Score | Tally | Total |
|---|---|---|
| 0 | | | 1 |
| 1 | || | 2 |
| 2 | JHT | 5 |
| 3 | | | 1 |
| 4 | || | 2 |
| 5 | | | 1 |
| 6 | | | 1 |
| 7 | || | 2 |

5.

| Month | Tally | Total |
|---|---|---|
| Jan | JHT ||| | 8 |
| Feb | JHT | 5 |
| Mar | || | 2 |
| Apr | ||| | 3 |
| May | ||| | 3 |
| June | || | 2 |
| July | || | 2 |
| Aug | || | 2 |
| Sept | ||| | 3 |
| Oct | JHT | 5 |
| Nov | || | 2 |
| Dec | ||| | 3 |

## Exercise 23B

1.

| Name | |
|---|---|
| Work | .................................... |
| Employer | .................................... |
| Holidays | .................................... |
| Hours etc . . . | .................................... |

## Exercise 23C

1.  (a) 2 (b) 3 (c) 3 (d) 7
2.  (a) Peugeot 306XL (b) Vauxhall Corsa 1.2
    (c) Peugeot 306XL, Ford Fiesta 1100XL, Vauxhall Corsa 1.2 (d) None (e) 2
3.  None
4.  Ford Fiesta 1100LX or Ford Escort 1.8
5.  Ford Escort 1.8 or Rover 214 Si

## Exercise 23D

1.  (a) Quantitative, discrete
    (b) Quantitative, continuous
    (c) Quantitative, discrete (d) Qualitative
    (e) Quantitative, continuous
    (f) Quantitative, discrete

## Exercise 23F

1.  (a) Alyssum (b) Red (c) Begonia or Dahlia
2.  (a) Lion (b) £11.70
3.  (a) Single year, single set, single day
    (b) More days of week and more sets of pupils
4.  (a)

| Breakfast food | Tally | Total |
|---|---|---|
| | | |
| | | |
| | | |

    (b) Ask how often they eat a) fruit, b) vegetables, c) chips
5.  (a) Cycling and swimming
    (b) How often do they take part in sport?
6.  Separate observation sheets for different parts of day and days of week.

| Vehicle type | Tally | Total |
|---|---|---|
| car | | |
| bus | | |
| lorry etc. . . | | |

7.  (a) Yes. Bus travellers have highest % of lates for number of days.
    (b) Sample additional days, more students, check times of travel (rush hour or not).

## Exercise 24A

1.  (a) (i) 70 (ii) 3 (b) Sharptown (c) Treetown

## Exercise 24B

1.

| Score | Tally | Total |
|---|---|---|
| 0 | JHT || | 7 |
| 1 | JHT JHT JHT JHT JHT | 25 |
| 2 | JHT JHT || | 12 |
| 3 | ||| | 3 |
| 4 | || | 2 |
| 5 | | | 1 |
| 6 | | 0 |
| 7 | | 0 |

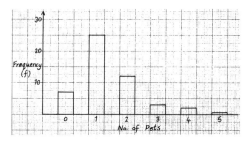

(b)

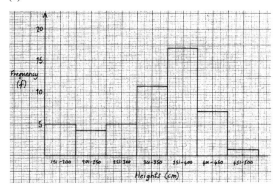

2.  (a)

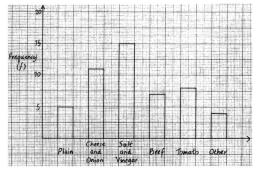

### Exercise 24C

1.  (a)

| Age | Tally | Frequency |
|---|---|---|
| 0 – 9 | IIII | 4 |
| 10 – 19 | IIIII IIIII | 10 |
| 20 – 29 | IIIII IIIII IIIII IIIII II | 22 |
| 30 – 39 | IIIII III | 9 |
| 40 – 49 | IIIII | 5 |

(b)

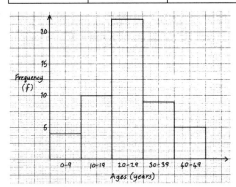

2.  (a)

| Height | Tally | Frequency |
|---|---|---|
| 150 – 200 | IIIII | 5 |
| 201 – 250 | IIII | 4 |
| 251 – 300 | IIIII | 5 |
| 301 – 350 | IIIII IIIII I | 11 |
| 351 – 400 | IIIII IIIII IIIII II | 17 |
| 401 – 450 | IIIII II | 7 |
| 451 – 500 | I | 1 |

### Exercise 24D

1.

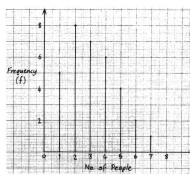

2.

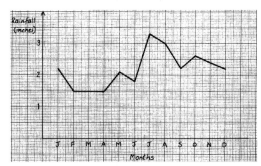

Higher rainfall in summer months and autumn. Low in Feb. to April.

### Exercise 24E

1.

**2.** (a)

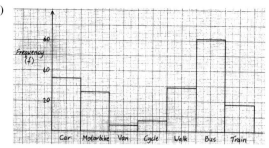

(b)

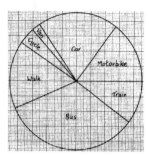

**3.**

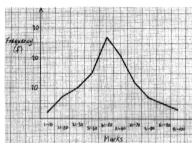

**4.**

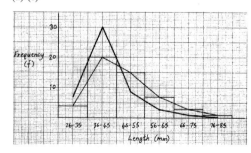

(d) In the previous year there were more shorter beans and fewer long ones

**4.** (a) (i) 81 litres (ii) $\frac{3}{20}$ (48.6 litres)
(b)

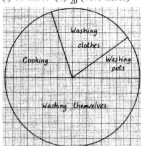

**5.** (a) (i) Pacific Ocean angle (178°) is twice Atlantic angle (89°)
(ii) 5.4 million square miles
(b) (i) $5.76 \times 10^7$ square miles (ii) 29.22%

**6.** (a) 90 (b) 13° (c) 0.22 (d) $\frac{3}{25}$

**7.** (a) (i) $\frac{1}{2}$ (ii) 3
(b) (i) No. This data implies that the area of forest in Latin America is exactly 3 times that in Asia and twice that in Africa.
(ii) 50%

**8.** (a)

| Item | Angle |
|---|---|
| Bus fares £12 | 48 |
| Going out £25 | 100 |
| Clothes £30 | 120 |
| Records £15 | 60 |
| Other £8 | 32 |
| **Total £90** | **360** |

(b)

(c) $\frac{1}{3}$

**9.** (a) (i) 14 (ii) 140 (iii) 20

**Exercise 24F**

**1.** (a) 50 (b) 35
**2.** (a) 1990 (b) 200 (b) 228 (estimate)
**3.** (a)-(c)

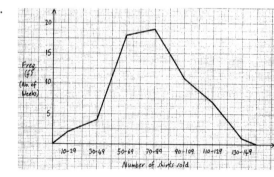

**Exercise 25A**

**1.** (a) (i) mean = 6.7 to 1 d.p.; median = 6; no mode; range = 12
(ii) mean = 27.25; median = 27.5; no mode; range = 15
(iii) mean = 59; median = 58; mode = 57, 58, 60; range = 7
(iv) mean = 6.49; median = 5.55; mode = 5.4; range = 10.6
(b) (i) median (ii) mean or median (iii) median (iv) median

**2.** mean = 78.3 kg to 1 d.p.; median = 76 kg
**3.** (a) mean = 21.9° C; median = 21.5° C ; mode = 22° C
(b) median as it is not distorted by extreme values
**4.** (a) mean = 169.27 cm to 2 d.p. (b) median = 169 cm

## Exercise 25B

1. (a)

| No. of pets ($x$) | Frequency ($f$) | $fx$ |
|---|---|---|
| 0 | 10 | 0 |
| 1 | 17 | 17 |
| 2 | 9 | 18 |
| 3 | 3 | 9 |
| 4 | 1 | 4 |
| Totals | $\Sigma f = 40$ | $\Sigma fx = 48$ |

(b) mean = 1.2; median = 1; mode = 1

(c)

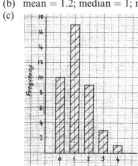

2. (a)

| Length ($x$) | Frequency ($f$) | $fx$ |
|---|---|---|
| 165 | 1 | 165 |
| 166 | 2 | 332 |
| 167 | 3 | 501 |
| 168 | 5 | 840 |
| 169 | 9 | 1521 |
| 170 | 13 | 2210 |
| 171 | 8 | 1368 |
| 172 | 6 | 1032 |
| 173 | 3 | 519 |
| 174 | 4 | 696 |
| Totals | $\Sigma f = 54$ | $\Sigma fx = 9184$ |

(b) mean = 170.1 cm ; median = 170 cm ; mode = 170

(c)

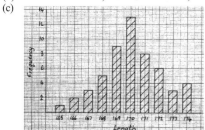

3. (a) mean = 14.5 to 1 d.p.; median = 14; mode = 14

(b)

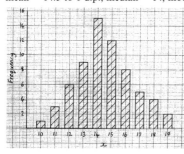

4. mean = 5.2 ; median = 5

## Exercise 25C

1. (a)

| Weight in kg | Number of sheep ($f$) | Halfway mark ($x$) | $fx$ |
|---|---|---|---|
| 20 to under 30 | 2 | 25 | 50 |
| 30 to under 40 | 5 | 35 | 175 |
| 40 to under 50 | 16 | 45 | 720 |
| 50 to under 60 | 25 | 55 | 1375 |
| 60 to under 70 | 13 | 65 | 845 |
| 70 to under 80 | 6 | 75 | 450 |
| 80 to under 90 | 3 | 85 | 255 |
| Totals | $\Sigma f = 70$ | | $\Sigma fx = 3870$ |

(b) mean = 55.3 to 1 d.p.

(c)

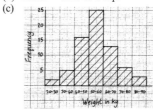

2. (a)

| Mark | Number of students ($f$) | Halfway mark ($x$) | $fx$ |
|---|---|---|---|
| 11 – 20 | 3 | 15.5 | 46.5 |
| 21 – 30 | 5 | 25.5 | 127.5 |
| 31 – 40 | 6 | 35.5 | 213 |
| 41 – 50 | 14 | 45.5 | 637 |
| 51 – 60 | 23 | 55.5 | 1276.5 |
| 61 – 70 | 30 | 65.5 | 1965 |
| 71 – 80 | 11 | 75.5 | 830.5 |
| 81 – 90 | 6 | 85.5 | 513 |
| 91 – 100 | 2 | 95.5 | 191 |
| Totals | $\Sigma f = 100$ | | $\Sigma fx = 5800$ |

(b) mean = 58

(c)

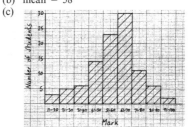

**3.** (a)

| Time (hrs) | Number of light bulbs (f) | Halfway mark (x) | fx |
|---|---|---|---|
| 0 to under 200 | 1 | 100 | 100 |
| 200 to under 400 | 4 | 300 | 1200 |
| 400 to under 600 | 7 | 500 | 3500 |
| 600 to under 800 | 10 | 700 | 7000 |
| 800 to under 1000 | 14 | 900 | 12 600 |
| 1000 to under 1200 | 33 | 1100 | 36 300 |
| 1200 to under 1400 | 20 | 1300 | 26 000 |
| 1400 to under 1600 | 6 | 1500 | 9000 |
| 1600 to under 1800 | 5 | 1700 | 8500 |
| Totals | $\Sigma f = 100$ | | $\Sigma fx =$ 104 200 |

(b) mean = 1042

(c)

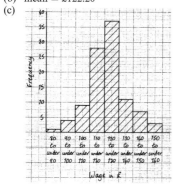

**4.** (a)

| Wage in £ | Number of workers (f) | Halfway mark (x) | fx |
|---|---|---|---|
| 80 to under 90 | 1 | 85 | 85 |
| 90 to under 100 | 4 | 95 | 380 |
| 100 to under 110 | 9 | 105 | 945 |
| 110 to under 120 | 28 | 115 | 3220 |
| 120 to under 130 | 37 | 125 | 4625 |
| 130 to under 140 | 11 | 135 | 1485 |
| 140 to under 150 | 7 | 145 | 1015 |
| 150 to under 160 | 3 | 155 | 465 |
| Totals | $\Sigma f = 100$ | | $\Sigma fx =$ 12 220 |

(b) mean = £122.20

(c)

(d) modal class = £120 to £130

**5.** (a) mean = 31.1

(b)

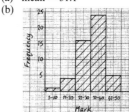

**6.** (a) mean = 23.9

(b)

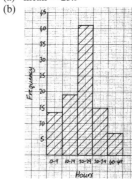

**7.** (a) mean = 9.51 miles

(b)

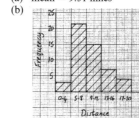

**Exercise 25D**

**1.** (a) mean = 2     (b) range = 4

**2.** (a) 11 to 15 kg

(b)

| Mid-point (m) |
|---|
| 3 |
| 8 |
| 13 |
| 18 |
| 23 |

(c) mean = 13.5 kg

(d)

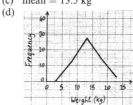

(e) No. The mean weight is less with GrowLots

**3.** (a) (i) mean = 50.1 seconds
(ii) modal class = 40 − 50 seconds
(b) modal class = 40 − 50; mean = 50.1; modal class

**4.** (a)

| Class interval | Frequency (f) | Mid-interval value (x) | fx |
|---|---|---|---|
| 1 – 5 | 16 | 3 | 48 |
| 6 – 10 | 28 | 8 | 224 |
| 11 – 15 | 26 | 13 | 338 |
| 16 – 20 | 14 | 18 | 252 |
| 21 – 25 | 10 | 23 | 230 |
| 26 – 30 | 3 | 28 | 84 |
| 31 – 35 | 1 | 33 | 33 |
| 36 – 40 | 0 | 38 | 0 |
| 41 – 45 | 2 | 43 | 86 |
| Totals | $\Sigma f = 100$ | | $\Sigma fx = 1295$ |

(b) (i) modal class = 6 − 10 (ii) median interval = 11 − 15
(c) 12.95

**5.** (a) £18.90    (b) 6.4 miles
**6.** (a) £41.64    (b) Colin; he sells the most items per hour.
**7.** (a) range = 25

(c)

| Class interval | Frequency (f) |
|---|---|
| 1 – 5 | 2 |
| 6 – 10 | 4 |
| 11 – 15 | 5 |
| 16 – 20 | 7 |
| 21 – 25 | 12 |
| 26 – 30 | 5 |

## Exercise 26A

**1.**

| Shoe size | Frequency (f) | Cumulative frequency |
|---|---|---|
| 4 | 2 | 2 |
| 5 | 7 | 9 |
| 6 | 16 | 25 |
| 7 | 30 | 55 |
| 8 | 45 | 100 |
| 9 | 26 | 126 |
| 10 | 14 | 140 |
| 11 | 8 | 148 |
| 12 | 2 | 150 |

**2.**

| Examination mark (x) | Frequency (f) | Cumulative frequency |
|---|---|---|
| 0 – 5 | 3 | 3 |
| 6 – 10 | 8 | 11 |
| 11 – 15 | 15 | 26 |
| 16 – 20 | 28 | 54 |
| 21 – 25 | 37 | 91 |
| 26 – 30 | 45 | 136 |
| 31 – 35 | 23 | 159 |
| 36 – 40 | 16 | 175 |
| 41 – 45 | 4 | 179 |
| 46 – 50 | 1 | 180 |

**3.**

| Weight in kg (x) | Frequency (f) | Cumulative frequency |
|---|---|---|
| 100 to < 110 | 4 | 3 |
| 110 to < 120 | 19 | 23 |
| 120 to < 130 | 39 | 62 |
| 130 to < 140 | 60 | 122 |
| 140 to < 150 | 53 | 175 |
| 150 to < 160 | 34 | 209 |
| 160 to < 170 | 16 | 225 |
| 170 to < 180 | 3 | 228 |
| 180 to < 190 | 2 | 230 |

## Exercise 26B

**1.** (a)

| Mark (x) | Frequency (f) | Cumulative frequency |
|---|---|---|
| 10 | 2 | 2 |
| 11 | 9 | 11 |
| 12 | 21 | 32 |
| 13 | 45 | 77 |
| 14 | 81 | 158 |
| 15 | 53 | 211 |
| 16 | 34 | 245 |
| 17 | 15 | 260 |
| 18 | 7 | 267 |
| 19 | 3 | 270 |

(b) Curve through points (10,2) (11,11) (12,32) (13,77) (14,158) (15,211) (16,245) (17,260) (18,267) (19,270)

**2.** (a)

| Weight (kg) (x) | Frequency (f) | Cumulative frequency |
|---|---|---|
| 20 – 29 | 8 | 8 |
| 30 – 39 | 13 | 21 |
| 40 – 49 | 41 | 62 |
| 50 – 59 | 20 | 82 |
| 60 – 69 | 14 | 96 |
| 70 – 79 | 3 | 99 |
| 80 – 89 | 1 | 100 |

(b) Curve through points (29.5,8) (39.5,21) (49.5,62) (59.5,82) (69.5,96) (79.5,99) (89.5,100)

**3.** (a)

| Examination mark ($x$) | Frequency ($f$) | Cumulative frequency |
|---|---|---|
| 130 – 135 | 2 | 2 |
| 136 – 140 | 5 | 7 |
| 141 – 145 | 13 | 20 |
| 146 – 150 | 22 | 42 |
| 151 – 155 | 36 | 78 |
| 156 – 160 | 57 | 135 |
| 161 – 165 | 87 | 222 |
| 166 – 170 | 37 | 259 |
| 171 – 175 | 21 | 280 |
| 176 – 180 | 7 | 287 |
| 181 – 185 | 1 | 288 |

(b) Curve through points (135.5,2) (140.5,7) (145.5,20)
(150.5,42) (155.5,78) (160.5,135) (165.5,222)
(170.5,259) (175.5,280) (180.5,287) (185.5,288)

## Exercise 26C

**1.** (a)

| Distance (km) | Frequency ($f$) | Cumulative frequency |
|---|---|---|
| 1 – 5 | 5 | 5 |
| 6 – 10 | 41 | 46 |
| 11 – 15 | 77 | 123 |
| 16 – 20 | 58 | 181 |
| 21 – 25 | 39 | 220 |
| 26 – 30 | 17 | 237 |
| 31 – 35 | 3 | 240 |

(b) Curve through points (5, 5) (10, 46) (15, 123)
(20, 181) (25, 220) (30, 237) (35, 240)
(c) (i) 1.5 km (approx.) (ii) 11 km (approx.)
(iii) 19.5 km (approx.) (iv) 4.5 (approx.)

**2.** (a)

| Age (years) | Frequency ($f$) | Cumulative frequency |
|---|---|---|
| 0 – 10 | 5 | 5 |
| 11 – 20 | 19 | 24 |
| 21 – 30 | 47 | 71 |
| 31 – 40 | 79 | 150 |
| 41 – 50 | 32 | 182 |
| 51 – 60 | 15 | 197 |
| 61 – 70 | 2 | 199 |
| 71 – 80 | 1 | 200 |

(b) Curve through points (10,5) (20,24) (30,71) (40,150)
(50,182) (60,197) (70,199) (80,200)
(c) (i) 34 yrs (ii) 26 yrs (iii) 40 yrs (iv) 14 yrs

**3.** (a)

| Weight (kg) ($x$) | Frequency ($f$) | Cumulative frequency |
|---|---|---|
| 30 – 39 | 3 | 3 |
| 40 – 49 | 11 | 14 |
| 50 – 59 | 24 | 38 |
| 60 – 69 | 56 | 94 |
| 70 – 79 | 123 | 217 |
| 80 – 89 | 70 | 287 |
| 90 – 99 | 13 | 300 |

(b) Curve through points (39,3) (49,14) (59,38) (69,94)
(79,217) (89,287) (99, 300)
(c) (i) 74 kg (ii) 66 kg (iii) 80 kg (iv) 14 kg
(d) 7% (approx.)     (e)   65% (approx.)

**4.** (a)

| Age (years) | Frequency ($f$) | Cumulative frequency |
|---|---|---|
| 0 – 8 | 71 | 71 |
| 9 – 16 | 110 | 181 |
| 17 – 24 | 186 | 367 |
| 25 – 32 | 131 | 498 |
| 33 – 40 | 88 | 586 |
| 41 – 48 | 52 | 638 |
| 49 – 56 | 25 | 663 |
| 57 – 64 | 7 | 670 |

(b) Curve through points (8,71) (16,181) (24,367) (32,498)
(40,586) (48,638) (56,663) (64,670)
(c) (i) 22 yrs (ii) 15 yrs (iii) 32 yrs (iv) 17 yrs
(d) 4.5% (approx.)     (e)   55% (approx.)
(f) 63.7% (approx.)

## Exercise 26D

**1.** (a)

| Age in years (less than) | 20 | 40 | 60 | 80 | 100 | 120 | 140 | 160 |
|---|---|---|---|---|---|---|---|---|
| Cumulative frequency | 6 | 18 | 36 | 74 | 119 | 154 | 186 | 200 |

(a) Curve through points (19.5,6) (39.5,18) (59.5,36)
(79.5,74) (99.5,119) (119.4,154) (139.5,186) (159.5,200)
(c)  170    (d) (i) 90 yrs (ii) 50 yrs
**2.** (a)  mean = 28.2 miles to 1 d.p.
(b) (i)

| Distance ($d$ miles) | $d \le 10$ | $d \le 20$ | $d \le 30$ | $d \le 50$ | $d \le 100$ | $d \le 140$ |
|---|---|---|---|---|---|---|
| Cumulative number of guests | 26 | 64 | 84 | 104 | 116 | 120 |

(ii) Curve through points (10,26) (20,64) (30,84)
(50,104) (100,116) (140,120)
(c) (i) median = 18 miles
(ii) the outlying values in the range $50 \le d \le 140$
distort the data when calculating the mean.
**3.** (a) Curve through (80,1) (90,5) (100,20) (110,37) (120,40)
(b) (i) median = 100 (ii) range = 12
(c) (i) Joy; less variation in her scores
(ii) Laura as her median score is lower than Joy's.
**4.** (a) Curve through points (19.5,0) (39.5,7) (59.5,16)
(79.5,34) (89.5,47) (99.5,59) (119.5,68) (139.5,74)
(b) (i) median = 82 (ii) range = 34

(c) The second group were much fitter than the first.

5. (a) Curve through points (20,1) (25,5) (30,14) (35,28) (40,66) (45,113) (50,164) (55,196) (60,200)

(b) (i) median = 44 seconds  (ii) range = 11 seconds

6. (a)

| House prices (p) in pounds 1993 | Cumulative frequency (%) |
|---|---|
| $0 \leq p < 40\,000$ | 26 |
| $40\,000 \leq p < 52\,000$ | 45 |
| $52\,000 \leq p < 68\,000$ | 67 |
| $68\,000 \leq p < 88\,000$ | 82 |
| $88\,000 \leq p < 120\,000$ | 91 |
| $120\,000 \leq p < 160\,000$ | 96 |
| $160\,000 \leq p < 220\,000$ | 100 |

(b) Graph through points (40 000,26) (52 000, 45) (68 000, 67) (88 000,82) (120 000,91) (160 000,96) (220 000,100)

(c) £82 000

## Exercise 27A

1. (a)

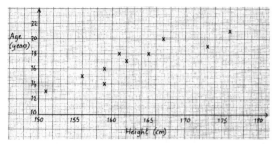

(b) Good, positive correlation

(c) Height increases with age during ages 13-21 yrs

2. (a)

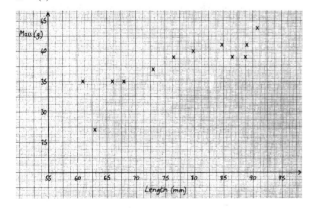

(b) Positive correlation – generally good

(c) Leaf mass increases with length

3. (a)

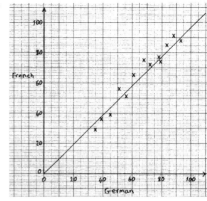

(b) Positive correlation – good

## Exercise 27B

1. (a)

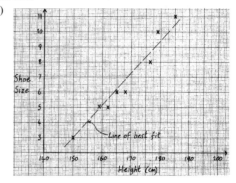

(b) Positive correlation – shoe size increases with height

(c) 155 cm    (d) 8

2. (a)

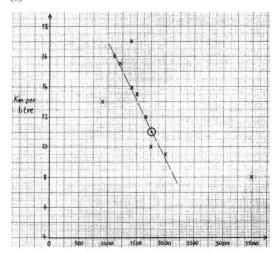

(b) Negative correlation – km per litre decreases as capacity increases.

(c) 1750 cc

3. (a)

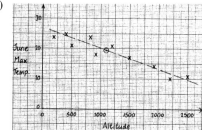

(b) Negative correlation – temperature decreases as altitude increases.

(c) 19.5

4. (a)

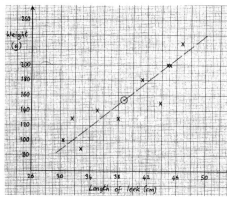

(b) Weight increases with length – positive correlation.

(c) 39 cm

## Exercise 27C

1. (a) (i) B, D (ii) C, E (iii) F

2. (a) (i)

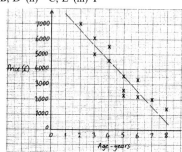

(ii) Price decreases as age increases

3. (a)

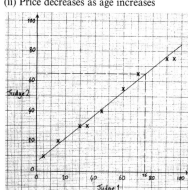

(b) 65

4.

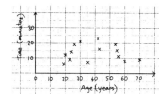

5. (a)

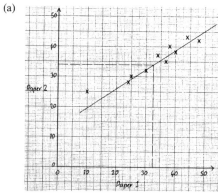

(c) (i) Estimated mark is 34

(ii) Read Paper 2 value where line of best fit has Paper 1 value of 32.

(d) Little or no correlation as subjects are different and require different talents for success.

6. (a) Yes generally but might expect less variation. Marks gained in both subjects are similar.

(b) (ii) 6

(iii) Pupil who gained 10 for Maths and 9 for Physics

## Exercise 28A

1. If dice lands on 1 or 2 Gulzar wins, if dice lands on 3 or 4 Sinead wins, if dice lands on 5 or 6 Tony wins. Each player now has an equal chance of winning

2. (a) Fair. Each player has a 1 in 2 chance of winning

(b) Not fair. Biased towards people whose surname is a letter in the first half of the alphabet.

(c) Not fair. Biased towards Alex who only has a 2 in 5 chance of doing the washing up. Georgie has a 3 in 5 chance.

## Exercise 28B

1.

| T | P | R | U | W V | S | Q |
|---|---|---|---|---|---|---|
| impossible | very unlikely | unlikely | evens | likely | very likely | certain |

2. A – very unlikely; B – evens; C – unlikely; D – very likely; E – impossible; F – very likely; G – likely

## Exercise 28C

1. (a) 

2. 

3. (a) e.g. A playing card picked from a pack is a Heart

(b) e.g. A playing card picked from a pack is a Heart

(c) e.g. A playing card picked from a pack is a Heart

(d) e.g. A dice when rolled lands with 1 uppermost

(e) e.g. A dice when rolled lands with either 1 or 2 uppermost

(f)   e.g. A green ball being picked out from a bag containing 9 green balls and 1 red ball

(g)   e.g. A pink ball being picked out from a bag containing 3 pink balls and 7 yellow balls.

## Exercise 28D

1.  (a)  $\frac{2}{5}$ or 0.4 or 40%     (b)  $\frac{7}{20}$ or 0.35 or 35%
    (c)  $\frac{3}{4}$ or 0.75 or 75%     (d)  $\frac{19}{20}$ or 0.95 or 95%
    (e)  $\frac{11}{20}$ or 0.55 or 55%
2.  (a)  $\frac{1}{4}$ or 0.25 or 25%     (b)  $\frac{3}{8}$ or 0.375 or 37.5%
    (c)  $\frac{1}{8}$ or 0.125 or 12.5%   (d)  $\frac{3}{4}$ or 0.75 or 75%
    (e)  $\frac{5}{8}$ or 0.625 or 62.5%   (f)  $\frac{1}{2}$ or 0.5 or 50%
    (f)  $\frac{3}{8}$ or 0.375 or 37.5%   (h)  $\frac{3}{8}$ or 0.375 or 37.5%
3.  (a)  $\frac{1}{4}$ or 0.25 or 25%     (b)  $\frac{3}{4}$ or 0.75 or 75%
    (c)  $\frac{1}{2}$ or 0.5 or 50%

## Exercise 28F

1.  0.4 or 40%
2.  (a)  0.32 or 32%   (b)  0.42 or 42%   (c)  0.26 or 26%
3.  4200
4.  4200
5.  6000
6.  Each probability should be $\frac{1}{4}$ or 0.25 .P(Club) = 0.24, P(Diamond) = 0.26, P(Heart) = 0.26, P(Spade) = 0.24. So there is no real bias.
7.  P(Heads) = 0.491, P(Tails) = 0.509. Expected value for both probabilities is 0.5 so expected actual number is 1000. Difference for Tails is 1000−982 = 18 or 1.8% of 1000. Difference for Heads is 1018 − 1000 = 18 or 1.8% of 1000. The coin is not biased.
8.  (a)  $\frac{2}{5}$ or 0.4 or 40%     (b)  9 600 000
9.  (a)  $\frac{1}{8}$ or 0.125 or 12.5%   (b)  125
    (c)  P(Any one letter) = 0.125 so frequency of spinner landing on any one letter should be 200 × 0.125 = 25. Frequencies in table are all approx. 25 so there is no evidence of bias.

## Exercise 28G

1.  0.15
2.  (a)  $\frac{1}{5}$ or 0.2 or 20%     (b)  $\frac{4}{5}$ or 0.8 or 80%
3.  80%

## Exercise 28H

1.  (a)  $\frac{1}{4}$ or 0.25 or 25%   (b)  0   (c)  $\frac{3}{4}$ or 0.75 or 75%
2.  (a)  $\frac{1}{2}$ or 0.5 or 50%     (b)  $\frac{3}{10}$ or 0.3 or 30%
    (c)  $\frac{1}{2}$ or 0.5 or 50%     (d)  $\frac{4}{5}$ or 0.8 or 80%
3.  (a)  0.33   (b)  0.37   (c)  150 times
4.  $\frac{13\,999\,999}{14\,000\,000}$
5.  $\frac{5}{12}$ or 0.417 or 41.7%
6.  (a)  $\frac{3}{10}$ or 0.3 or 30%     (b)  $\frac{1}{5}$ or 0.2 or 20%
7.  80 times
8.  $\frac{7}{500}$ or 0.014 or 1.4%
9.  (a)  0.45   (b)  55 times
10. (a)  $\frac{1}{50}$ or 0.02 or 2%     (b)  $\frac{1}{2}$ or 0.5 or 50%
    (c)  $\frac{11}{50}$ or 0.22 or 22%   (d)  $\frac{3}{10}$ or 0.3 or 30%
    (e)  $\frac{8}{25}$ or 0.32 or 32%   (f)  $\frac{22}{25}$ or 0.88 or 88%
11. (a)  $\frac{19}{50}$ or 0.38 or 38%   (b)  8 930 000
12. (a)  0.19   (b)  190 times
    (c)  The number 4 as this has the greatest probability of 0.21
13. (a)  $\frac{3983}{9800}$ or 0.406 or 40.6%   (b)  $\frac{1617}{2450}$ or 0.66 or 66%
    (c)  $\frac{833}{2450}$ or 0.34 or 34%
14. (a)  He recorded the amount of time each light was illuminated for.
    (b)  0.15   (c)  0.85

## Exercise 29A

1.  (a)

    (b)  10

2.  (a)

| dice/spinner | A | B | C | D | E |
|---|---|---|---|---|---|
| 1 | A,1 | B,1 | C,1 | D,1 | E,1 |
| 2 | A,2 | B,2 | C,2 | D,2 | E,3 |
| 3 | A,3 | B,3 | C,3 | D,3 | E,3 |
| 4 | A,4 | B,4 | C,4 | D,4 | E,4 |
| 5 | A,5 | B,5 | C,5 | D,5 | E,5 |
| 6 | A,6 | B,6 | C,6 | D,6 | E,6 |

    (b)  30
3.  (a)  (1,4) (4,1) (2,3) (3,2)   (b)  5 ways
4.  (a)

| Grace/Wesley | Win | Lose | Draw |
|---|---|---|---|
| Win | W,W | L,W | D,W |
| Lose | W,L | L,L | D,L |

    (b)  6 outcomes
5.  (a)  (H,H,T) (H,T,T) (H,T,H) (T,H,T) (T,T,T) (T,T,H) (H,H,H) (T,H,H)
    (b)  16 outcomes   (c)  $2^n$ outcomes

## Exercise 29B

1.  (a)  $\frac{1}{3}$   (b)  $\frac{1}{2}$
2.  (a)  $\frac{5}{8}$   (b)  $\frac{3}{8}$   (c)  $\frac{3}{4}$

## Exercise 29C

1.  $\frac{1}{36}$
2.  $\frac{1}{16}$
3.  (a)  $\frac{2}{10}$   (b)  $\frac{3}{50}$   (c)  $\frac{3}{10}$
4.  (a)  0.42   (b)  0.195112   (c)  0.074088
5.  (a)  45%   (b)  30%   (c)  15%   (d)  10%
6.  0.16

## Exercise 29D

1.  (a)  $\frac{2}{25}$   (b)  $\frac{4}{25}$   (c)  $\frac{15}{25}$
2.  (a)  $\frac{1}{9}$   (b)  $\frac{2}{9}$   (c)  $\frac{1}{6}$
3.  (a)  0.432   (b)  0.648

## Exercise 29E

1.  $\frac{1}{3}$
2.  0.54
3.  0.52
4.  $\frac{8}{13}$
5.  $\frac{67}{100}$
6.  $\frac{11}{36}$
7.  0.82

## Exercise 29F

1.  (a)  0.25   (b)  0.45   (c)  0.9
2.  (a)  $\frac{1}{6}$   (b)  $\frac{1}{3}$   (c)  $\frac{1}{3}$
3.  (a)  .000027   (b)  0.087327

**4.** (a)

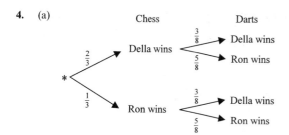

     (b) $\frac{1}{4}$ or 0.25   (c) $\frac{3}{4}$ or 0.75

**5.** (a) 0.125   (b) 0.5

**6.** $\frac{47}{100}$

**7.** (a) 0.18 or $\frac{18}{100}$ or 18/100   (b) 0.72 or $\frac{18}{25}$

**8.** (a) $\frac{7}{12}$   (b)

    First bag         Second bag

                   $\frac{3}{5}$ → Chocolate

   $\frac{5}{15}$ → Chocolate

                   $\frac{2}{5}$ → Mint

\* <

                   $\frac{3}{5}$ → Chocolate

   $\frac{7}{12}$ → Toffee

                   $\frac{2}{5}$ → Mint

   (c) (i) $\frac{1}{4}$ or 0.25 (ii) $\frac{31}{60}$ (iii) $\frac{23}{30}$

**9.** (a) 0.0008   (b) 0.032   (c) 0.096   (d) 0.488

**10.** (a) (2,3) (2,4) (2,5) (2,6) (4,3) (4,4) (4,5) (4,6)
     (6,3) (6,4) (6,5) (6,6)

   (b) $\frac{1}{9}$

**11.** (a) 1   (b) 34

   (c) (i) $\frac{1}{5}$ or 0.2 (ii) $\frac{4}{5}$ or 0.8 (iii) $\frac{11}{40}$ or 0.275

**12.** (a) 0.08   (b) 0.23

# Index